from guinea pig
to computer mouse

from **guinea pig**
to **computer mouse**

alternative methods for a progressive, humane education

2nd edition

Nick Jukes, BSc
Mihnea Chiuia, MD

InterNICHE

The views expressed within this book are not necessarily those of the funding
organisations, nor of all the contributors

Cover image (from left to right): self-experimentation physiology practical, using Biopac apparatus
(Lund University, Sweden); student-assisted beneficial surgery on a canine patient
(Murdoch University, Australia); virtual physiology practical, using SimNerv software
(University of Marburg, Germany)

2nd edition
Published by the International Network for Humane Education (InterNICHE)
© InterNICHE 2003

InterNICHE
19 Brookhouse Avenue
Leicester LE2 0JE
England

tel/fax: +44 116 210 9652
e-mail: coordinator@interniche.org
www.interniche.org

Design by CDC (www.designforcharities.org)
Printed in England by Biddles Ltd. (www.biddles.co.uk)

Printed on 100% post-consumer recycled paper: Millstream 300gsm (cover), Evolve 80gsm (text)

ISBN: 1-904422-00-4

British Library Cataloguing-in-Publication Data
A catalogue record for this book is available from the British Library

Contributors

Jonathan Balcombe, PhD
Immersion Medical, USA

Hans A. Braun, PhD
Institute of Physiology, University of Marburg, Germany

Gary R. Johnston, DVM, MS
Western University of Health Sciences College of Veterinary Medicine, USA

Shirley D. Johnston, DVM, PhD
Western University of Health Sciences College of Veterinary Medicine, USA

Amarendhra M. Kumar, BVSc, MVSc, MS, PhD
Department of Biomedical Sciences, Tufts University School of Veterinary Medicine, USA

Mykola Makarchuk, PhD
Faculty of Biology, Kyiv National Taras Shevchenko University, Ukraine

Lara Marie Rasmussen, DVM, MS
Western University of Health Sciences College of Veterinary Medicine, USA

R. Ashley Robinson, BVSc, MPH, PhD
Western University of Health Sciences College of Veterinary Medicine, USA

Garry C. Scroop, MBBS, MD, PhD
Department of Physiology, University of Adelaide, Australia

Daniel D. Smeak, DVM
The Ohio State University College of Veterinary Medicine, USA

Henk van Wilgenburg, PhD
Department of Pharmacology, University of Amsterdam, The Netherlands

Nick Jukes

Nick Jukes graduated in the physical sciences from the University of Leicester, England, in 1988. He has been active in progressive social change through campaigning for civil rights, environmental responsibility and animal freedom, particularly where these fields intersect. Since the mid-1990s he has co-ordinated InterNICHE, helping to build a diverse and active network of individuals and campaigns working for curricular transformation and humane education within the life sciences. He was co-author of the 1st edition of *from Guinea Pig to Computer Mouse*, and co-produced the multi-language video *Alternatives in Education*, both award-winning resources for teachers and students. He has helped co-ordinate the international development of a range of other resources and projects on alternatives, and has spoken widely at events across the world. Nick is also interested in empowerment through psychosynthesis, in photography, and in exploring the human relationship to nature.

Mihnea Chiuia

Mihnea Chiuia studied medicine in Bucharest, Romania, and obtained his MD degree in 1999. After a year spent as a junior doctor at the Emergency Hospital in Bucharest, he moved to England, where he plans to continue his medical career. From 1994-2000 he was InterNICHE national contact for Romania, working to improve the quality of life science education within the country by promoting alternatives to animal experiments. In 1998 he co-organised the network's 11th International Conference, held in Sighişoara, and later focused on alternatives research for the 2nd edition of *from Guinea Pig to Computer Mouse*. He has been involved in Romania's post-communist transition to civil society by working for the political magazine '22' and its publisher, the Group for Social Dialogue. He has also co-edited the memoirs of one of Romania's leading surgeons, who documents the changes to the medical profession in the country under communism. Mihnea enjoys music, cycling, and hiking in Romania's mountains.

Acknowledgements

This book would not have been possible without the input of energy and resources from a wide community of individuals and organisations.

We would like to give special thanks to the funders of this project: Maggie Jennings and Arthur Lindley from the Royal Society for the Prevention of Cruelty to Animals (RSPCA); Karin Gabrielson from the Swedish Fund for Research Without Animal Experiments; the Universities Federation for Animal Welfare (UFAW); Theo Capaldo from the New England Anti-Vivisection Society (NEAVS) and Ethical Science and Education Coalition (ESEC); Max Moret and Marina Zumkeller from the Swiss League Against Vivisection (LSCV); Tina Nelson and Katherine Lewis from the American Anti-Vivisection Society (AAVS) and Animalearn. Thank you for your moral and financial support, and your patience.

Many thanks also to Voicu Rădescu from Green Hours (www.jazz.ro) and to Radu Filipescu from the Group for Social Dialogue (www.ong.ro) for providing free internet access in Bucharest to research the *Alternatives File*.

We are very grateful to the contributors who have written chapters for the book, for sharing their invaluable experience with developing, implementing and assessing alternatives: Jonathan Balcombe, Lara Marie Rasmussen, Hans Braun, Henk van Wilgenburg, Mykola Makarchuk, Garry Scroop, Amarendhra Kumar, Daniel Smeak, Shirley Johnston, Ashley Robinson, and Gary Johnston. Very many thanks as well to Gill Langley from the Dr Hadwen Trust for Humane Research for her foreword, and to Michael Balls, Mary Midgley and Barbara Smuts for their reviews.

Ursula Zinko deserves special mention for her work in researching the 1st edition of the book, which provided information upon which to base the early product research for this edition. In the preparation of this edition, Siri Martinsen helped considerably with a number of important tasks, and Thales Tréz, Bruno Lecomte and Monika Perčić contributed at other times.

All the other InterNICHE national contacts provided their input as well: Marina Berati, Alina Bodnariu, Jana Bohdanová, Deidre Bourke, Cynthia Burnett, Sonja Desnica, Dávid Karátson, Heleen van Kernebeek, Liza Kodym-Flanagan, Hanna Kurppa, Bente Lakjer, Anne Leenknegt, Tamir Lousky, Elena Maroueva, Makiko Nakano, Markéta Pecková, Shiranee Pereira, Ulpiano Pérez Marqués, Nuria Querol i Viñas, Evald Reintam, Astrid Schneider, Vanna Tatti, Irina Tsirkvadze, Dražen Vicić, René Votion, Gina Walsh, Maria Eugénia Webb, and Anya Yushchenko.

Thanks also to James Argent, Jasmijn de Boo, David Bowles, Manuel Cases, David Dewhurst, Maneka Gandhi, Sheelagh Graham, Sérgio Greif, Franz Gruber, Brian Gunn, Ana Miškovska Kajevska, Lexo Khubulava, Leslie King, Andrew Knight, Tannetje Koning, Joy Leney, Valentina Maroueva, Esther van der Meer, Victoria Meshcheryakova, Dita Michalickova, Gisela Murillo, Jason Nardi, Helena Pedersen, Sunčica Remenar, Riitta Salmi, Roy Schneider, Adrian and Karina Smith, Jasminka Štimac, Ewa Suskiewicz, Tamara Tarnavska, Massimo Tettamanti, Jan van der Valk, Les Ward and Marja Zuidgeest.

We would like to acknowledge the important role of the creators and producers of alternatives, for their contribution to best practice within life science education; and of the student conscientious objectors who have helped transform higher education with their humane awareness and action.

Credit is due to Matthew Kay and Dolma Beresford from CDC - Consortium: Design for Charities for their excellent graphic design and layout work; to Hanna Kurppa for the icons used to illustrate the medium for each product; and to Biddles Ltd. for their printing expertise.

Nick Jukes would like to thank Kala Subbuswamy for her critical thinking, patience and partnership. Mihnea Chiuia thanks Viorel Nistor (www.gess.ro) for his invaluable technical assistance.

Finally, thank you to all the animals that have enriched our lives; and to all the people with vision and ideals, and the skills to make them real. This book is dedicated to the human-animal bond; to heart and mind; and to progressive social change.

Nick Jukes
Mihnea Chiuia

Leicester, England
January 2003

Foreword

When I was studying at Cambridge University in the 1970s, concepts such as respect for all life and a student's freedom of conscience were dismissed within academia. As one of many second year students of the Natural Sciences, I entered the physiology practical classroom to be faced with dozens of decerebrated rabbits which we had to dissect and whose reactions to drugs we had to monitor, as part of our learning experience. A request that only one demonstration rabbit should be used, or a film made for future classes, was brushed away by lecturers without a second thought.

More disturbing even than this unnecessary and profligate waste of animals' lives was a creeping awareness that my enthusiasm and excitement for science began very quickly to drown out my concern. So starts the process of desensitisation, to which every life science student is susceptible when taught by conventional animal-based methods. Part of that learning process, deliberate or not, was to view animals for their instrumental value rather than their intrinsic value. Later, my memories became vague about the purpose and outcome of many of the classes which used animal 'preparations'. In contrast, I remember well and with a clear conscience the other practicals, where we students experimented harmlessly on ourselves to demonstrate key physiological principles.

When you are campaigning for an issue you believe is important, especially if it requires a paradigm shift in intellectual and social cultures, it is easy to feel discouraged at the apparently snail-like pace of progress. Worthwhile efforts to change the status quo often meet implacable resistance due to the power of tradition, a lack of vision and the unwillingness of most people to leave their 'comfort zone'.

Those who believe in humane education in the life sciences - a concept of teaching and learning which avoids harm to animals and encourages critical thinking - may occasionally have felt discouraged. Students who have had to change courses or were marked down because they were not offered alternatives to invasive animal use, and educators who have tried to improve the way biological sciences are taught, may feel that the teaching model will never change.

Having been professionally involved in alternatives to animals in science for more than 20 years, I can offer a different perspective. There has been a dramatic evolution in thinking, attitudes and practice regarding the use of animals in life science education. Today, conscience and respect for life can be discussed in academic circles without the expectation of ridicule or defensive over-reaction. It is also possible to speak of empathy with the suffering of other animals without being dismissed as squeamish.

For today's student with a conscience, the choice is not only between using animals or self-experimentation. Neither is the choice restricted to going along with the mainstream view; or to dropping out or changing courses. There is now an effective range of sophisticated humane education tools, ranging from mannekins and surgical models to interactive multimedia software packages on CD-ROM. These can replace animal-based practicals in disciplines such as anaesthesia, critical care, anatomy, surgical skills, physiology, pharmacology and others. Furthermore, when animals are genuinely needed for skills acquisition, the use of ethically-sourced animal cadavers and beneficial work with animal patients can replace conventional practicals that involve laboratory animal experimentation.

This new edition of *from Guinea Pig to Computer Mouse* is much more than a catalogue of products available for teaching life sciences in a humane and progressive way. As well as providing descriptions of these alternatives, this book also offers intelligent, original and well-argued essays explaining why and how to alter the educational process to the benefit of students, teachers, animals and the life sciences. This isn't just a future goal: curricula have already changed in many higher education establishments, and non-animal or animal-friendly methods of teaching are being implemented worldwide. Annual statistics in Britain, for example, show a two-thirds decrease (from 12,000 procedures in 1991 to 3,760 in 2001) in animal use for education over the last 10 years.

Within these covers you will find information, innovation and inspiration on almost every page. The editors and contributors, in a genuinely international collaboration, write with an appealing mix of the intellectual and the idealistic. From explanations of the types of alternative methods and assessments of their teaching value, to personal experiences of designing non-animal techniques and developing humane education curricula, the scope and content of the book challenge old assumptions and offer a new reality.

The acceptance of alternatives in life science education has been paralleled by similar changes in biomedical research and testing. Animals are used widely in research, especially as 'models' for studying human diseases and developing treatments; they are also used in safety tests for medicines, industrial and household chemicals, pesticides and novel foods. However, serious questions have been raised regarding the relevance and reliability of the data from such experiments when extrapolated to humans. There has been a growing interest in creating new methods, incorporating cutting-edge knowledge and technologies, which could replace - and improve on - animal experiments. Molecular studies, cell culture approaches, test-tube genetics and clinical and population studies offer humane, multi-disciplinary ways to achieve progress.

Humane education is thus part of a wider context of scientific change, in which other animals are increasingly recognised as sentient beings with a right not to be harmed. These related fields are linked in a positive feedback loop: as more science students graduate with their sense of compassion intact, encouraged to appreciate other life forms and to question dogma, they will look for professions and employment paths which reflect these qualities. As young researchers they are likely to choose fields which avoid animal use, and their ideals and creativity will benefit immeasurably the on-going development of non-animal research and safety testing methods.

Paradigm shifts in society rarely happen without considerable effort and commitment. InterNICHE, the organisation which has produced this book, has campaigned and worked tirelessly, with students and teachers who were willing to listen and who were in turn inspired by the InterNICHE vision.

Often, against all the odds, one person in the right place, at just the right moment, can achieve remarkable and unprecedented results. Some of those people have contributed to this book. Others are about to read it, and be empowered in their turn to leave their 'comfort zones' and become part of the solution: the humane teaching and practice of the life sciences.

Dr Gill Langley, MA PhD (Cantab) MIBiol CBiol
Scientific Adviser to the Dr Hadwen Trust for Humane Research

Contents

Introduction

Within biological science, medical and veterinary medical education, animals often play a central role in laboratory practical classes. The relationship between the animals and the students, however, is usually one of harmful use. Tens, if not hundreds of millions of animals across the world are used for experiments or killed for dissection every year.

The InterNICHE vision is one of a fully humane education, where teaching objectives are met using humane alternative methods, and where compassion, respect for life, and critical thinking skills are valued and developed. Students have freedom of conscience and the negative relationship with animals has been transformed to the positive through full replacement of harmful animal use.

By working with teachers to introduce alternatives and with students to support freedom of conscience, InterNICHE is committed to supporting the most ethical and effective ways of gaining knowledge and skills in the life sciences.

This book presents a concise collection of resources concerning curricular transformation and alternatives to harmful animal use in education, with a view to informing and empowering the reader. It contains comprehensive and up-to-date information on alternative products and approaches, researched and collated by InterNICHE, and includes papers written by teachers sharing their personal experiences of developing, implementing and assessing alternatives. It describes the background to animal use and alternatives, and brings together links to hundreds of further resources.

Since the publication of the 1st edition of *from Guinea Pig to Computer Mouse* in 1997, a number of significant developments have taken place. One is the establishment of alternatives as the norm in many life science departments, offering clear evidence that students of biology and the medical sciences can and do graduate without animal experimentation, and often with above average knowledge and skills. Another development is the spread of new computer technology. This has brought computer hardware to a large number of people and institutes, and made available software of increasing depth and quality. There has been a massive growth in the availability and use of educational CD-ROMs in particular. Computer technology has also allowed for an expansion of the internet, with its growing role in communication, information retrieval and marketing. For many, e-mail has facilitated global communication, and the creation of university and company websites has facilitated the gathering of information for this book.

Alternative methods and curricular transformation

The book begins with a definition of alternatives in education, and describes the different types of alternative that have replaced or can replace harmful animal use. From alternative tools such as mannekins for clinical skills training and computer software for virtual laboratory experimentation, to the alternative approaches of clinical work with animal patients and the use of ethically-sourced animal cadavers, their pedagogical advantages and potential are discussed in detail.

The multiple benefits of alternatives are further described in the next chapter. The use of alternatives rather than animal experimentation helps reconnect life science education with its roots: *healing* rather than *harming* in medicine, and the study of *biology* instead of *necrology*. Honouring the life-affirming fundamentals of medicine, veterinary medicine and the biological sciences helps provide an ethical anchor to modernisation and curricular change. Moreover, questioning the animal experimentation orthodoxy - as a teacher or a student - is an expression of critical thinking, and some alternatives are designed to support the development of problem-solving skills through the use of the scientific method, itself a formalisation of critical thinking.

The value of emotional literacy to science, self and society is also addressed. The qualities and skills of sensitivity, empathy and compassion are often validated and nurtured when harmful animal use is replaced with alternatives. Together with critical thinking, they are necessary for ethical awareness and the gaining of confidence and competence in ethical decision-making amongst students. The life sciences, as with all professions, cannot exist in an ethical vacuum. The introduction of alternatives evidences a commitment to ethics and social responsibility with impact in education and beyond: as well as the clear benefits to animals of not being killed or harmed in the classroom, familiarity with alternatives and with ethical thought also supports the growth of humane science within research and testing. Moral imperatives for the implementation of alternatives in education are often supported by legislative requirements that alternatives are to be used 'wherever possible'. Other practical advantages include financial savings, the wise use of resources, and reduced environmental impact.

In his chapter, Dr. Jonathan Balcombe reviews the published literature concerning assessment of the pedagogical efficacy of alternative methods across a range of disciplines. Collectively, the empirical evidence fully supports the replacement of harmful animal use such as dissection and animal experimentation: the alternatives are equal or superior to conventional animal use. Anecdotal evidence also supports such replacement. The elements of good study design are explored in detail in the chapter, in order to encourage the performance of more studies, specifically those with a high level of scientific rigour. A large-scale international assessment study that investigates process as well as content learning is also recommended.

The majority of published studies compare one non-animal alternative with one conventional animal experiment or with dissection. The broader definition of alternatives proposed by InterNICHE includes alternative approaches that involve neutral or beneficial work with animals, such as the use of ethically-sourced cadavers and clinical work. Moreover, combinations of alternatives will invariably be employed throughout the curriculum, so studies should also reflect the diversity of tools and approaches used to gain knowledge and skills.

Some teachers, therefore, talk less of 'alternatives' but simply of better ways of meeting teaching and learning objectives, and of meeting a broader range of objectives, through humane and innovative approaches. In her chapter, Dr. Lara Rasmussen explores the process of curriculum design within the life sciences with a view to students gaining a diversity of skills, knowledge and attitudes in a fully humane way, and of developing an appreciation of and respect for life. Addressing inclusive curricular aims, focused curricular goals, and purposeful learning objectives, as well as different learning methodologies, the potential of thoughtfully designed curricula to support effective and high quality life science education is clearly shown. The importance of evolution of the curriculum is also explained; the curriculum can be seen as a metaphor for a scientific investigation that progresses with the input of new information and from assessment. Accompanying this change is the excitement of creative course design and of being an effective educator.

Conscientious objection to harmful animal use is sometimes the catalyst for the introduction of alternatives, and the roles and responsibilities of students and teachers when ethical conflict emerges is addressed in the next chapter. Objectors are usually critical thinking students who care deeply about animals and their education. They are prepared to question established norms and risk academic and psychological penalty by pushing for alternatives. Understanding the motivation of conscientious objectors, and responding appropriately to their intellectual challenge, can reduce student-teacher conflict and help ensure co-operative win-win solutions.

Finally in this section, the history, structure and process of InterNICHE is presented. Working for replacement of harmful animal use with alternatives, and supporting student conscientious objection, InterNICHE is both an organisation and a network. Resources such as the international Alternatives Loan System, the Humane Education Award, a comprehensive website and an award-winning multi-language video, are described along with other local and global projects.

Case studies

Teachers and heads of departments who are at the forefront of new approaches in life science education have contributed chapters for the second part of the book. Their diverse experiences with progressive, humane teaching methods, including full replacement of harmful animal use, cover a range of disciplines and alternative media.

Dr. Hans Braun shares his experience of developing and implementing multimedia simulations of physiology and pharmacology experiments after facing widespread student conscientious objection to animal experiments. The award-winning *Virtual Physiology* series, designed to encourage active learning with practice-oriented tasks in a virtual laboratory, was found by both students and teachers to be pedagogically, scientifically and ethically superior to the conventional animal practicals. This assessment has prompted further development of cutting-edge multimedia design for physiology education - progress that is described in the chapter.

The tradition of using animals as models for human physiological and pharmacological processes is questioned by Dr. Henk van Wilgenburg. Teachers' attitudes concerning alternatives and different learning methods, particularly the acceptance of computer-based alternatives, are addressed in detail. Emphasis is put on the importance of careful preparation of the steps required for successful implementation of new methods, including an analysis of needs, preparation of staff and support, student involvement in the process, and evaluation. The benefits of locally-editable freeware and of collaborative production of alternatives are also described.

Dr. Mykola Makarchuk questions the conventional belief in the 'indispensibility' of animal experiments in biology education. He shares how his own views have changed from accepting animal use - including performing experiments on frogs and rats - to embracing only alternatives. This change has paralleled the cultural evolution of human values concerning animals, and a growing

3

awareness of the negative impact of harmful animal use. The challenges of implementation of alternatives such as computer simulation in the educational system of the Ukraine are explored, and the benefits of such alternatives described.

The value of self-experimentation projects for gaining an appreciation of the scientific method and learning problem-solving strategies is described by Dr. Garry Scroop. Semester-long team-based practicals follow the postgraduate research approach to ensure not only effective physiology education in medical training but also to enhance students' life-long learning skills. The advantages of this alternative over recipe-driven animal experiments - with their contrived results and associated lack of practice of critical thinking skills - are explained, and the design and performance of the projects are described in detail along with an assessment of the approach.

The process of meeting the cadaver requirements of anatomy, surgery and clinical skills training for veterinary students in a fully ethical way is explained by Dr. Amarendhra Kumar. The exemplary 'client donation program' at Tufts University in the USA provides ethically-sourced cadavers in sufficient numbers for student needs. The establishment, maintenance and working of the program are described, and typical questions concerning donated cadavers are answered. For those students who genuinely require hands-on experience of animal tissue for their profession, this alternative approach provides a sustainable solution.

Dr. Daniel Smeak addresses the requirement for veterinary students to be competent surgeons upon graduation by focusing on effective skills acquisition. The use of autotutorial video programs in combination with suture trainer and hollow organ simulators has provided opportunities for basic skills mastery, and employing these ethical, cost-effective simulators has proved better than animal experimentation for effective hands-on training. The use of ethically-sourced cadavers, and clinical work with animal patients through a sterilisation program, provide the experience of real tissue and real patients that allows the application of the basic surgical skills gained using simulators.

Dr. Lara Rasmussen, with Drs. R. Ashley Robinson, Gary Johnston and Shirley Johnston, describes the ongoing realisation of a vision of a progressive, cutting-edge veterinary curriculum. The new College of Veterinary Medicine at Western University of Health Sciences in the USA provides innovative student-centred learning, a commitment to 'reverence for life', and enhanced clinical experience with animal patients and volunteers. No animals will be harmed or killed for the sake of education, nor will students be allowed to graduate without the required knowledge and skills mastery. The approaches used to achieve this mastery, such as a focus on a broad range of identified teaching objectives, creative course design, and employment of high-quality alternative tools and approaches, are explained in detail.

Alternatives file

Based on original research, the *Alternatives File* describes in detail the applications, specifications and source for over 500 alternative products, listed according to discipline and medium. Mihnea Chiuia carried out meticulous and exhaustive product research for this edition, and was therefore responsible for the content and quality of the *Alternatives File*. The book also includes information of some products pre-launch, presents some products never before marketed or shared, and includes details from catalogues not yet published. Over two-thirds of the products included in this edition are new to the book.

The main criterion for deciding whether to include a product in the *Alternatives File* concerned its potential to replace harmful animal use and to improve knowledge and skills acquisition. The priority areas for replacement are gross animal anatomy, animal and human physiology, pharmacology, clinical skills, critical care and surgery. The majority of products are therefore designed for implementation at the university level, but many are suitable for secondary (high school) teaching, and some also for professional training/re-training.

No products that support laboratory animal experimentation in research and testing are included, but some training models and other alternatives from this field may be useful for students to gain practical skills in preparation for a range of animal-based professions. Few human anatomy products are included because human cadavers, human anatomy software and clinical work are already widely in use in medical schools across most of the world. The tradition in some colleges of dissecting frogs and cats for teaching human anatomy needs no further comment. It is likely that the remaining lab animal-based practical courses for learning human physiology, pharmacology, clinical skills and surgery will disappear, but in the meantime, products for replacement of animal use in these human medical disciplines are included. Other changes in the development of life science education include the growing focus on genetics and cell and molecular biology, on the one hand, and on ethology and ecology, on the other. These offer opportunities to move away from the conventional invasive animal experiments and dissections, and therefore some products relating to this indirect replacement are included. Further information about the entries can be found at the beginning of the section itself.

There are certainly other teaching aids available that are not listed. The amount of information on the world wide web - the medium of much of the book research - is almost limitless, but time and human resources are not. Moreover, some teaching aids are limited to individual institutes, developed to improve teaching quality locally, but not marketed or shared. The authors welcome details of available products of which they are not aware.

Further resources

The final section of the book provides links to nearly 800 further resources related to alternatives in education. These include databases and reviews of alternatives, websites of curricular resources, details of alternatives loan systems, a broad range of recommended reading, and the contact details of campaigning and scientific organisations from around 40 countries. Also included are the details of producers and distributors for the alternatives featured in the *Alternatives File*.

With comprehensive world wide web references and the full contact details for producers and distributors included in this edition, it is hoped that future research for InterNICHE and for the reader has been made much easier. It is also hoped that the product and other information in this book will be useful for updating and expanding other databases and resources on alternatives; readers should contact InterNICHE if interested in using any of the information in this way.

The level of the debate has already been raised. The question is no longer whether harmful animal use is a problem, nor whether alternatives are pedagogically valid. Alternatives are already implemented in universities across the world, and it is now time that the remaining harmful animal use is replaced - using some of the excellent alternative tools and approaches described in this book, and others that are under development by teachers. Discussions should instead focus on design strategies to meet teaching objectives effectively and to maximise the broader positive impact of humane education. User reviews and assessment of existing products, and studies of replacement, are also strongly encouraged.

Until curricular transformation involving full replacement has been achieved, ethics and animal care and use committees should deny permission for all harmful animal use in education. They should also support teachers in effective information retrieval on alternative tools and approaches, and on curricular design issues. Legislation itself should reflect the widespread availability, existing use and multiple benefits of alternatives by banning harmful animal use for education and training. Where appropriate, student choice policies should be implemented so that conscientiously objecting students are not denied access to superior learning methods.

Producers of alternatives should ensure that the process of development involves no harmful animal use. There is also a large demand for translated versions of software and video, and for the opportunity to edit material locally.

Many teachers have invested considerable energy and resources in producing state-of-the-art alternatives for their students. Life science education deserves further investment to provide all students with the most effective and ethical methods for acquisition of knowledge and skills. Such investment in alternatives will not only help the learners, the teachers and the animals, but will positively impact on the professions and wider society as well. All will benefit from a commitment to humane education.

part a **alternative methods & curricular transformation**

1. Types of alternative and their pedagogical impact

Defining alternatives

It is now possible to refine the conventional definition of an alternative. Developments in technology and in ethical thought, and creative examples of the replacement of harmful animal use that have been achieved across all the disciplines of the life sciences, mitigate for such a refinement. Specifically, the definition of alternatives within education can be made more strict so as to comprise only replacement alternatives; and can be broadened to include approaches that involve neutral or beneficial work with individual animals. Such a definition goes beyond 'reduction, replacement and refinement' of animal experiments, as described by Russell and Burch[1]. It is more appropriate to the nature of knowledge and skills acquisition within life science education, and reflects the present-day possibilities and opportunities for replacement.

Alternatives, therefore, are humane educational aids and teaching approaches that can replace harmful animal use or complement existing humane education. Typically used in combination to meet existing teaching objectives and to provide other educational outcomes that cannot be met through animal experiments, they comprise:

- Film and video
- Models, mannekins and simulators
- Multimedia computer simulation
- Ethically-sourced animal cadavers and tissue
- Clinical work with animal patients and volunteers
- Student self-experimentation
- *In vitro* labs
- Field studies

This chapter describes in detail the above types of alternative, and explores their pedagogical impact and potential. InterNICHE policies that relate to specific alternatives, and to the humane production of new alternatives, are elaborated in the *Appendix*.

Film and video

Historically films have been used to a large degree within life science education to illustrate those parts of the curriculum that particularly benefit from visual representation, that need further explanation, or that are hard to show in the lab. Most films have over time been replaced by video. Some video material has in turn been used in clips within multimedia software on CD-ROM and DVD.

Modern high quality video is used at virtually all institutes, and can play an important role as a visual alternative to harmful animal use. For institutes with limited financial resources, video can be a realistic alternative to animal dissection and experimentation, especially when combined with other low-cost approaches to meeting teaching objectives. Though passive, video can provide good background to a subject and is often used as preparation and support material for work with other alternatives, such as surgery practice on simulators or clinical work with human and animal patients.

Videos of professionally-performed dissections can often impart much more information to students than dissections performed by the students themselves, and can provide a sufficient alternative for students who will not use animals in their careers. For the minority of students who do need dissection skills in their careers, videos can be used to train them before they do real dissections on ethically-sourced cadavers. Videos of experiments in pharmacology and physiology, like their software counterparts, can also demonstrate procedures that would be ethically unacceptable to continue performing on living animals, or difficult to illustrate effectively. Many videos incorporate graphics as well as footage and audio.

Digital video

Recent digital technology presents new opportunities to creatively develop and maximise the potential of video-based teaching resources in conjunction with computer software[2]. The digitising of video is simple and low cost. The editing of digital video, including the addition of auditory comments, stills and graphics, and its copying and distribution, can be managed with average computer hardware, the appropriate software, and basic computer skills. Digitisation allows video-clips to be accessed quickly and used with ease during a lecture or practical lab, and streams can be provided on the web. Creative use of this technology can provide a highly effective learning aid.

Models, mannekins and simulators

These non-animal alternatives comprise both synthetic training objects designed to simulate organs, limbs or whole animals, and apparatus for training and simulation of physiological functions or clinical skills and scenarios. The descriptive terms are used flexibly and sometimes interchangeably. In general, 'models' refer to objects designed for appreciating anatomical structure; 'mannekins', or sometimes 'phantoms', are life-like representations of animals or humans designed for clinical skills training; and 'simulators' are tools for clinical skills, surgery and critical care practice, and include computerised mannekins, surgical training devices, and suture trainers.

Plastic models of animals, showing their internal structure, are commonly used for teaching morphology across the world, and real animal cadavers can be dissected and preserved, for example using plastination. Within orthopaedics in human and veterinary medicine, plastic bones are used widely to illustrate fractures.

Simple and inexpensive simulators can be used for effective practice of psychomotor and clinical skills such as eye-hand co-ordination, instrument handling and suturing. Skin and hollow organ simulators, intestinal anastomosis simulators, microsurgical trainers and others are made from specially prepared plastics or latex to realistically simulate the relevant tissue or organs. Pathologies such as cysts can be included in certain simulators to practice excision. Even bicycle tyre inner tubes are sometimes used as easy-to-obtain, practical training devices appropriate to the basic level of skills acquisition.

Dynamic simulators

One surgical simulator used for minimally-invasive surgical training can accommodate ethically-sourced animal organs, which are perfused and practised on[3]. Another, under development, employs perfusion of an ethically-sourced human cadaver, or part thereof, to offer a realistic alternative to live surgery[4]. The veins and arteries are dynamically filled with coloured liquid by a specially designed pump. This also applies pulsating pressure that can be transmitted to the vessels, and thereby reliably simulates the vascular tree, all within a closed system. Dissection and a range of surgical and microsurgical approaches such as vascular suturing, anastomosis and repair, aneurysm clip applications, intra-parenchyma resection, bleeding management, and endoscopic procedures can all be performed. Realistic surgery can therefore be practised, and the technique potentially applied to both human and animal cadaveric sources.

Other simulators include apparatus built by instructors to illustrate dynamic processes such as the physiology of circulation. These can easily be created using basic lab resources such as pumps, tubing, valves and coloured liquid; or may be electronic circuit simulators for illustration of neuro-physiological processes.

Hands-on training

Human patient mannekins are used frequently in some countries for training students and profes-sionals in clinical skills and procedures, as well as critical care. The most advanced mannekins have artificial skin, bones and organs, sometimes including beating hearts, and artificial fluids simulating blood and bile. The anatomically correct nature of the organs may be derived from advanced scanning techniques and precision moulding by engineers. Some mannekins are computerised, for presenting real-time emergencies and allowing for real-time monitoring of how successful the trainee is in his or her performance of critical care or surgery. Trainee surgeons and doctors can therefore learn in an environment that is risk-free for patients, and the monitoring can also help ensure consistency and uniformity of training. Like all similar alternatives used to their full potential, they allow for mastery of a skill, not just exposure to it. Having been through the simulated clinical situations, students will have gained the practical, mental and emotional skills required for the real-life situation - skills which can be further refined.

Animal mannekins can facilitate training in handling, blood sampling, intubation, thoracentesis and CPR techniques, amongst others. Different mannekins have different degrees of anatomical and physiological realism. For challenging procedures such as female canine urinary catheteri-sation, anatomically correct mannekins can allow the student to follow the visual and tactile clues for mastering the technique. Technically demanding procedures and those involving risk and/or stress to an animal can therefore be mastered by students without live animals, and critical care cases explored in advance of clinical opportunities, building confidence and competence. Experience in dealing with individual variability in animals can be addressed by using a range of mannekins, and progressing on to ethically-sourced cadavers and then clinical work with animal patients.

Mannekins and simulators offer cost-effective and ethical hands-on training. They give more freedom to students to practice at their own rate, to learn by trial and error, and to repeat proce-dures, without the high cost to animals. Some basic simulators can also be used by students in their home environment as well as the lab, potentially releasing some faculty resources. The time and resources formerly used to prepare animal labs for basic skills practice can be re-allocated to devel-oping and using simulators and the learning opportunities associated with patients in the clinical setting. The latter include more complex surgical skills and other training that would necessarily require human and animal patients.

Multimedia computer simulation

The computer mouse

The emergence and application of computer technologies have revolutionised science and society as a whole. High-speed processors and powerful software have transformed the way that data is gathered and processed, how biological processes are modelled and explained, and how knowledge is transferred. The opportunities associated with the development of computer-based technology in contributing to effective life science education have grown exponentially within the last decade. The internet, and multimedia software available on CD-ROM and DVD, are playing powerful roles in many universities, with applications in labs and lectures, tutorials and project work. From virtual dissections and experiments in well-equipped labs that students can perform on-screen, to full virtual reality simulations of clinical technique with tactile facilities, the possibilities of computer-assisted learning are limited only by technical and imaginative boundaries.

While the first computer simulations were little more than textbooks on disk, today's interactive multimedia programs may integrate a virtual laboratory, 3D photographic images and graphics, videoclips, and textual information to significantly enhance the quality and depth of learning. Created by teachers to better meet the teaching objectives of specific courses, these professionally-designed packages can facilitate students' ability to visualise and understand structure and process, to experiment and learn problem-solving strategies, and to gain a range of other skills.

Enhancing anatomy study

In a virtual dissection or anatomy program, students can perform tasks step-by-step, repeating as necessary, and learn functional anatomy as they work through the program. The range of facilities varies between programs. They may include libraries of colour photographic images, from gross to micro-anatomy, with the opportunity to zoom in and out of the images; allow morphology between species to be compared at the click of the mouse, with auditory comments or text boxes providing explanatory information and questions; offer the facility to highlight or incrementally dissolve away specific organs or organ systems, by controlling their opacity within a composite image; present physiological processes such as digestion or the activation of muscles through the technique of 'morphing'; spin organs and skeletal systems, and present animations and fly-throughs for any part of the body. These opportunities, absent in the real lab but available on demand at high-speed in the simulation, can provide a very rich and sensory experience which allows a much fuller appreciation of structure and structural relationship.

It is worth noting that as newer disciplines such as genetics, molecular and cell biology, and neuro-science take learning time away from more traditional fields, multimedia educational software can also revitalise and modernise the study of anatomy and help keep an appropriate balance between fields during the evolution of the life sciences. This has already begun with high-resolution 2D imaging, such as the *Visible Human* digital atlas, and the latest anatomy simulations. And as new imaging technologies, such as 3D ultrasound, Computer-Assisted Tomography (CAT) and Magnetic Resonance Imaging (MRI), become more accessible and are applied more widely, visual-isation in anatomy and physiology, diagnostics, preparation through simulated surgery, and actual surgical performance, will all be enhanced. Virtual Reality (VR) already uses some of these advanced technologies.

The virtual laboratory

Software which includes a virtual laboratory presents a range of equipment on-screen and may offer a very high degree of interactivity. Typically, such programs simulate classical animal preparations and experiments within physiology, pharmacology and critical care. These disciplines lend themselves well to multimedia because of the need to correlate multiple and simultaneous events, and to gain an understanding of the interplay between complex and related phenomena.

Simulations provide practice-oriented tasks building on students' theoretical knowledge. Before students use such simulations, teachers may choose to present aspects of the program using a data projector in front of the whole class, to help clarify specific teaching objectives. A lecture-style presentation in support of their individual or group experimentation may be welcomed by students. Importantly, a balance needs to be found between the challenge inherent within a new learning tool, and the students' knowledge and skills at that point in time, so that learning is optimised.

Virtual laboratories detail the preparation, essential equipment and method relevant to the practical, and students then actively perform experiments themselves with simulated tissue responses to stimuli or pharmacological agents as they would in an animal practical or clinical scenario, monitoring and recording data with on-screen oscilloscopes, chart recorders and other apparatus. This can be in real-time, or adapted to requirements; student experimentation to find solutions to specific challenges can benefit from the opportunity to work faster and at lesser expense than in a conventional animal lab.

Various parameters in the experiments, such as pressure and volume in a virtual cardiovascular physiology practical, can be modified by users to generate data sets for analysis, and there may be options for different levels of complexity within one program. Instructors will give students a degree of control appropriate to the teaching objectives. The responses themselves may derive from previous animal experiments no longer performed, or from algorithms, and may include random variables to simulate biological variability and thereby produce varied results amongst the students. Some simulations enable the illustration of concepts or the performance of tasks that would be unethical, difficult, or impossible in the real situation, such as the effects of breathing low oxygen concentrations, measuring cerebrospinal fluid, or the re-use of preparations.

Web applications

Web-accessible software for student use is an approach that is increasingly being explored in the development of computer-assisted learning (CAL), and can provide increased ease of delivery and use both within an institute and for distance learning. Some alternatives and training courses are already available on-line, but the internet as a medium could be further exploited in order to maximise the creative use and positive impact of such technology on the learning process. For example, such programs could offer on-line experimentation; students could work where and when they choose, and re-visit their individualised on-line lab to revise or to continue with specific experiments. Tutors could also monitor and analyse individual results with greater ease. As well as creating the teaching material itself, such a vision requires from instructors and their collaborators knowledge of web applications and the technical skills for web design and programming in order to be realised. It also requires adequate computer hardware and software.

When designing courses, instructors typically deconstruct existing instructional resources, create some of their own, and then combine the different components in order to meet their chosen teaching objectives. One concept being explored at the forefront of design and of web applications for educational purposes is that of sharing these design components, or 'learning objects'. Well-designed pieces of virtual laboratory equipment and well-written algorithms from existing alternatives are examples of learning objects that could be useful to other instructors involved in software design for new alternatives. Most current software design does not allow individual components of the software to be de-contextualised. Releasing learning objects that were previously only available for use within specific programs, and ensuring that new software is designed with content as reusable learning objects, can provide more resources for instructors to choose from. Building this concept into a mutual aid facility could be achieved via a database available on-line, with users both contributing and taking individual elements of programs. Existing freeware could also be contributed. Sharing these resources is a democratising task that will support the process of good course and software design: software developers able to reuse learning objects can avoid repeating design work already performed, and are free to focus on their own individual design strengths and location requirements, thereby pushing the boundaries of best practice in course design and delivery.

Design and support

Using software, students can largely be self-directed and work at their own pace. They can repeat parts of the program, and use the support material that is provided by tutors or that is available within the program itself, until they are satisfied that they understand the experimental procedure and the principles being taught. Sufficient theoretical knowledge should provide the basis upon which the new skills and knowledge can be built using the program. Self-assessment questions and feedback within the programs, opportunities for presentation of results and conclusions, and tutor support and review, can confirm this.

Support material such as student workbooks and teachers' notes may be available from the producer of the software, and locally-editable 'wraparound' support may provide the ideal tool for effective implementation. Teachers may also choose to make their own accompanying literature.

Good design of educational software can lift students to higher conceptual levels as well as providing a better understanding of the specific topics being addressed. Moreover, fundamental and crucially important aspects of the life sciences can be appreciated and practised by students, independently or in groups. In particular it can encourage self-directed exploration and problem-solving strategies that support initiative, creativity and scientific thinking. And by being firmly grounded in the student's own experience, such active learning is highly effective. With realistic experimental conditions simulated, experimental design can also be practised.

The integration of different media and the design of different levels of learning experience within one program can provide a complex teaching aid that is highly sensitive to the requirements of the practical course and the individual student. Effective visioning and design of the software requires an element of interdisciplinarity and collaboration between, for example, physiologists, educationalists, graphic designers and programmers. Student involvement in the process of production of new software, such as testing *beta* versions and making suggestions for refinement, can both improve the quality and educational potential of the software and intimately involve students in the field under study.

The innovative nature of new technological developments, such as multimedia software, can be exciting for students and teachers alike, which adds to the learning experience and is an important part of the informal training for professions where computer skills will play a crucial role. Nevertheless, computer simulation should always be complemented by non-harmful practical experience with living humans or animals, so that technology is kept as a powerful tool, not an alternative to reality.

Virtual Reality

All simulations, whether computer software or plastic models, are virtual models of reality, but the term 'virtual reality' (VR) is generally understood to refer to advanced interactive software with exceptional 3D graphics and an immersive nature which allows for psychomotor skills and procedures to be practised with a high degree of sensory experience. VR dramatically increases the opportunities for real-time interaction with a dynamic model of reality, through the computer-human interface.

It has taken until the late 1990s for the processing requirements of real-time VR simulators to became available on personal computers, so the field is very young and involves cutting-edge technologies. VR has been used in other areas such as flight simulation and disaster management training due to the importance of highly effective preparatory training for such high-risk scenarios and the obvious practical or ethical limitations on real-life experience. The adoption of VR by the medical profession is driven by the same concerns about the importance of expert training, and by the growth of innovative minimally-invasive diagnostic and therapeutic techniques. Such techniques already have a 'virtual' nature with the development and use of high-quality endoscopes, digitally-enhanced video imaging, and new instrumentation; and they involve many skills-oriented techniques. They are therefore well suited to VR simulation.

Currently, little VR is used at medical schools, the applications being mainly for object visualisation and data analysis in clinical practice and research, for learning new skills at trainee and professional level, and for skills maintenance by surgical specialists. Interest in VR within veterinary medical education is currently even less common, and there is relatively little money invested in improving veterinary education. Despite under-funding, and the resource-intensive nature of VR, computer scientists in collaboration with a small number of veterinary colleges have developed trial VR simulations such as horse ovary palpation and canine anatomy exploration[5].

Within both the medical and veterinary medical fields, VR will increasingly be adopted in response to the demand for specific skills in graduates, and as recent developments in technology filter down into the educational environment and get adapted to meet the specific demands of teaching objectives. These demands will include improved visualisation of anatomical structure and physiological and pharmacological processes, as well as clinical skills. As it evolves, VR could also be used to perform more complex experiments in the virtual environment, providing a further enhancement to the simulations currently available to students, and adding to the momentum of replacement in every area.

Skills training using VR

VR is particularly useful for training in endovascular and endoscopic procedures, through the use of a virtual patient. Images of the patient may be created using technologies such as CAT scanning and advanced computer graphics. Different scenarios and complications are presented in VR simulations; the trainee practices by holding a wand, which represents an instrument such as a needle or scalpel, and performs the required procedure in front of a screen which images the anatomy and tracks the movement of the instrument in real-time. Headsets may provide a stereo-scopic view, but there are several other methods of immersion in the virtual environment, including situating the trainee in a cubic room, and projecting, on to each wall, images which correspond dynamically to the trainee's movements.

A range of different views of the live simulated procedure can be chosen. Specific tissues can be dissolved away so that an increased awareness of and sensitivity towards specific anatomical landmarks are developed, supporting the successful completion of a procedure. As well as visual feedback, that of haptics - the tactile sense that can be simulated in VR - plays an increasingly important role. Specially designed data gloves can be used, offering resistance as an endoscope or proxy needle interacts with the virtual patient's body. This force feedback means that roll, pitch and yaw can clearly be felt, and that challenging techniques such as negotiating a needle around a vein, manoeuvring a catheter into the coronary arteries, or navigating curves in the colon, can be practised and improved upon. Other feedback can include 'comments' from the virtual patient - such as an expression of discomfort or pain - and on-screen visual evidence of bruising or bleeding. Various parameters can also be measured and analysed later for more detailed feedback on performance.

VR fits well with and can enhance problem-based learning (PBL) curricula in education through the extra facilities it can offer to examination of clinical cases. Research into this application for clinical practice and education is on-going. Web-based simulations using dynamic VRML (Virtual Reality Modelling Language) are also being explored for selected clinical skills training, such as practice of catheterisation, but their nature is not as immersive as full VR.

Virtual surgery and robotics

As scanning and imaging techniques further improve in quality, speed and degree of application, data from individual real patients may be inputted more frequently into the VR environment. Visualisation by surgeons will be improved, and surgical procedures that are specific to individual patients' needs may be performed virtually in advance. The actual procedure may use endoscopic techniques, and in time perhaps also robots as surgical tools. Experience in VR by students at university and by surgeons in their on-going professional training will help prepare them for endoscopic procedures: as well as specific VR simulations in endoscopy, the technique itself is 'virtual' in nature, with action at a distance and with visualisation through monitors.

The same is true for robotic surgery. This can extend and enhance human performance and reach parts of the body difficult to access conventionally. Trials of minimally-invasive cardiac surgery have already taken place using robots. The robotic arms and instruments can cut and graft arteries, making sutures and tying knots at the micro level, mimicking the surgeon's moves at the macro level nearby - but without the tremor. This greater mechanical sensitivity, dexterity and precision enhancement, and the freeing of the surgeon to focus more on the mental tasks, can only be positive for the patient.

VR will also be applied in the future in remote applications such as clinical examination of a patient, where the physical presence of a medical team is limited or impossible. Networked virtual environments will allow for collaborative sharing of expertise, and human resources can be combined and projected using supercomputers and telecommunications, including satellite, for effective responses to medical emergencies. Telementoring is the most likely immediate application, but remote surgery is a real possibility.

Ethically-sourced animal cadavers and tissue

For many zoology students and all future veterinarians, the study of anatomy would not be complete without some degree of hands-on experience of animals and animal tissue. Similarly for surgery, training would not be sufficient if actual experience of real tissue and the associated skills practice was absent. Ethical alternatives to the killing and harming of animals do of course exist for such requirements, specifically the use of ethically-sourced animal cadavers and tissue.

The term 'ethically-sourced' in this context refers to animal cadavers and tissue obtained from animals that have died naturally or in accidents, or that have been euthanised secondary to natural terminal disease or serious non-recoverable injury. Animals that have been harmed or killed to provide cadavers and tissue are not considered ethically-sourced, nor are those sourced from places where harming or killing is commonplace. Moreover, a market should not be created or supported for the acquisition to be considered ethical.

The use of ethically-sourced cadavers is not a new approach. Within human medicine it is standard practice. The acquisition of human cadavers that are donated by consent may not always be sufficient at current levels of donation, but nevertheless willed body programs and other mechanisms do meet some of the needs of medical students for anatomy study. The ethical sourcing of animal cadavers should be no different, and is potentially much easier than that of human cadavers.

Replacement

Dissections of ethically-sourced cadavers can replace dissections of killed animals in anatomy practicals, for those students who genuinely require dissection skills in their careers. Such dissections can complement multimedia and other alternatives or students can progress from the gaining of basic skills using models, mannekins and simulators on to the use of cadavers. For both students and professionals (for example, where surgeons need to train new procedures), cadavers are also excellent clinical skills and surgery training tools. As a valuable resource, they should not be used for basic skills training, but for the next stage of training they provide an excellent tool to gain an appreciation of the 'feel' of real tissue, and to learn techniques such as exposure, surgical anatomy and closure. Ethically-sourced organs and tissue may also be used for training surgical techniques such as intestinal anastomosis, and the organs or whole cadavers may be perfused in simulators to provide opportunities for practising various procedures and using specific surgical tools.

Ethically-sourced cadavers and tissue can therefore be used to develop and hone students' practical skills to a sufficient level in preparation for apprentice work with live patients. Published studies have shown that students using cadavers for surgery training are at least as competent as those using live animals, and students who have used ethically-sourced cadavers are also very positive about the learning experiences[6].

Fresh animal tissue from ethical sources can also be used within some biochemistry, pharmacology and physiology practicals, in those situations where multimedia is not considered a more appropriate tool. Leftover tissue from beneficial operations on animal patients, when not needed for the benefit of other animals, may be suitable for practicals in these disciplines. When convention dictates that specific organs of particular species are used in experiments and preparations, then the same tissue may be ethically-sourced to transform the experiment into an alternative. If obtaining sufficient guinea pig ileum or rabbit jejunum is considered impossible, then an alternative that uses real tissue may still be possible: with minimal adaptation the experiment could be performed using the ethically-sourced ileum or jejunum from small animals of other species.

Body donation programs

Amongst the most practical sources of animal cadavers are veterinary teaching hospitals and independent veterinary clinics. Ethically-sourced cadavers can be obtained from 'body donation programs', where clients of the clinics consent to donating the cadaver of their companion animal to teaching, after the animal's natural death or euthanasia. Also known as 'willed body', 'client donation' and 'educational memorial' programs, they have proved workable and sustainable at a number of universities for supplying cadavers to meet anatomy and surgery training needs, and should be explored by all departments that genuinely need cadavers for teaching (see Kumar, in this volume).

Body donation programs provide an excellent example of the multi-benefit solutions that the process of implementing alternatives can offer. With very many animal cadavers being disposed of or cremated, such programs make use of this existing but neglected resource, saving energy, money, and most importantly animal lives by directly replacing the killing of animals. With the animals' medical histories available, there is a guarantee of disease-free cadavers, and opportunities to observe pathologies as well as normal anatomy. Students will be happy that no killing is required, the need for conscientious objection is obviated, and the learning environment is improved as a result. The profession can display compassion and empathy, and build trust with the public, by showing respect for the human-animal bond and commitment to an ethical education. The family of the companion animal are offered an opportunity to alleviate some of their grief by being able to help educate future veterinarians and thus help other animals. And the public can be educated about the need for cadavers and tissue within teaching and research - as long as the profession can demonstrate that it will respect and use ethically the bodies of former companion animals that are entrusted to them.

It is a positive challenge for universities to make the right connections either between departments or with independent clinics, and to build a sustainable infrastructure in order to utilise cadaver resources effectively. Nevertheless, provisional organisational structures, perhaps with student involvement, are worth setting up in order to begin the process of ethical sourcing; evolution and refinement of the program can happen over time. The increase in the number of body donation programs - for example in the USA - is testament to the common sense of making good use of a wasted resource.

Animal tissue banks

Centralised animal tissue banks for ethically-sourced material could also be set up within regions of countries to provide a wider variety of animal tissue (and cadavers), and to support a more reliable and consistent ethical source for education. Collection and almost immediate use of fresh tissue would also be possible if the acquisition and distribution processes were of a sufficiently high standard. Animal blood from healthy companion animal volunteers, stored for life-saving transfusion medicine and an increasing number of other therapeutic purposes, could also be used within education to replace blood sourced from lab animals. Investment in and publicity for existing animal blood banks, as well as support for new projects, would be needed to help provide sufficient blood for both clinical use and education. Animal blood banks could be closely linked to new networks of animal tissue banks.

Lessons from the establishment of human tissue banks, such as the new European network, can be applied to animal tissue banks as they become established. The former allow for the ethical, safe and controlled acquisition of human surgical waste, post-mortem material and non-transplantable tissue for biomedical research and testing. Although the donation of human tissue and its use as a replacement for killed animal tissue within research and testing still requires widespread adoption, the use of excess human tissue is feasible for human and veterinary medical education as well.

Students themselves could also consent to donating their own blood for use in practical work, as long as transfusion services are not deprived of the resource. The use of human or animal blood must accord with ethical, health and safety guidelines, of course. And in many countries, transportation of cadavers and tissue may be controlled by health and safety legislation. Awareness of the regulations is important, and challenges to inappropriate practical restrictions may be called for.

Other sources of supply

University pathology departments constantly receive animal cadavers. Large and small animals are autopsied and used for pathology teaching, and the public is known to bring in dead wild animals on occasion. With increased co-operation between the departments of pathology, anatomy and surgery, diseased animal cadavers could be used more widely for educational purposes. For example, parts of animals such as limbs that are not used in pathology teaching could be used within anatomy, surgery and some clinical skills training.

Other potential sources of cadavers and tissue include dead animals and fish from pollution incidents (where there is no toxic hazard), and 'road kill' of animals whose cadavers are sufficiently useable. Student and nature protection groups helping with the annual frog migration in some countries will be able to source some material in this way, for example.

Borderlines and compromises

The above two examples illustrate the ethical difficulties surrounding some sources of cadavers; they are borderline 'ethical' because the animal deaths would not occur if it weren't for inappropriate economic development, criminal negligence and an anthropocentric society that does little to respect the boundaries and rights of other species. On rare occasions, or where uncommon species are required for study, ethically-sourced animals may not be easy to procure. Non-ideal sources such as animal breeders, research facilities, some animal shelters, farms, slaughterhouses and sporting events - i.e. places where the harmful use, killing or marketing of animals is typical - may for some students provide an acceptable compromise, but only when the cadaver or tissue was genuinely destined for disposal and the sourcing contributes nothing to the continuation of harmful practice. Slaughterhouse waste organs may be acceptable, but not whole animals; a terminally ill, euthanised dog from a shelter may be used, but not one that was killed because re-homing was 'difficult'. The sourcing of animal cadavers and tissue should prioritise body donation programs, where the positive ethics are clear, and non-ideal sources employed only when absolutely necessary. Biological supply companies usually source killed healthy animals and these are always unacceptable ethically.

Preservation and storage

The next important issue that needs to be addressed is that of the preservation and storage of cadavers. Certainly some cadavers will be fresh and can be used immediately or within a few days. Cold storage within anatomy or pathology labs will keep the cadaver in good condition and minimise autolysis. But re-use of the cadaver, and storage for future use, will require more than a cool room. Ensuring a sufficient number of cadavers to meet training needs will require careful planning and long-term storage.

Freezing the cadavers is one solution. Careful preparation before freezing, such as the emptying of blood, immediate cooling by removal of fur or by skinning, and rapid access to the freezer, can help with successful preservation of tissue and help ensure even thawing before use. Embalming fluids, which usually contain the toxin and pollutant formalin, are also very often used to fix cadavers. Combinations of different chemicals can be used for different tissues and for different end-results, such as diversity in tissue texture and longevity.

There is room for further development of preservation techniques, but freeze-drying, silicone impregnation ('silyophilisation') and a range of plastination techniques are increasingly being used for preservation of cadavers, organs and thin slices. In plastination, the water and lipid within the cadaver are replaced by curable plastic polymers which are then hardened, resulting in real specimens with textures and structures that are very well preserved. Different polymers, including silicone rubber, epoxy resin and polyester, are chosen to produce specimens of varying flexibility and opacity, and dyes can be used to highlight specific structures. The specimens are more durable and practical to handle than in the conventional 'wet' lab. Silyophilisation and plastination also offer the advantage of a safer and less toxic environment for those involved in both the preservation work and the use of specimens within teaching.

Clinical work with animal patients and volunteers

It is expected that the training of medical students will involve experience with real patients, and the more experience - at the right level and the right time - the better the training. From interpersonal and clinical skills, to opportunities to learn anatomy, physiology and more, the clinic and the hospital provide excellent learning environments for medical students. Problem-based learning, using clinical cases, is also recognised as a powerful educational approach and is increasingly being applied across the world. Both are replacing animal experimentation in those countries where animals are still used for human medical education.

Realistic training

Veterinary students can effectively gain clinical skills and surgical experience through beneficial or neutral work with animal patients and animal 'volunteers'. For some students around the world, this is already the norm, with a tradition of beneficial clinical work rather than vivisection being standard practice[7]. As well as replacing the use of killed animals and stressful and invasive or terminal live animal use, such an alternative approach encourages respect and consideration for the animal, and can allow students to be aware of or actively involved in the whole process of animal care, from diagnosis through to post-operative care and recovery. Other skills that are essential for the professions, such as experiencing and dealing with the clinical environment and its demands, appreciation of the diversity of patients and clinical situations, and communication skills with work colleagues and animal guardians, can also be gained using these alternatives. As such, the clinic can provide a highly realistic and relevant training, and allow for true apprenticeship. The use of 'clinic' animals, kept and used repeatedly for training procedures, and of course the use of experiments and terminal surgeries, teach none of these and work against the veterinary ethic of animal care and healing.

Skills acquisition

Animal 'volunteers' are those such as students' own companion animals that are encouraged to participate in non-invasive, non-harmful clinical skills training. Handling skills, physical examinations, blood sampling and bandaging are examples of clinical work that are appropriate with an animal volunteer. Rewards rather than intimidation and punishment, and the right of the animal to stop his or her participation the moment that fear or discomfort is evidenced, can provide an ethical and fully respectful environment.

Other clinical skills training that may involve invasive procedures are justified when performed as part of beneficial clinical work on animal patients. Harm caused to an animal patient during a clinical procedure and/or treatment is acceptable only when it is the minimum harm necessary for successful work aimed at healing the animal. Involvement by students in all clinical work requires that they have the appropriate level of skills mastery. Non-animal alternatives such as models, mannekins and simulators can help students accomplish this mastery within the clinical skills arena, and computer simulation can provide experience in crisis management, critical care and various procedures. The safety and well-being of an animal patient should never be jeopardised by students, and constant supervision by qualified instructors is necessary during any learning process that involves live animals.

Wound management, intubation, and simple or more complex surgery can also be learned best and ethically in the clinic and with real patients. There are plenty of opportunities to learn surgery skills in ways that not only avoid harm to animals, but contribute to their well-being. Veterinary teaching hospitals and independent veterinary clinics have a constant flow of patients; observation of procedures, student-assisted surgery, and finally performance of basic procedures by students can contribute not only to effective and rewarding student education and the replacement of harmful animal use, but to support for veterinarians as well.

Some of this alternative track clinical work, however, will also involve extra work for the veterinarians, particularly during the establishment of the program. Curricular and organisational changes within universities would be required in order to increase the emphasis on clinical work with animal patients. This is already happening, however: attached to over half of all American veterinary teaching hospitals are 'community practice clinics', established to provide students with clinical experience of primary care work within the community. When there are time and personnel limitations, then developing links with independent practices could be prioritised. Many students already work as assistants in clinics during their studies and their breaks in order to gain valuable experience, and this practice could be mainstreamed so that all students can benefit.

Shelter animal sterilisation

There are other significant opportunities for work with animals that can be explored in order to replace animal experiments and to provide students with more practical experience. In particular, animals in shelters (pounds) can benefit from supervised basic veterinary care and from sterilisation performed by students. As with the successful ethical sourcing of cadavers, the challenge is to build and sustain the infrastructure required, and to ensure that all parties can benefit. Students may offer to work for free, but they will gain valuable experience in exchange.

The castration and spaying of companion and stray dogs and cats - two of the most common operations that graduate vets will face - are typical procedures that students can participate in at shelters. Both, of course, require sufficient student competence and initial supervision. Castration is a fairly simple operation that can be learned quickly, but spaying needs more practice. All universities should be providing many more opportunities for students to perform spays, for example through sterilisation programs. Such 'service learning' is sometimes arranged through co-operation between universities and animal protection groups. Adoption of sterilised animals is higher than the average animal adoption rate, and a reduction in the number of future stray animals is likely.

Increasing potential

The learning potential of clinics, especially within teaching hospitals, can be maximised by allowing students from different disciplines and levels to observe clinical work on patients. This can be live or recorded, and watched in small groups or projected on to a screen for larger groups. Instructors may talk through a procedure, appropriate to the level of the students; not only surgery, but anatomy, physiology, pharmacology and critical care can be illustrated too. Recordings can also be edited into making video or multimedia alternatives. Material from the clinic, including urine, faeces, and blood, may also be used in the teaching of pharmacology, parasitology and immunology, for example. The potential can therefore extend well beyond the clinic itself.

Student self-experimentation

For most life science students the importance of practical work with the living body cannot be over-emphasised. The effective understanding of physiological processes, and the practice of clinical skills, does require experience of the living body. The consenting student is an excellent experimental animal, and student self-experimentation is a non-invasive humane alternative. The intense involvement and self-reference of all self-experimentation practicals can make them memorable as well as enjoyable - qualities that are highly significant in terms of learning.

Biology and human medicine

Self-experimentation and clinical skills training with students are used by most institutes as part of normal practice. Blood sampling, blood pressure measurements and venous catheterisation on students is typical of medical education. Common self-experimentation practicals using standard lab equipment may include urine and blood analysis before and after exercise or the ingestion of various substances. More complex self-experimentation apparatus with associated hardware and software can allow for measurements of EEG/ECG activity and skin temperature in resting, exercising and mentally active situations; of nerve conduction velocity and EMG; of pulmonary function, and for other tests[8]. These may offer a choice between pre-programmed lessons for demonstrating fundamental physiological principles, and opportunities for generating local lesson templates. Opportunities also exist for data collection (and subsequent analysis) from physiological measurements during more extreme circumstances such as fairground rides, using flexible telemetry technology[9].

Of course, self-experimentation practicals must accord with the highest ethical standards, including the necessity of informed consent and the right to withdraw; supervision by a qualified teacher; avoidance of risk, harm and embarrassment; and anonymity of data, where appropriate. Local ethical review committees would generally need to assess experiments in advance.

Relevance for veterinarians

The human body can be used in all the life sciences, including general biology and veterinary medicine. Veterinary students would benefit from self-experimentation, as humans can also be models for non-human animals. Training specific clinical skills with a student as the first 'patient', rather than an animal, can help create an environment that is more conducive to learning skills and building confidence: no animals will be stressed or harmed in the process, and students will not face this ethical problem; the training can be more controlled, and the 'patient' can respond to suggestions and give feedback. It also offers the opportunity to understand how it feels to be the patient, an experience that veterinary students usually lack compared to their colleagues in human medicine. The students will of course also need to learn the techniques on the relevant animals, but they will be better prepared: taking blood from a rabbit and a horse are two very different things, but taking blood from a fellow student is an experience in between.

In vitro labs

The rapid development and uptake of *in vitro* technology in research and testing is based on both the scientific and ethical advantages of tissue and cell culture. The lower cost and faster rate of screening for assessment of toxicity, and the superior reliability and repeatability of *in vitro* testing, are complemented with the ethical advantages of not using animals *in vivo*. This shift in practice needs to be supported by student familiarity with the techniques, and *in vitro* practicals can provide this experience. A greater emphasis on cellular pharmacology and physiology studies, for example, could contribute significantly to the replacement of animal experiments. Animal tissue and cells used for *in vitro* work can be sourced ethically, and recent developments in non-animal serum replacements and serum-free cell culture media overcome the ethical problems of using the conventional foetal bovine serum. Moreover, within some cell biology practicals, the use of animal tissue and cells can be replaced directly with plant material: for studying cell respiration and electron transport, for example, mitochondria can be sourced from turnips, potato or beet instead of rat liver[10]. With ethically-sourced animal preparations, or with plant material, therefore, such *in vitro* practicals can then be considered as alternatives.

Field studies

Students within the fields of biology, zoology, ethology and even ecology may often find themselves in situations where animals are studied in a laboratory setting as a model for nature, or where inter-action with animals in the field is harmful to the animals or their habitat. But biology is not just experimentation, nor does its study require harm. Much of the knowledge gained about animals and nature has come from observation and other non-invasive fieldwork. This tradition of studying animals within their natural environment is a particularly rewarding alternative to harmful animal use which could be developed and explored in order to replace some harmful animal use in the above disciplines.

Such field studies offer opportunities to study animals expressing natural behaviour rather than the limited or stereotyped behaviour presented by isolated individuals or groups within the lab. They can provide a richer learning experience for the student, and support the appreciation of animals as free individuals of integrity, existing within a complex and dynamic web of social, cultural and ecological realities.

Locations and impact

The ideal fieldwork should contribute to the animals' protection and well-being, directly or indirectly. It should not involve harm, and should cause zero or minimal disturbance. Assessing to what degree any activity may be invasive, and choosing to minimise that impact, should of course be done during the planning and design stages of the fieldwork. The impact depends on the location, the species, the method, and many other factors. Ecologically-sensitive areas and endangered species should be avoided unless significant benefits for either are expected, and instructors must have the appropriate training for whatever animals and habitats are part of the study. Evaluation of the methods chosen should always be performed afterwards to support thorough analysis of results and to allow improvement in design in the future.

Fields and forest clearly provide opportunities for field studies, and insects, birds and many other animals can easily be studied with minimal disturbance. Student and instructor sensitisation to the animals and their habitats can benefit both the field work and the animals, and techniques such as scats analysis and observation or monitoring from a distance can further reduce disturbance.

Towns and cities are also rich in possibilities to study wild or semi-wild populations of local animals such as pigeons, rats, foxes, and in some countries cows and non-human primates[11]. Insects, domestic dogs and cats, and stray animals can also form part of student fieldwork, as can humans themselves. Conservation work, rehabilitation centres for wild animals, rescue shelters for farm animals, and no-kill shelters for stray animals are further ethical locations; these may provide opportunities to study specific species that may not be ethically acceptable or practicably available for study elsewhere. Zoos and other permanent captivity locations rarely provide an environment that is sufficiently natural or free of harm to justify their use for fieldwork, though they may be used to illustrate suffering, and how animals should not be kept.

Human-animal interaction

Existing human interaction with animals can also be studied. Investigation of animal populations before, during and after interaction from which the animals benefit - for example, nesting behaviour in pigeon populations in pigeon towers, or social interaction in a stray cat population being spayed and offered food and housing - can provide interesting material for analysis as well as direct benefits for the animals.

A challenging approach to fieldwork that involves the investigation of human-animal relationships is to design experiments where animals interact with humans on their own terms. Good knowledge of and sensitisation to animal behaviour and interspecies interaction is a prerequisite to such experiments, and the challenge is to create a situation where the animals themselves choose to interact and thereby participate in the study. They are not coerced into it, and can walk, hop or fly away from it at any time. This 'positive experimentation' gives to the animals the opportunity to express agency, rather than takes that agency away; it should also bring them benefit. This is an analogue to some experiments with humans, based on the ethics of informed consent for involvement. As with all such experiments, however, the designers of the study should ensure that choosing to participate is as genuinely free a choice as possible. Examples of positive experimentation include studying interactions between sensitive dogs and their guardians, or other established close human-animal relationships; and ethically-responsible interactions between human and non-human primates[12].

Notes and references

1. The Principles of Humane Experimental Technique - W.M.S. Russell & R.L. Burch (UFAW, 1992)

2. Interactive video and laser videodiscs are other less common digital video media

3. See entry for *P.O.P. Trainer* in *Part C - Alternatives File*

4. See entry for *Surgical Training System (Aboud's Model)* in *Part C - Alternatives File*

5. For example, Glasgow University (UK) is developing a virtual reality simulator for veterinary clinical skills training

6. For a summary of these papers, see Ethically-Sourced Cadaver Surgery: A Submission to Murdoch University's Division of Veterinary and Biomedical Sciences (Knight, A., 2000). See also Balcombe, and Kumar, in this volume.

7. For example in the UK. British human medical education also involves little harmful animal use.

8. See entry for *Biopac* in *Part C - Alternatives File*

9. For example, see Axelsson. M., J. Altimiras & K. Pitsillides (2002). TeleHeart: Using Telemetry to Teach Function and Control of the Human Heart - from face-to-face to distance education. Bioscience Explained Vol. 1.1. www.bioscience-explained.org. See also entry for *TeleHeart* in *Part C - Alternatives File*

10. The Excellence of Turnip Mitochondrial Fractions. Joaquim A.F. Vicente and Vitor M.C. Madeira (2000). Biochemical Education, volume 28, pp. 104-6.

11. Cohen, P.S. & M.L. Block (2001). Field-Based Animal Research Approach for Teaching Learning & Motivation. NUCASE. www.casdn.neu.edu/~nucase/library/cohenandblock.html

12. For example, see Smuts, B. (2001). Encounters with Animal Minds. Journal of Consciousness Studies. Vol. 8, nos. 5-7, pp: 293-309

2. The broader impact of humane education

Introduction

Most teachers who have developed alternatives and implemented them into the curriculum have done so primarily for their pedagogical advantages, as described in the previous chapter and in *Part B - Case Studies*. The positive ethical, social and economic impacts of progressive teaching methods have also played a role in the decision-making of some course designers. The multiple benefits of a curricular transformation that establishes humane education within the life sciences are now explored in detail. Awareness of these impacts, and of the problems created by harmful animal use, provides clear evidence in favour of alternatives. It can also directly inform the process of curricular design. The quality of the design, and therefore of the learning experiences presented to students, depends not only on the effectiveness of delivery of the main objectives, but also on the positive impact created beyond the classroom.

Life science philosophy

Affirming life

The physician's life-affirming commitment to healing, and the imperative *Primum non nocere*, or *First, do no harm*, have provided the philosophical basis to human medicine. The harmful use of animals, therefore, is contrary to the fundamental tenets of medicine: the widespread harming and killing of animals for dissection and experimentation in both medical and veterinary medical education teaches students that disrespect for life and the violation of an individual's integrity are acceptable practices. While the physician may on occasions harm in order to heal, this is not the case when educating the future professional with harmful animal use.

Such practices are equally counter-intuitive when addressing practical work within biological science, such that the study of life has in many ways become not *biology* but *necrology*. The focus on cadavers from killed animals, and the practice of invasive use teaches that life is not to be approached with sensitivity and respect, but instead experimented on, or killed and cut up with a scalpel.

Harm is caused to an animal when his or her well-being is limited in any way (see *Appendix*). The capture, transportation and housing of an animal is harmful, as it denies the opportunity for the animal to express its full natural behaviour and be part of a social structure and ecosystem. Experiments themselves may cause pain, fear or distress, and killing is a major harm, as life itself is denied to the animal.

A reconnection with *life* and with *healing*, through the use of alternatives such as student self-experimentation, work with animal patients, and interactive software that models living processes, will benefit life science education and impact positively on human and animal patients, and life itself.

Critical thinking

Critical thinking is the process of rigorous questioning and effective problem-solving. Critical thinkers use a healthy scepticism to assess information, question beliefs and practices, to face intellectual and practical challenges creatively, to construct and evaluate an argument, and to apply knowledge appropriately. These skills are necessary for true scientific thought: the scientific method itself is a formalisation of critical thinking.

The ability to think critically is gained through practising the process itself, with guidance from teachers; it cannot be taught effectively in abstraction. If life science education is teaching the scientific method effectively, then critical thinking skills are being employed. Questions such as 'Why is it so?' and 'How do we know?' are typical. Thinking beneath the surface, and identifying hidden assumptions are part of the process. An increasing awareness of one's own thinking processes and intellectual potential should develop, and intellectual self-reliance is encouraged. Learning *how* to think is very different to learning *what* to think. Overcoming intellectual laziness so that students are actively engaged in real thinking may require motivation at first, but the process is an empowering one and the skills gained have life-long learning and broad social impact. Critical thinking doesn't cease off the university campus or after graduation.

Conventional animal experiments often involve little critical thinking - students usually just follow instructions to deliver a contrived result. Genuine experimentation, using the scientific method, is often not available to students, or indeed encouraged, because of a lack of commitment to the process, or the ethical, practical, financial and time limitations associated with animal labs. Alternatives such as virtual laboratory work allow students to use their critical thinking skills to investigate and solve problems, and to learn how to make use of their knowledge, without the same limitations. They can experiment freely, learning both the subject matter and the scientific method itself in the process, and because they have more control over the practical class by working by themselves or in teams, they are able to repeat the experiments or discuss any problems until they know they have acquired a degree of understanding and mastery.

The use of simulations of clinical scenarios, such as anaesthesia management software, or advanced mannekins designed for critical care training, can challenge students to learn to think fast and to act appropriately, before involvement in live situations with human or animal patients. Such simulations are more realistic than recipe-driven animal experiments as they are focused on working with actual cases and exploring the range of likely scenarios. Clinical work itself, as an alternative, also provides real life situations that develop critical thinking and problem-solving skills. Other non-lab animal alternatives, such as research project practicals (see Scroop, in this volume), allow students to use the scientific method and hone their thinking skills within projects that are modelled on research methodologies.

Emotional and ethical literacy

Cultural values and practices such as sensitivity, respect, empathy, compassion and love play essential roles in holding society together. They help lift human behaviour and social norms above and beyond coarseness, lack of care, social division, prejudice and exploitation. The latter are expressions of psychological imbalance and cultural decay which negatively affect and often harm others within human society as well as the animals with whom we share our social and natural environment.

Life science practicals that involve major harm, such as killing or experimentation, are actually acts of violence when they are not necessary for the well-being of an individual animal. Operating on a patient, or euthanising an animal who is suffering and terminally ill, however, comprises a commitment to the animal's well-being. On the current scale of killing and suffering, harmful animal use could be considered a reflection of human barbarism which is holding back cultural development.

Sensitivity

Sensitivity is one of the major casualties of life science education when harmful animal use is the norm. Instead of valuing this positive quality and aspiring to enhance it, many teachers trivialise, dismiss, and knowingly or unknowingly destroy it. Animal experiments and the dissection of killed animals desensitise students through violation of the integrity and rights of the animal and of the students' own moral values. They therefore have a negative effect on respect, empathy and compassion for others.

Sensitivity is important because it is the quality by which we can receive signals from others and from our environment, and communicate back. It is necessary for understanding others and for knowing boundaries, and therefore for being able to respect integrity and rights. It is also needed for positive explorations of interpersonal and interspecies interaction, and for testing or challenging questionable boundaries in an ethical way.

Desensitisation is a process that develops as harmful animal use becomes a familiar sight and practice for students (and for teachers). For many it reaches a stage where the loss of sensitivity is no longer consciously recognised, and its absence seems normal. Such a loss, however, is an emotional crippling which has a significant negative effect on the nature of the individual's interpersonal and interspecies relations, as well as on their deeper psychological health.

Objections to harmful animal use are sometimes dismissed as 'squeamishness'. The use of this pejorative term implies that students aren't able to deal with the harsh reality of the life sciences - the use of a scalpel, the sight of blood, etc. They are 'too sensitive', 'non-objective', 'too feminine', 'not man enough'. Conscientious objection in higher education, however, is most often based on ethical disagreement with killing and harming healthy animals, and on demands for better learning experiences than harmful animal use can provide. Many veterinary students object, and yet their career choice is to deal with the suffering of animals, including repairing wounds and operating when required. Objectors are also prepared to 'get their hands dirty' by dealing with ethical issues, rather than avoiding them.

All students, particularly from their teenage years onwards, are exploring the moral universe and understanding the concepts of freedom, boundaries, and personal responsibility. Some new and challenging experiences may involve distancing or provoke revulsion from students until they are more fully understood. Some 'squeamishness', therefore, is an aspect of personal moral and emotional development and should be welcomed as part of a valuable reflexive experience and the evolution of a sense of identity. However, some students suffer trauma associated with a threat to their emotional or ethical integrity when witnessing or participating in harmful animal use. Psychological withdrawal, full dissociation, and avoidance are typical ways of trying to cope with this trauma. With the continuing systemic practice of harmful animal use, the widespread denial of the existence of an ethical problem, and with no support to deal with the trauma, effects such as unpleasant memories and guilt may last many years (see Makarchuk, in this volume).

Desensitisation is often defended as a necessary evil which helps students to learn how to deal with emotionally challenging situations both in their education and for future careers. How can veterinary students learn to make the first surgical cut on an animal, perform euthanasia on a terminally ill patient, or even think objectively, if they are not divorced from feeling and hardened to suffering?

The answer is that by defending sensitivity, by exploring emotional reactions to real and hypothetical situations, and by supporting ethical discussion, students can gain the psychological skills and strength to be able to deal effectively with most situations. Staying sensitive helps keep an awareness of possible scenarios or solutions to a crisis situation, and losing sensitivity can therefore limit the ability to act appropriately and apply effective judgement - for example to limit suffering. This emotional literacy, or intelligence, avoids the denial of problems and instead allows the student or professional to process the complex feelings associated with the work. A doctor who has not managed to save a patient will suffer personally by not dealing with the issue effectively, and trivialising the feelings may well affect future professional work in a negative way. A disaster paramedic needs to think and act quickly, and to be sensitive to degrees of suffering and to appropriate treatment. Insensitivity and uncaring approaches are neither desirable nor acceptable.

Promoting desensitisation, denying one's feelings, and blustering through situations may have been popular in decades and centuries past, but the techniques didn't work. Moreover, the dualistic split between emotion and reason is a social construct; it is not emotion that hinders objectivity, but a lack of critical thinking and awareness of the whole picture. The denial of emotion, and the denigration of emotional qualities and skills, can contribute to a lack of self-awareness that can also impact negatively on objectivity (after all, there is always someone behind the claim of objectivity). The more one is involved with sentient beings - animals or humans - the more important is sensitivity and sensitisation. Well-developed hearts and minds are surely prerequisites for all medical and veterinary medical work, if not for all professions.

In unavoidable situations such as disasters where full awareness of suffering could be overwhelming, then some denial and desensitisation can help one survive emotionally. For victims it may help guarantee physical survival, unless it limits perception of danger and an urgent need for action. However, these examples are self-imposed and temporary solutions, and subsequent emotional support through counselling will encourage the processing of the experiences. Phobias, or hypersensitivity to specific animals or activities, are also atypical situations where targeted desensitisation can help people. Desensitisation through harmful animal use is completely different: it is an imposed process, and should certainly not be necessary for survival through life science education.

Empathy and compassion
Sensitivity by itself cannot ensure positive interpersonal and interspecies interaction, or a positive contribution to better science; it can even be used as a tool for increasing harm to another. Combined with respect for others, however, sensitivity allows for empathy - the awareness of and

identification with another's feelings and lived experience. A prerequisite for empathy is that one is aware of and can identify one's own emotions. Scientific rationalism, 'maturity' and the male world have dismissed emotions and their importance, so this awareness is often an evolving process of recovering one's emotional self.

Sensitivity towards and empathy with students will require that coercing them, or dismissing their experience and their values, cannot be sustained ethically. Similarly, sensitivity towards and empathy with animals will require that denying their integrity and their ability to suffer, by objectifying, harming or killing them, should stop. Understanding this - understanding that we can all suffer - helps bring compassion. If we can be agents in avoiding the harm and creating well-being instead, then that is what we should do. The motivation for action comes from a sense of conscience, informed by emotional intelligence and by knowing oneself and one's responsibilities.

Denying an ethical problem exists, or not owning one's role in harming others, evidences a lack of conscience. This may come from insensitivity, empathic failure, and the elaborate defences we build to shield ourselves from the feelings that we ourselves have buried or lost. Rationalising animal harm, defending it through doctrine or the use of shallow emotional and sentimental arguments, are typical avoidance strategies.

History teaches us that in extreme situations, the lack of empathy can have disastrous consequences. During the second world war, whole groups of people were dehumanised: they were objectified and treated as 'vermin' in Germany, 'logs' in Japan, and 'the enemy' everywhere. Respect and empathy were discarded, and violence was rife. Medical education was used to further racist and fascist ideologies, with human experimentation, torture and killing performed by respected scientists. More recently, Harold Shipman, a practising doctor from Britain, was discovered to be a serial killer who had murdered around 300 patients. Importantly, he was described as exhibiting "clinical detachment" and being "unable to empathise", with no recognition of people's intrinsic value. He enjoyed "exercising dominion over others" and seemed to be without conscience or compassion[1,2].

Aspiring to 'clinical detachment' is still seen by many as a positive thing. Seeing animals as objects, as disposable tools with no intrinsic value, is commonplace. It is true that many people try to compartmentalise their life and their ethics, but nothing truly exists in isolation: lack of respect and empathy within a laboratory doesn't end at the door. Harmful use of animals in life science education contributes to an environment where extreme expressions of a lack of respect and empathy, like the above, can develop. It also supports the problem of medical practitioners who see the disease but not the person, and the harmful use of hundreds of millions of animals in research and testing, despite the alternatives. Why contribute to the problem by supporting harmful practices in the lab, a place where teaching respect for life is not only possible but urgently required?

Beauty, grace and love

In stark contrast to the above, there is beauty, grace and love. For some scientists, the appeal of research is in the beauty of the scientific method and of a well-designed and executed experiment. A carefully designed course for students where all the elements fit together synergistically into a powerful whole is also a work of art, as are some of the best learning tools. Some teachers enthuse students with a fascination and awe at the complexity and beauty of nature, animals and the human body; and show a passion for teaching, for learning, and a love of life.

Ethical literacy

Ethically literacy is the ability to understand the concepts and principles of moral thinking, to think critically about moral norms, and to apply these skills in personal and professional life. It involves both cognitive and emotional skills. Following a chain of thought logically will help make the connections between issues and bring the thinker to awareness of the consequences of an activity. Sensitivity, respect and empathy help inform the person about interpersonal and inter-species connections, including the nature of relationships, and an understanding of impact and boundaries. They also evidence an emotional literacy that is part of the self-awareness needed for taking full responsibility for one's actions - an essential part of ethical literacy.

Ethical literacy therefore contributes to self-development: the evolution and flourishing of a student with regard to their values and integrity, their engagement in local and world communities, and their competence and ethical commitment in their profession. Part of this self-development is an understanding of the impact of personal and collective ethical standards on society, and the role of ethical literacy within progressive change.

Recognising ethical issues, and being able to think them through critically, have long been identified as essential skills for the medical and veterinary medical professions. Work with a patient requires ethical literacy to help guide day-to-day action and to provide support for particularly challenging situations. Rapid advances in technology are giving rise to new and often difficult questions for which ethical literacy is needed. It is clear that the level of these skills is currently not high enough amongst the professions, the legislative and regulatory bodies, or the general public, to deal effectively with many of these issues. Science, along with many other areas, is too often seen as existing in an ethical vacuum, and the real consequences of this illusion are reflected in the problems all around us. But ethical debate must be an essential element throughout all policy and practice; it should not be added on to courses or policies, or seen as a separate issue, isolated from the rest of reality.

Ethical discussion is more likely to be initiated by critically-minded teachers and students, including those that have worked to introduce alternatives; it is often avoided when animals are used harmfully in courses. This avoidance suggests the denial of an ethical problem, and evidences a lack of critical assessment of the information concerning animal use and alternatives. To really support ethical literacy requires that teachers and students are able to challenge themselves, their beliefs and their frameworks; if neither are willing, then the very nature of science is betrayed. The widespread avoidance of discussions on the ethics of animal use and alternatives within the life sciences provides a *de facto* lesson in ethics: that ethical concerns do not matter. The hidden curriculum teaches that life is cheap and animals can be considered disposable tools.

When the issues are explored, however, there are many benefits. Teachers can demonstrate emotional and intellectual courage, by facing difficult issues; the process of dealing openly and responsibly with ethical questions is shown to be preferable to avoiding them; and the process of conflict resolution and achieving win-win solutions can be demonstrated - even more so when the student community is valued as an integral part of ethical decision making in the classroom.

Ecological worldview and social responsibility

Understanding the multiple negative impact of harmful animal use is part of a wider process of developing (or perhaps recovering) a deeper ecological or holistic awareness of interconnection and of taking responsibility for one's actions. The relationship between a policy, or choice of learning tool, on the one hand, and its pedagogical, social and environmental impact on the other, becomes clearer as this awareness grows. The denial of connection is harder to maintain.

Recognising oneself as a participant in the world community - which involves humans and animals - is both daunting and liberating: daunting because we increasingly recognise our current impact on the world (much of it negative), our responsibilities towards others, and the amount of tasks ahead; liberating because we increasingly see where and how we can sever negative relationships and impact positively instead. Every decision and action has multiple effects, and ethical choices should be made and organisational structures built that maximise the potential for good and minimise the potential for harm. Individual and collective commitment to genuine progressive social change through ethical choice is the hallmark of an evolved culture.

Keeping aware of the whole picture while being able to focus on specific elements, or fluently moving between the two, is a valuable skill. Reductionistic science finds this tricky, preferring to deny the whole for the sake of the parts. Denial of connection (such as the negative impact of harmful animal use), and even denial of the reality of ethical problems (that harmful animal use is an issue) are therefore commonplace.

In contrast, well-designed courses bring in many elements from different sources to create an effective 'whole'; the process of design requires awareness of both the detail and the whole picture. A sensitivity towards effective skills acquisition, designing combinations of alternatives that can most effectively support that acquisition, and awareness of the multiple benefits of alternatives, reflect an ecological worldview.

The creation of genuinely sustainable structures requires the same consciousness; building the right links or relationships between elements of a system can allow for the needs of the system to be met mostly from within it. For example, the needs of veterinary anatomy and surgery training (ethically-sourced cadavers), and existing resources (euthanised animals from teaching hospitals or local independent clinics), can be linked through body donation programs. The quality of the connection can be further improved, and the sustainability increased, with, for example, good client counselling on one side and effective storage strategies at the other. Having to raise money from outside sources in order to buy healthy animals to meet the needs is not sustainable; indeed, in countries where centralised funding has collapsed, there are sometimes shortages of animals within education. Alternatives combined with an ecological awareness can therefore provide fully ethical solutions which contribute to sustainable development.

Ethics and power

The history of the humane movement illustrates the interconnection between social movements and between different forms of prejudice and exploitation. Some social reformers in late nineteenth century Britain fought for children's rights alongside animal protection, and a number of early feminists also promoted vegetarianism or animal welfare reform. Before this, links between animal freedom and anti-slavery campaigns were being made. Many humane education groups working with children today clearly recognise that the cultivation of humane qualities, and the encouragement of critical thinking skills and personal responsibility, have multiple benefits that impact on individual people, animals and wider society. Within adult life science teaching, humane education deals with the same issues in greater depth, and also addresses how to acquire knowledge and specific skills in ways that are humane both to the animals and to the learner.

The harmful use of animals in education is in fact a form of exploitation. Comparing the exploitation of animals throughout society with domestic violence, sexism, racism and imperialism shows that they all use similar justifications, dynamics, strategies and tools, and have domination as the common element. They therefore mutually support each other, and so challenging one form of exploitation will impact on all. So the replacement of harmful animal use in education is part of a wider multi-pronged challenge to the unethical use of power over another. And when alliances between campaigns are explored, the potential for sweeping change is increased further.

Giving up the 'privilege' of using animals for experiments does not mean that teachers or students lose out. Like giving up any privilege or exploitative practice, it frees both the subject of exploitation and the exploiter. By dissolving the hierarchical power relationship, one returns to a diverse community of equals, and regains some humanity. Such a change allows for many new opportunities, including the development of positive interspecies relationships, and the practice of a true multiculturalism that extends to all life.

Accessibility and civil liberties

Accessibility to higher education is an issue that helps define social inclusion and which impacts on civil rights issues. Increasingly, governments are stating that they support accessibility, and policies have been drawn up to that end. Genuine commitment to it is lacking, however, and the barriers to full accessibility have not been removed. Harmful animal use limits accessibility and the development of diversity within education through discrimination against women, people of specific religious beliefs and spiritual approaches, and some critical thinking, ethically-committed and sensitive men and women.

Women are already under-represented within science and life science education. The reasons for this are multiple and complex, but self-perception concerning ability, stereotypical male values dominating science, and discrimination within the workplace all play important roles. Harmful animal use also contributes to the exclusion of women from education and therefore from the professions: reports and anecdotal evidence from the USA suggests that objection to harmful animal use is more likely from young women than from young men[2], although this does vary by country and according to the specific situation. Many women and some men have certainly avoided taking life science courses because they were not prepared to compromise their ethical principles or harm their sensitivity through involvement in animal experiments. Denying the relevance or value of the emotional realm in the life sciences is a further exclusive practice to some women and men.

These are accessibility issues because the students will not be able to benefit from a science education and career; moreover, their skills, and their sensitivity, are lost to science. For those that are already on life science courses, the academic or psychological penalty often associated with objecting can preclude opportunities for advancement, or demand changes in career paths from students, if alternatives are not provided.

Students with some religious beliefs may be discriminated against if harmful animal use is the norm in education. Compassion and reverence for life are fundamental tenets of Jainism, for example. Jains were advised by a spiritual leader in the twentieth century that they should not study medicine because of the dissection and vivisection required in some countries at that time[3]. Most other religions also have strong ethical elements within their teachings, although the degree of application of such elements in the world often leaves a lot to be desired. Accessibility and multi-culturalism are limited by discrimination against those who do hold reverence or respect for life as a spiritual or otherwise significant belief and practice.

The use of multimedia software and web-based training can increase accessibility for disabled, special needs and distance learning students, and many alternatives are well-suited to such media. Courses designed with a range of quality tools and approaches specially chosen to meet teaching objectives can also make life science education more suitable to the diversity of learning styles required by students. And with high quality, ethical training being offered, it also becomes more appealing.

Many students are given no choice whether to participate in harmful animal use for their practical work. Despite the increasing number of student choice policies being installed at state level or within some institutes, in other institutes students have no formal right to object or to be provided with alternatives. Students who disagree with harmful animal use may find they are discriminated against and their freedom of conscience violated. While a few may drop out or be forced to change discipline, others are encouraged or coerced into performing dissection and animal experiments with the threat or reality of psychological and academic penalty.

All students have the moral right to opt out of harmful animal use and have access to alternatives. International directives and conventions, national laws, constitutional amendments and state or local regulations usually favour accessibility and counter discrimination, at least in theory. Where these are not granted, the discrimination is an infringement of the students' civil liberties. Student rights or civil liberties campaigners may choose to sue an institute (or a government education department) on grounds of violation of freedom of conscience, religious discrimination, and limits to accessibility, including that of access to high quality and ethical education and training. A number of cases have already been to court, particularly in the USA and Germany, with judgements tending towards the protection of civil liberties.

Practical impact

Environmental impact

The use of alternatives removes the majority of the negative environmental impact associated with practical courses, and makes wise use of existing resources. It's 'ecological footprint' is significantly smaller than that of harmful animal use. The capture, breeding, housing, killing, preservation and transportation of millions of animals every year has a significant environmental impact. This involves pollution and disruption of local ecosystems, threats to endangered species, and the use of energy and other resources for transportation, housing and other aspects of animal use.

Taking animals from the wild has contributed to the decline of some species, such as leopard frogs and bullfrogs in the USA. The spiny dogfish shark is used widely for high school education, and yet is an endangered species. Turtles and other animals are also taken from their habitats, killed and used for education. Removing elements of healthy, sustainable ecosystems can disrupt them, sometimes permanently: frogs in particular may play a major role in an ecosystem's stability, as they are both predators and prey. When frogs from tropical countries are used, the insect population at the site of capture is likely to increase significantly, presenting an increased risk of malaria for humans.

Toxic chemicals such as formaldehyde are often used for preparing the millions of animals killed each year, particularly for dissection; they have a damaging environmental impact as pollutants, and pollution incidents involving illegal dumping of waste have been documented.

The production and use of alternatives, along with most (but not all) of human activity, does have some negative environmental impact. The production of computers, for example, involves the mining and refinement of oil for plastics and for transportation, and of rare earth minerals for circuit boards. This mining has significant local and global environmental impact, and often involves the infringement of the human rights of those living near the sub-surface resources. Pressure on corporations and governments to stop the human rights abuses is increasing, however, and the environmental impact of mining and production could easily be limited. The constant upgrading of computers also creates immense waste, but re-use and recycling could become typical if individuals and corporations took responsibility for their waste.

The ability to re-use alternative products such as computer software, videos and models over many years, however, means that there is no new production, limiting the impact of the alternatives to the initial production work only. Clinical work with animal patients uses existing resources, as does work with ethically-sourced cadavers. In fact, the latter makes use of cadavers that would otherwise be incinerated, itself a polluting process.

Economic benefits

Studies by the Humane Society of the United States (HSUS)[4] and the Physicians Committee for Responsible Medicine (PCRM) have compared the economic costs of dissection to the use of alternatives, and found a considerable difference in favour of the alternatives. Buying software, videos and models is in most cases cheaper that the purchase of animals for a single year's practical courses, and as they are usually re-used in the following years they are invariably cheaper in the long term than the annual purchase and housing of animals. For practical courses using cats, foetal pigs and bullfrogs, assessed over a 3-year period, the HSUS found that alternatives saved between $2,700 and $9,600, as well as providing a diverse selection of media for more effective learning.

If the many hundreds of high quality photographic images on some CD-ROMs were printed in a book, the cost would be prohibitive, particularly if class size is increasing. Similarly, the cost of equipment in a virtual laboratory is limited to the cost of the software itself, unlike a real lab. Body donation programs incur storage costs and sometimes transportation and preservation expenses, but the initial resource of animal cadavers is free. Clinical work with animal patients uses existing resources, although introducing new student involvement does of course require some financial input. Computer alternatives may require a high initial investment if there is little existing hardware in a department, but the outlay is recovered over time; moreover, the increase in computer re-use and recycling worldwide allows for cheaper purchase options. Beyond economics, the educational and other benefits of investment in progressive alternatives are often apparent immediately.

The development of alternatives such as multimedia software can support new localised economic activity, using the human resources and experience of teachers and other skilled workers found at the institutes themselves. Few outside resources are needed, meaning that self-reliance for the institute - and for the country as a whole - is supported. For those countries where the transfer and loss of skills and resources to others is typical, such localisation can provide significant economic and social benefits. Some income can also be generated if the products are sold.

The capture and shipping of animals from countries with little hard currency to those with much - the selling of Indian frogs and Mexican cats to the USA, for example - only perpetuates an unjust economic system where life and resources from those countries are commodified, and sold at prices that can never reflect their real value. Most resources, including finance, usually travel in one direction only, and the economic playing field is certainly not level. Meeting needs locally wherever possible frees both the source countries and the recipients from this unjust economic relationship, and can allow for local economic regeneration in both areas.

Working conditions

For the workers at biological supply companies and for the students dissecting killed and preserved animals, exposure to formaldehyde and other toxins is a serious health and safety issue. Despite recommendations for protective clothing, few students are usually protected. The pungent odour may also be the main memory of the dissection learning experience for students, rather than any anatomy lesson.

Working in jobs where the killing of animals is routine can only harden and harm the spirit of employees. As with factory farming and meat processing, a disproportionate number of workers at biological supply companies may be women or others from low-income and minority backgrounds. The 'dirty work' is carried out by traditionally exploited groups, often paid very little.

Needless to say, the production of alternatives can in general offer much better workplace conditions, although it is not without impact, nor without potential for improvement.

Personal and institutional reputation

Many developers of alternatives have found their personal and departmental reputations enhanced by their work. As well as adoption by other institutes, some high quality software has won awards within the fields of multimedia design or teaching innovation. New approaches can also attract students to specific institutes. Many academic papers dealing with new alternatives and their implementation have also been published. Learning about alternatives and their potential is beginning to be accredited as part of some 'professional development' courses, and in a growing number of countries alternatives training also comprises mandatory professional education for selected fields.

Even more important has been the enhanced reputation of teachers amongst students and work colleagues within an institute when innovative learning methods are employed and when ethical conflict is resolved. The resultant improvement in interpersonal relations and the learning environment can benefit all parties. Free distribution of alternatives, such as freeware CD-ROMs, also generates reciprocal goodwill and opportunities for collaboration.

Positive links between academia and the general public can be made through the practice of some alternative approaches. Establishing body donation programs for ethically-sourced animal cadavers provide one example. Members of the public that have companion animals can donate the body of a deceased animal towards veterinary anatomy and surgery training, aware that they are not only replacing harmful animal use but also contributing towards the effective and ethical education of future veterinarians. Body donation programs that prioritise sensitivity towards grieving animal guardians, that provide clear explanations of the need of cadavers and tissue within education, and that can demonstrate responsible use of the donations, show that veterinarians care about animals, their guardians, and the quality of veterinary graduates. Moreover, they can also help rebuild trust that has been breached by the historical (and in some places contemporary) reality of companion animals having been kidnapped for use in education and research, and by the occasional retention of human organs or tissue without informed consent.

Personal and institutional reputations can be seriously damaged by negative media publicity or legal challenges surrounding animal harm or the violation of students' civil rights. Several institutes in the USA have been forced to provide alternatives for students and to respect the constitutional and moral right to freedom of conscience after headline newspaper articles or legal judgements in the students' favour. Resolution of such problems long before these is clearly preferable, especially as win-win solutions can usually be found.

Legislative requirements

From an ethical point of view, the coercive nature of legislation suggests that personal and collective responsibility for change is preferable to that forced by diktat. Taking responsibility at the grassroots for curricular transformation is therefore not only an expression of academic freedom, but a democratic assertion. Until such responsibility is widely taken, however, legislation is a necessary tool to limit harm and discrimination, and to help establish alternatives as the norm.

Within Europe, the European Convention 123 states that in their basic university courses students should not use animals at all. The European Directive 86/609 states that alternatives should be used wherever possible, although the letter of the law excludes education. Many national laws are similar in stating that alternatives should be used where they exist, and some countries also have national or state / regional laws banning animal use at some levels of education. As well as conventions and laws against discrimination, the right to conscientiously object and the right to freedom of religion and conscience are enshrined in some national laws and constitutions. A growing number of institutes are incorporating student choice policies into their regulations and providing quality alternatives for conscientiously objecting students. Others are replacing the harmful animal use entirely.

The European Centre for the Validation of Alternative Methods (ECVAM), part of the European Commission, has also promoted replacement alternatives for life science education at workshops for scientists and teachers from countries in central and eastern Europe. Familiarity with alternative methods and conformity to the relevant alternatives legislation are necessary conditions for accession into the European Union. There is also a need, however, for countries already within the EU to improve their own scientific practice with further replacement at all levels.

Matters needing urgent attention, however, include updating of legislation to reflect today's science and ethical thought, ensuring the defence of animals, students and good science rather than established practice, and securing proper implementation of the laws. The keeping of better statistics, including numbers of animals killed before use in a procedure, would also provide the basic information needed to accurately assess the degree of harmful use in education and beyond.

Notes and references

1. Gove, M. The motives of a murder addict. The Times, 20 July 2002.

2. Stuttaford, T. Psychopath with no guilt and no regret. The Times, 20 July 2002.

3. See for example, Keeping Girls and Women in the Sciences. Ethical Science and Education Coalition (ESEC) website. www.neavs.org/esec

4. Dr. Natubhai Shah. Personal comm. 10 May 2002

5. Dissection vs. Alternatives: A Cost Comparison. Humane Society of the United States (HSUS) (2002). www.hsus.org/ace/15305

3. Assessment of alternatives in education

Jonathan Balcombe

Immersion Medical, USA

Introduction

The use of laboratory animals for teaching in the life sciences involves several costs. These include the expense of purchasing and/or maintaining the animals, the time required to prepare and conduct animal-based labs, ethical costs to animals, and social/ethical costs to students, most of whom wish them no harm. These costs have provided much impetus to develop alternative means of teaching in the life sciences, and the pace of this development has increased greatly over the past three decades alongside advances in computer technology and moral concern toward animals.

As so-called 'alternatives' to traditional animal labs have proliferated, so too have studies designed to assess how well they function as learning tools. To date, over thirty published studies and student theses have assessed the performance of these newer learning methods. This chapter summarises the findings of these studies. Because the quality of a study design influences its rigour, I also discuss the elements and provide examples of good study designs for assessing alternatives in education, to aid those considering conducting a study of their own. Finally, I briefly address the value of anecdote in the assessment of alternatives.

Assessment in education versus validation of alternatives to animal testing

This chapter is concerned with the assessment of learning methods, as distinct from the assessment of individual students. However, these two assessment levels are closely linked, because student performance is the typical yardstick by which a learning method is evaluated. More important is to distinguish the assessment of alternative methods in education from the validation of alternative methods to animal testing - used to estimate potential human hazards from exposure to drugs, industrial chemicals, and other products. While there are parallels, they are fundamentally different. In all cases of validation of animal testing alternatives, the traditional animal-based method is the standard against which the alternative is measured. However, in animal testing this *de facto* 'gold standard' is artificial because of the unreliability of extrapolating from non-humans to humans. This shortcoming is worsened by the fact that the animal tests themselves have been shown to be grossly unreliable: different labs have reported disparate results after performing the same animal test protocols (e.g. Zbinden & Flury-Roversy 1981).

In the case of education, a true gold standard exists: how well the students learn using different methods. One can compare the traditional animal method and the alternative method squarely, with humans as the true arbiter. This is because the data to which the alternative is compared are from tests performed on students, not tests performed on animals. No fuzzy extrapolation from animals to humans is needed. Thus, whereas animal testing measurements are one step removed from the human, data comparing the efficacy of lab animal-based learning methods with alternative learning methods can be compared directly on the same subjects. As a result, alternatives in education may be found to be superior to their traditional counterparts, while alternatives to testing are handicapped by the presumption that they can only be as good as the animal test.

Studies performed to date

To date, over thirty published studies have assessed learning methods designed to replace or reduce teaching methods that harm animals, such as animal dissections, invasive animal physiology labs, and terminal dog labs in medical and veterinary schools. This body of research is by no means exhaustive, and it represents only a small sampling of the thousands of available alternative teaching methods. However, it is substantial enough to make some comparisons and some general conclusions about the efficacy of such methods. In this section, I briefly summarise the research findings, organised by discipline within the life sciences. In the subsequent section, I examine the methods used in these studies. More detailed descriptions of the findings can be found in Balcombe (2000).

General biology

Evidence from several studies of students at both pre-college and college learning levels demonstrates that animal dissection is not superior, and may be inferior, to other learning methods with respect to acquiring basic knowledge of animal structure and function. Computer-based labs have resulted in equivalent (Kinzie et al. 1993, Strauss & Kinzie 1994) or significantly better test scores (Leonard 1992, More & Ralph 1994). Videotapes (Fowler & Brosius 1968) and 3-dimensional models (Downie & Meadows 1995) have also been found to generate equal or better learning performance compared with animal dissections. And both Lieb (1985) and McCollum (1987) found that lectures alone evinced post-test scores that were, respectively, equivalent and better than those of students who dissected earthworms and frogs.

Collectively, the eight studies cited above report on the performance of 4,149 students studying a variety of vertebrate and invertebrate organisms (e.g. rats, frogs, fish, earthworms, crayfish) in both the United States and Britain. In only one study (Matthews 1998) of 20 American college students have test scores been found significantly higher for dissection than for another learning method (computer program), but there has been criticism of Matthews' methods (see below).

Physiology and pharmacology

Physiology and pharmacology are fields that have traditionally used a preponderance of invasive live animal lab exercises. Here, too, a number of studies have been published, and the findings once again do not support commonly-held claims that lab animal-based learning exercises are superior to other learning methods not harmful to animals. These latter methods have performed equally or better in physiology or pharmacology courses taken by medical students (Samsel et al. 1994), veterinary students (Fawver et al 1990), nursing students (Phelps et al. 1992), pharmacology majors (Henman & Leach 1983), and physiology undergraduates (Dewhurst & Meehan 1993, Dewhurst et al. 1994). With the exception of Henman & Leach (1983), who compared use of a biovideograph with animal organ labs, each of these studies compared computer-based learning modules with traditional live animal labs. Collectively, these studies involved at least 300 undergraduate level students in both the United States and Britain.

Medicine and allied professions

Five additional studies of students in medicine or allied fields corroborate the findings of the studies cited above. In the United States, Guy & Frisby (1992) reported equivalent performance of 473 pre-nursing and pre-medical students using either interactive videodiscs or taught with cadaver-demonstration labs. Prentice et al. (1977), reporting on learning performance of 16 physician's assistant students, concluded that use of labeled sequential slides of anatomical dissections provided a viable alternative to human cadaver dissection. One hundred freshman medical students achieved equivalent learning performance using films, computer assisted instruction and prosected human cadavers to those taught by traditional lecture and cadaver dissection (Jones et al. 1978). And Lilienfield & Broering (1994) reported that 252 medical and graduate students who used a computer simulation achieved a significantly higher grade than their classmates in the cardiovascular section of the final exam. In Britain, Leathard & Dewhurst (1995) evaluated the performance of 105 pre-clinical medical students and found no significant difference between students who used a traditional live animal lab (for which rats were killed and segments of their intestines isolated) and those who used a computer simulation on intestinal motility.

Several additional studies, while not evaluating student learning performance directly, have nonetheless reported student preferences and time and cost savings for alternatives to traditional animal labs. Dewhurst & Jenkinson (1995) analysed responses to 40-question questionnaires from 50 institutions around the world that were using at least 3 from a set of 16 available computer packages. The responses indicated that the packages saved money and staff teaching time, were an effective and enjoyable mode of student learning, and significantly reduced animal use (*ibid*). In a study involving 110 U.S. medical students who used both computer demonstrations and animal (dog) demonstrations, the students rated the former higher than the latter for learning cardiovascular physiology (Samsel et al. 1994).

A relatively new application of computer technology in medicine is to the acquisition and maintenance of surgical procedural skill. Virtual reality training modules have been developed for training intravenous, endoscopic, endovascular and other procedures. Traditional training methods for some of these procedures (endoscopy and endovascular) involve practising on human patients in a clinical setting, and using live pigs, dogs, and sheep as surrogate human patients. Recent studies have shown that such simulations not only significantly improve practitioner performance (Rowe & Cohen 2000, Colt et al. 2001), but that they exceed traditional training methods in the acquisition of procedural skill (Ost et al. 2001). Other studies have confirmed that these simulators measure what they are intended to (Wong et al. 2001), and can discriminate users based on procedural experience (e.g. Mehta et al. 2000, Datta et al 2001).

Veterinary medicine

Non-animal surgical training devices are used extensively in veterinary schools to help hone skills prior to their application to live animal tissue. Anatomical models, for example, have proven effective in the training of veterinary skills and techniques. Soft-tissue plastic models of dog abdominal organs developed at the University of Illinois were found to have comparable handling properties and were useful for teaching a range of common surgical procedures (Greenfield et al. 1995). The *DASIE* (Dog Abdominal Surrogate for Instructional Exercises), developed at the Ontario Veterinary College, has also been successfully used to reduce animal use in teaching abdominal surgery at several institutions (Holmberg et al. 1993, Holmberg & Cockshutt 1994). More rigid plastics have been used to make bone models, and these are used effectively for demonstrating and teaching many aspects of bone-related surgical procedures (DeYoung & Richardson 1987; Johnson & Farmer 1989; Johnson et al. 1990). Of 27 respondents to a survey of all 31 veterinary schools in the U.S. and Canada, Bauer (1993) reported that plastic bones were being used in 8 schools (30 percent) to teach fracture repair.

Several other published studies in the veterinary field support the use of animal friendly learning methods in place of traditional animal consumptive ones. In their study of 82 U.S. veterinary students, Erickson & Clegg (1993) found that students rated computer-based active learning the highest of fourteen learning methods for basic cardiac teaching and electrocardiograph interpretation. Carpenter et al. (1991) reported no significant differences between the surgical performance of two groups of 3rd year students, one trained using live animals, the other using cadavers. (Unfortunately, the authors don't report the source of their cadavers, but ethical sources are certainly available, for example, from companion animals euthanised for medical reasons.) White et al. (1992) reported on seven 4th year veterinary students in an alternative (animal-friendly) track; the students showed hesitancy in their first live tissue surgery, but subsequently performed on par with students with standard lab experience.

A study by Pavletic et al. (1994) compared surgical abilities of 12 graduates from the Tufts University veterinary class of 1990 who had participated in an alternative small animal medical and surgical procedures course with 36 of their counterparts. The subjects were rated for surgical competency by their employers at the time of their hiring and again twelve months later. No significant differences were found on either occasion for any of the measures, which included ability to perform common surgical, medical and diagnostic procedures; attitudes toward performing orthopaedic or soft tissue surgery; confidence in performing procedures; or ability to perform procedures without assistance. This study is especially noteworthy because it assesses the learning experience at the point where its outcome is most important: on-the-job performance.

The above veterinary studies involved 290 students at all stages of their training, including on-the-job performance one year post-graduation. Collectively, they provide a strong case for the replacement of traditional labs in which healthy animals are killed. The initial hesitancy of 'alternative track' students when faced with live animal surgery, as mentioned in the study by White et al. (1992), is short-lived and has no lasting effect on surgical performance, as illustrated by that study and the study of Pavletic et al. (1994). The demonstrated validity of alternative track curricula in veterinary training, combined with growing student dissatisfaction with traditional methods, is fostering progressive changes at North American veterinary schools (Patronek 1998, Bauer et al. 1992a, b). More than half of these 31 schools now have alternative tracks, and the newest, Western University of the Health Sciences, whose veterinary program is scheduled to open in 2003, aims to have a completely non animal consumptive curriculum (Lara Rasmussen, DVM, personal comm. 28 November 1999).

Sometimes overlooked among alternatives is the use of ethically-sourced cadavers and clinical / therapeutic work on animals within curricula. These approaches are particularly relevant to veterinary training, where direct contact with live animals is indispensable. There is a considerable amount of literature supporting surgical training with animal cadavers over live animals.

Bauer et al (1992b), for example, found that students who had access to animal cadavers showed more self-confidence in performing surgeries, and developed and maintained more positive attitudes toward their work. According to a recent survey (Anon. 2000), 16 of 31 North American veterinary schools now offer cadaver surgeries as part of their alternative programs, and of these, 12 have client donation programs to secure ethically-sourced cadavers. Kumar et al. (2001) discuss a number of advantages to the use of client donation programs for veterinary training, based on their experiences at Tufts University.

While most veterinary schools now participate in spay/neuter programs with local animal shelters as a means to train surgery, there is a dearth of studies examining the results of this alternative to using purpose-bred animals. Hart et al (1993) reported on the successful use of shelter animals for supervised spay/neuter surgery, and the increased adoption rate that ensued. That students are helping to save lives in their training is a strong motivator to learn, and would seem to be a more agreeable environment for the aspiring veterinarian than one in which healthy animals are terminated.

Study design

With a few exceptions, the research papers cited above have followed a similar basic study design. Students are divided into two groups: one who learn using traditional animal-based methods, the other who learn using the newer or alternative method. Following the learning period, each group is evaluated using a standardised test that permits comparison between the two groups. Fowler & Brosius (1968) were the first to use this approach in the evaluation of learning methods that could replace animal dissections in the biology curriculum. They used a series of standardised tests to evaluate 156 high school students both before and after they studied four animal species (earthworm, crayfish, frog and perch) using either films or by performing dissections. The two methods yielded no differences in the ability to solve problems, to develop understanding of the methods and aims of science, to improve students' attitude toward science, or to improve manual skill; the film treatment was found more effective than the dissection treatment in the learning of factual information regarding each specimen (*ibid*).

Within this basic study design, many refinements are possible. Pre-tests can be used to confirm that the two treatment groups are comparable to begin with. Larger sample sizes will tend to increase the degree of uniformity between treatment groups, reducing such potential confounding possibilities as one group being smarter, more experienced, or more confident. A suite of post-tests will provide a more rigorous evaluation of two learning methods than will just one. Delayed post-tests further evaluate the capacity of learning methods to affect retention of information.

Two examples of strong study designs are provided by Kinzie et al. (1993) and Greenfield et al. (1995). Kinzie et al. (1993) examined the performance, achievement, and attitudinal effects of an interactive videodisc-based (IVD) simulation as both a substitute and a preparatory tool for frog dissection. Their subjects were 61 high school biology students, who participated in the study over a 4-day period. All of these students were taught by the same instructor and at the same school, thereby minimising effects that may result from different instructional environments. In this study, students were randomly assigned to one of four groups: 1) 16 students who used IVD simulation as a preparation for frog dissection; 2) 15 students who viewed a linear videotape containing the same video materials used in the IVD simulation, (i.e. without interactivity); 3) 15 students who conducted the frog dissection without preparation; and 4) 15 students who used the IVD simulation but did not dissect. Preliminary analyses of students' course grades attained to that point in the semester indicated that there were no significant between-group differences.

The students knew they were participating in a study but were not told what its goals were. They were also told that their performance on the post-test would count toward their final grade and that they should try hard to do well. In addition to the examination of their course grades, the students were given a pre-test, which yielded no significant differences in achievement, attitude, or self-efficacy among the four groups. Each group spent comparable amounts of time with their assigned learning materials. All the dissections (done by groups 1, 2, and 3) were conducted on the same day, with four trained researchers observing and evaluating each team's dissection performance (evaluations were compared, yielding congruent ratings among the observers). Finally, all students completed a post-test which measured achievement, attitude and self-efficacy. The achievement post-test contained a diversity of elements: three diagrams to be labelled, four prosected frogs with pins to be labelled, and nine multiple-choice questions. The attitude post-test, which was initially reviewed, critiqued, and modified by twelve high school science teachers and education technologists, contained 20 items, half positively- and half negatively-phrased. The self-efficacy post-test contained 25 statements eliciting respondent confidence in both performance of dissection and knowledge of anatomy, with which students indicated their level of agreement. Inter-item consistency was evaluated for each of the above three post-tests. Finally, four questions were given soliciting student preferences for the various study activities used in this study. (Students using the simulation as a preparation scored higher than students who received no preparation: they performed a subsequent dissection more effectively, and they learned more about frog anatomy and dissection procedures. The authors conservatively concluded that the interactive videodisc was at least as effective as actual dissection in promoting student learning of frog anatomy and dissection procedures.)

Greenfield et al. (1995) compared the acquisition of surgical skills in 36 third-year veterinary students randomly assigned to two treatment groups: one trained with soft-tissue plastic models, the other with anaesthetised dogs who were euthanised at the end of each session. Each group had two sessions with their surgical training mode, during which mock videotaping of surgical performance was done to accommodate students to being filmed. The students' surgical competence was then assessed during two additional sessions in which each surgery group performed spay surgery on a dog or cat from a local animal shelter (and later returned for possible adoption). Faculty members supervised these sessions, and determined whether the students' cognitive and motor skills were acceptable or not. Faculty were not aware of which training method the students had used. These spay surgeries were also videotaped, edited for clarity and arranged in random order, and evaluated by 8 surgeons at 4 veterinary schools. These evaluators were told whether or not the student's performance had been rated as acceptable or not, but were not told how the students learned, and they were instructed not to penalise based on personal preferences in surgical approach.

Students were re-evaluated a year later, during their 4th year small animal surgical rotations, to determine if there were any differences in performance of the two treatment groups. To help ensure that treatment groups were comparable to begin with, overall academic performance was assessed at the study outset by comparing the grade-point averages (GPA) of all students in the study and by comparing GPAs between the two groups; each of these comparisons yielded no significant differences.

Smeak et al. (1994) used a similar study design to evaluate forty veterinary students on their ability to perform hollow organ (stomach) closure, and they included an innovative test in which the organs were placed underwater and filled with air at increasing pressure so that leakage could be used to measure the effectiveness of surgical closure. (Unfortunately, the properties of the simulated organ turned out to be unsuitable for this test.) A more qualitative approach, used by Samsel et al. (1994), involved only one treatment group. Students received both computer and animal demonstrations and were asked to rate each for their educational merit. The computer demonstration was rated higher.

The approach of Dewhurst & Jenkinson (1995), who mailed surveys to alternatives customers, provides a less rigorous assessment of any one learning method than does the direct comparison approach used by Kinzie et al. (1993) and Greenfield et al. (1995). However, it benefits from the breadth and diversity of the sample (50 institutions in 14 countries around the world). It should be noted that Dewhurst and his collaborators have employed a range of methods to evaluate their instructional packages, and this work has made significant contributions to the development and legitimacy of alternatives to animal labs.

The only study published to date that found a significantly better performance from students using a traditional animal-based method over those using an alternative was reported by Matthews (1998). The control group were 8 undergraduate students who spent twelve hours (four 3-hour study periods) dissecting foetal pigs; coverage of the subject was fairly in-depth, with students expected to learn the location and function of 140 anatomical structures. The treatment group studied foetal pig anatomy using *MacPig*, a computer program produced by Intellimation (which became defunct, ca. 1996). Following the study period, students from both groups were each given two tests, one being a 2-question quiz included in the computer program, the other a 25-question oral practical in which students were required to point to a structure and describe its function. Both student groups performed similarly on the computer test, but the dissecting students performed significantly better on the oral test with prosected pigs.

Several problems with the design of this study shed doubt on the veracity of the findings. These problems arise from the less detailed coverage of the subject by this particular program. The author reviewed *MacPig* in 1994 and deemed it most suited to a middle-school (7th-9th grade) audience (Balcombe 1998). *MacPig* describes some 50 to 75 structures of the foetal pig, barely half of the 140 covered by the students in Matthews' dissecting group.

With this in mind, control group students can reasonably be expected to have covered all of the structures on the *MacPig* test, but not so for the experimental group of students on the oral examination. Furthermore, it is improbable that the content of *MacPig* would be sufficient to occupy a student for twelve hours of study. Finally, Matthews administered the oral exam herself; her study design would have been better if the oral practical were administered 'blind,' by a neutral party unaware of the method by which the students had learned the material.

An ideal study would involve a range of replacement methods being compared to traditional animal-based methods at a variety of institutions. The inclusion of several institutions in a single study would give valuable information on the degree of inter-institutional variation that might occur. Large sample sizes would minimise the effects of initial differences in the student samples (e.g. aptitude, prior knowledge, prior experience with different learning methods), but pre-tests should also be done to satisfy this assumption. A range of instructors will tend to nullify the effects of individual instructor bias (for instance, students may detect and respond to an instructor's preference - however subtle - for a given learning method). Blind study designs, in which students are unaware of the aim of the study and the evaluators unaware of what learning method(s) the students used, will further minimise the influence of bias. Post-test evaluations should be done both short- and long-term, so that retention of the lesson's aims can be assessed.

Finally, the use of combinations of alternative methods in replacing harmful animal use should be encouraged, as it combines the strengths of different resources into one learning experience. It would be useful to see more studies that specifically evaluate combinations of alternatives compared to traditional animal-consumptive methods.

The value of anecdote

As an increasing number of teachers develop and implement alternatives, and more and more students demand humane learning methods, a growing body of anecdotal evidence is becoming available as both groups report on their experiences. While not statistically rigorous, anecdotes provide real-life scenarios of alternatives being used as intended, and are a useful supplement to published studies assessing alternatives.

Hepner (1994) was one of the first to publish the personal experiences of student conscientious objectors to harmful animal uses in education; her examples include unfair treatment of students by resistant instructors, and some uplifting stories of students who successfully negotiated mutually agreeable solutions with their schools. One student reports having sat at one end of the class working on models and diagrams while her fellow students dissected cats, and getting an 87 percent score in the course. Another reports having constructed organs of clams and rats using clay - a constructive way to learn an animal's anatomical relationships - but makes no mention of how she ultimately fared in the course. Two other useful repositories of students' anecdotes are the InterNICHE website (www.interniche.org) and Pedersen (2002). Within the InterNICHE website, testimonies by veterinary student Andrew Knight and zoology student Denise Humphreys further illustrate the value of anecdote. Knight's efforts to modernise the curriculum at his Australian veterinary school resulted in his performing many more surgeries (all in the clinical setting) than his peers, thereby providing him with more extensive training and greater confidence. Humphreys was warned by instructors that she would not be offered a job if she refused to dissect animals during her course. On contacting 30-40 life science organisations, including the Institute of Zoology (London), however, she was told by each that while they did not want to encourage her to oppose the wishes of her university, they would definitely consider employing such a student.

Unfortunately, very few student anecdotes report the use of specific alternatives and how the student fared academically. This sort of anecdote would be of greater value. Case studies of the development and implementation of alternative methods by instructors are very useful, and may address students' academic performance (see for example the paper by Braun, in this volume). Journals such as *The American Biology Teacher* and the *Journal of Biological Education* regularly publish anecdotal reviews of new teaching material, and borrowers of alternatives held in loan systems are encouraged to provide some evaluation to the lending organisations. The European Resource Centre for Alternatives in Higher Education (EURCA) commissions detailed reviews of alternatives from teachers, and includes these and other anecdotal assessments on their website (www.eurca.org). This is a valuable contribution worth emulating.

Conclusion

The studies described in this paper do not cover the extensive range of applications possible for education and training in the life sciences (see this book for many other such applications). However, they are for the most part methodologically adequate for assessing the efficacy of animal-friendly learning methods in comparison with animal-consumptive methods. Collectively, the empirical evidence provides solid support for the replacement of traditional learning methods that involve harming and/or killing animals. Even in cases of equivalence in learning performance, ethics should dictate that the alternative learning method be used.

Non-animal learning methods are often criticised for not providing 'hands-on' experiences. Without doubt, computer programs and 3-dimensional models provide different learning experiences to preserved cats or anaesthetised dogs, but there is no basis for concluding that such experiences are any less hands-on or interactive. First, there are many other hands-on materials and approaches for learning biology - 3-dimensional models, patient simulators, virtual reality modules, and surgical training models, for example - that do not require killing or harming animals. When Washington State University (WSU) modernised its veterinary surgery training program in the early 1990s by replacing traditional invasive animal labs, they did not reduce the manual skills training. On the contrary, the quality and magnitude of that training was increased by introducing an early skills program and a psychomotor skills lab (Borje Gustafsson, former dean of WSU vet school, personal comm. 21 January 2000).

Second, a hands-on learning activity is not by definition a better learning activity. There are many hands-on activities that we could have students carry out in school, but for social or moral reasons we do not - for example, constructing and detonating explosives in chemistry class. Hands-on activities are only effective for learning if the students' heads are being kept as busy as their hands (Michael 1993). This point has particular relevance to animal dissection, where the behaviour of poorly supervised students can degenerate to the exclusion of meaningful learning (Solot & Arluke 1997).

One valid criticism that can be made against most of the research evaluating replacements of animal consumptive teaching methods is that there is a dearth of emphasis on the learning process itself. With the exception of a few studies of surgical proficiency in veterinary and medical students, the emphasis has been on measuring 'content' knowledge (e.g. a student's ability to memorise names of anatomical parts and systems) instead of 'process' skills (e.g. a student's ability to design and perform experiments and analyse data). Yet, much of the focus of reform efforts in biology/science education today pertains to how students learn rather than what it is they are learning. The U.S. National Science Education Standards are emphatic in their recommendation that science education place greater emphasis on students being actively involved in doing scientific studies, including designing the studies, acquiring and analysing data, and generating new questions and hypotheses (U.S. National Academy of Sciences 1995).

Unfortunately, as long as students are evaluated on standardised tests designed primarily to measure content knowledge (and teachers evaluated on their students' performance on those tests), there is little impetus to shift curricula towards process learning, despite its demonstrated benefits (Modell & Michael 1993, Heiman 1987). What is perhaps most needed now is a large-scale international study comparing traditional with alternative learning modes and examining them from both content and process learning perspectives. An international study has been proposed (van der Valk et al. 1999), but it is not yet clear whether or not it will be conducted, or whether it will include aspects of process learning.

References

Anonymous. 2000. Comparison of alternatives offered by veterinary schools. Alternatives in Veterinary Medical Education, 14: 6-7.

Balcombe, J.P. 1998. Letter to the editor. The American Biology Teacher 60(8): 565-566.

Balcombe, J.P. 2000. Animals in Higher Education: Problems, Alternatives and Recommendations. Humane Society Press, Washington, D.C.

Bauer, M.S. 1993. A survey of the use of live animals, cadavers, inanimate models, and computers in teaching veterinary surgery. Journal of the American Veterinary Medical Association 203(7): 1047-1051.

Bauer, M.S., N. Glickman, S.K. Salisbury, J.P. Toombs & J.M. Prostredny. 1992a. Surgical vs. terminal animal laboratories to teach small animal surgery. Journal of Veterinary Medical Education 19(2): 54-58.

Bauer, M.S., N. Glickman, L. Glickman, J.P. Toombs & P. Bill. 1992b. Evaluation of the effectiveness of a cadaver laboratory during a 4th-year veterinary surgery rotation. Journal of Veterinary Medical Education 19(3): 77-84.

Bauer, M.S. & H.B. Seim III. 1992. Alternative methods to teach veterinary surgery. Humane Innovations and Alternatives 6: 401-404.

Carpenter, L.G., D.L. Piermattei, M.D. Salman, E.C. Orton, A.W. Nelson, D.D. Smeak, P.B. Jennings & R.A. Taylor. 1991. A comparison of surgical training with live anesthetized dogs and cadavers. Vet. Surg. 20: 373-378.

Colt H.G., Crawford S.W., Galbraith O. 2001. Virtual reality bronchoscopy simulation: A revolution in procedural training. CHEST 120: 1333-1339.

Datta V.K., Mandalia M., Mackay S.D., Darzi A.W. 2001. Evaluation and validation of a virtual reality based flexible sigmoidoscopy trainer. Gut (Supplement) 48: A97-A98.

Dewhurst, D.G. & A.S. Meehan. 1993. Evaluation of the use of computer simulations of experiments in teaching undergraduate students. British J. Pharm. Proc. Suppl. 108: 238.

Dewhurst, D.G., J. Hardcastle, P.T. Hardcastle & E. Stuart. 1994. Comparison of a computer simulation program and a traditional laboratory practical class for teaching the principles of intestinal absorption. American Journal of Physiology 267 (Advances in Physiology Education 12/1): S95-S104.

Dewhurst, D.G. & L. Jenkinson. 1995. The impact of computer-based alternatives on the use of animals in undergraduate teaching. ATLA 23: 521-530.

DeYoung, D.J. & D.C. Richardson. 1987. Teaching the principles of internal fixation of fractures with plastic bone models. Journal of Veterinary Medical Education 14: 30-31.

Downie, R. & J. Meadows. 1995. Experience with a dissection opt-out scheme in university level biology. Journal of Biological Education, 29(3), 187-194.

Erickson, H.H. & V.L. Clegg. 1993. Active learning in cardiovascular physiology. Pp. 107-108 In Modell, H.I., & Michael, J.A. (editors). Promoting Active Learning in the Life Science Classroom. Annals of the New York Academy of Sciences, Vol. 701. New York, NY.

Fawver, A.L., C.E. Branch, L. Trentham, B.T. Robertson & S.D., Beckett. 1990. A comparison of interactive videodisc instruction with live animal laboratories. American Journal of Physiology 259 (Advances in Physiology Education 4): S11-S14.

Fowler, H.S. & E.J. Brosius. 1968. A research study on the values gained from dissection of animals in secondary school biology. Science Education 52(2): 55-57.

Greenfield, C.L., A.L. Johnson, D.J. Shaeffer & L.L. Hungerford. 1995. Comparison of surgical skills of veterinary students trained using models or live animals. JAVMA 206(12): 1840-1845.

Guy, J.F. & A.J. Frisby. 1992. Using interactive videodiscs to teach gross anatomy to undergraduates at The Ohio State University. Academic Medicine 67: 132-133.

Hart, L., D. Anderson & R. Zasloff. 1993. Alternatives to the use of live animals in veterinary school curricula. Humane Innovations & Alternatives, 7: 499-503.

Heiman, M. 1987. Learning to learn: A behavioral approach to improving thinking. Pp. 431-452 In Perkins, D.N., Lochhead, J., & Bishop, J. (editors) Thinking: The Second International Conference. Lawrence Erlbaum Associates, Hillsdale, New Jersey.

Henman, M.C., & G.D.H. Leach. 1983. An alternative method for pharmacology laboratory class instruction using biovideograph video tape recordings. British Journal of Pharmacology, Vol 80: 591P.

Hepner, L.H. 1984. Animals in education: The facts, issues and implications. Albuquerque: Richmond Publishers.

Holmberg, D.L., J.R. Cockshutt. & A.W.P. Basher. 1993. Use of a dog abdominal surrogate for teaching surgery. J. Vet. Med. Educ. 20(2): 61-62.

Holmberg, D.L. & J.R. Cockshutt. 1994. A non-animal alternative for teaching introductory surgery. Humane Innovations and Alternatives 8: 635-637.

Intellimation. 1995. MacPig (computer program of foetal pig anatomy). Santa Barbara, CA, USA.

Johnson, A.L. & J.A. Farmer. 1989. Evaluation of traditional and alternative models in psychomotor laboratories for veterinary surgery. J. Vet. Med. Educ. 16(1): 11-14.

Johnson, A.L., J. Harari, J. Lincoln, J.A. Farmer & D. Korvick. 1990. Bone models of pathologic conditions used for teaching veterinary orthopedic surgery. Journal of Veterinary Medical Education 17: 13-15.

Jones, N.A., R.P. Olafson, & J. Sutin. 1978. Evaluation of a gross anatomy program without dissection. Journal of Medical Education 53: 198-205.

Kinzie, M.B., R. Strauss & J. Foss. 1993. The effects of an interactive dissection simulation on the performance and achievement of high school biology students. Journal of Research in Science Teaching 30(8): 989-1000.

Kumar, A.M., R. Murtaugh, D. Brown, T. Ballas, E. Clancy & G. Patronek. 2001. Client donation program for acquiring dogs and cats to teach veterinary gross anatomy. Journal of Veterinary Medical Education 28(2): 73- 77.

Leathard, H.L. & D.G. Dewhurst. 1995. Comparison of the cost-effectiveness of a computer-assisted learning program with a tutored demonstration to teach intestinal motility to medical students. ALT-J 3(1): 118-125.

Leonard, W. H. 1992. A comparison of student performance following instruction by interactive videodisc versus conventional laboratory. Journal of Research in Science Teaching, Vol 29 No 1, pp 93 - 102.

Lieb, M.J. 1985. Dissection: A valuable motivational tool or a trauma to the high school student? Unpublished Thesis, Master of Education, National College of Education, Evanston, Illinois, USA.

Lilienfield, L.S., & N.C. Broering. 1994. Computers as teachers: learning from animations. American Journal of Physiology. 11(1): Advances in Physiology Education, pp. S47 - S54.

Matthews, D. 1998. Comparison of MacPig to Fetal Pig Dissection in College Biology. The American Biology Teacher 60(3): 228-229.

McCollum, T.L. 1987. The effect of animal dissections on student acquisition of knowledge of and attitudes toward the animals dissected. Unpublished Doctoral Dissertation, University of Cincinnati, USA.

Mehta A.C., Ost D., Salinas S.G., Sanchez D.E., DeRosiers A., Tasto J.L., Britt E. 2000. Objective assessment of bronchoscopy skills by a bronchoscopy training simulator. American Journal of Respiratory and Critical Care Medicine 161: A234.

Michael, J. A. 1993. Teaching problem solving in small groups. Pp. 37-48. In Modell, H.I., & Michael, J.A. (editors). Promoting Active Learning in the Life Science Classroom. Annals of the New York Academy of Sciences, Vol. 701. New York, NY.

Modell, H.I., & Michael, J.A. (eds). 1993. Promoting Active Learning in the Life Science Classroom. Annals of the New York Academy of Sciences, Vol. 701. New York, NY.

More, D. & C.L. Ralph. 1992. A test of effectiveness of courseware in a college biology class. J. Educational Technology Systems 21: 79-84.

National Academy of Sciences. 1995. National Science Education Standards. National Academy of Science Press. Washington, D.C.

Ost D., DeRosiers A., Britt E., Fein A.M., Lesser M.L., Mehta A.C. 2001. Assessment of a bronchoscopy simulator. American Journal of Respiratory and Critical Care Medicine 2001; 164:2248-2265.

Patronek, G.J. 1998. Spotlight on a school: Tufts University. Alternatives in Veterinary Medical Education 8: 4-5.

Pavletic, M.M., A. Schwartz, J. Berg, & D. Knapp. 1994. An assessment of the outcome of the alternative medical and surgical laboratory program at Tufts University. JAVMA 205(1): 97-100.

Pedersen H. 2002. Humane education. Animals and alternatives in laboratory classes: Aspects, attitudes and implications. Stockholm, Humanimal 4.

Phelps, J.L., J.O. Nilsestuen & S. Hosemann 1992. Assessment of effectiveness of videodisc replacement of a live-animal physiology laboratory. Distinguished Papers Monograph, American Association for Respiratory Care.

Prentice, E.D., W.K. Metcalf, T.H. Quinn, J.G. Sharp, R.H. Jensen & E.A. Holyoke. 1977. Stereoscopic anatomy: Evaluation of a new teaching system in human gross anatomy. Journal of Medical Education 52: 758-763.

Rowe, R.. & Cohen, R. 2000. Virtual reality bronchoscopy simulator (abstract). Anesthesiology. 93(3A): A-1219.

Samsel, R.W., G.A. Schmidt, J.B. Hall, L.D.H. Wood, S.G. Shroff & P.T. Schumacker. 1994. Cardiovascular physiology teaching: Computer simulations vs. animal demonstrations. Advances in Physiology Education 11: S36-S46.

Smeak, D.D., L.N. Hill, M.L. Beck, C.A. Shaffer & S.J. Birchard. 1994. Evaluation of an auto-tutorial-simulator program for instruction of hollow organ closure Veterinary Surgery 23: 519-528.

Solot, D., & A. Arluke. 1997. Learning the scientist's role: Animal dissection in middle school. Journal of Contemporary Ethnography 26(1): 28-54

Strauss, R.T. & Kinzie, M.B. 1994. Student achievement and attitudes in a pilot study comparing an interactive videodisc simulation to conventional dissection. The American Biology Teacher 56(7): 398-402.

van der Valk, J., D. Dewhurst, I. Hughes, J. Atkinson, J. Balcombe, H. Braun, K. Gabrielson, F. Gruber, J. Miles, J. Nab, J. Nardi, H. van Wilgenburg, U. Zinko, and J. Zurlo. 1999. Alternatives to the Use of Animals in Higher Education (ECVAM Workshop Report 33). Alternatives to Laboratory Animals 27: 39-52.

White, K.K., L.G. Wheaton & S.A. Greene. 1992. Curriculum change related to live animal use: A four-year surgical curriculum. J. Vet. Med. Educ. 19: 6-10.

Wong T., Darzi A., Foale R. & Schilling R.J. 2001. Virtual reality permanent pacing: Validation of a novel computerized permanent pacemaker implantation simulator. Journal of the American College of Cardiology (Supplement) 37(2): 493A-494A.

Zbinden, G. & M. Flury-Roversy. 1981. Archives of Toxicology 47: 77-99.

Biography

Jonathan Balcombe was born in England, was raised in New Zealand and Canada, and has lived in the United States since 1987. He received his bachelors degree in biology from York University, in Toronto, his masters in biology from Carleton University, in Ottawa, and his doctorate in ethology from the University of Tennessee, where he studied communication in bats. From 1993 to 2000 he worked at The Humane Society of the United States (HSUS), focusing on the issues surrounding animal use in education. In addition to published papers on the behavioural ecology of bats, birds, and turtles, Jonathan has written more than thirty articles on the animal dissection issue, and in 2000, the Humane Society Press released his first book: *The Use of Animals in Higher Education: Problems, Alternatives and Recommendations*. He has been President of the East Tennessee Vegetarian Society, Vice President of the Vegetarian Society of the District of Columbia, Alternatives Adviser to InterNICHE, and is currently a member of the Scientific Advisory Council of The HSUS and an adviser for the European Resource Centre for Alternatives. In 2001, Jonathan took the position of Research Co-ordinator with Immersion Medical, a company that develops virtual reality simulators for training in minimally-invasive surgery. He lives with his wife and daughter in Maryland, USA, where his primary interests are bird watching, watercolour painting, bicycling, and writing.

Jonathan Balcombe, PhD

Research Co-ordinator
Immersion Medical
55 West Watkins Mill Road
Gaithersburg, MD 20878
USA

tel: +1 301 984 3706 x345
fax: +1 301 984 2104
e-mail: jbalcombe@immersion.com

www.immersion.com/medical

4. Curricular design: Choosing and planning a humane approach to life science education

Lara Marie Rasmussen

Western University of Health Sciences College of Veterinary Medicine, USA

Introduction

from Guinea Pig to Computer Mouse is all about education - humane education, but education nonetheless. Its message is one of a better way to learn. This message would not be complete without consideration of how we facilitate learning, and how we choose what is important for our students, i.e. curricular design. Achieving a humane educational experience for the life science learner is about more than merely substituting an inanimate model or a computer program for an animal dissection. As well as effectively addressing the traditional aims and goals, humane education has this bigger mission of expanding the potential for learning to include such concepts as appreciation for life, compassion, interpersonal/interspecies communication and under-standing, altruism, and the interrelatedness of life. Curricular design/re-design must therefore go beyond simply selecting a non-harmful tool in order to replace a harmful tool. Emphasis must be placed on developing goals and objectives that are all-inclusive to this bigger mission and analysing learning methods to highlight their risks and benefits to it. Assuming that education in the life sciences is simply about learning a known group of facts, principles and skills is a short sighted, objectivist view[1]. What we 'know' now is different than what Darwin 'knew' or what our grand-childrens' children will 'know'. Today's popular notion of 'humane' is likely to be different to that of preceding generations and future generations. The premise of this chapter is that the above mentioned mission - a better way to teach - is desirable and worthy; in order for our society to advance in this direction, our educational system must evolve. This chapter provides an outline for the curricular design process; a thorough approach that draws from wider audiences, orients to a broader scale of considerations, and gives credence to the positive societal implications of humaneness.

Learning in the life sciences

The life sciences consist of a broad group of complex, ever-changing disciplines in which successful participation requires many diverse skills, knowledge and attributes. Addressing and accomplishing this diversity in a curriculum is an often-overlooked challenge. The focus has tended to be knowledge alone in abstraction. But mastering scientific knowledge is just the beginning. Students of the life sciences must also go further in the cognitive domain to comprehend, apply, analyse, synthesise and evaluate knowledge (Bloom's Taxonomy[2]). Additionally, the life sciences must be approached through the affective and psychomotor domains. Students must be able to receive and respond to information; they must be prepared to value, organise and characterise information. Those entering these fields must be adept in the practical skills necessary for successful partici-pation in their chosen discipline. The over-riding tenet, given that this is life science learning, must be to instil an appreciation and respect for life, as these students have the potential to be our future experts, educators, policy makers, and role models. Preparing them for these lofty ambitions by maintaining their excitement for learning, their inquisitive nature, their compassion towards all will support a positive future for civilisation and this planet.

Curricular planning in the life sciences

When designing or revising a curriculum, the process must begin with educators divorcing ourselves from methods and concentrating on desired outcomes. Beginning with the big picture, we should determine the aims of the life sciences curriculum relative to the entire curriculum[3]. Next, focus is achieved for each life science course or discipline by outlining goals with more specific behavioural characteristics attached (i.e. actions that must occur for the goal to be satisfied). Thereafter, the road map for the course can be developed in the form of well constructed objectives. Choosing methods for imparting these aims, goals and objectives is the next step. Attention must be paid to the concept that how something is taught or learned may be as important to imparting these aims, goals and objectives as is the content that is presented. Assigning relative importance to the various learning domains (cognitive, affective, psychomotor) with respect to academic level and future expectations is a daunting, commonly unconsidered task. As the learners mature and focus their attentions toward specific disciplines, the aims, goals, objectives, and methods must be aligned appropriately without forgetting that the 'picture' remains quite big. The college-age and postgraduate learners must come to appreciate the scope of their chosen fields - not just the facts and principles, but the skills and attributes and activities inherent to successful participation. Selecting the aims, goals, objectives, and methods to maintain this breadth is a challenge to the curricular design process, though highly rewarding for the learner. Even with the considerable investment of time and resources in this curricular planning experience, educators must not consider this a static, completed project. Evolution of a curriculum is essential.

Upon delivery of a curriculum, evaluation of the outcomes relative to the means then becomes critical to the success and growth of the curriculum. Traditional standardised tests may not adequately assess the students' progress; the testing methodology must take into account the methods by which a student learned the information and the specific information learned. Again, this assessment must go beyond testing for facts and principles; communication, compassion and collaborative effort, for example, must be assessed. Additionally, the assessments must focus not only on the students' progress, but the curriculum's progress. A curriculum fits well the metaphor of a scientific investigation; it develops and evolves over time directed by feedback and new information (e.g. program assessment data)[4]. To ignore the data is to stifle the investigation. Humane educational methods allow the potential for learning in the traditional areas as well as many diverse, as yet minimally appreciated or assessed, areas of the life sciences (see the paper by Balcombe, in this volume.)

Inclusive curricular aims

The aims of learning in the life sciences are quite broad[5]. Students must understand and/or be able to access the extensive knowledge base in the various disciplines (such as physiology, zoology, and biology). They must come to know many complex interrelations, and participate in deductive reasoning. The various scientific disciplines require the student to engage their perceptual and physical abilities as well. The area of learning not specific to the life sciences, though essential to it, is in life skills. These encompass communication, critical thinking, self-regulation, group interactions, problem solving, life-long learning, etc. And core to all life science fields is an appreciation for life. So when educators formulate the aims of a particular curriculum or program of study, we must broaden the field from which we gather our expectations - going beyond simply asking the students to accumulate knowledge; asking them to learn to be life scientists. The curricular aims are thus ideas having "enduring value beyond the classroom"[6]. Making these ideas inclusive versus exclusive allows for student development with far-reaching potential.

Practical application

These inclusive aims are not objectively measurable; rather they give direction to the curriculum. They are conceived and written to define the curriculum for the curricular developers and participants. Inclusive aims may be written with general terminology such as 'understand', 'appreciate' and 'develop'. They should be explicit and inclusive of all anticipated aspects of learning in the curriculum, as suggested above.

Examples of inclusive aims in life science learning for the veterinary student might include:

• Develop skills and knowledge basic to veterinary medicine
• Understand communications essential to clinical veterinary medicine
• Appreciate the learning skills necessary for life-long self-improvement in veterinary medicine
• Understand the needs of the patient and guardian

Examples of inclusive aims in life science learning for the university student might include:

• Understand the knowledge basic to the discipline
• Develop the skills essential to the design and conduct of a scientific investigation
• Appreciate the communication skills necessary for disseminating data within the scientific community and the lay community
• Understand the needs of the scientific community and animal populations

Examples of inclusive aims in life science learning for the high school student might include:

• Appreciate the classification of 'life' or 'living'
• Understand the distinguishing features of the animal and plant kingdoms
• Develop the skills necessary for learning in the life sciences
• Develop an awareness of the interconnectedness of plant and animal life on this planet

Focused curricular goals

From this broad pool of aims we can distil goals. Goals are more specific to the context of a specific discipline or course, yet fulfil curricular aims. For example, a student learning about physiology will apply the aims of an overall life science curriculum in more specific contexts of the physiology discipline (e.g. the means of communication in physiology may be somewhat different than other disciplines; the methods for information transfer or scientific investigation or problem solving may all be different than those used in anatomy or botany or ecology). Learning is more efficient and effective when allowed to occur in proper context; the student must be able to relate information to a tangible experience or situation (i.e. contextual learning model)[7]. Goals begin the process of providing this context.

Practical application

Goals are written with more attention to observable terms; they describe the actions that must be demonstrated by the student to confirm successful learning in the specified area. If a course is not part of a well constructed life science curriculum, then educators should take the time to step back and design the aims of a life science curriculum in which the specific course would ideally fit. We should consider from where the student has come and to where the student is going. This reflection and preparation will allow more inclusive considerations to emerge.

Examples of goals in life science learning for the veterinary student might include:
- Acquire knowledge related to the normal and abnormal cardiovascular system in dogs
- Master clinical skills basic to the cardiovascular system in dogs
- Identify and perfect the communications essential to cardiovascular diagnostics and therapeutics in veterinary medicine
- Perfect the learning skills necessary for life-long self-improvement in veterinary cardiology
- Define and address the needs of the cardiology patient and guardian
- Demonstrate appropriate compassion and professionalism relative to the practice of veterinary cardiology

Examples of goals in life science learning for the university zoology student might include:
- Acquire knowledge basic to the mollusc life-cycle
- Master the skills essential to the design and conduct of a scientific investigation
- Identify and perfect the communication skills necessary for disseminating data within the scientific community and the lay community
- Define the needs of the scientific community and animal populations as related to the zoology discipline
- Explain the relationship between invertebrates and their environment

Examples of goals in life science learning for the high school biology student might include:
- Acquire knowledge basic to genetics and evolution
- Outline and distinguish between the life cycles of invertebrate versus vertebrate life forms
- Demonstrate the role of water and organic molecules in animal and plant life forms
- Identify and perfect the skills necessary for learning in the life sciences
- Explain the interconnectedness of plant and animal life

Purposeful learning objectives

We may then use the above focused curricular goals to create objectives for a course of study; a purposeful learning objective must be a statement of an observable behaviour, with minimally acceptable performance standards, given specified conditions under which the student performance is to occur. These should be written with full consideration of the course position within a curriculum, time requirements, level of student development, the needs inherent to subsequent student studies or activities, the goals of the course as well as other related courses, and the aims of the curriculum. They can be organised by priority to further guide student activities. Well constructed learning objectives will provide the framework from which learning tools and methods as well as assessment means will be designed. The objectives should be detailed and inclusive, requiring actions of the student that demonstrate learning and understanding in the many important areas of life sciences identified in the curricular aims and goals.

Practical application

The list of learning objectives for a course should be detailed enough to be used as a guide during the course and/or as a checklist at the end of the course. The language of an objective must include specific observable terms so that methods of assessment will clearly develop (e.g. conduct, analyse, perform, calculate, verify, demonstrate, compare). 'General' learning objectives are written from the teacher's point of view; they tell the student what to expect from the course and the teacher. 'Specific' learning objectives are written from the student's point of view; they tell the student what the teacher will expect from the student. An interesting possibility in this process is to have the students submit their own specific objectives as the course progresses.

Examples of objectives in life science learning for the veterinary student might include:

In the fourth year of the veterinary medical curriculum, the student will be able to:
- Correctly interpret the ten most common electrocardiographic abnormalities seen in the canine patient during actual clinical examinations
- Communicate in written format to referring veterinarians following a diagnostic evaluation of the five most common feline cardiac presentations
- Provide oral critique of ten veterinary cardiology internet resources for fellow students
- Role-play the interaction between the equine cardiologist and the guardian given a case of syncope in a four-month-old foal
- Master techniques for arterial blood sampling and provide written physiological evaluations of ten clinical presentations using the artery simulator, clinical samples and two blood gas analysers
- Identify the living, gross anatomy of the heart and great vessels during the videographic demonstration of canine cardiopulmonary bypass surgery to correct congenital anomalies

Examples of objectives in life science learning for the university zoology student might include:

At the conclusion of this course, the student will be able to:
- Sketch the life-cycle of the bivalve and teach principles to pre-university students
- Prepare a scientific grant application using U.S. National Institutes of Health standards
- Present the findings of scientific investigations to a professional audience
- Design and implement a grade school zoology field trip experience
- Prepare a vertebrate environmental impact report
- Lead a community forum meeting addressing a pressing wildlife concern
- Master the ultrastructural microscopic anatomy of the cell
- Critique the components of experimental study design

Examples of objectives in life science learning for the high school biology student might include:

By the end of the second year, the student will be able to:
- Predict progeny for genetically known pairings in the plant kingdom
- Identify a species and justify phylogenetic classification
- Prepare a scientific study investigating mammalian water balance

- Analyse the effects of physical exertion relative to the mammalian cardiovascular, respiratory and metabolic systems
- Describe the components of successful written scientific communication
- Critique four learning tools used in biology teaching and learning
- Track a molecule of water in a raindrop to the bladder of a mountain lion

Multidimensional learning method selection

Accomplishing learning objectives requires decisions on methodology. The risks and benefits of each method should be identified and weighed. Since how we deliver education will have impact on some of the aims/goals/objectives (i.e. through learning processes such as observation and role-modeling), brainstorming[8] each method is a helpful planning exercise. (By using brainstorming techniques one is prompted into new ways of thinking about how a learning method directly and indirectly satisfies stated aims/goals/objectives.)

When a person in a position of authority is seen by students to harm another through the use of a certain learning tool or method, students may learn that to harm is acceptable behaviour. A term employed to define this concept is desensitisation. Its ramifications are quite far-reaching. Do we want a paediatric physician or veterinarian to refrain from treating pain in children or animals? There is evidence to suggest that desensitisation takes place in current veterinary educational systems[9], and pain treatment in children is only now getting the attention it deserves[10]. Are these findings related to how we learned - to the desensitising experiences we had in our learning years?

Without specific identification, recognition, and assessment of each method's benefits, these benefits remain intangible; learners may not appreciate their importance[11]. And if the curricular designer has identified these issues as important, then this 'learner appreciation' is indeed important. Additionally, without specific identification and recognition of each method's detriments, we as educators cannot properly weigh risk versus benefit for our students. Yet we must.

The area of learning methodology offers creative opportunities for the curriculum designer. We may choose learning methods and tools that have been validated for their intended objectives, or modify validated methods and tools to new objectives. We may pilot test new methods and tools for subsequent application to specific objectives, or create new methods and tools for these objectives and validate them through their own use. There is a wealth of resources currently available and relatively underused that will assist the curriculum designer in learning method and learning tool selection. This book seeks to be one of these resources such that the user may have easier access to learning tools. And there is a wealth of information in the education literature to facilitate learning method selection.

Some examples of learning methodology include:

- Active learning: A method of educating that allows students to participate in class rather than assume the role of passive listener and note-taker. It may include small group discussion, role playing, hands-on projects, and teacher-driven questioning. This is a learning methodology quite popular in today's literature; many successful methods of active learning have been evaluated, ranging from lecture delivery to participatory exercises[12-15].

• Service-learning: Two concepts are central to this learning methodology. First, service experiences are used to enhance learning (i.e. serving to learn). Involvement in service activities can increase student motivation, substantiate learning of classroom activities, and introduce the student to real-world complexity. Second, service-learning allows the student to recognise, develop, and refine the act of service (i.e. learning to serve.) Helping students to develop a spirit of service can be a key goal of undergraduate education. This methodology is used and has been evaluated in a variety of disciplines; it is very well suited to the life science arena.

• Computer-assisted learning: This methodology, in the form of computer-generated virtual reality, interactive software, and simulations can be a powerfully engaging tool when applied appropriately.

• Experiential learning: Using this methodology, students become active participants in events beyond the classroom, facilitating the accumulation of knowledge, skills and values deemed important to the curriculum. This approach takes into account the reality that we 'learn by doing';[21,22] a creative curriculum designer has enormous potential to capitalise on this concept in the life sciences.

The methods chosen to facilitate learning can be diverse and multidimensional, with one method satisfying a range of distinct learning objectives. One objection sometimes voiced is that the learning tools emerging from these diverse methodologies are just not good enough. The computer image isn't sharp enough, the content is too simplistic, the time commitment is too great, the price is too high. As evidenced by the examples and supportive data in this book, many of today's products and opportunities show that these concerns are unfounded. Additionally, if appropriate boundaries and expectation are applied to the learning tool (in the form of individual learning tool protocols), then the student can focus on the tool's strengths and maximise learning in those specific areas. A properly prepared protocol prevents student disappointment with a tool because expectations are appropriate prior to engagement. Moreover, producers of tangible learning tools will follow the end-user's lead; if we as educators demand and participate in the development of novel learning tools and methods, the producers will fulfil our needs. We cannot stand by and expect others to invest the time and effort if they are not shown the market potential. Educators must create the demand; supply will follow.

When choosing learning methods, we must go beyond the bench top. We must not assume there is one inanimate model or one software program to 'teach' an entire topic. We must not assume that seeing one physiology demonstration and hearing one lecture will 'teach' the concept at hand. Learning is multidimensional and thus requires appropriate methods to facilitate the process. We should look outside of the classroom, step away from the lectern, move through the variety necessary to engage and fulfil the learners.

Again the analogy connecting education to a scientific approach is quite valid here. The choice of learning methods must follow evidence where evidence is available[24], and we should actively engage in the creation and dissemination of evidence where it is lacking (see Balcombe, in this volume). This process of curricular development or reform also parallels the constructs on decision-making put forth by both Dewey[25] and Wales et al[26]. The message is one of logical thought process - define the problem, set the goals, gather information, define constraints, suggest solutions, support solutions with evidence, choose a solution and evaluate the solution.

At this stage, when aims/goals/objectives are concrete and learning methods are being matched to objectives, I suggest that this is where the choice to be humane enters into practice. The above mentioned overriding aim must be to value life - for that ultimately is why we study it. We are in awe of it. We seek to understand it. But to destroy it in our pursuit is to snuff out that which we so appreciate. To do this with maturing learners is a terrible disservice to them, the community and our future - and we do shape our future as we design how our students learn. We can choose learning methods and tools that do not harm animals, the environment nor our learners. And even learning through the non-detrimental and beneficial participation of animals is a privilege which we should reserve for those who have earned and need it. Through this process we can promote a reverence for life so eloquently described by Albert Schweitzer in the early twentieth century[27].

> "At sunset of the third day, near the village of Igendja, we moved along an island set in the middle of the wide river. On a sandbank to our left, four hippopotamuses and their young plodded along in our same direction. Just then, in my great tiredness and discouragement, the phrase, 'Reverence for Life,' struck me like a flash. As far as I knew, it was a phrase I had never heard nor ever read. I realised at once that it carried within itself the solution to the problem that had been torturing me. Now I knew that a system of values which concerns itself only with our relationship to other people is incomplete and therefore lacking in power for good. Only by means of reverence for life can we establish a spiritual and humane relationship with both people and all living creatures within our reach. Only in this fashion can we avoid harming others, and, within the limits of our capacity, go to their aid whenever they need us."

> "The ethic of reverence for life prompts us to keep each other alert to what troubles us and to speak and act dauntlessly together in discharging the responsibilities that we feel."

This approach does not limit our choices; rather, it forces us to examine and justify our actions relative to animals and each other. This critical thinking, introspection and resultant creativity will benefit not only the life science learner but society as well.

Fully satisfying aims, goals and objectives in the life sciences without harm

As originally stated in the discussion of curricular aims, the potential learning available and important to the life science student is immense and diverse. All too often we narrow our expectations to just the facts and principles about a living organism. We ask students to learn the gross anatomy and physiology of the frog or the pig or the cat, but we do not ask them to learn how to communicate this knowledge or to advance it. We can. We can ask them to justify or judge the information. We can ask them to demonstrate their perceptual abilities so fundamental to scientific investigations. We can ask them to design means to answer their own questions. The key to achieving these more inclusive objectives is to identify them, put them to paper, make clear the expectation, and assess student progress with each one. All major desired outcomes must be assessed, or they will not be outcomes[11].

When considering the topic of humane methods for education, philosophical and practical curricular planning provides perspective; it assigns relative importance to learning issues and thus the methods employed. I would argue that aims such as instilling an appreciation of and propensity toward scientific thought are as important, if not much more important, to the maturing life science learner than knowing what a formalin-preserved kidney looks like and where it resides. And the kidney's function to the living body is likewise more important, and so very easily learned in context while accomplishing multiple other objectives during multidimensional experiences. For example, in the earlier academic grades, the kidney can be used as the context in which learning objectives centred around technical writing, technical verbal communication, scientific method, scientific measurement (volumes, weights, etc.), osmosis, and an appreciation for life are satisfied. A learning objective that asks a student to know what the dead, formalin-preserved kidney looks, feels and smells like pales in comparison to the aforementioned six objectives. Or more pertinently, the student mastering only the later objective suffers in comparison to a student versed on the first six objectives. Maybe some educators think they need the cadaver specimen to engage the student. Given its very limited use and potential to satisfy learning objectives outside medical training (i.e. simply to convey what a dead, formalin-preserved kidney looks, feels and smells like), why not choose an equal or superior method of engaging students that fulfils a more inclusive list of objectives?

Can this approach to life science learning be integrated into existing curricula - a task likely to be more difficult than that of beginning afresh? Outright reform or a staged, gradual approach are both achievable. If a staged approach is chosen, only the implementation should be staged; the design phase should encompass the entire plan. If the design is done in stages, the big picture is lost. Curricular reform may seem a daunting task. To avoid much of the initial frustration in the perceived enormity of the task, an important first objective must be to formulate curricular aims and goals without consideration for means. Freeing oneself from potential obstacles to implementation allows for the generation of creative and inclusive aims and goals. Without this freedom, creativity will not emerge. This process is best achieved with input from multiple participants during focused brainstorming sessions. Professionals, academics, and users of the discipline(s) in question all can provide insight into the development of these aims and goals. Surveys completed by users of the discipline(s) are also useful tools for compiling inclusive aims and goals.

Creating an evolution of humane education in the life sciences

The motivation for curricular reform may or may not originate with the desire to employ humane educational methods. Even if the reform is motivated by the perceived need for 'better' education, it is probable that the new curriculum will indeed be humane if all agree that learning about such things as compassion, altruism, life, and non-violence is important. For example, teaching ultimate superiority of our species (by using animals to their detriment, because we can) is necessarily contrary to learning to appreciate diversity within our own species or in relation to other species, the intelligence of other species, and the complexity of life itself. The life sciences are not exact; they are a continuum. We do not know 'the truth'. To suggest that other species are 'known' to be inferior and at our disposal, does not allow for the humility we need to seek the truth[1]. Choosing learning methods instead that support the important concepts mentioned above will move us forward.

Active evaluation of a curriculum is as essential to educational progress as is hypothesis testing to scientific discovery. Educators must participate in this process such that we may benefit from it as well. Our student assessment methods must be as diverse as our learning methods, and we must assess what we hope for students to learn. Our program assessments must not hinder our students, and they must be focused enough to answer the questions posed.

The process of curricular design must be purposeful and well considered. It is easy to focus on the facts to be learned as the only objectives. A much broader scope of knowledge, abilities and attributes is an achievable goal. This larger potential is what creates the excitement for the designer. If we create a curriculum that facilitates an inclusive learning experience, one which does not harm the student, does not harm others, and one which seeks diverse learning goals through diverse learning methods, we will 'create' a graduate whose life is defined by both compassion and intellect. How and what we teach does impact the world through these individuals.

Conclusion

This process of developing something new or reforming something old, using creative (perhaps unproven) methods, and asking students to explore and demonstrate novel or uncommon learning objectives is likely to be unsettling to the curriculum designer. Members of our species (and others) perform at their best when the adrenaline is flowing, the heart is beating faster, and the mind is clear and sharp. Sitting on the edge of this educational uncertainty gives us the challenging circumstance to create something better. Risk bounded by rationality allows us to move forward in a logical, controlled manner seeking solutions to the problems we face. Education is a challenge. Doing it the way we have always done it and expecting of our students what we have always expected is contrary to human nature and scientific discovery. Learning through humane education and expecting our students to demonstrate kindness and compassion alongside their intellect are both achievable and ultimately more supportive of a civilised society.

Bibliography

1. Palmer P.J. The Courage to Teach. New York: Jossey-Bass, 1997.

2. Bloom's Taxonomy. 1996. Last accessed 25 February, 2002. www.coun.uvic.ca/learn/program/hndouts/bloom.html.

3. Karuso P. Systematic Curriculum Design? HERDSA News. 1999;21:3.

4. Goad T.W. Delivering Effective Training. San Diego, CA: University Associates, 1982.

5. Schmidt W.H., Raizen S.R., Britton E.D. Many Visions, Many Aims: A Cross-National Investigation of Curricular Intentions in School Science. Dordrecht, The Netherlands: Kluwer Academic Publishers, 1997.

6. Wiggins G., McTighe J. Understanding by Design. 1998. Association for Supervision and Curriculum Development. Last accessed 24 May 2002. www.ascd.org/readingroom/books/wiggins98book.html.

7. Coles C. Is problem-based learning the only way. In: Boud D. and Feletti G., eds. The Challenge of Problem-Based Learning. 2nd ed. London: Kogan Page Limited. 1997;313-325.

8. Change Your Life and Career with Advanced Brainstorming. Sheffield, England: Infinite Innovations Ltd, 2001. Last accessed 24 May 2002. www.brainstorming.co.uk/tutorials/definitions.html

9. Paul E.S., Podberscek A.L. Veterinary education and students' attitudes toward animal welfare. Veterinary Record. 2000;146:269-272.

10. Fernandez C.V., Rees E.P. Pain management in Canadian level 3 neonatal intensive care units. Cmaj. 1994; 150:499-504.

11. Evensen D., Hmelo C. Problem-Based Learning: A Research Perspective on Learning Interactions. Norwood, NJ: Lawrence Erlbaum Associates, Inc., 2000.

12. Bonwell C.C., Eison J.A. Active Learning: Creating Excitement in the Classroom. Washington, D.C.: The George Washington University, School of Education and Human Development, 1991.

13. Yelon S. Active learning: A taxonomy of trainee activities. Performance and Instruction. 1995;34:38-41.

14. Schomberg S.F. Strategies for Active Teaching and Learning in University Classrooms. A Handbook of Teaching Strategies. University of Minnesota: ERIC Database # ED380665, 1986.

15. Draper R.J. Active Learning in Mathematics: Desktop Teaching. Mathematics Teacher. 1997;90:622-625.

16. Roach R. The virtual classroom. Black Issues in Higher Education. 1997;14:20-23.

17. About National Tele-immersion Initiative (NTII). Last accessed 29 January, 2002. www.advanced.org/teleimmersion.html.

18. Hoffman H.M. Virtual Reality in Medical Education. 1999. Last accessed 29 January, 2002. http://medschool.ucsd.edu/Presentations/NYU/.

19. MacDonald S. A Knowledge-based Learning and Testing System for Medical Education. In Proceedings of the ED-MEDIA 94 - World Conference on Educational Multimedia and Hypermedia June 25-30, 1994; 7.

20. Christensen U.J., Heffernan D., Barach P. Microsimulators in Medical Education: An Overview. Simulation & Gaming. 2001;32:250-262.

21. Kuh G.D., et al. Student learning outside the classroom: Transcending artificial boundaries. ERIC Digest. 1994. Last accessed 20 March, 2002. www.ed.gov/databases/ERIC_Digests/ed394443.html.

22. Center for Teaching and Learning. Active learning beyond the classroom. 1989. Last accessed 20 March, 2002. www.unc.edu/depts/ctl/fyc3.html.

23. Johnson A.L., Farmer J.A. Evaluation of traditional and alternative models in psychomotor laboratories for veterinary surgery. Journal of Veterinary Medical Education 1989;16:11-14.

24. Nobis N. Animal dissection and evidence-based life-science and health professions education. Journal of Applied Animal Welfare Science. 2002;5.

25. Dewey J. Democracy and Education. New York: Macmillan, 1924.

26. Wales C.E., Nardi A.H., Stager R.A. Thinking Skills: Making a Choice. Morgantown, West Virginia: Center for Guided Design, 1987.

27. Schweitzer A. Reverence for Life. Kiernan T., ed. Philosophical Library, 1965.

Biography

Lara Marie Rasmussen completed an undergraduate Bachelors of Science degree in Biological Sciences and Policy Studies at the University of California (Davis) in 1989. She went on to receive a Doctor of Veterinary Medicine degree from UC Davis as well in 1993. A portion of her surgical training was accomplished during a summer surgical course at Washington State University. Her interest in small animal surgery as a career took her through a small animal internship at South Shore Veterinary Associates in Massachusetts and a three-year small animal surgery residency at the University of Minnesota. She later received Diplomate status in the American College of Veterinary Surgeons. Her beliefs about the inappropriate and detrimental use of animals in education were challenged at every stage of her educational experience, yet she prevailed and now succeeds as a board-certified surgeon. She spent one year as a clinical instructor at Washington State University in the surgery department, and then went into private referral practice with Veterinary Referral Services in Spokane, Washington. In 1999, she was recruited to develop and direct the surgery and clinical skills program at the new veterinary school in Southern California (Western University of Health Sciences, College of Veterinary Medicine.) The program will involve the non-detrimental use of animals and will incorporate extensive live animal experiences that benefit the animals involved. Dr. Rasmussen's approach to this new curriculum will be to capitalise on the wealth of education science available, and to require student mastery of skills rather than simple exposure to skills.

Lara Marie Rasmussen, DVM, MS

Diplomate, American College of Veterinary Surgeons
Assistant Professor
College of Veterinary Medicine
Western University of Health Sciences
309 East 2nd Street
Pomona, CA 91766
USA

tel: +1 909 469 5668 (office)
fax: +1 909 469 5635
e-mail: lmrasmussen@westernu.edu

www.westernu.edu

5. Conscientious objection: Roles and responsibilities for teachers and students

The context

For any discussion about harmful animal use and alternatives in education, the issue of conscientious objection must be considered. Like conscientious objection to war, it is an individual or group act whereby the objectors refuse to participate in practice which is against their moral beliefs. It is a civil rights issue relating to freedom of conscience, and in education it has impact right across the curriculum. Where alternatives have not replaced harmful animal use in the life sciences, and requests for their implementation are denied, then objection by students is a likely scenario. As well as refusing to participate in dissection of killed animals or in animal experimentation, objectors will of course request humane alternatives.

Conscientious objection by students can therefore create a challenging situation for teachers, as it raises questions about established practice and academic freedom. Nevertheless, it is rooted in positive cultural values such as respect for life, and a commitment to healing rather than harming. Moreover, well-developed critical thinking skills and ethical literacy are often evidenced by students who conscientiously object. As a process, objection may therefore play a significant role in the resolution of existing ethical conflicts, and the modernisation of education through the introduction of alternatives.

Degree of objection

The number of students who object often seems low. This is understandable considering the social and academic pressures of being a student, and the psychological and academic penalty often threatened to those who question the status quo. But the situation is misleading, as the literature shows that when the inherent ethical issues surrounding harmful animal use are discussed openly, many more students are prepared to voice their discomfort or disagreement with the practice[1].

Private, silent disagreement from students, however, does not solve the ethical problem, and nor does it limit the harm caused to animals. Students may participate in experiments against their will, or choose to observe from a distance. In some cases they may decide to change course or drop out rather than defend and follow through their beliefs by challenging the experiments. Conscientious objection itself involves students choosing to broach the issue of harmful animal use with their teachers, and express their views, in an attempt to reach a mutually agreeable solution that involves replacement. It is likely to involve taking a more public stand against the experiments, and asking for the right to alternatives with a firm personal or collective commitment to achieving their implementation. This often involves a small number of determined students, but on some occasions whole classes have been known to object.

Responses from teachers

Teachers' responses in these situations vary considerably, often reflecting their ability or choice to deal creatively with challenge, and personal and institutional confidence with the process of transition. In the best of cases, they may respond by investigating existing alternatives and implementing a combination of humane tools and approaches which meet the teaching objectives and replace the harmful animal use. They may also develop their own alternatives. Ideally these curricular changes will be for the whole class, so that all students can benefit; otherwise, where alternatives are not mainstreamed, they may only be for students who choose the 'alternative track'.

Teachers may also leave students to find their own ways of meeting the teaching objectives for particular practicals using alternatives. Veterinary students, for example, may find ethically-sourced animal cadavers for anatomy study and clinical skills practice, or arrange extra-curricular surgery practice with supportive independent veterinarians. The faculty may consent to recognising this activity as part of the course credits, and monitor the students' progress.

Some students, however, face highly defensive emotionally-charged opposition from their teachers, and occasionally even from fellow students, such that calm and rational discussion about the issues is not possible. Conscientious objection is sometimes taken personally by teachers, rather than as a challenge to the denial of student choice or as a criticism of practice. Aggressive questioning of students and dismissive treatment of their concerns are surprisingly common, and many have suffered the threats and subsequent reality of low grades, no grades, and even expulsion.

Student choices

In the face of opposition, or where they consider that self-organised alternatives reflect an abnegation of the institute's responsibility to provide the educational experiences, students may choose to campaign harder for widespread official implementation of alternatives. Routes chosen by students may include gathering support from fellow students and sympathetic teachers, student advocacy groups, civil liberties organisations and other conscientious objectors; presenting submissions to the university authorities with well-researched arguments and details of relevant alternatives and their pedagogical advantages; and as a last resort bringing the issue to the attention of the media or launching a legal challenge.

Finding win-win solutions to ethical problems is almost invariably possible. It is worth looking closer at the qualities and approaches of many conscientiously objecting students, as recognition of the positive aspects of objection will help support mutual understanding, reduce teacher-student conflict and encourage co-operative resolution.

Qualities and values

Students who object are likely to be active critical thinkers, and therefore good potential scientists. Being able to question the orthodoxy is a sign of critical, scientific thinking. There would not have been any innovation - or any science - if it weren't for creative thinking and the challenging of established norms. Many objectors are also amongst the brightest of students, and this intelligence often has a direct relationship with their willingness and ability to challenge.

Risking opposition or penalty from their teachers, as a potential consequence of objection, is a choice not taken lightly. Students who do object care deeply about their education, and have a high level of motivation and commitment to it. They are conscientious in more ways than one.

As well as their interest in best practice through the use of alternatives, they may also be involved in extra-curricular training work, student science clubs or animal protection to gain further experience in their field.

They are likely to be emotionally literate, valuing sensitivity, respect, empathy and compassion. Students who value their own and others' emotions have a self-awareness which is intrinsically valuable and which has a positive impact in terms of successful learning: with an awareness of themselves and their own learning processes they are likely to learn more effectively. Student efforts to support the implementation of alternatives in a well designed curriculum derive in part from this awareness about the learning process and effective learning environments. Such awareness is supported by the evidence from published academic studies, which show that alternatives are at least as effective as animal experiments in terms of student performance (see Balcombe, in this volume).

Together with their critical thinking skills, emotional literacy informs their facility to deal with ethical issues. Ethical literacy is of crucial importance in the life sciences, and familiarity with the ethical terrain at an early stage is a valuable skill and resource. Support and encouragement in the process of developing emotional and ethical literacy is important for everyone. Conscientious objection is also an expression of taking responsibility for one's actions, both by refusing to participate in practice that is against one's morals, and by calling for alternatives. Moreover, students are usually committed to pushing for co-operative solutions, and engaging responsibly with teachers on the issue. Taking responsibility and developing these qualities of true leadership should be welcomed and rewarded.

Resolving ethical conflict

Students who object are catalysts for the resolution of existing and often unspoken tension. It is up to teachers to respond appropriately when the tension surrounding harmful animal use is named and explored. Teachers could deal with the challenge by meeting the intellectual energy and passion of the students. Sadly, some teachers avoid this, and resort to imposing authority and penalty, or practising non-engagement. Conflict resolution can significantly improve the learning environment, including the student-teacher relationship. Students will appreciate the efforts made by teachers to deal with the issues and to implement alternatives, and will feel valued and encouraged in their thinking, learning, and commitment to ethics. The improved communication that accompanies a more respectful, partnership approach within education means that the wisdom and experience of teachers are more likely to be successfully passed on to the students. Genuine respect flowing in both directions can create a very free environment, where growth and learning can flourish. And teaching students who care deeply about their education and have a high level of respect for their teachers may be very rewarding for the teachers themselves. Such respect comes from a very different source to that demanded by authority.

Catalysing change

Resolving conflict concerning harmful animal use will lead to some introduction of alternatives. As catalysts, therefore, students may bring about significant change. If teachers' academic freedom is seen as being limited by the replacement of cherished conventional methods, then it should be remembered that academic freedom always has ethical constraints, and that its practitioners must be answerable to society. Informed by the evolution of cultural values and the impact of techno-logical developments, the process of dialogue and the establishment of social consensus help define what these constraints are. Moreover, any freedom that denies another's freedom is absurd: denying students their freedom of choice, or animals the freedom to live, is not ethically consistent. In contrast, academic freedom to develop progressive humane ways of teaching is an unlimited freedom - one that is there for the taking. This positive orientation, rooted in the freedom of creativity, is the powerful counterpoint to any loss of academic 'freedom' to harm animals or deny student choice.

Potentialities and opportunities condense around any call for progressive change. Bringing in new ideas and new energy, students could be welcomed as partners with the teaching establishment in helping to modernise and make humane the current practice. If students have energy for discussing and progressing this issue, then some of that energy can be channelled by teachers. In the devel-opment of alternative tools, such as new software, students can input their ideas, do some of the work, and test *beta* versions. For alternative approaches such as the use of ethically-sourced cadavers, student energy can help establish the infrastructure. This participation in and joint ownership of the process of change will also help students to commit to the learning process. And harmful animal use and alternatives together provide an excellent case study for further developing critical thinking and ethical literacy skills.

Empowerment

For the students themselves, the implementation of alternatives is of course a successful outcome. But the whole process of conscientious objection can be enlightening and empowering. Whether it begins with merely a discomfort about animal experiments, or is seeded from a well-developed ethical position, finding the courage to speak up sets in motion a process of empowerment whereby one's agency for catalysing change becomes increasingly apparent and strong.

Existing strengths and qualities can be enhanced through objection, although the process is certainly not always easy. Challenging and being challenged develops one's critical thinking, and can force a critical refinement of one's ethical position. It is rewarding to exercise and develop an incisive mind, and to overcome intellectual laziness. Becoming more ethically literate and true to one's emotions is also liberating. The practice of authenticity is surprisingly radical, and combined with self-confidence can be very effective for communication. Feeling more alive and engaged with the world by thinking more, feeling more, and honouring one's evolving ethics is the alternative to denial, conformity and obedience. These life-negating practices help sustain harmful animal use, and limit the unique contributions to cultural diversity and progressive change that each person could make.

Conscientious objection therefore facilitates empowerment, which in turn supports more effective objection. With a well-designed vision of humane education, a realistic appraisal of the existing situation, and knowledge of one's skills, progressive change can certainly be brought about by one or more dedicated individuals. The exact strategy, or route map, does not need to be known in detail in advance: the path of least resistance will become apparent, especially as one begins to live more in the present and more in one's power. But an optimistic outlook, and faith in some form of success, will make the realisation of the vision more likely.

Developing the will plays a crucial role in self-development, and therefore in catalysing change. A strong will is in fact the energy of self-determination, and reflects an identification with decision and commitment (rather than the effort of 'willpower' and 'trying too hard', or the 'duty of stern self-restraint'). A skilful will helps direct and apply energy appropriately and with ease. And goodwill provides the required ethical base[2].

Sources of information and support will often present themselves once a commitment to oneself and to change is made. New communities of thinking, caring people may become visible. Moreover, there may also be strong respect for students who refuse to give up or compromise from teachers who would not disagree publicly with their colleagues, but who are certainly against harmful animal use and supportive of curricular change. Expressing that support, or helping in other ways, can be very valuable for the students.

Any action, including objection and the subsequent responses from teachers, should open up possibilities for further co-operation and initiatives, rather than limit or preclude them. Ensuring that the means to the end are responsibly carried out, co-operatively wherever possible, will help guarantee this. 'Non co-operation' through conscientious objection, however, is the only option available when harmful animal use is compulsory. Nevertheless, when a student refuses to compromise on ethical issues, all other avenues for co-operation with teachers are still open. It is up to both parties to explore these avenues, and to aspire to win-win solutions.

Notes and references

1. For a summary of published studies of attitudes towards animal use in education, see Balcombe, J. (2000). The Use of Animals in Higher Education: Problems, Alternatives and Recommendations. Humane Society Press, Washington, D.C.

See also Pedersen, H. (2002). Humane Education: Animals and Alternatives in Laboratory Classes. Aspects, Attitudes and Implications. Humanimal 4.

2. For a fuller exploration of the will, see Ferrucci, P. (1995). What We May Be: Techniques for Psychological and Spiritual Growth through Psychosynthesis. Thorsons, London.

6. InterNICHE: Philosophy and practice

Structure and process

InterNICHE is an open and diverse network comprising students, teachers and animal campaigners. There is no membership, but free association around the issue of progressive, humane life science education. InterNICHE is one part of a movement for humane education and ethical science, and provides a communication medium and discussion forum for all those involved. InterNICHE works in partnership with any individual, organisation or department that shares the common goals of replacement of harmful animal use and investment in high quality ethical science.

Practically, those who see themselves as part of InterNICHE tend to be the national contacts and their close associates, actively involved in campaigning. All share a commitment to full replacement, and to peaceful and responsible action. Other organisations, various teachers and some producers of alternatives work more in partnership with InterNICHE and liaise on common ground.

InterNICHE is also an international organisation, with a structure to facilitate its activity. It is represented by a co-ordinator at the international level, and by individual national contacts in each of the participating countries. For democracy and efficiency, decision-making is made at the lowest appropriate level. Most general and some specific decisions regarding international activity are made by the committee of national contacts, who work by consensus, communicating mostly by e-mail and meeting at least annually.

The co-ordinator performs most of the international work, and guides and maintains the network. An alternatives adviser, Alternatives Loan System co-ordinator, webmaster and financial assistant comprise the other main roles at the international level. They form a small core group that takes most of the specific decisions relating to on-going activity and project work. The co-ordinator has autonomy where appropriate, but is answerable to the core group and committee. National contacts are encouraged to join the core group, on a rotating basis, to take more responsibility and to learn new skills. Structure and process also evolve over time, and need constant review to ensure that they maximise the opportunities for participation and empowerment, and minimise those for bureaucracy.

The alternatives work of national contacts includes participation in major InterNICHE projects, such as the planning and distribution of this book, and autonomous activity using local or international resources, such as support for local conscientious objectors or the promotion of alternatives from the Loan System. News of most activity is shared internationally, and the degree of activity varies according to capacity and available resources. All national contacts are volunteers for InterNICHE, performing significant work in this and related fields. The community of national contacts has its own energy and forms part of a wider support network for campaigners.

InterNICHE facilitates the evolution of an empowered global network and movement for humane education, exploring the mutual benefits of alliances rather than aspiring to building an empire.

To create this sustainable change requires respect for diversity and an inclusive process - a recognition that everyone can be an agent for progressive change. There are few forums where both abolitionists and animal experimenters can meet to discuss, argue, and search for common ground upon which to build some progressive change involving replacement.

Successful campaigners keep a focus on replacement alternatives in education whilst staying aware of the broader impact of conventional and progressive approaches in the scientific, ethical, pedagogical, social, and economic spheres. Working with this awareness creates more opportunities for connections and alliances to be explored, avoids shifting problems from one sphere to another with an illusion of success, and allows for genuine progressive change with multiple impacts to be achieved.

History

The European Network of Individuals and Campaigns for Humane Education (EuroNICHE) was formed in 1988 by a diverse group of student conscientious objectors, anti-vivisectionists, ethologists and animal welfare researchers from several European countries. With initial support from animal protection organisations in the Netherlands and Britain, and from the European Commission via Eurogroup for Animal Welfare, EuroNICHE served very much as a networking medium between individuals and groups that were promoting alternatives in higher education and supporting students' freedom of conscience. Regular newsletters, meetings and annual conferences helped this communication, brought in more people, and built the foundations for the growth of the international network and various national groups.

This 'first wave' of activity within Europe emerged contemporaneously from several western European countries, and paralleled a growing environmental awareness. Those involved in EuroNICHE could draw on the established - though marginalised - tradition of humane education, which already utilised some alternative approaches and tools, including the very earliest computer simulations which were being developed for use in life science education. National activity in some countries had grown and had helped bring about change at various institutes, and people from new countries in western and central Europe had become active.

By the early 1990s, organisational difficulties associated partly with the transience of student involvement left a need to consolidate the growth and ensure sustainability. This was increasingly achieved from the mid-1990s onwards. The emergence and subsequent empowerment of NGOs in central and eastern Europe led to the movement's further growth, and the production of multi-language literature resources and the 1st edition of this book provided practical support for campaigners. EuroNICHE was awarded the 1997 Nordic Prize for Alternatives to Animal Experiments for its international work.

High quality multimedia software alternatives with significant pedagogical advantages over animal experiments were increasingly being produced and implemented at this time. New contacts were also being made in the USA and Japan, and EuroNICHE began to work more closely with some teachers. By the late 1990s, particularly with the increasing use of the internet, co-operation with alternatives campaigners in countries such as Australia was growing. The EuroNICHE video *Alternatives in Education* was made in 1999 and was widely distributed and translated, supporting another wave of activity and involvement from many of the remaining European countries, such as the Ukraine and those of former Yugoslavia. New contacts were also being made in Brazil, Cuba, Georgia, India and South Africa.

In 2000, with contacts firmly established worldwide, EuroNICHE formally transformed to a global network: InterNICHE, the International Network for Humane Education. The profile of the network had been growing significantly, supported by the work of many national contacts, and by increased opportunities for the co-ordinator to speak at national and international conferences on alternatives - including as a European Commission 'expert'. An enlarged Alternatives Loan System and a new website, both established in 2001, further contributed to awareness about alternatives in education and support for replacement, and new countries joined the network.

The distribution of this book will support activity in new regions such as Asia and across Latin America, especially as students and NGOs gain strength and as modern technology is increasingly applied to life science education. It will also support further replacement and help to consolidate progressive change in countries already involved in the network.

InterNICHE is a non-profit charitable organisation which relies on grants from sponsors for much of its activity. Voluntary commitment and resourcefulness also play major roles. The network has been doubling in size every two years since the late 1990s, and is the only international campaigning network focusing on alternatives within higher education.

Projects and practice

from Guinea Pig to Computer Mouse

This 2nd edition of *from Guinea Pig to Computer Mouse* reflects the massive growth of the field of alternatives in education, and the growth of InterNICHE itself. Compared to the 1st edition, it is very much a new book in terms of its content and scope: as well as the updated product information, it provides detailed background, case studies and further resources, and the print-run is over 10 times greater.

It is useful to have practical information about alternatives in printed form as well as on-line in databases, and to be able easily and quickly to look through a whole publication. A diversity of media reaches more people and is more inclusive: in some countries and regions, the printed word rather than the computer is the main medium for information retrieval; computers are not universally available or affordable, despite their near ubiquity in the west, and fast and inexpensive internet connections are not standard. A book is therefore the most culturally appropriate and practical tool for some areas. Translations into at least 12 languages are under production, supported by the RSPCA, and internet and CD-ROM versions will also be created.

Alternatives video

The InterNICHE video *Alternatives in Education* was launched in 1999, sponsored by a number of groups including the Swedish Fund for Research Without Animal Experiments and the Dr Hadwen Trust for Humane Research. It provides another medium through which to promote alternatives and to demonstrate exemplary products from a range of disciplines. The 33-minute film features a number of teachers demonstrating alternatives that they have developed and/or use in practical courses. State-of-the-art tools such as multimedia software and high-quality video, and alternative approaches such as student self-experimentation and the dissection of ethically-sourced cadavers, are shown graphically and with positive anecdotal assessment by teachers and students.

The video is suitable for life science teachers and students, for ethics committees, legislators and animal campaigners. It has been used as reference material for educating students and faculty about alternatives and product innovation, as course material within life science education and lab animal welfare training, and as a promotional tool for campaigners. Over 2,000 copies have been distributed directly to university libraries, teachers and others in around 60 countries. The World Society for the Protection of Animals (WSPA) has helped support translations into 20 different languages. It has also been viewed at a number of national and international conferences on alternatives, and clips shown on national television in several countries. The Naef Prize for Alternatives was awarded to EuroNICHE in 1999 for the video and for its work in eastern Europe.

Alternatives in Education is also available for downloading via the InterNICHE website (www.interniche.org) and will be added to the CD-ROM version of this book.

Alternatives Loan System

The opportunity to trial alternatives is an important factor in the familiarisation with and assessment of alternatives by teachers and students. In 2001 InterNICHE radically enlarged its existing Alternatives Loan System to include over 100 different products from a range of quality CD-ROMs, videos, mannequins and simulators. Covering major areas such as anatomy, physiology, pharmacology and clinical skills, the alternatives held within the Loan System have been chosen for their pedagogical quality and potential for replacement (see *Part D - Further Resources* or the InterNICHE website for the current list of products).

Currently the most comprehensive library of alternatives in education, the Loan System offers alternatives for free loan to most areas of the world. Borrowers pay the return postage to Slovenia, where the Loan System is currently based. The facility allows individual products to be assessed by teachers for their relevance in particular courses, and provides an opportunity to see the quality and range of alternatives for those less familiar with recent developments. Products are also used for replacement of specific animal practicals by conscientiously objecting students, for displays and demonstrations at institutes and conferences, and to support the diverse work of InterNICHE national contacts. For those working to replace harmful animal use, the Loan System can provide encouragement and motivation as well as practical help.

Within its first year, loans averaging 5 items each have been made to teachers, students, organisations, ethics committees and government ministries in over 25 countries. As well as increasing teacher and student familiarisation of alternatives by bringing the products into offices and labs, other direct results of the facility have included actual replacement of animal experiments with the purchase and implementation of alternatives subsequent to the loans.

With its location in Slovenia, the Loan System has an extra focus on the countries of former Yugoslavia through a Special Collection of alternatives set up at the Veterinary Faculty of the

University of Ljubljana. The Special Collection gives easy access to products via the university library and through regional bibliographic databases, and also allows for lending between teachers from neighbouring countries. As a medium-term loan, the Special Collection will move to another part of the world after a suitable period of time. Four small-scale 'micro-Loan Systems' are also being established in Brazil, Russia, India and Japan to provide demonstration and loan items in these regions. As the libraries are evolving resources, recommendations of new alternatives to include are invited from readers in order to keep them up-to-date and of optimum relevance.

Website and listserve

In 2001 InterNICHE launched the world's largest website on alternatives in education. Available at www.interniche.org, this resource provides a wide range of material for all parties involved in animal use and alternatives. The site provides news updates and background information on the issues. It details the resources that InterNICHE offers, provides links to other organisations and their resources, and lists the latest contents of the Alternatives Loan System, with links to producers. There is advice and support for conscientious objectors, including testimonies from students around the world, and several image galleries.

Substantial parts of this book, including the database of products in *Part C - Alternatives File*, will be available on the site. On-line databases on alternatives are increasingly being specified as 'required visiting' before teachers and researchers apply to animal ethics/animal care and use committees, as part of the moral and legal burden of proof on teachers that they have investigated 'all possible alternatives' to animal procedures. The InterNICHE site has an increasing number of visitors, and was registering around 30,000 hits per month by the end of 2002. Translations of the site into new languages are beginning with Russian, Polish, Portuguese, Spanish, Greek and Japanese. Regional variations of selected content will honour the cultural diversity relevant to the issue and within the network, providing an appropriate degree of localisation.

The InterNICHE listserve focuses on alternatives in education and conscientious objection, and is open to everyone. New members can join via the website.

International awards

An annual Humane Education Award was launched in 2002 by InterNICHE, with financial support from the Dutch anti-vivisection organisation Proefdiervrij. Teachers and students from specific geographical regions are invited to submit funding proposals for the replacement of harmful animal use, which are judged according to overall ethical design, potential to replace harmful animal use, potential pedagogic effectiveness, and student involvement in the project. Proposals are encouraged for the creation of freeware CD-ROMs, videos, models or mannekins for replacement in practical courses; buying a range of established products for similar use; setting up a body donation program for ethically-sourced animal cadavers for veterinary anatomy or basic surgery training; and setting up a student-based program for training medical students who currently use animals.

In the first year, 20,000 Euro was made available for the countries of south-eastern Europe, and seven projects were accepted. At the University of Belgrade in Yugoslavia, the award has enabled the purchase of existing multimedia software and the local creation of a new freeware CD-ROM.

One initiative has brought about replacement within pharmacology and toxicology teaching at the Faculty of Veterinary Medicine, and another will provide an alternative for the many conscientiously objecting students within the experimental physiology course at the Faculty of Biology.

Teachers at the Faculty of Veterinary Medicine in Bucharest, Romania, have developed a new freeware CD-ROM for veterinary physiology teaching with support from the Award. This will replace the annual use of 1,000 frogs, rats, mice and rabbits, and will also be promoted actively throughout Romania with a view to multiplying this replacement within many similar courses. Further support includes a donation of 16 reconditioned computers, recycled from Britain, which will create a new Alternatives Lab for the Faculty and support the use of the new CD-ROM and other alternatives. The University of Medicine and Pharmacy in Iaşi, Romania, is also being given recycled computers along with funds for the purchase of existing alternatives.

In Croatia, the Department of Animal Physiology at Zagreb University has been awarded an Advanced System *Biopac* apparatus for student self-experimentation, as a full replacement for invasive and terminal physiology experiments on at least 100 animals. The range of experiments possible with the apparatus will also allow for some new practical courses not done before, which will further improve teaching quality.

Finally, the development of a range of small and large animal models and mannekins for anatomy and clinical skills training is being supported at the Faculty of Veterinary Medicine at the University of Sarajevo in Bosnia & Herzegovina.

The 2003 Humane Education Award offers a similar amount of funding support to initiatives from within India. 1,000,000 Rupees will support existing grassroots interest in alternatives, and complement government-level initiatives for replacement.

Conscientious objection and support for students

Support for student conscientious objectors is crucially important in the face of emotionally-charged opposition to humane science and the threat of academic or psychological penalty from some teachers. The presence of a network offering advice and information, and the experiences of other students who have been through similar situations, can give power to those objecting and help sustain them through the process. A booklet of testimonies from 12 student conscientious objectors has been produced, and these and other testimonies are included on the InterNICHE website. Practical advice on how to object, step-by-step, and the range of other InterNICHE resources such as the *Alternatives in Education* video and the Alternatives Loan System, are also available to students.

InterNICHE conferences

InterNICHE now holds a major international conference every two years. These events offer leading international and national speakers, challenging workshops, an alternatives room with some of the latest teaching products, and space for plenty of discussion and networking. Delegates include teachers, product developers, students and campaigners, amongst others. Until 1998, conferences were held annually in a different country each year, providing a regular alternatives event in regions as diverse as Italy, Sweden and Romania, co-organised by local national contacts.

The 1ˢᵗ InterNICHE Conference, held in Belgium in 2001, involved over 100 people from 15 countries, including the USA, Brazil and India, and many from within Europe. Such conferences are tightly focused events, yet acknowledge the links between issues. They are also optimistic and positive in spirit, and aim to give a very practical and empowering message about replacement.

Outreach work

As part of their outreach work, InterNICHE national contacts often help organise and participate in local and national events. These range from seminars and conferences on alternatives, presentations at academic meetings, and various animal protection events, to small-scale demonstrations of alternatives to teachers and students. The InterNICHE co-ordinator also helps organise and has spoken at a range of national and international conferences on alternatives and related issues.

Outreach tours in a number of different countries, organised by national contacts together with the co-ordinator, have also brought the InterNICHE vision and practical support to large numbers of students and teachers at their own institutes. A tour to several universities in Moscow and in Tartu (Estonia) took place in 1995, and was followed by visits to three Polish cities. The Russian and Polish trips also involved several co-producers of the *Virtual Physiology* series of alternatives, who demonstrated the newly produced software and met with local teachers.

In 2000, a smaller tour of Croatia was followed by a large tour of the Ukraine where the co-ordinator visited eight institutes in Kharkov, Kyiv and Odessa to present the case for alternatives and show the newly translated Russian and Ukrainian versions of the *Alternatives in Education* video. Opportunities for discussion with students and individual teachers also helped identify potential collaborators for the RSPCA / InterNICHE Ukraine Alternatives Project, which was initiated soon afterwards.

Following a major alternatives conference in New Delhi, a 2003 speaking tour of veterinary and medical institutes in eight cities across India has been organised. This will be supported by the nationwide distribution of this book, and the launch of the 2003 Humane Education Award.

Joint projects and collaboration

Much of the work of InterNICHE comprises joint projects - with funders, with teachers, with others. InterNICHE also collaborates with NORINA and groups such as the European Resource Centre for Alternatives in Higher Education (EURCA).

The Ukraine Alternatives Project is a successful joint project for replacement that builds on the InterNICHE speaking tour of the Ukraine, RSPCA investment in an alternatives lab at Kyiv State University, and various local initiatives. A nationwide library of alternative products was set up in 2001 to lend products to teachers across the country. In advance of its launch, a number of products were donated to institutes. Some replacement of animal experiments has already taken place, and a 2002 alternatives conference helped share experiences and plan for future replacement.

A diversity of future projects are possible. Readers are invited to make contact and to explore common ground with InterNICHE.

part b **case studies**

1. Virtual versus real laboratories in life science education: Concepts and experiences

Hans A. Braun

Institute of Physiology, University of Marburg, Germany

This report is based on many semesters' teaching experience with both 'real' and 'virtual' laboratories in practical courses for medical and human biology students at the University of Marburg. When massive student protest in the early 1990s led us to stop using animal preparations in practical courses, classical experiments like those with the frog sciatic nerve and others which we considered of high educational value were eliminated. In our search for alternatives we created virtual realisations of the original experiments. These are the computer programs *SimNerv*, *SimMuscle*, *SimVessel*, *SimHeart* and *SimPatch*, together called the *Virtual Physiology* series. The programs are distributed by Thieme Publ., Stuttgart/New York and have been in regular use for several years not only in Marburg but also in medical, biological science and related faculties at several hundred universities and high schools across the world. They are used in lectures, seminars, and - most widely - in practical courses, and they often have replaced the original experiments which used animal preparations.

This report therefore also considers comments from other colleges with a similar teaching background, as well as students' assessment of the virtual labs, specifically referring to an evaluation of *SimNerv* with a detailed questionnaire. As one of the developers of the *Virtual Physiology* series, I will also give some background information about the history of these programs, and explain how they reflect our principal philosophy - that educational software packages can and must be more than animated textbooks. I also describe our new series of virtual computer laboratories, called *cLabs*. More detailed information is given at our homepage www.cLabs.de, with free access to several applets of our latest release *cLabs-Neuron*.

History of the *Virtual Physiology* series

Our first teaching program, *SimNerv* (originally called *MacFrog*), was developed in the mid-1990s. At that time, the medical faculty in Marburg had already stopped using animal preparations in physiology courses. This was a consequence of massive, sometimes aggressive student protests against animal use which finally made regular teaching with animal preparations impossible. In our faculty I was probably most strongly exposed to the student protest because I was teaching the remaining two courses which involved animal preparations - the classical frog nerve and muscle experiments. I was heavily defending these experiments because I considered them to be the best examples for effective practice-oriented learning.

We therefore looked for alternatives, and saw that they did not exist. But we soon recognised that rapidly developing computer techniques could provide an opportunity to make virtual laboratories where the students can do experiments similar to the real lab. These ideas were realised in collaboration with our then students Martin Hirsch, an expert in multimedia design, and Martin Huber, a specialist in computer modeling for neurodynamics. As a private venture, but with support from the Director of our institute, Karlheinz Voigt, we developed our first virtual lab, *MacFrog*, which later, as part of the *Virtual Physiology* series, was renamed *SimNerv*. Coverage of the program in diverse media (newspapers, TV) led to external support from Apple Computers and the Hessian State Ministry of Science and Arts (HMWK).

The program was winning awards almost from its inception. In 1994 *MacFrog* won the German/Austrian Software Award for the Best Teaching Software in Biology and Medicine, the Award for the Best Multimedia Application, and the MacWorld Editors Award for Trendsetting Multimedia Software. With this background we received, in contract with Thieme Publishers (Stuttgart/New York), a substantial grant from the German Ministry of Education and Science (BMBF). This support allowed us to take *SimNerv* into its final form for public distribution, and to develop three more programs, *SimMuscle, SimVessel* and *SimHeart*.

These programs together reproduce exactly the experiments which before had been done with real animal preparations in integrated physiology/pharmacology courses for medical students in Marburg. A fifth and final program, *SimPatch*, was added by Horst Schneider and Martin Hirsch, completing the *Virtual Physiology* series.

Martin Hirsch is now the owner of a successful multimedia company (iAS, Marburg/Berlin, see www.brainmedia.de). Martin Huber is successfully continuing his scientific computer modeling studies at the Department of Psychiatry and Psychotherapy, still in close co-operation with us. Horst Schneider had left the university for industry but recently came back to our group and has contributed to our new series of teaching software *cLabs*.

Background and concepts of the virtual labs

The development of our virtual computer laboratories was guided by the same criteria which had previously led me to defend the 'real' experiments. The criteria are related to the high teaching impact of practical courses which can be achieved when well-prepared students do the experiments on their own. The prerequisites are that the students understand the experimental set-up, i.e. they don't have to deal with over-complicated devices, and that the physiological tasks are practice-oriented but closely related to the theoretical knowledge. The ideal situation would be 'learning by doing', with free experimentation by students.

Therefore, we designed a user-friendly computer interface where fully equipped labs appear on the computer screen and where all instrument settings are freely adjustable by mouse-clicks. In parallel, we developed mathematical algorithms for the heart of the program, which, according to the device settings chosen, reproduce realistic responses from the preparations. Moreover, we use random variables to account for the natural variability of the preparations, which also has the advantage that no student will have the same preparation or the same results as his/her neighbour. In this way we came very close to the situation in the real lab, and, in addition, could take advantage of some specific features of the virtual world, as described below.

The programs allow students to perform experiments at different levels of complexity. There is the experimental situation, which is relatively easy to grasp - for example, when students have to reproduce classical textbook illustrations like isotonic and isometric maxima of muscle contractions.

The idea is that students who successfully do these recordings on their own will never again have problems with the understanding of basic biological characteristics. They will also be well practised in procedural skills. Additionally, as a more general aspect, the students will learn (sometimes the hard way) that successful experimentation also requires profound theoretical knowledge. They will see that this is needed for the systematic collection of problem-relevant data as well as for critical, qualified data analysis and appropriate presentations of the results. It is also needed for correct interpretation of the experiment itself. For example, interpretations of most recordings in the nerve experiment require theoretical knowledge about ion channel gating, which means that the students, in a more demanding task, have to bring together knowledge from quite different physiological levels.

These teaching aims go far beyond learning and reproducing factual textbook knowledge. Here, students learn how to make use of their knowledge, and this is certainly much more closely related to the problems that they will have to face later in their career - for example, as a medical doctor who has to decide about the appropriate treatment of a patient on the basis of systematic inspection and correct diagnosis. It is worth noting that this is exactly the area where the 'Program for International Student Assessment' (PISA) only recently detected major educational deficiencies in Germany and internationally.

Teaching experiences with real and virtual labs

The main argument against the virtual labs generally is that students cannot practice the preparation of living biological tissue with mouse-clicks. Indeed, this cannot be achieved even with the most excellent computer simulation. When this is the objective of a course the experiments necessarily have to be done with animal preparations. However, the major question is how far it is justified to practice these specific skills in regular biology, physiology and pharmacology courses or at high schools.

The answer essentially depends on the need and the efficiency of such training. I myself often have argued that at least medical students, before they treat patients, should know from their own experience how sensitive living tissue reacts and how easily proper functioning can be destroyed by improper handling. But I am no longer sure about these arguments because medical doctors are becoming more and more specialised and those who perform operations will be trained in this respect anyway. The efficiency is also questionable, specifically in relation to the actual situation at our university where we now have 16 students in one practical group, compared with the 6 or 8 when I last did experiments with animal preparations in a student lab.

It is hard to do such work with a group of 16 inexperienced students. Indeed, I know of several departments where the students receive ready-prepared tissue from the tutors. Hence, many courses which involve the use of animal tissue do not in fact include preparation of that tissue by students. The experiments following the preparation, however, can be done better in the virtual lab. In the following I am going to illustrate this specifically referring to our and others' experiences with *SimNerv*, because this is the program which has been in use longest and for which we have a recent detailed students' evaluation.

When we introduced *SimNerv/MacFrog* into the regular physiology course we didn't have time to write the instructions in advance. We used the instructions and protocol forms which were left from previous courses with the animal preparations. With no difficulties, the students followed the same instructions and did exactly the same experiments as previous students did with the real nerve - and with even better success. This illustrates how closely this simulation resembles the real lab, something that was confirmed by many other groups ("This simulation allows the students to experience virtually everything that they would see in the real nerve"). Indeed, there are several institutes where I know that the teachers originally wanted to use *SimNerv* as an introduction to the real experiments but who then decided that "this follow activity may be unnecessary" (quotations from a report by D. Wilson, Miami University, Oxford, Ohio).

However, over the course of time, we noticed that we were in fact doing a better job with the virtual than with the real preparations. We realised - admittedly only from our new experience from the virtual labs - that it was an illusion that students were doing their own experiments in the animal lab. They always strictly followed the instructions and, whenever some settings had to be changed, they would ask the tutors whether the settings were correct before they continued with the experiments. The reason for this is obvious. The students were afraid that wrong settings might destroy the preparation, and that as a consequence they might not get the certificate or might have to kill another animal (which we, by the way, would never have allowed).

So we were unexpectedly confronted with surprisingly active students in the virtual labs which, step-by-step, led us to modify the instructions. Specifically, tasks have been included for which we do not explain the experiment in detail but let the students investigate. Some of these experiments would have been very difficult to carry out in the real lab but are of particularly high didactic value. For example, in the real nerve experiment it is almost impossible to block the nerve conduction or even to change the positions of stimulating and recording electrodes without unpredictable changes in the whole situation. This can easily be done in the virtual lab. So we ask the students to induce mono- and biphasic or inverted action potentials, or to find out which electrode is connected to the positive and negative stimulator output or the inverting and non-inverting input of the differential amplifier, respectively. By the time the students have succeeded in answering this question through their own experimentation they have understood a lot about the generation and recording of compound action potentials, and, as a more general aspect, should have seen that the experimental settings can interfere profoundly with the outcome of an experiment.

As another example, in *SimHeart* we encourage the students to examine heart activity at its limits, in addition to the standard experiments. We let them induce and compare cardiac arrests in the systole and the diastole, or ask them to apply glycosides to an already pre-activated heart to see not only the positive effects of therapeutic substances but also their potential toxicity. We believe that the students can learn a lot from such extreme situations of heart contractions which, in the real lab, are mostly avoided because you never can be sure that the preparation recovers.

Hence, experimentation in the virtual labs is more rich, and students are more active. It is my impression and that of other tutors that teaching has become not worse but more effective. There are no students who are frustrated due to preparations or instruments that sometimes fail. They are not confused by instruments that have extra controls which they should not touch. Requests for help from tutors are less numerous and the students' own initiative is clearly improved. Last but not least, experimentation and learning do not suffer from the negative emotions of using killed animals.

Of course, there are still teachers who definitely want to have 'animal experiments' in student physiology or biology courses. Our programs seem to be dangerous to their concepts. This would partly explain the curious criticisms, especially from German colleagues, that the programs are "worse than television", "toys", or "tamagotchies". Such comments (R. Klinke, H. Wiese in Uni-Spiegel 2/2001), however, are the exception. Most reports in German newspapers and journals, especially those with the highest reputation, praise our programs and emphasise, for example, that "the authors, undoubtedly, did excellent work" (Frankfurter Allgemeine Zeitung, FAZ, 22.07.98), or, more recently, that these programs "are more instructive than classical experiments" (Zeitpunkte 1, 2001) and "have set international standards for high quality teaching software" (Die Zeit, 28.12.00).

These positive reviews of our programs were recently confirmed by an evaluation of *SimNerv* with a detailed questionnaire that was anonymously answered by 155 medical students in our regular physiology course. Questions about user-friendliness revealed that there were no difficulties associated with the use of the virtual devices. The students felt that *SimNerv* helped to increase their understanding of nerve physiology, and most assumed that they may even have learned more than in the real experiment. As the *SimNerv* experiment was held towards the end of the course when the students had already done most of the other experiments, we also asked them to compare *SimNerv* with other training experiments, and this again gave excellent positive results (>80%). This is even more remarkable considering that nerve physiology usually does not belong to medical students' favourite topics and that *SimNerv* had to compete with clinically very important exercises (EEG, ECG, blood plasma analysis etc.) performed in very well equipped labs.

The students were also asked whether they consider multimedia simulations as valid alternatives to real experiments. This question was asked prior to using *SimNerv*, revealing a principally positive opinion on computer simulations. When the students were asked again following the *SimNerv* experiment there was an additional, statistically highly significant shift toward still more positive values. It is therefore no surprise that the students showed an interest in the development and use of further simulation programs.

Current situation and plans: the *cLabs* concept

Our present work continues with an advanced series of virtual computer labs, called *cLabs*, which expands the *Virtual Physiology* concept in several respects.

Firstly, the cLabs programs will further facilitate students' own experimentation and therefore also include more simple animations and simulations to prepare step-by-step for the experiments in the more complex virtual labs. For one of our programs, *cLabs-Neuron*, part of these applets are already running on our homepage www.cLabs.de. For the other program, *cLabs-SkinSenses*, they will soon be available, and we are going to develop similar resources for the *Virtual Physiology* series too.

The *cLabs* series also includes experiments which, like *SimPatch*, are too difficult to be physically carried out in student coursework but which can be realised *in silico*. This is the case for *cLabs-Neuron*, which provides virtual labs for ion-channel recordings and current/voltage clamp experiments, as well as for *cLabs-SkinSenses* which simulates single-fibre recordings from mechano- and thermosensitive afferents from the skin.

Moreover, our principal approach with the use of mathematical simulations, including random components, fits perfectly with the idea of an advanced 'Virtual University' because it allows control of individual experiments by the students themselves as well as by the tutors - and also via the internet. For example, whenever a user opens one of our virtual labs he/she will find his/her personal preparations. However, what for the user will appear as principally unpredictable variability is mathematically clearly defined. This makes it possible to develop a control software for immediate check of individual results. Here we see the most promising solutions for highly effective teaching software for the future.

This was, unfortunately, not the opinion of some unknown referees. In a major initiative, the German Ministry of Education and Science (BMBF) spent about US$100 million for the development of new teaching software, but refused any support for us although we are still the only German group with teaching software of international reputation, at least as far we are aware within the fields of biology and medicine.

We have been continuing our efforts and have made good progress with some support from 'transMIT', Giessen. We have already presented parts of the *cLabs*-programs with great success at international conferences, including the teaching exhibition of the 2001 Neuroscience Meeting in San Diego. The dates of upcoming exhibitions are given on our homepage www.cLabs.de. To speed up the progress and to realise our plans with the integrated control software we would be happy to explore potential co-operation. We are confident that these programs, even more than the *Virtual Physiology* series, will find hundreds of interested institutes with many thousands of users all over the world.

Biography

Hans Albert Braun is head of the Neurodynamics Group at the Institute of Physiology at the University of Marburg in Germany. He trained as an electronic engineer at the Technical University in Karlsruhe, where he obtained a degree in 'Electrobiology'. In a supplementary study of 'Human Biology' he obtained his PhD at the Medical Faculty of the University of Marburg. His research involves experiments and models of neuronal encoding and neuromodulatory processes in peripheral sensory receptors and hypothalamic neurones, including computer modeling studies of affective disorders. The aim is the understanding of neuronal systems dynamics at different levels and to elucidate their common functional principles. With the background of these experiences, the Neurodynamics Group has developed teaching software with virtual computer laboratories for practice-oriented learning, including the award winning teaching software *SimNerv*. Hans A. Braun is a member of several scientific societies and has been honoured with the fellowship of the Biophysics Division of the American Physical Society.

Hans A. Braun, PhD

Institute of Physiology
University of Marburg
Deutschhausstr. 2
D-35037 Marburg
Germany

tel: +49 6421 286 2307
fax: +49 6421 286 6967
e-mail: braun@mailer.uni-marburg.de

2. Implementation of computer-based alternatives in biomedical education

Henk van Wilgenburg

Department of Pharmacology, University of Amsterdam, The Netherlands

Alternatives for alternatives

Animals as model for humans

Interest in the study of anatomy and physiology goes back to Leonardo da Vinci (1452-1519), and beyond. That animals could be used for understanding unexplained processes became clear when the Dutchman Jan Swammerdam (1637-1680) proved that the volume of muscles does not increase upon contraction due to the inflow of fluidum, as was believed in his time. Instead, he showed in an experiment that the volume of a submerged isolated frog muscle remains the same upon contraction, since the water level did not change when the relaxed muscle was stimulated. Darwin's publication of *The Origin of Species* in 1859 gave rise to the new disciplines of Comparative Anatomy and Comparative Physiology. Since then, animals have been not only the objects of study, but also models for human anatomy and (patho-)physiology. Or in other words: Animals became alternatives for humans.

New models for animals

Anything can be a model of anything, if they share some properties. In science, models are used for different purposes. *Exploratory models* are typical of fundamental research. In more applied research, *predictive models* are widely used with the intention to extrapolate from the model to the real situation. Animals are very often used to study patho-physiological processes and the effects of new drugs within biomedical research. Finally, *explanatory models* are used in teaching and for the transfer of knowledge in general. A scheme on a blackboard, a practical course with animals, a computer program - all are examples serving this purpose.

Although animals are still used as explanatory models within education at some institutes, it should be clear that with modern technologies there is little justification for using them. For developing specific practical skills too, many alternatives are available, especially when the skill is focused on obtaining and interpreting data. For example, for understanding pharmacodynamic effects, i.e. the interaction of a substance with a receptor, students in biomedical sciences often use the guinea pig ileum in a practical course. A guinea pig will be killed for this purpose and a piece of the intestines (ileum) will be isolated and transferred to an organ bath. The effect of different concentrations of drugs - agonists and antagonists - can be studied from the rate of contraction of the ileum. The contraction will be recorded and later on measured for further elaboration, i.e. graphical representations of the results and calculation of different parameters. In general, a technician will prepare the isolated ileum, and the students will add the drugs to the organ-bath and acquire the data. For these practical skills, however, no animal is needed, because for the generation of the data very realistic simulations are available. We might even wonder whether it is still necessary to simulate animal experiments, since animals have been introduced as alternatives for humans, as we saw above, and with modern technologies we can directly simulate the appropriate processes in humans. It can be concluded that by using modern facilities, the old approach of using animals as alternatives for humans can now be replaced by new alternatives. And these alternatives are not necessarily alternatives to animal experiments.

Acceptance and implementation of alternatives in education: pros and cons

Although alternatives are now widely available, and have replaced many animal experiments, in some regions the number of animals used in education seems to be decreasing only slowly. Many factors contribute to the acceptance of alternatives, but acceptance is just a starting point. Many challenges have to be addressed before alternatives are actually introduced. For successful intro-duction of alternatives the following steps should be considered: Awareness of alternatives; analysis of needs; acquiring the appropriate alternatives; preparing staff, support and the location; the actual implementation; and finally the evaluation before proceeding.

Fig. 1. Flow diagram of steps to be taken for the introduction of alternatives

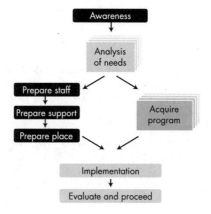

Awareness

Awareness of the need to introduce alternatives can begin at different levels, not necessary at the level of the teachers themselves. Students are often the first to request alternatives to animal experiments, and in some countries students now have the right to use alternative methods. Outside pressure also comes from society and from policy makers. Other factors, not directly related to finding alternatives to animal experiments, can provide the impetus for replacement - such as the introduction of CAL (computer-assisted learning) based on staff reduction.

Some teachers, however, are resistant to change and need to be convinced of the benefits of using alternatives. Sceptical attitudes exist, and should therefore be addressed.

Typically, these may include:

- 'Animal-based practical exercises are part of the learning paradigm and guarantee quality and authenticity in education'
- 'Educational technology is a dead end in the modern process of enlightenment'
- 'Technology is a retrograde step - the best are animal experiments'
- 'New learning models rely on the assumption that students are curious and have initiative, and have the social skills and attention span required to co-operate in teams'

Other obstacles may include the following:

- Teachers resenting being told what to do in the classroom
- Teachers being overloaded with material from different sources, without any real balanced interpretation of the information
- A tendency to stick with tradition, based on assumptions such as the overriding importance of anatomy compared to other interesting fields such as cell biology
- Teachers may consider alternatives inferior
- Textbooks, labs, etc. are still animal experiment oriented
- Training teachers is very difficult due to time limitations
- Training the teachers makes no sense when there is no perceived need

Analysis of needs

Simply replacing an animal experiment with a non-animal model is often not possible, since the new model may require a different level of support and involve new learning styles. Accepting the introduction of alternatives to animal experiments often means that new technologies, such as CAL, might be introduced for the first time in the learning environment.

The penetration of new technologies can also dramatically redefine the teacher-learner relationship. For example, new technologies open up new ways to learn by:

- Simulating real-life environments
- Enabling self-paced learning
- Increasing one-to-one interaction
- Providing access to more information
- Implementing situated learning, 'just-in-time', and 'education-on-command'
- Boosting of curiosity, creativity and teamwork
- Breaking down the walls of the classroom, integrating home, town and the world

Educational paradigms will change. For example:

Old Model	New Model
Classroom teaching	Individual exploration
Passive absorption	Apprenticeship
Individual work	Team learning
Omniscient teacher	Teacher as a guide
Stable content	Fast-changing content
Homogeneity	Diversity

Learning objectives have to be re-defined, and new objectives will be added. In order to make the right choice, teachers must be provided with the right information, including full descriptions of the alternative, the hardware requirements, independent reviews and evidence of educational effectiveness. Learning objectives and context should always be the guiding principles in the introduction of alternatives in education. From this point, the appropriate choice of medium can more easily be determined.

Implementation

After a detailed needs analysis and the establishment of the characteristics required of the technology for the educational task, the next step will be the implementation of the alternative. This involves decisions about the new learning environment, and the acquisition of programs and/or creation of alternatives.

The new learning environment can still be based on the classical classroom concept. Instead of using the lab for practical courses, the class moves to the computer room. Restrictions and conditions, for example the limited number of available computers and limited time that the classroom is available, can frustrate the use of computer-based alternatives. Another option is that students in their own time visit open learning centres or use stand-alone computers. In this case, the modules should be very well structured. Some institutes now provide laptops to the students and a free connection to the internet. This requires that the modules are available over the internet and that the courseware is well protected. For the implementation of computer-based alternatives in general, the types of computers that are available is a factor to be considered. To equip a room with computers is expensive, and the hardware will therefore be used for several years. The courseware, however, makes use of the latest technologies and can therefore be useless if the hardware is no longer appropriate.

Although alternatives to animal experiments are widely available, acquiring the right software can be a problem. Courseware is sometimes expensive. The content of the courseware should be appropriate to the objectives of the teacher.

Costs and hidden costs

Sometimes educational technologies have soaked up huge capital expenditure without providing the expected return on the investment. Hidden costs result from software that does not meet the needs, hardware that does not properly fit into the training environment, and insufficient support. In the established system, requirements such as support have been included, and so the maturity of the system is a measure of the hidden costs.

A golden rule is that a maximum of 50% should be spent on hardware, 30% on software, and a minimum of 20% on support.

Computer-based alternatives

Computer-based alternatives for replacing animals are available for most practical courses. Information can be found on various websites and is disseminated in many other ways. Most of the programs are interactive multimedia productions. They may be tutorials with feedback to the students, simulations mimicking more-or-less realistic situations, databases providing information, or question banks - or a combination of these features.

For successful introduction of computer-based alternatives, students themselves should be involved in the choice of alternatives. Students should therefore have education about and access to information on alternatives. It should also be realised that students may dislike CAL programs if the language is not their own. It is recommended that teachers co-operate in developing programs, because the objectives of available courseware do not always cover their own teaching objectives. Using collaborative software lets teachers work with faculty members on their campus and worldwide to design and develop a new curriculum.

Microlabs: Animal experiments without experimental animals

Replacement, Reduction and Refinement

Microlabs is a series of computer-based modules with the primary aim of replacing animal use in education by simulating the effects of drugs on isolated tissues *in vitro* and the effects of drugs on whole animals *in vivo*. Some modules deal with reduction of the numbers of animals used in experiments and refinement of the methods - for example in toxicology and pharmacology. Data obtained from the simulations, for example, can be analysed in a program for calculating Quantitative Structure Activity Relations (QSAR). In this way students become aware that many animal experiments can also be excluded on theoretical grounds.

The programs available in the *Microlabs* package are:

- Pharmacokinetics/pharmacodynamics, simulating drug distribution, elimination and effects *in vivo* in humans and animals
- Probit analysis, simulating the quantal response of drugs *in vivo*
- Experimental design
- Anaesthesia of the rat
- Mouse behaviour - an animation
- Heart rate and blood pressure *in vivo*
- Guinea pig ileum *in vitro*, simulating the effects of agonists and antagonists
- Vas deferens of the rat *in vitro*
- Frog rectus abdominus *in vitro*
- Nervus phrenicus-diaphragm preparation *in vitro*
- Sciatic nerve-anterior tibialis preparation *in vitro*
- Human case studies and pharmacokinetics
- Drug development
- Animal behaviour: digital video (on CD-ROM) demonstrating drug induced behaviour in mice, rats and rabbits
- A drug list linked to the program providing information about the drugs used

Teacher-developer relationship

As stated above, teachers like to be involved in the development of alternatives in order to have the learning objectives according to their requirements. Students prefer to have the modules and instructions in their own language. In most *Microlabs* modules the data and text have been stored in MS-Access databases and can easily be modified in terms of content and language. In general, the modules are simulations, and as for a practical course with animals, the instructions and exercises can be found in a workbook. The student selects a species or animal preparation; an experimental procedure; the drug, dose or concentration, and the route. The student is guided through the experiment, and experimental data can be collected for further (statistical) elaboration in a student workbook. An example of a workbook is provided in ASCII text which can easily be customised.

Microlabs has been developed for Windows 95 and higher, and can be obtained on CD-ROM from the author for mailing costs.

Conclusions

There is a wide range of animal-free models available for use in life science education today. The key to successful integration of any alternative into the teaching and learning environment is the closeness of fit between the educational requirements, the context in which the alternative is to be used, and the choice of the medium. The success of replacing existing animal experiments with new material is dependent on careful preparation at all the steps necessary for implementation.

References

Bates, A.W. (editor) (1990). Media and Technology in European Distance Education. Proceedings of the European Association of Distance Teaching Universities (EADTU) workshop on Media, Methods and Technology.

ECVAM Workshop Report 33 (1999): Alternatives to the Use of Alternatives in Higher Education.

Reinhardt, A. (1995) New ways to learn. Byte 20 (3), 51-73.

van Wilgenburg, H. (1997). Computer simulations in education. In Animal Alternatives, Welfare and Ethics. Ed. L.F.M. van Zutphen & M. Balls), pp. 469-475. Amsterdam, The Netherlands: Elsevier.

Vervest, P. & Sherwood, P. (1992). A report for the Commission of the European Communities: Task Force Human Resourses, Education Training and Youth. Technology Options for Distance Education.

Biography

Henk van Wilgenburg trained as a biologist and is currently Head of the Department of Pharmacology at the University of Amsterdam in the Netherlands. Since the first computers became available for teaching he has been making computer simulations which have replaced animal experiments in practical courses. With funding from the Platform for Alternatives in the Netherlands and from the European Union he and his colleagues have developed *Microlabs for Pharmacologists - Animal experiments without experimental animals*. This still growing collection of alternatives is available at cost price from the author.

Henk van Wilgenburg, PhD

University of Amsterdam
Dept. of Pharmacology, AMC J01 155
Meibergdreef 15
1105 AZ Amsterdam
The Netherlands

tel: +31 20 566 4669
fax: +31 20 691 9149
e-mail: h.vanwilgenburg@amc.uva.nl

3. Teaching physiology is possible without killing

Mykola Makarchuk

Faculty of Biology, Kyiv National Taras Shevchenko University, Ukraine

The fundamental principle behind all life is the principle of development, for which one form of life is replaced by another more perfect form. Awareness of this principle should inform our practice. The gradual development of the life sciences at the end of the twentieth century has led to an important and fundamental conclusion about the need to change our general ideology regarding the relationship between humans and all other manifestations of life. Taking into account both the uniqueness, and, at the same time, the indissoluble connection between these forms of life, the question of ethics is paramount.

In general, the theoretical recognition of a change of ideology does not lead easily to practical realisation. Those who stand for the preservation of the status quo provide the main difficulty. Their reasoning for the defence of animal use, for example, may include the issue of quality of teaching, for the specialist or for the general biologist. The question of the morals and ethics of the traditional approach to education, which as an obligatory component includes the killing of animals, is eclipsed by the practice of such teaching, or, more precisely, by the *a priori* belief of the 'indispensability' of such practice.

So much for theory. The philosophers conclude that practice is the sole criterion of truth. I will address the reality of the current situation in the Ukraine, and my own practice as Head of Physiology at Kyiv National Taras Shevchenko University. I am aware that the changes are not as large as I would wish, but also not so small for me to avoid making some preliminary conclusions. Often the first steps are the most difficult.

I belong to those scientists who from the beginning of their study of biology, particularly physiology and anatomy, were brought up on the traditional approach. The authority of the teachers and adherence to tradition, the lack of other opportunities, and no personal experience of alternatives, meant that I had no great reflections on this approach to education at first. But during practical lessons in physiology, which involved the killing and dissection of frogs, some unpleasant and disturbing sensations were left in my soul. And despite the fact that over twenty years have passed since then, I clearly remember those negative feelings. And if I, a physiologist, remember this, then such unpleasant memories must have remained with the majority of the biologists. Indeed, during conversations with biologists who finished university many years ago and who are now involved in activity far removed from physiology or anatomy, at the mention of their course or faculty all of them recollect the killed frogs. Personally, I was most struck by so-called 'sharp' experiments on dogs. This wasn't so much the dissection itself, but the behaviour of the dogs before they were narcotised.

Only recently have I begun to reflect on the price and value of such experiments during the study of physiology. After graduation I worked for many years with animals, investigating their behaviour, or more correctly their emotions. Studying the physiological mechanisms of such behaviour, I frequently operated on animals, and at the end of the experiment killed them. Did I feel any special remorse? Probably not. My enthusiasm for science and for research justified all this activity. However, from the beginning of my practical scientific activity I completely refused similar work with dogs. I simply could not overcome a 'complex of pity' towards them. As a result, I carried out all my scientific research solely on laboratory rats.

Working with students, I continued to use only frogs and rats for practical work. It was a blessing that despite being engaged in research into animal behaviour, the courses I conducted did not involve sharp experiments on dogs.

My reading of lectures in zoopsychology for the students of psychology at the university played a crucial role in the formation of a new awareness and belief. I more deeply understood the unity of the mental processes of humans and animals, and the absence of a basic difference in our feelings. Pain and suffering in both cases remain only pain and suffering.

In 1999 I was elected Head of the Department of Human and Animal Physiology. The department is in the Faculty of Biology and covers teaching of human and animal physiology and anatomy to students of our faculty and to those of Psychology and of Physics (Department of Radio Medicine). Only those students of the Biology Faculty studying physiology and anatomy had to take part in the large practical course involving work with animals.

It had been traditional until recently that the practical courses involved various species of animals. Frogs and rats were used in general, and rabbits and dogs for special practical work for the physiologists. But over the last few years the Department of Physiology has been actively introducing alternative methods and approaches to teaching - connected to financial difficulties in the purchase and housing of experimental animals, and a general change in psychology within Ukrainian society regarding animals.

First of all we considerably reduced the number of animals used during practical courses. We modified them and carried out some with the participation of student volunteers. We applied non-invasive tools such as myography, registration EEG and ECG, measured heart rate variability, etc. Also introduced into the educational process were techniques of psycho-physiological investigation of volunteers using original computer programs from long-term departmental scientific development. We used blood from student donors as another alternative to animal use, but in connection with the HIV / AIDS problem we are now obliged to buy a small amount of blood from transfusion clinics.

In connection with the general democratic changes occurring in independent Ukraine, with a closer dialogue between public and state organisations, and with growing links to other countries, the question of humane attitudes towards animals has arisen. It is sad, but in our country before there were many examples of severe treatment of animals. And such attitudes were not condemned by the majority of people, nor punishable legally.

Over the last few years, due in particular to the active campaigning and practical activity within Ukraine of the International Society for the Protection of Animals 'SOS', and its president Tamara Tarnavska, the situation has been changing. A shelter for homeless animals in Kyiv, financed by international NGOs, TV and radio coverage, and articles in newspapers and magazines have led to many people changing their attitudes towards animals. Followers and active workers for the protection of animals have appeared in Kyiv and other large cities.

These processes have found a reflection in the organisation of the educational process in our department. The activities of 'SOS' and its president have been the main catalysts for changes in the approach to teaching the students of physiology and anatomy, and indeed for changes in my own point of view. I was invited to be a reviewer of the 'SOS' project for a new national *Law for the Protection of Animals*. Work on the law, and my visit to an international conference on alternative methods within physiology and anatomy teaching, held in Poland in 1998, convinced me of a real opportunity to teach physiology with all or most animal practicals replaced. Several educational products were donated to us, providing the opportunity to use computer techniques as alternatives to traditional methods of teaching.

In the 1999 academic year we changed the program of the practical course and for the first time used computer modeling of the contraction of frog muscle and the use of various agents. Before, a full class of 170 students used tens of frogs. The students and teachers were very happy with the new approach and its results. This was proof that the replacement of animal experiments could be made without damage to the level of assimilation of knowledge.

In the same year we arranged meetings between David Bowles, Head of the International Department at the RSPCA, and 'SOS', on the one hand, and the management, students and teachers of the faculty on the other. There was a positive response in the hearts of our students, and a good dialogue between the parties. Our first experience with alternatives, followed by these meetings, have convinced us of the necessity of widespread introduction of alternative methods in education. These methods not only allow us to teach and prepare highly skilled specialist-biologists, but also to encourage new thinking on the principle of a humane attitude towards all life. They also give hope that in the future the students will build their professional activity and life on this principle.

With financial support from the RSPCA and active participation of 'SOS', in the following educational year our department was able to equip a classroom with computer hardware and educational programs. We have now changed the entire program of practical lessons for physiology and anatomy and have completely refused to use animals in the educational process. Within anatomy, the programs allow the students to see bodies and structures from various angles and in various planes. The students have the opportunity to see on the screen, simultaneously with an overall view, the internal structure or thin section of any part of the human or animal organism. The style and depth of presentation in the subject matter is significantly higher, which is very important. Our experience is that the computer programs considerably raise the level of education in this rather difficult discipline.

Within physiology, the use of the programs allows us to save many animals from being killed, and allows us to work well with those students whom for ethical reasons do not wish to cause pain and suffering to an animal. They let us simulate and visualise those physiological processes which cannot be reproduced in usual laboratory conditions during education, such as changes of membrane potentials. Secondly, they allow each student to work independently at their optimum rate, to review any stage, and to repeat critical parts of the experiment which would be impossible to do with animals. Thirdly, the teacher can supervise and estimate the success of adoption of the subject matter from printouts of experimental results and the students' analyses and conclusions.

The introduction of such programs into the educational process has faced some difficulties. First of all it needed significant preparatory work. It was necessary to carry out preliminary training to include the programs within all the teaching and auxiliary structures of the department, and to select the appropriate sections of each program, as some are too broad and cannot be used fully within the framework of one laboratory session. Such preliminary work was completed by writing suitable instructions for the students' use of the program.

The introduction of the appropriate program is of course possible only when it corresponds to the subject matter in our courses. We currently have a lack of material in some areas and so cannot use our computer class to the full. But we are gaining new programs, and, moreover, the presence within the department of highly skilled teachers and employees allows us to hope for the creation of our own teaching programs, which in turn can be offered for use at other universities. But this project can be realised only with sources of funding.

Doubts and criticisms always accompany new undertakings. Moral support is therefore crucial, particularly shared appreciation of the importance and necessity of new approaches. I and my employees have been given this to the full through acquaintance with the activity of InterNICHE and its co-ordinator Nick Jukes. It is a broad and deep theme to write about, but most important is that InterNICHE propagates and popularises the vision and the new approaches in teaching students, and supports those who try to realise these new approaches in practice. Invaluable in this was the 1st InterNICHE Conference held in Brussels in 2001. The discussions I had there with other teachers and with developers of alternatives, and the evidence of changes that have already happened, were practical proof that the teaching of physiology and anatomy can completely do without the killing of a huge quantity of innocent - though laboratory - animals. The theoretically understood importance of the preservation of any life can be proved practically.

With the assistance of 'SOS' we are trying through press conferences and the mass media to acquaint others in the Ukraine with the application of alternative methods in our faculty. The use of computer programs and non-invasive methods on student volunteers has been the primary interest of representatives from other departments of physiology. This has provided further confirmation to us that alternative methods are the future.

However, the introduction of such programs and approaches in practical courses in the Ukraine is not going as quickly nor being applied as widely as would be desirable. There are many reasons for this, but the most important is the adherence of many teachers to traditional methods, particularly dissection. We are planning several conferences to bring together teachers from across the country to discuss in detail the introduction of alternatives in the Ukraine, and to look at examples of successful implementation elsewhere. And as it is told in the Bible, 'The road will be made by those who travel.' So despite all the challenges, it is necessary to continue the work that has begun, and only then to expect powerful results.

Biography

Mykola Makarchuk is Head of the Department of Human and Animal Physiology in the Faculty of Biology at Kyiv Taras Shevchenko University, Ukraine. He lectures students of the Faculties of Biology and Psychology, including teaching the course of 'Animal Psychology'. For more than 20 years he has been investigating the role of emotions in the behaviour of animals. Recently his scientific interest has concentrated on the study of the neuro-physiological mechanisms of the development of anxiety and depression, both in animals and humans, and the role of the olfactory analyser in these processes. He studies the possibility of optimisation of the functional condition of humans by aromatherapeutic methods. He carries out active work with talented schoolchildren biologists and is the head of the jury of the National Biological Olympiad of the Schoolchildren of Ukraine, whose winners participated in the XII International Biological Olympiad in 2001.

Mykola Makarchuk, PhD

Head of Department
Department of Human and Animal Physiology
Faculty of Biology
Kyiv National Taras Shevchenko University
64 Volodymyrska Street
01033 Kyiv
Ukraine

tel: +38 044 266 9283
fax: +38 044 252 0828
e-mail: nikmak@biocc.univ.kiev.ua

4. Research project practicals for undergraduates in the biological sciences: Learning problem-solving strategies without animal experimentation

Garry C. Scroop

Department of Physiology, University of Adelaide, Australia

Prologue

Practical teaching classes in physiology for university undergraduates in dentistry, medicine and science have long been focused on traditional recipe-driven animal experiments. These classes are designed to provide practical examples of living physiology in support of the didactic material presented in lectures and tutorials. Their format is based on long-established protocols designed to ensure that all students obtain the same contrived result. Such a teaching process not only suppresses the essential scientific message of biological variability but ignores the contradiction of using results from animal experiments to illustrate the human physiology being taught in their lectures and which will form the foundation of their future professions.

In recent years, much of the newer information technology has been applied to give a modern face to such practical classes, yet the unwavering principle of reinforcing established dogma with contrived practical experiments remains. Since their outcome is known in advance, the ability of such practical classes to motivate students and teaching staff is poor and the recycling of results from previous years is common student practice. It has often been argued that such animal practical classes provide preclinical students with essential experience in handling living tissues and organs. Yet any observer of such sessions quickly recognises the fallacy of this argument. Any experience is brief, poorly supervised, often confined to one or two students in a given practical group, derived from unusual animal species and never to be repeated in their professional lives.

Let alone the moral objections to such experiments, undergraduate practical teaching sessions of this type are a contradiction of the scientific principles which we, as academic staff, hypocritically espouse to the postgraduate students in our research laboratories. Importantly, these long-established, recipe-driven animal experiments provide no life-long learning experiences for graduates to use in their future professional careers.

The way forward

While there has been a long-standing dissatisfaction with the educational merit of traditional practical class teaching, little has been done other than attempts to enhance their impact with new technology. In 1990, a decision was made by the Department of Physiology at the University of Adelaide to abandon the traditional animal-based practical teaching classes which had been provided for second year students of dentistry, medicine and science over many years. The new idea was to provide the students with an appropriate medium for learning problem-solving strategies. The medium chosen for this was a variety of semester-long research projects in human cardiovascular, respiratory, renal and neural physiology. The objective of this initiative was to use the research project as a practical experience for students to learn the scientific method of problem-solving.

These new 'practical classes' are termed, rather clumsily, Research Project Practicals (RPP), where the students work as small (4 to 8) research teams, designing their own project and completing it over a full semester. The Department provides all the necessary research infrastructure and each project lasts a full 13-week semester, with each student completing 2 projects in 2 different physiological systems during a full academic year.

Design

At the start:

• The students, with general staff assistance, form into small groups and are given advice on forming an interactive research team. Each team is then assigned to one of four laboratories targeting research in four of the principal physiological systems: cardiovascular, respiratory, neural and renal. Detailed prior knowledge of the particular physiological system doesn't matter, as the central theme is to provide a learning experience in the scientific method of problem-solving, and the physiological learning experience is coincidental.

• Each laboratory provides the essential minimal equipment and space to support 3 research teams in any given 4-hour practical session each week for one semester. The actual process of data acquisition is deliberately kept as simple as possible yet needs to employ the most modern technology. The technical aspects of equipment use, while critical in postgraduate research studies, should not be a significant part of the learning exercise at this stage of instruction in the scientific method. Nevertheless, each laboratory should be seen as a self-contained research unit supporting 3 research teams with access to all the required consumables, equipment, computer software, etc. which are peculiar to that particular physiological system and characteristic of most research laboratories.

• An academic staff member is assigned to each of the 4 laboratories to encompass the role of Research Supervisor and act as the mentor for the 3 research teams in a given laboratory. It needs to be continually reinforced that these are research sessions are not 'practical classes' in the old sense, and the staff member must adopt a 'hands-off' approach. The student research team must be encouraged to run with their project and, as far as is seen reasonable, solve their own problems as they arise. There is a separate central Resource Unit run by general staff serving all 4 laboratories in terms of consumables, photocopying, submission of assignments, maintaining student records, etc.

In the beginning (weeks 1 and 2):

• The research team needs firstly to decide on a research project theme. The handbook which accompanies the Research Project Practical sessions lists 10 or more broad potential research areas in each of the 4 systems which can be encompassed by the available laboratory infrastructure. For example, the Cardiovascular Laboratory focuses on the measurement of only 2 cardiovascular variables, namely heart rate (using Polar Heart Rate computers) and blood pressure (Automatic Sphygmomanometers with hardcopy print-outs), both of which are measured clinically and therefore appropriate to their career structure. The laboratory allows these variables to be measured during either of 2 cardiovascular stressors, namely postural change (head up or head down with or without the use of a simple tilt table) or cycle ergometer exercise (*Monark*, where work loads and corresponding approximate oxygen uptake values are well known). Each laboratory has both computer file and hardcopy of published work on the physiology of cardiovascular responses within this basic stressor framework, i.e. orthostasis and exercise. This infrastructure then allows the student research team (with the guidance of the Research Supervisor, if required) to develop a research area and proposal of their choice. A senior Academic Resource Person, whose research is within the laboratory's discipline (e.g. cardiovascular), is also available for consultation at other times by the Research Supervisor and student research team leader.

• Once the research team has agreed on the project theme they must prepare and submit a formal Research Proposal. To this end a purpose-designed Research Application Form is available for downloading from the Departmental website. This 4-page document is structured like a simple funding grant-in-aid request form and seeks details of the Project Title, Project Summary, Members of the Research Team, Hypothesis to be tested, Specific Project Aims, Significance of the Project, Background to the Research Proposal, Research Plan with experimental protocols, and Equipment requirements and the methods to be employed in data analysis. Signature approvals of the completed and submitted forms are required from several persons before the project can commence. These include the student research team leader (ensuring consensus from the team on the research direction), Research Supervisor (ensuring a sound scientific theme), director of the Resource Centre (ensuring the consumable and equipment requests can be met by the Department), the Academic Resource Person with expertise in the physiological system (to give general advice on the structure of the research project if necessary), and the Ethical Clearance officer. Since the experiments are all human-based, an in-house departmental ethics committee is essential and liaises with the main University Committee on Human Ethics which receives brief summaries of all projects. Therefore students have to provide an Information Sheet for potential volunteers to ensure that the volunteers' signed consent is informed, both in writing and orally. Students must attach their proposed Information Sheet and Consent Form to the Research Application Form for the approval of the Ethical Clearance Officer. The Research Application Form has a final submission deadline of the last Friday of the second week from commencement of the 13-week semester. This deadline may be extended if there are problems detected during the several signature processes which must be addressed by the student research team before final approval can be given.

Running the project (weeks 3 to 9):

• The research team recruits experimental subjects based on a power analysis and using standard recruiting procedures.

• The team members become familiar with the equipment (operation, accuracy, reproducibility, etc.) and experimental protocol and procedures, conduct pilot experiments and establish Excel subject data files. This can begin to occur during weeks 1 and 2.

• The progress of the project follows the basic scientific method used in any human experimental research project, with appropriate use of controls and scientifically sound experimental protocols. Advice on these procedures is provided by the Research Supervisor but is also covered in an accompanying Course Handbook. Furthermore, copies of Scott and Waterhouse, *Physiology and the Scientific Method* (1986) are made available to all students and are recommended reading.

• Students have access to appropriate computer-based software for both past research literature access and data acquisition and processing throughout the project.

• The Research Supervisor adopts a gentle guidance/non-interference ('hands-off') approach in a manner familiar to most academics in their supervision of Honours and Doctoral students. In point of fact the student research team quickly establishes and protects the ownership of their research project and becomes very committed.

Final data analysis and Poster preparation (weeks 10 and 11):

• During this period the research team spends much of their time in finalising data spreadsheets, performing statistical analyses and preparing data tables and figures for presentation in their poster and final written reports.

• The Poster Presentation is prepared as a computer file and the Resource Centre prints a colour poster in standard large poster format for all research teams. Again, this is modern research procedure and avoids students wasting valuable learning time in laborious artwork.

Assessment and Evaluation

Assessment (total of 30 marks for the semester project):

• There are 2 individual student assessments in the form of (1) a 600-word Background Literature Review (semester week 5), which contributes 5 of a total of 30 marks, and (2) a final 3,000-word Written Report (last week of the semester - week 13), prepared in the style of a research manuscript, which contributes 10 of 30 marks. Detailed guidance for preparation of the final report is provided in the Course Handbook.

• There are also 2 forms of group assessments. One of these is in the form of a Peer Group Assessment at 3 time points during the conduct of the project (weeks 4, 9 and 13), allowing the student research team to monitor their individual performances (total of 5 of 30 marks). The other is a Poster Presentation of the project and its Oral Defence (week 12), contributing 10 of 30 marks for the RPP.

• All assessments are scheduled at appropriate times during the semester and the Assessment Criteria to be used by examiners in making their assessments are included as hardcopy in the student's Course Handbook.

Evaluation - Is it worth it?:

• The RPP concept was reviewed favourably in a report (No. 28, 1994) commissioned by the Australian National Board of Employment, Education and Training and published in August 1994. The report followed an on-site visit and discussions with staff and students. It was identified as an example of Best Teaching Practice in Australia, promoting life-long learning principles.

• When introduced in 1990 it was a first among problem-solving educational practices at our University but which has now permeated widely and in several forms through undergraduate teaching programs, particularly in Science and the Health Sciences.

• Instruction in the scientific method of problem-solving is the essential theme of the practical sessions, given that it is such an enormously valuable life-long learning experience in all career directions, regardless of the faculty. However, in Science and the Health Sciences it is clear that the areas of systematic physiology forming the basis of the student research projects and the associated experience in data acquisition and in the basic principles of statistical analysis are learnt in a manner which results in greater information retention. This may derive from the students' acknowledged ownership of the research project and its outcomes.

• Ownership and pride in their project are very evident group outcomes, and the necessity of having a true team effort if there is to be a worthwhile achievement is strongly reinforced.

• Inevitably the team concept fosters the development of interpersonal and communication skills throughout the entire semester. The diverse ethnic backgrounds of our student cohort provides a further benefit to the concept by promoting bonding cultural exchanges and interactions.

• The academic and general staff supporting the research teams also gain great pleasure and valuable experience from being involved in the research projects and seeing their students grow academically and achieve good outcomes.

• The basic concept of providing a suitable vehicle for instruction in the scientific method can be applied to any scientific discipline, and to primary, secondary or tertiary students. Prior knowledge is not a requisite to success in learning the discipline of problem-solving with the scientific method. Just the question, "Why is it so?" and then establishing the project concept within the constraints of the given student population and the available infrastructure.

• In each of 2 semesters over a period of 2 years (1993 and 1994) in Adelaide, the same course in second year physiology (lectures, tutorials and the RPP concept) was provided to approximately equal size classes (~130 students in each) of students in Medicine and Science. The students in these classes gained entry to either Science or Medicine at the University of Adelaide based on marks obtained in their final year of secondary schooling. The mark required for entry into Medicine is significantly higher than that for science yet both derive from the same examination process, generally based on assessing factual recall rather than problem-solving skills. Not surprisingly, the marks gained by the Medical Class in factual recall written examination questions in Physiology in each semester were significantly higher than those for the Science Class. However, the final marks for the RPP assessments in any of the 4 semesters studies were not different between the two student populations, nor were they different for the one problem-solving question deliberately included in each of the formal written assessments. This preliminary result, more than anything, raises substantial questions about educational methodologies and direction in the tertiary sector.

Conclusions:

In the best of all worlds, the transition from student practical class experiments using animals to those where human volunteers are used to illustrate the scientific method of problem-solving, would be justified on the basis of the moral indefensibility of animal experimentation. In point of fact and, sadly, not surprisingly, the turn around, which is now widespread, has occurred because tertiary academic teachers have come to recognise that the research project practical concept and similar problem-solving methodologies are just educationally vastly better than the old-fashioned didactic sessions. For those of us committed to protecting animals from human exploitation it would have been preferable for the change to have been stimulated by the realisation that using animals for experimentation is just plain wrong. While the outcome has been the same in the teaching sphere, failure to make the moral transition leaves addressing the experimental exploitation of animals in research an unresolved issue at this time.

Bibliography

1. Scott, E.M. and Waterhouse, J.M. (1986). Physiology and the scientific method. Manchester University Press, ISBN 0 7 190 2262 2.

2. Scroop, G.C. (1993). Research project practicals in the Department of Physiology. A 16-page in-house publication available from G.C. Scroop, Department of Physiology, University of Adelaide, South Australia 5005.

3. Scroop, G.C. (1993). Research and the scientific method in practical teaching in the biological sciences. Proceedings of the Australian Physiological and Pharmacological Society, 24, 186P.

4. Candy, P.C., Crebert, G. and O'Leary, J. (1994). An inquiring mind. B Science (Physiology). In: Developing lifelong learners through undergraduate education, Commissioned Report No. 28 (ISBN 0644 35349X), National Board of Employment, Education and Training Commission (Australian Government Publishing Service), pp 201-209.

5. Scroop, G.C. (1995). Use of research project practicals and the scientific method to develop problem-solving skills: a new teaching methodology in the biological sciences which does not require the use of animals. In: Animals in Science: Perspectives on their Use, Care and Welfare, Monash University Clayton Campus, Ed. NE Johnston, (ISBN 0 7326 0636 5), pp. 208-214.

Biography

Garry Scroop is a medical graduate of some 40 years standing, during which he has engaged in basic human research and teaching, both in Australia and overseas. During his research career he has published in the diverse fields of hypertension, foetal physiology, exercise physiology and chronic fatigue syndrome. His teaching, which spans a similar time frame, has been principally in the field of physiology, to both undergraduate and postgraduate students in Medicine and Science. He is a founder member of the MAWA Trust (Medical Advances Without Animals) which provides a doctoral scholarship annually in support of students engaged in research which is directed at removing animals from biological research. The educational methodology encompassed in the accompanying article derived from both his desire to remove animals from student practical classes and to educate students in the scientific method of problem-solving as a life-long learning strategy.

Associate Professor Garry C. Scroop, MBBS, MD (Adelaide), PhD (London)
Department of Physiology
University of Adelaide
South Australia 5005

tel: +61 8 8303 5331
fax: +61 8 8303 3356
e-mail: garry.scroop@adelaide.edu.au

Current address:

Lung Function Laboratory
Level 7 Outpatients Block
Royal Adelaide Hospital
South Australia 5000

5. Client donation program to meet the needs of veterinary medical education: Alternatives to healthy animal sacrifice

Amarendhra M. Kumar

Department of Biomedical Sciences, Tufts University School of Veterinary Medicine, USA

Knowledge of anatomy is essential for the practising veterinarian. Anatomical science is the foundation of biology, essential for understanding various normal and abnormal body functions as well as for clinical diagnosis. Anatomy is perhaps the oldest medical science. Stone age people attempted drawing animal forms about 30,000 years ago, displaying some knowledge of topographical anatomy of animals. Recent recorded history indicates that attempts at the systematic study of anatomy began with the work of Greek scientists Alcmaeon and Empedocles (approximately 500 B.C.). These scientists were probably the first ones to dissect a human body, but most of what they disseminated was not anatomically accurate. Not until the time of Aristotle (384-322 B.C.) did physicians perform animal dissections carefully enough to extrapolate human organ function. Galen (ca. 129-199 A.D.) systematically dissected monkeys to learn human anatomy, and he was the first to correctly describe differences between veins and arteries and provide a reasonable description of the brain. Subsequently, Leonardo da Vinci (1452-1519), and the father of modern anatomy, Andreas Vesalius (1514-1564) documented human anatomy by systematic dissections. William Harvey (1578-1637), the English physician and anatomist, published an anatomical treatise on the motion of the heart and blood in animals, based on careful dissections and observations of various organs[1].

Rapid advances in radiological techniques during the twentieth century allowed scientists to recognise significant connections between anatomy and physiology and to integrate anatomy with clinical sciences as well as basic sciences. Recent advances in scanning techniques such as ultrasonography, computer assisted tomography (CAT), magnetic resonance imaging (MRI) and positron emission tomography (PET), permit clinicians to look inside the body and observe internal anatomy without performing surgery. These imaging techniques are major advances in the history of anatomy, and with the rapid development of computer technologies the way that anatomy is taught to the professional student will gradually move away from traditional animal dissections.

At present, teaching veterinary gross anatomy often involves sacrificing live animals and then embalming them. In most Asian countries, veterinary students in their first year dissect primarily a ruminant animal and learn comparative anatomy of the horse and dog based on a faculty-dissected animal. Stray dogs are a major source of teaching specimens in many developing countries. At most veterinary anatomy departments in the United States, dogs and cats are procured from the following sources: 1) unclaimed animals from animal shelters; 2) purpose-bred animals that are bought from a United States Department of Agriculture (USDA)-approved vendor; or 3) from biological supply companies selling embalmed animals (which may also be acquired from animal shelters). A fourth source for dogs are greyhounds that are retired from racing or breeding by the animal owners.

For many years, students at Tufts University School of Veterinary Medicine (TUSVM) dissected donated greyhounds. The greyhound donation program gradually became unsustainable due to the reluctance of greyhound owners to donate culled animals for the anatomy laboratory, the objections raised by some students, and the increased adoptions facilitated by the Greyhound Rescue League. Since Massachusetts State regulations prohibit use of shelter animals for teaching and research, including embalmed animals from biological supply companies (as they are usually shelter animals) for student dissections, the only remaining option available was to purchase purpose-bred dogs from USDA-approved vendors.

Purpose-bred dogs are used by researchers at various biomedical research facilities in Boston. These animals are certified healthy on delivery. I had serious ethical concerns euthanising healthy dogs for anatomical dissections. The catalytic element in motivating us to explore alternative ways to procure animals for our teaching program was one veterinary student, True Ballas (now a DVM). She offered time and the means of transportation in order to initiate a client donation program. This was established six years ago, and in the initial stages, many people spent a lot of personal time contacting local veterinary clinics and our teaching hospital clinicians to educate clients in the benefits of such a program - particularly the opportunity to spare healthy animals. During its first year, Dr. Ballas often transported donor animals from the clinics in her car to the Boston campus for embalming. At that time, TUSVM had two campuses - North Grafton (veterinary clinics) and Boston (basic sciences). The split-campus situation presented additional challenges for us to resolve. As the client donation program evolved, embalming procedures were centralised in the pathology necropsy room. Donor animals were embalmed on the Grafton campus pathology facilities, and transported to the Boston campus by a licensed hazardous chemical transport company. This required a tremendous amount of effort initially to co-ordinate the program at first. But considering the alternative of putting healthy animals to death, the choice for us was easy.

Anecdotal reports suggest that difficulties in obtaining animals for teaching, and the ethical concerns expressed by veterinary students, are major factors in modifying the anatomy curriculum and reducing animal dissections in some veterinary colleges. The various alternatives to the use of purpose-bred animals include incorporating plastinated specimens or computer programs and decreasing the animal dissections. However, a recent survey conducted by Dr. Judy Provo[2] indicates a significant number of veterinary gross anatomists prefer animal dissections in order to impart a 3-dimensional perspective of the body to students. Students at TUSVM also practice medical procedures and clinical skills (including basic surgical skills) on animal cadavers before working with animal patients. It was important therefore to develop a program that could supply the demand for animal dissections and other needs and at the same time comply with the ethical concerns expressed by students and faculty.

The first step in establishing a successful client donation program is to convince the university administration that the program is an important component of the training of students. Without the administration's support, the program is difficult to run. It is also crucial to include the clinical department chair in the process. The next step is to recruit staff and faculty who have total commitment to the program. Finally, policy guidelines are developed, which take into account the USDA as well as Institutional Animal Care and Use Committee (IACUC) protocols on the use of animals in teaching.

The following are key elements of the TUSVM donor animal policy:

1. Animals donated to teaching programs must belong to a regular TUSVM client. This ensures high ethical standards. If a decision on euthanasia is arrived at, it is due to the incurable terminal condition of the animal. The case reports on the donated animals are easily available at the hospital.

2. The decision for euthanasia is arrived at in the usual way, by consensus of the client and the veterinarian attending the case. The client has access to the humane euthanasia information brochure from the attending veterinarian, which sensitively addresses the issue and which briefly describes the options for disposal of the remains. Once the client makes an informed decision to proceed with euthanasia, the attending veterinarian discusses with him/her in more detail the choice between supporting the client donation program, a cremation, necropsy, or return of the body. The hospital waives the euthanasia fee for donors, but this is not mentioned initially in order to ensure the client is not induced to donate the animal primarily for financial reasons.

3. The euthanasia brochure explains the client donation program as follows: "Donating your pet's remains to the veterinary school can be a way of letting the spirit of your pet live through the education of future veterinarians, who are being trained to heal other animals. In addition, your willingness to participate in the program supports a humane approach to obtaining resources for this training. Animal cadavers are invaluable in teaching veterinary students about animal anatomy and the skills they need to master to become competent veterinarians."

4. The client signs the euthanasia consent form, marking the appropriate box for disposal of the remains. The form is also signed by the attending veterinarian. Copies of the signed forms are distributed for filing as follows: Medical Records, Division of Laboratory Animal Medicine, Accounting, and the technician. Proper record keeping is important in order to be in compliance with federal regulations, as well as to avoid any potential legal problems later on.

5. The technician makes a decision on the destination of the cadaver, based on the condition of the animal and the need for cadavers in various laboratories at the veterinary school. Cadavers are used for the following laboratories: gross anatomy teaching, clinical skills, medical procedures, junior surgery and final year students' anatomy elective laboratories. The cadaver condition or size may not be suitable for all laboratories, but this has no bearing on whether the client is allowed to donate the remains. The anatomy program has utilised dogs and cats of all sizes for teaching purposes.

6. The animals used for gross anatomy teaching are embalmed. They receive 100,000 units of heparin IV prior to the injection of the euthanasia solution. Heparin prevents blood clotting, which is crucial to the successful embalming of the animal. Embalming is done within 24 hours if possible, otherwise cadavers can be stored at 4°C and embalmed when convenient within 3-4 days after death. We have successfully embalmed donated animals 4-5 days after death and used them in teaching laboratories.

7. If the cadaver is destined for the anatomy laboratory, the anatomy secretary is contacted immediately and a copy of the signed donation form, with case number, is faxed to the anatomy office. The secretary contacts the gross anatomist as soon as possible. The cadaver is bagged, tagged and stored in a cold room until it is ready for embalming.

8. Donor animals destined for other laboratories are stored in chest freezers prior to their use.

Embalmed animals are tagged with numbered ear tags. The case file on the animal is identified using the ear tag number. In our experience, approximately 95% of the donated animals were properly fixed by our methods. Thoracic and/or abdominal organs on a few occasions fail to fix properly, but students have used good parts from these animals to learn anatomy. No appreciable differences in tissue fixation were noticed among animals fixed within 10 hours and those embalmed 4-5 days after euthanasia (see Appendix of this chapter for details on embalming procedure).

We have evaluated students' responses on the client donation program in a study which spanned a 3-year period. The student response to the client donation program was overwhelmingly positive (Table 1).

Table 1. Responses from first year veterinary students on client donation program:	Number of respondents out of 80
Given a choice, would you rather:	
a. Dissect and learn anatomy from a donor animal:	78 (97.5%)
b. Dissect a purpose-bred animal that is sacrificed:	0
c. Dissect either donor animal or purpose-bred animal:	2 (2.5%)

A significant proportion of first year students preferred donor animals for dissection. Of those, many felt that the program is very important (68.0 %) or important (30.7%) because of their objections to sacrificing a healthy animal (Table 2). A significant proportion of the class, preferring donor animals for dissections, felt donor animals sometimes have a pathological or clinical condition that may help them appreciate the importance of understanding normal anatomy (Table 2). Table 3 shows the clinical conditions most commonly encountered in the donor animals.

Written comments from students were positive, and strongly supportive of the client donation program. I have not encountered a single negative comment from students who have used donor animals for learning anatomy and clinical procedures. The program is now in its seventh successful year, and has become one of the major attractions for student recruitment at TUSVM.

Table 2: Responses from students who preferred to dissect donor animals
(averaged over 3 years):

A   Donor animal may have important pathological or clinical condition
that may help me understand the importance of knowing normal
anatomy

B   Donor animal program is important because of ethical objections I
have dissecting an animal that was healthy but sacrificed

	Very Important	Important	Not Important
A	36 (46.2 %)	38 (48.7 %)	4(5.1 %)
B	53 (68.0 %)	24 (30.7 %)	1 (1. 3 %)

Table 3: Common clinical conditions for which the dogs were euthanised:

1. Intra-abdominal neoplasia
2. Pancreatic tumour
3. Haemoabdomen (trauma)
4. Right ventricular tumour
5. Grand Mal Seizures
6. Mast cell tumours on limb
7. Thoraco-lumbar intervertebral disc disease
8. Vertebral fracture
9. Gastric dilatation and volvulus
10. Osteosarcoma of limb bones
11. Muscular dystrophy
12. Gastrointestinal haemorrhage
13. Thyroid tumours
14. Lymphosarcoma
15. Haemangiosarcoma
16. Hit by car (HBC)

We now procure all of the animals needed for teaching through the client donation program. The cadaver needs of the first year gross anatomy course, as well as those of our clinical skills and medical procedure laboratories, are fully met. No healthy animal is sacrificed for the purpose of teaching.

According to medical records, TUSVM has a typical caseload of 21,484 (dogs and cats). Approximately 240 animals per month (canine to feline ratio is about 2:1) are euthanised at the request of the clients, and approximately 20 animals per month are donated to teaching programs. Based on our experience, therefore, approximately 8% of the clients who request euthanasia for their pets donate the remains to TUSVM teaching programs. Based on these figures, we believe the client donation program is a sustainable program at any teaching hospital.

A survey of various veterinary colleges in the USA indicates that TUSVM is the first to successfully implement a client donation program that meets 100% of teaching animal need. There is momentum towards setting up or enlarging client donation program at a number of veterinary colleges.

Texas A&M University College of Veterinary Medicine currently sources about 10% of cadavers required for gross anatomy teaching as donations from local veterinary clinics, and the remainder are from animals euthanised at pounds or shelters. Cadavers from the teaching hospital are used for necropsy teaching in the pathology department[3].

The Ohio State University College of Veterinary Medicine currently sources its teaching animals from local shelters. Animals that are sick, or those that will not make good companions because of health or behavioural problems, are euthanised and donated to the veterinary college. There is strong interest in setting up a client donation program to ensure a more consistent source of cadavers[4].

The University of Wisconsin School of Veterinary Medicine instituted a client donation program in the teaching hospital 15 years ago[5]. This initially met 20% of the teaching animal need. The program became inactive over the years, partly due to changes in faculty, but is currently being revitalised. Donor animals are used in gross anatomy teaching and in the elective courses of supplementary small animal surgery and dental procedures. The aim is to meet 100% of the need for small animal cadavers from the client donation program within 3 years. A pilot project is currently linking local practitioners with the School in order to bring in more cadavers.

At the University of California College of Veterinary Medicine (Davis), animals are generally acquired from commercial sources and from shelters. In order to accommodate the ethical concerns of some students, however, cadavers are also derived from "suitable sources", i.e. client donation[6]. At the Virginia Tech College of Veterinary Medicine, donor animals are used in pathology necropsy teaching only[7]. The teaching hospital provides the majority of these cadavers. Euthanised pound animals are used for anatomy teaching.

Other veterinary schools have expressed interest in client donation programs but are reluctant to implement them. Such a reluctance on the part of anatomy faculty is partly based on the following assumptions:

a. The programs are labour-intensive because client donations occur sporadically, and sometimes at odd hours of the day.

Client donation programs do not require a full-time technician to manage. It is not necessary to rush in at all hours of the day in order to embalm donated animals immediately. We have successfully embalmed donated animal 4-5 days after euthanasia. Small groups of animals donated over a 3-4 day period are embalmed together. It is easy to recruit one or two veterinary students and train them in embalming techniques. This saves time and labour for the teaching faculty.

b. Donor animals are often castrated and therefore not ideal for teaching the reproductive component of anatomy.

Approximately 90% of the animals donated to TUSVM are castrated. I am assuming this may reflect a nationwide statistical figure of the proportion of animals that are castrated by their owners. At TUSVM, we have developed teaching procedures to compensate for the high numbers of castrated animals that are used in anatomy teaching laboratories. We usually have 2-3 intact animals among the pool of donated animals for teaching every year. Instructors demonstrate the anatomy of the male and female reproductive system to the entire class using these intact male and female animals. At the end of the course, the abdominal and pelvic regions are dissected out and saved, and used for the subsequent class. Over a period of 2-3 years, we have collected enough intact specimens to teach the reproductive anatomy component adequately. The specimens may also be plastinated to enhance their utility.

c. Animals that are donated may not embalm properly, facilitating dangerous fungous growth.

In my personal experience, based on 6 years of teaching gross anatomy using donor animals, this has not been a problem. I developed embalming protocols based on Tufts Medical School human cadaver donation program, run by a certified mortician. We have not experienced mould growth on these donated animals.

d. Donor animals may have infectious diseases that may be harmful to people.

A major advantage of client donated animals is that we can access the medical records of the animal from the teaching hospital. In contrast, there is absolutely no way of determining the medical history of commercially procured animals, or those that are euthanised by animal shelters. Whether a disease in an animal is reportable to the state veterinary agencies depends on individual state regulations. In Massachusetts, rabies is considered endemic and is not reported. Other diseases of interest, such as canine brucellosis or tuberculosis, are rare, and the agencies may require tracking of these diseases, which precludes the animal's use in teaching programs. In the 6 years of using donor animals at TUSVM, we have not encountered a single case of an infectious disease.

Our experience with the client donation program has been positive. Students have a better appreciation of anatomy and exhibit more mature behaviour in taking care of the cadaver and performing their dissections with a sense of responsibility.

The client donation program also provides the potential option of integrating other important learning themes into the education of future professional veterinarians. For example, at TUSVM students are given case histories of the dog (and cat) they are dissecting. These case histories could be integrated with their Problem-Based Learning (PBL) sessions. The students could be asked to write individual term papers emphasising the anatomical or physiological basis of the dog's illness.

The client donation program is a workable program that can be implemented by veterinary schools. It is cost-effective and presents a number of advantages over acquiring animals via the traditional route. These advantages include providing students with a valuable education that emphasises clinical aspects of anatomy and the ability to integrate the ethical values of veterinary medicine beginning from the first year of veterinary education.

Appendix: Procedure for embalming donor animals

Dogs: After the cadaver is stretched to full extension, an incision is made midventrally. The trachea is exposed, opened and plugged with paper towels. This prevents leakage of embalming fluids from the lungs and allows proper fixation of the body. On the dorsolateral aspect of the trachea, the common carotid artery is exteriorised. An appropriate size metal cannula is inserted (slip hub cat #s 708701, 708719 or 708727; The Dodge Company Inc., 165 Cambridge Park Drive, PO Box 400193, Cambridge, MA 02140, USA; tel +1 800 443 6343). The cannula is fastened within the artery and infused with the following solution: Permaflow (Dodge Chemical Company) diluted 1:2 with lukewarm water and injected into the cannula at a flow rate of 300 ml/min with a peristaltic pump (Fisher Scientific). The Permaflow solution is allowed to remain in the animal for approximately 10 mins. (or longer if time permits). The embalming solution is pumped into the animal at a flow rate of approximately 300 ml/min. Stock embalming solution is procured from Hydrol Chemical Company (Commerce Drive, Yeadon, PA 19050, USA; tel +1 800 345 8200). The concentrated embalming solution is made up of the following chemicals:

Formaldehyde 37%	13%
Phenol	13%
Ethanol	32%
Propylene Glycol	42%
Maquat (Thymol)	1%

The stock embalming solution is diluted 1 part with 3 parts of water and pumped into the animal (yielding an effective formalin level of 3.25%). As the embalming solution starts flowing into the animal the external jugular vein is punctured to force out blood along with the previously injected Permaflow solution. The animal is exsanguinated until the flow from the jugular vein indicates fixed blood (light-dark dirty brown). The external jugular vein is tied off and the embalming solution infusion is continued until the muscles feel firm.

In our experience, a large dog (30 kg and above) requires 7-10 gallons (30-40 litres) of embalming solution. If the abdomen is found to be bloated, the stomach is trocarised with a 14 Ga needle to evacuate gas. This reduces intra-abdominal pressure and permits passage of embalming solution into the pelvic limbs. 100-200 ml of the embalming solution is injected into each of the abdominal and thoracic cavities. If any of the muscles feel soft, they are spot injected with an appropriate amount of embalming solution.

Cats: The initial procedure for dogs is followed, and after isolating the common carotid artery a 23 Ga catheter (Wingless 'quick-cath'; Baxter Healthcare Corporation, One Baxter Parkway, Deerfield, IL 60015, USA; tel +1 847 948 2000) is introduced into the artery and the needle is withdrawn and discarded. The cannula within the artery is secured with a thread. The catheter is connected to a small-bore tube attached to the peristaltic pump and embalming fluid is pumped at a flow rate of 50 ml/min. A 4 kg cat usually takes 1 litre of embalming solution to fix properly. Spot injection of cavities and muscles is done if necessary, as described above.

Although it is possible to double inject the donor animals with blue (for veins) or red (for arteries) latex, we chose not to, as vascular injection is a labour-intensive process. Students were able to discriminate arteries and veins without latex.

References

1. National Library of Medicine, History of Medicine Division
2. Dr. Judy Provo, Kansas State University College of Veterinary Medicine
3. Dr. Anton Hoffman, Texas A&M University College of Veterinary Medicine
4. Dr. Daniel Smeak, Ohio State University College of Veterinary Medicine
5. Dr. Norm Wilson, University of Wisconsin School of Veterinary Medicine
6. University of California College of Veterinary Medicine (Davis) website (www.calf.vetmed.ucdavis.edu)
7. Dr. Ludeman Eng, Virginia Tech College of Veterinary Medicine

Biography

Amarendhra M. Kumar obtained his veterinary medical training from the Mysore Veterinary College, Bangalore, India. He subsequently received a Masters Degree in Veterinary Anatomy from the same place, taught Gross Anatomy at the Mysore Veterinary College and the Ahmadu Bello University College of Veterinary Medicine, Nigeria, before coming to the USA. He obtained graduate degrees from the Kansas State University (MS in physiology) and the University of Florida (PhD in neuroscience). He has been teaching Veterinary Gross Anatomy at Tufts University since 1983. He has around 100 abstracts and publications on various research topics and is also one of the associate editors for the journal *Small Ruminant Research*.

M.S.A. Kumar, BVSc, MVSc, MS, PhD

Professor of Anatomy
Department of Biomedical Sciences
Tufts University School of Veterinary Medicine
200 Westboro Road
North Grafton, MA 01536
USA

tel: +1 508 839 7967
fax: +1 508 839 7969
e-mail: m.kumar@tufts.edu

6. Ethical surgery training for veterinary students

Daniel D. Smeak

Department of Small Animal Surgery, The Ohio State University College of Veterinary Medicine, USA

Surgical training evolution[1]

Since the beginning of written history, animal and human subjects have been utilised by educators to help teach students important surgical techniques and principles. Surgical training, until recently, existed as a kind of an 'apprenticeship system'. Students observe and learn while they assist surgeons during operations on clinical patients (hence, many surgeons still use the adage, 'see one, do one, teach one'). In more recent times, the need to train large numbers of qualified surgeons has forced educators into considering a different, perhaps more efficient, approach to surgery training. Healthy animals were felt to be good subjects for teaching surgical principles and procedures to students instead of relying on a limited and inconsistent number of clinical patients. The use of healthy animals allowed instructors to develop surgical training laboratories to teach procedures in an effort to ensure a more consistent level of surgical competence and experience for the entry-level medical doctor. Unfortunately, many animal lives were lost as a result of this shift in teaching methods. The recent 'information explosion' has drawn the medical student further away from the practice laboratory into the classroom. Currently, partly due to ethical and budget limitations, human medical students desiring additional surgical training have a well-developed postgraduate system to consider. As a result, there is little need for the surgery laboratory now so human surgical training has come full circle and, again, continues to be principally based on the 'apprenticeship system' using clinical patients as teaching subjects.

The public does not expect the newly graduated human medical doctor to be capable of performing anything more complicated than minor laceration repair. This is unlike veterinary graduates in most of the world who are still expected to be capable of performing more complicated surgeries after they graduate. In the veterinary profession, basic public demands (both private and industry) for competent surgeons remain. Unlike the case with human medical students, however, very few postgraduate surgical training opportunities are, or will be, available. Thus, veterinary schools must continue to train their students to become competent entry-level surgeons.

Veterinary surgical laboratory courses have customarily taught psychomotor skills using a 'procedure-oriented' approach. That is, the student practices a required surgical procedure on a live animal and acquires fundamental surgical skills much by trial and error during the exercise. The limited number of surgery instructors available in teaching hospitals cannot offer each student enough time for adequate training of required basic skills in these live animal laboratories. Therefore, most introductory training procedures for the student are mistake-ridden and prolonged. This negative experience has lead to poor confidence and frustration for the student as well as the instructor. However, this approach has a proven track record for training basic surgery skills to veterinary students. Indeed, this was the way I was trained in veterinary school.

It can be argued that this 'procedure-oriented' laboratory simulates the clinical surgery experience adequately, but it does have major drawbacks. Evaluation of student skills is difficult because each animal reacts differently to trauma and bleeds variable amounts. The procedure is typically practised only once which is hardly enough time to gain confidence and skill retention. Additionally, multiple students have to gain experience using one animal, reducing individual practice time. Increasing pressure on faculty for scholarly activity has further reduced the time available for the instructor to individually teach skills. Furthermore, most videotapes available to the student for surgical instruction depict procedures rather than satisfactorily addressing the fundamental skills required for any operation.

I believe that students can be better prepared for clinical surgery using alternative teaching techniques. The time 'wasted' as the student tries to learn basic skills by trial and error in the live situation could be better used to learn the more important aspects of 'live' surgery such as tissue handling, results of poor haemostasis, and reaction of specific tissues to trauma. Veterinary medicine must continue to search for alternatives to the extensive use of live animals in surgery training. Recent budgetary constraints, mounting laws and regulations, the current and increasing sensitivity to animal use by the public, faculty, and students, and the lack of evaluation of alternative teaching techniques emphasise the need for further research into alternatives.

Introduction of autotutorial programs and simulators in our curriculum

If psychomotor skills could be taught effectively using simulators (models) and standard video presentations then the number of purpose-bred live animals required for teaching could be dramatically reduced or eliminated. The procedure-oriented laboratory reinforces students' attitude that they cannot perform a procedure successfully unless they have done it before. Students with fully-tuned basic surgery skills learned using inanimate models, on the other hand, quickly find that they can perform a procedure with supervision and study even if they have not witnessed the procedure previously. This leads to an attitude more conducive to learning and often results in improved student confidence and less frustration. Surgical skill evaluation tends to be more objective using a standard model for training skills rather than using live animals.

Use of simulators has distinct advantages over traditional laboratories that use cadavers or live animals. Ethical, cost-effective, and portable simulators are used along with autotutorial lessons allowing each student to practice when and where they choose. Thus, practice time can be tailored to the individual student. Some students without prior surgical experience or those with weak psychomotor skills may require more time or repetitions to become adept at a skill. In most traditional surgery laboratories, only one animal is provided for three or more students, and the exercise is conducted only during specific supervised laboratory settings. Time restrictions and the laboratory environment may not be as conducive for learning for some students. Students using simulators, through repetitive practice, strengthen their motor skills and increase their confidence and efficiency.

When I critically review my own teaching methods and results, I have found that without a means to practice a skill depicted on a video autotutorial, students miss the subtle but important steps shown in that exercise. Video presentations, although helpful for the student to understand general concepts and steps, do very little to teach psychomotor skill. Students cannot develop psychomotor skills manipulating computer programs or videotape presentations. Furthermore, the student needs to see the cause and effect of the important steps required for basic skill technique before they develop the confidence to perform it. Indeed, highly effective future teaching alternatives will rely heavily on student interaction with the teaching media.

The model/video instruction concept is not new. Probably the most successful use of this approach is practised in human and veterinary graduate continuing education programs regarding internal fixation of fractures. Plastic bones are used as practice models and the technique is taught by carefully planned and illustrated standard video presentations. I have used foam models and knot tying models for years in introductory surgery classes and I feel the results are very encouraging (Basic Suture Patterns, Basic Hemostatic Technique Videotapes, The Ohio State University, College of Veterinary Medicine). Early in my curriculum development, I found no controlled experimental trials evaluating this kind of instruction compared to more traditional methods of surgery training. Clearly, the first step in the quest to develop alternatives was to evaluate the effectiveness of this teaching technique before it was implemented into surgery curricula.

The haemostasis model was chosen for my initial evaluation of a video/model autotutorial program because: 1) Ligature placement is an universal technique required for successful surgery, 2) The technique has been notoriously difficult to master by beginning surgery students, 3) It is easy to evaluate and simulate, and 4) It should take a relatively short time to practice to become proficient. Twenty first year veterinary students with no prior experience in surgery were randomly paired and assigned into two study groups. Ten students (group V) viewed a haemostatic technique videotape until they thought they could competently perform and assist in performing a hand-tied ligature on a blood vessel in a live animal. Ten students (group VS) were also given a simulator for technique practice. Paired students were video recorded and blindly evaluated on their ability to perform and assist proper ligation of a bleeding vessel.

Inexpensive haemostasis models were very helpful for teaching students essential surgeon and assistant skills involved in hand-tied ligature placement. Students who practised with simulators performed significantly better as surgeon and assistant, and in total psychomotor skill evaluation, than students watching the video only. Students using simulators performed ligation with significantly more accuracy and tended to be more expeditious at this task. Further training is needed, however, for students to acquire skills necessary for efficient bleeding vessel exposure and isolation.

The results from this pilot study indicated that the inexpensive, simple to construct, haemostasis model enhanced the amount of instruction gained from the videotape and that students could effectively apply the skills learned with the model directly to the live animal[2]. It was subjectively felt that these freshman students who used a model for practice were at a level of proficiency (for hand ligature placement in the live animal) equal to, or better than, the majority of junior students having completed at least three traditional (procedure-oriented) laboratories. Conclusions from a subsequent, similarly constructed, study examining the training of a more complex set of technical skills (hollow organ closure) did not result in a clear-cut difference in closure between student groups. Students were ill-prepared to handle mucosal eversion during stomach closure, a problem the hollow organ model did not simulate well[3]. Clearly, the available models do not mimic the live situation entirely and live animal experience with supervision may be required for adequate student training of the more complex surgery techniques. More realistic life-like models need to be developed to better prepare students for the live experience.

My ultimate goal is to design a complete teaching video/model set that can easily be adopted by other veterinary colleges to better prepare the student for surgery on live animals. With additional preparation, more operative time can be utilised by the student to learn important aspects of surgical and procedural techniques. This less stressful and objective means of teaching and evaluating surgery should ultimately result in less live animal experiences required to produce a capable veterinary surgeon.

The primary goal in our surgery curriculum is to provide the most ethical and effective surgical training program available. We introduce simple simulators during early surgical training exercises in our second year curriculum. Later, cadavers from ethical sources offer a more realistic way for students to further strengthen their basic surgical skills. Severely injured, and sick dogs from our regional animal shelter are humanely euthanised and these provide most cadavers for our laboratories. We also receive cadavers from clients donating their pets' remains for the purpose of teaching. Once fundamental basic skills are mastered, students put the whole surgical experience together during mandatory, ethically responsible, spay/neuter and clinical rotation experiences. As simulators have been introduced into our core curriculum, fewer cadavers and live animal experiences have been required to ensure that our students possess essential entry-level surgical skills required for veterinary practice.

Our *Skin and Suture Pattern Simulator* is now used to begin teaching eye-hand co-ordination, suture patterns, and early wound closure principles in our second year Introduction to Surgery course. It was specifically designed to simulate skin to help demonstrate how tissues respond to suture patterns, and for teaching basic suture and instrument handling skills. The working surface is a flat sheet of woven nylon-laminated polyurethane 'skin' similar in feel and thickness to dogs' skin. This 'skin' covers a foam 'subcutaneous' pad, all of which is housed in a standard VHS format videotape case. The case top is removed to expose the 'skin' surface during practice. Sticky rubber feet on the bottom of the base keep the simulator from moving during use. This special polyurethane material reacts with water and certain other plastics so the protective cover is replaced when the model is carried in a backpack or during storage.

The unique laminated polyurethane surface responds like other soft tissues during suturing. Rough instrument handling or excessive intrinsic suture tension causes tears through the fragile skin. Incisions created on the 'skin' can be made to evert, invert, or appose depending on the desired action of the chosen suture pattern. If the tactile element is important for simulating how sutures and needles pass through live tissue, glycerin can be used to 'grease' the needle and suture for smooth passage. The skin surface can be used over and over again if given appropriate care. Currently, the price of the simulator is US$32.00 plus shipping charge. In addition, hollow organ models are used in early skills laboratories to teach how to create a water-tight inverting closure, and how to manipulate organs with stay-sutures. Right now we are testing an intestine model, complete with an attached mesenteric sheet for use in teaching intestinal anastomosis technique.

At The Ohio State University, second year veterinary students are required to purchase the simulators as part of a laboratory kit. Instruments, gowns, gloves, needles, suture material, and video autotutorials are also included in these kits. When weekly 'homework' suturing assignments are completed, the simulators are evaluated and returned to students for the next exercise. Basic instrument and suture handling, instrument knots, suture patterns, vessel ligation, and basic skin closure skills are taught in these exercises. In the third and fourth year professional curriculum, students repetitively practice these basic skills to improve their efficiency, and new techniques such as intradermal closure are taught with the aid of these simulators.

Although simulators have not reduced the total amount of laboratories in our curriculum, they have dramatically reduced the number of animals used for surgical training. The *Skin and Suture Pattern Simulator* is not a good substitute for the 'live' laboratory, but it offers distinct advantages over traditional laboratory experience for teaching certain basic surgical skills, and it provides excellent preparation for students before more advanced live surgery laboratories. Several universities in the United States and abroad are using these simulators successfully in their surgery courses.

Alternative live animal experience opportunities

During the third year, students participate in our operative practice course. Here, we focus on basic skills development using models, cadavers, and, ultimately, live animal laboratories in the clinical setting. Instead of using purpose-bred dogs for our students' early live animal surgical experience, seeing-eye (service) dogs and shelter dogs are spayed and neutered, recovered and monitored, and are found homes. Most important basic surgical skills and post-operative principles can be taught effectively during a spay or castration procedure. After the operative practice course, students can elect to participate in a surgical procedures course in which many common procedures (such as intestinal anastomosis, gastropexy, skin reconstruction, and cruciate stabilisation) are taught using ethically-sourced cadavers.

As the surgical caseload in our teaching hospital has become more complicated, fewer final year students receive adequate hands-on experience in the operating room. To address this issue, we were awarded a grant from an animal welfare endowment to fund two full-time faculty members to teach surgery students at regional animal shelters and humane societies. During our students' 5-week rotation though small animal surgery in their final year, students spend 6 days through this elective co-operative surgery program. Healthy cats and dogs are sterilised, and animals needing uncomplicated surgical care (for example, skin or mammary tumours, ear haematomas, wounds, and simple ophthalmic conditions) are repaired by students under the supervision of the elective surgery program.

Students each perform about 6-8 surgeries and participate in anaesthetic management during surgeries performed by their peers. During the last 5 years, we have spayed and neutered over 5,000 animals. The adoption rate for these animals is reaching 100%. Surgically altered animals are more desirable to many companion animal guardians and the adoption rate has nearly doubled since the onset of the program. We are hoping that because no animals are now released from the shelters without being sterilised, we will also be helping reduce our companion animal over-population.

In addition to this valuable experience, each student performs about 4-6 procedures during their two-week soft tissue rotation. We have seen a dramatic difference in confidence and skill level in students who have rotated through the co-operative elective surgery program compared to students without this valuable experience.

Summary

Our surgery training program will continue to evolve with the primary goals to increase early hands-on training, and to provide better basic skills training. After basic skills are mastered, cadavers from ethical sources are excellent aids for teaching tissue layers and exposure, surgical anatomy, and basic closure methods. Students finally 'graduate' to live animal surgery using patients from humane animal organisations that need to be neutered or spayed, or to have simple surgical conditions corrected. I believe that our training program, model/video autotutorials, cadaver, and finally live animal experience provide the best ethical solution in the surgical training of veterinary students.

Resource list of video autotutorials at OSU

• Smeak D.D., Beck M.L.: "Technique of beginning and ending a continuous suture pattern" (VT #2594), 1997. (Video tape is used during sophomore Introduction to Surgery course; accompanies the suture pattern videotape and suture pattern model).

• Smeak D.D., Beck M.L.: "Open and closed gloving technique" (VT #2583), 1996. (Video tape is used during sophomore Introduction to Surgery and Junior Operative Practice courses).

• Smeak D.D., Beck M.L., Shaffer C.A., Jenne B., Sherman R.: "Buried Continuous Intradermal Suture Closure Technique" (VT #2381), produced in co-operation with Pitman Moore Inc. grant, 1992. Approved and accredited by the AVMA, 1993. (Used in senior clinics as an alternative wound closure technique for elective surgeries; suture simulator used for teaching this technique).

• Smeak D.D., Beck M.L., Shaffer C.A.: "Hollow Organ Closure Technique" (VT #2463), Student Council of the American Veterinary Medical Association Autotutorial Excellence Award, 1991. One autotutorial is chosen from all entries from all North American Veterinary Schools. Student representatives choose the best autotutorial for content, quality, importance. (Used in senior clinics and third year operative practice laboratories, demonstration hollow organ model in Introduction to Surgery Course for second year students).

• Smeak D.D., Beck M.L., Shaffer C.A.: "Vessel Exposure and Isolation" (VT #2462), 1990. (Video tape is used in conjunction with the Basic Hemostatic Technique Tape in operative practice laboratories and for senior clinics instruction to show actual live technique).

• Smeak D.D., Beck M.L., Shaffer C.A., Jenne B., Sherman R.: "Basic Hemostatic Technique" (VT #2431), funded in part by Hildegard Foundation grant, 1988; presented at AVMA Convention, 1989. (Used in a model laboratory in operative practice before live animal laboratories to show eye-hand efforts used to place ligatures on a simulator - see below).

• Smeak D.D., Beck M.L., Shaffer C.A., Jenne B., Sherman R.: "The Forehand Stitch, Instrument and Suture Manipulation (Basic Suturing Technique)" (VT #2433), AVMA 1989. (Used by second year students for practice of motor skills involved in suturing, used by third year students for review during model laboratory).

Resource list of surgical simulators used at OSU

• Smeak D.D., Kitchen B.: Intestinal Anastomosis Simulator (Classroom, laboratory, individual student model). Used for demonstration in Introduction to Surgery Course Laboratories, actual simulation of anastomosis before live animal sessions in operative practice. Available now from Sawbones Inc., Seattle, Washington, USA.

• Smeak D.D., Evenhouse R.: Hollow Organ Simulator (Classroom, laboratory, individual student model). Used for demonstration in Introduction to Surgery Course Laboratories, actual simulation of gastrotomy closure before live animal sessions in operative practice.

• Smeak D.D., Beck M.L., Shaffer C.A.: Vessel Ligation Simulator (Laboratory model). Used in third year operative practice model laboratory. See Reference 1 below - illustrates how to make the model.

• Smeak D.D., Evenhouse R., Shaffer C.A., Beck M.L.: Skin and Suture Pattern Simulator (Classroom, laboratory, individual model). Used in Introduction to Surgery Course to demonstrate suture pattern use and suturing skills.

References

1. Smeak D.D.: Simulator/Media Based Teaching of Basic Surgical Skills. Proceedings of the First Annual International Foundation for Ethical Research Workshop. Alternatives to Live Animals in Veterinary Medical Education, 1989.

2. Smeak D.D., Beck M.L., Shaffer C.A., Gregg C.G.: Evaluation of video tape and simulator for instruction of basic surgical skills. Vet Surg. 20:30-36, 1991.

3. Smeak D.D., Hill L., Beck M., Shaffer C.A., Birchard S.J.: Evaluation of an autotutorial-simulator program for instruction of hollow organ closure. Vet Surg. 23:519-528, 1994.

Biography

Daniel Smeak received his DVM degree from Michigan State University, College of Veterinary Medicine in 1979. After completing an internship at Colorado State University, he began a Small Animal Surgery residency at The Ohio State University. In 1983, following his residency, he accepted a surgery faculty position in Ohio. He became board certified in the American College of Veterinary Surgeons in 1986. He is currently Head of Small Animal Surgery, and since 1994 he is a Full Professor of Surgery at The Ohio State University. His main academic interests are in the field of surgical training of veterinary students and residents, and in soft tissue surgery. He has produced over 15 teaching video autotutorials and 4 surgical simulators. Many of his research grants and publications have been related to methods to better prepare students for the live experience in surgery. He has been the keynote speaker at many veterinary surgery symposia in Europe, North America, Korea, and Japan about this subject.

Daniel D. Smeak, DVM

Head, Small Animal Surgery
The Ohio State University
College of Veterinary Medicine
601 Vernon L. Tharp Street
Columbus, OH 43210
USA

tel: +1 614 292 3551
fax: +1 614 292 0895
e-mail: Smeak.1@osu.edu

7. A pedagogically sound, innovative, and humane plan for veterinary medical education

Lara Marie Rasmussen

R. Ashley Robinson

Gary R. Johnston

Shirley D. Johnston

Western University of Health Sciences College of Veterinary Medicine, USA

The College of Veterinary Medicine at Western University (WesternU-CVM) is a product of many critical thinkers in veterinary academia, the veterinary profession, and general health professions education. In 1999, with historical reflection and information from many veterinary medicine educational symposia, a plan was created to further the successes of existing veterinary medical education, to capitalise on the innovations and progress of many diverse pedagogies, and to promote the needs of the modern veterinary profession. Societal considerations, professional trends, student needs and fiscal responsibility were all considered in the development of this innovative plan. The program evolved around three founding principles:

1) Commitment to innovative, student-centred, life-long learning;
2) Commitment to 'Reverence for Life'; and
3) Commitment to excellence in clinical education through reliance on strategic partnerships and alliances.

Each component of the developing curriculum finds connection to these three core principles. This interconnectedness is key to the less tangible goals of this program (to be discussed later), and makes the discussion of the approach to 'humane education' dependent on a discussion of the program *in toto*.

WesternU-CVM offers a four-year curriculum culminating in a Doctor of Veterinary Medicine professional degree. The prerequisites for admission include fairly extensive preparatory coursework in a university setting and significant animal and/or veterinary-related experiences. A commitment to education and animals, an understanding of the rigours of veterinary medical education, and an appreciation of the scope of the veterinary profession are all expected of applicants seeking admission to WesternU-CVM.

Phase I of the curriculum includes two years of a Problem-Based Learning (PBL) curriculum emphasising the basic sciences, a clinical skills curriculum and a veterinary issues course. Phase II (3rd year) begins in earnest the student transition to the practice of veterinary medicine. During this period, groups of three students rotate through thirteen two-week rotations. These rotation topics range from clinical veterinary medicine, such as small animal, equine, shelter medicine, production animal, and zoo/wildlife, to non-clinical applied settings, such as food and feed safety, environmental/public health, and diagnostic laboratory. Students in the clinical settings will spend 50% of their time participating in the conduct of the private veterinary clinic/hospital to which they are assigned (receiving outpatients, managing inpatients, etc.) and 50% of their time working with their group members mastering prescribed learning objectives and researching cases. Non-clinical rotations will be staged from campus, utilising field trips, student projects, expert consultations, and seminars to achieve the goals of the rotations. Phase III (4th year) is comprised of eight four-week rotations in areas of veterinary medicine chosen by the individual student in consultation with a faculty committee (Committee for Specialty Instruction). Rotation selection criteria in the 4th year include the student's professional goals and mobility during this final year; locations might include local, national or international private veterinary hospitals, Centres of Excellence[1] in other national or international veterinary teaching hospitals, local or national governmental agencies that impact on animals, and animal-related non-governmental organisations, such as those in research, industry and service areas.

The expectation is for the WesternU-CVM student to graduate with the knowledge, skills and attributes necessary to immediately begin serving a contributory role as a veterinary medical professional. Fundamental to this expectation are the variety of outcomes/learning goals that will be promoted, taught and assessed throughout the four-year curriculum. Some of these outcomes are quite traditional and intuitive when considering the goals of veterinary medical education, such as the mastery of facts and principles of various scientific disciplines core to veterinary medicine, including anatomy, physiology, immunology, nutrition, microbiology, and cardiology. Some other outcomes are as intuitive, though addressed less traditionally in veterinary academia, such as mastery of life-long learning, practice management, grief management/counseling, and animal behaviour. Additionally, there are a large group of outcomes that are not linked specifically to the veterinary profession, but are requisite for any member of an interactive community, such as oral and written communication, personnel management, time management, personal responsibility, common sense, and service to the community. Finally, there is a group of outcomes that are somewhat intangible, yet essential for members of a medical profession, especially those serving animal populations, such as humaneness, empathy, respect for others, morality, knowing one's abilities and limitations, and respect for the human-animal bond. A holistic approach to planning and implementation has been necessary to satisfy outcomes in one area, such as pharmacology, without compromising outcomes in another area, such as humaneness. The approach for all outcomes is multidimensional. Learning styles vary across the population; utilising variety in teaching thus facilitates learning. Moreover, the keys to achievement of the WesternU-CVM outcomes is both to present opportunities to learn them, and to actively assess student mastery of desired outcomes. WesternU-CVM students will be assessed again with variety, using everything from the traditional exam to group critiques to one-on-one reviews to self-assessment.

As an example, a discussion of how the outcome 'humaneness toward animals' will be achieved in the WesternU-CVM curriculum is provided. First and foremost is the mandate that for a veterinary professional to truly exhibit humaneness relative to animals, he/she must be a competent veterinarian. Without this competence, the veterinarian risks acting inhumanely (e.g. inflicting harm) through naïveté, error and poor judgment. Central to this mandate are satisfactory outcomes in the various scientific disciplines core to veterinary medicine, such as surgery.

Students will first encounter the learning goal 'humaneness toward animals' when they are introduced to our program. Upon entry into the program, students will learn that the WesternU-CVM animal use policy is that animals will not be used to their detriment in the curriculum.

All experiences with and uses of animals will either be neutral or beneficial in their effect on the animals. Their second exposure to this learning goal will be encountered when they receive an explanation of 'mastery'. Mastery of a skill, generally to a level of introductory competence, is required of all students. WesternU-CVM will not graduate students without competence in designated skills.

The approach to learning surgery will be multidimensional; it includes both the art and science of surgery as well as the practice of surgical skill. The program will ask the student to explore and develop in the understanding of and decision making relative to surgical disease, will facilitate learning of various identified skills and, importantly, will coach students on methods of learning that will help them grow (and stay current in their field) throughout their career. Given the flexibility of the PBL curricular design, students will engage clinical cases from which naturally emerge the breadth of learning goals set for them. In the context of these cases and through various means, such as self-directed study, literature reviews, lectures, laboratories/applied experiences, and expert consultation, students will identify and learn the basic and clinical sciences, such as the art and science of surgery. Concurrently, they will identify and learn the less concrete learning goals, such as 'humaneness toward animals', through self-directed study, literature reviews, role playing, simulated client exercises, client interviews, expert interviews, and observation.

In the design of the skills curriculum, each end product, such as a complex surgery skill that the student is required to master, is broken down into its composite parts. From the simple to the complex, each skill is assigned a variety of learning tools designed to facilitate student mastery of that skill. A 'learning tool' is defined as an object, exercise, or experience used by a student to learn a designated skill, concept, fact, or principle. Learning tools vary in design and are organised under several categories: 1) Failure consequence, 2) Time restriction, 3) Availability of repetition, 4) Complexity scale, 5) Degree of simulation, and 6) Degree of student independence. During their first week of the curriculum, students are provided lists of skills to master, and the level to which they must master each skill prior to the beginning of the 3rd year. The concept of mastery is important[2]. The skills lists include skills used with all domesticated species, and include the many diagnostic and therapeutic clinical skills expected of an entry-level graduate veterinarian. Each student initially will be capable at a different skill level based on inherent abilities and past experiences; they 'plug themselves in' to these lists at the level that is appropriate. They are then given access to the learning tools appropriate to each skill. Student use of learning tools will be self-directed and self-scheduled. As the curriculum is centred around a PBL format with minimal scheduled time, students will assume responsibility for their learning activities immediately. Each piece of our plan is integral to the rest; the individualised use of time by students throughout the entire curriculum will allow for individualised learning in the skills curriculum.

The learning tools for mastering all skills related to and including a complex surgical skill are diverse. They will include inanimate, synthetic models (e.g. 'See with your hands' sized peg board, knot tying board, procedural organ models); animate, synthetic models (e.g. electronic suture board); computer simulations (e.g. *The Virtual Anesthesia Machine*); video and live demonstrations (e.g. procedure videotapes, live video surgery rounds); role-playing simulations (e.g. equine anaesthesia induction, operating room navigation); anatomical cadaver dissections (e.g. formalin-fixed cadavers); cadaver clinical procedures (e.g. frozen-thawed cadavers/body parts); animal 'volunteers' (e.g. non-invasive examinations and procedures); and clinical patients (e.g. prophylactic or required procedures).

Each learning tool will have a written protocol[3]. This protocol is comprised of four sections: 1) How to use/orientation to the learning tool; 2) Expectations students may have of the learning tool; 3) Expectations faculty have of the students, including conditions and constraints for completion and a definition of what comprises successful completion; and 4) Significance of the learning tool. The purposes of these protocols are to orient the student to the tool, create proper learning expectations for the learner, and excite the learner by linking abstract tools to future real-life experiences. Without proper orientation to a tool, students may be unprepared for the learning tool or use it improperly; the frustration that results can negatively impact the learning motivation of the student. If faculty or students expect more than a tool offers, disappointment and dismissal of the tool may follow. Additionally, some students may lack the foresight necessary to appreciate the need to utilise an abstract learning tool (understandably, given their level of experience); this may manifest as disinterest in the tool, and a loss of critical skill practice. These rationales for learning tool protocols parallel the rationales for properly prepared syllabi for non-skill learning experiences[4].

Cadaver-based exercises, animal 'volunteers', and clinical patients have been classified as 'learning tools'. The manner in which students engage these learning tools will directly affect their learning relative to 'humaneness toward animals'. All cadavers will be supplied through a client donation program (similar to Willed Body Donation in human medical schools) whereby the bodies of animals who have died or been euthanised secondary to natural disease/injury will be donated to the school. Outreach and education about this program will be provided on the college's website, and through adjunct faculty. In choosing animals as 'volunteers', a heavy responsibility rests with the faculty and students involved in these exercises such that all procedures are non-invasive or neutral in their immediate effect on the animal. Pain and anxiety will be avoided. Participation from the animal is encouraged through positive reinforcement (e.g. food, social interaction, exercise), and termination of the experience will be required if pain or anxiety are evidenced by the animal. Sources of animal 'volunteers' include companion animals of faculty, staff and students, animals housed in shelters and rescues, and animals managed through a local agricultural college.

Clinical patients will be used as learning tools in direct apprentice-type experiences. An on-campus primary care companion animal clinic with contract clients and patients and a desig-nated small caseload will allow students the time and supervision necessary to 'graduate' into live performance of skills. Small animal and large animal ambulatory/mobile services for local animal shelters, rescues and sanctuaries also will provide the students the opportunity to gradually increase their participation in clinical skills based on their level of expertise. Health fairs and events, designed to provide service to the animals of a low-income human population, will give students both the opportunity to begin assuming the 'doctor' role in professional communications and case management, and to experience a variety of species and clinical skills benefiting those animals.

Having mastered the introductory clinical skills necessary for primary care veterinary medicine, students then will enter the clinical setting of the 3rd year in fee-for-service veterinary practices. Here students primarily will focus their energy on the practice of veterinary medicine with animals in need of care by generating problem lists, differential diagnoses, diagnostic and therapeutic plans, prognoses, and client communication plans. In so doing, they will hone their clinical diagnostic and therapeutic skills in an apprentice-like manner. The 4th year will bring the student gradually into more advanced clinical skills, capitalising on the abilities mastered in the first two years and fine-tuned in the 3rd year. Independence will increase as they demonstrate their expertise. The percentage of successful 'solo flights' when performing skills can be increased dramatically with this gradual and patient approach to learning skills[2].

The primary focus of this discussion was the learning goal of 'humaneness toward animals', but bound into that learning endeavour are the goals of learning surgery, anatomy, life-long learning, practice management, oral and written communication, personnel management, time management, personal responsibility, morality, the human-animal bond, and more. This is just part of the curricular web that makes up the WesternU-CVM plan for veterinary medical education.

There are important references that support the various areas of the WesternU-CVM curriculum. The ability of PBL to produce not only the traditional discipline outcomes but the other important outcomes mentioned above has been documented[5-7]. Assessment has been determined to be critical to the achievement of identified outcomes; without the assessment, learning goals are not perceived to be important[8]. Johnson and Farmer[3] found that through observation and critique of several clinical skills laboratory settings, the most appropriate and successful structure of a laboratory experience could be determined. Successful factors included clearly stated objectives, obvious clinical relevance, and appropriate tasks for given levels of skill. Other components essential to motivating learners in technical training are checklists, procedures, end goals and adequate materials. Another factor critical to achieving self-directed learning in mandated programs is that of making sure the learner is fully aware of the outcomes of the skills training - negative and positive, tangible and intangible. Allowing multiple forms of delivery, offered at all hours, with easy access for students will create situations where students may practice a skill simply because it is within reach[9]. Several studies have questioned the moral development (or deterioration) and desensitisation that occurs as students progress through veterinary medical education[11-12]. In a field such as veterinary medicine, where compassion must share centre stage with intellect, curricular efforts to prevent desensitisation and bolster moral development must be integral to veterinary medical education. These data and more support the structure of the WesternU-CVM curriculum.

There are many challenges to the approach we have taken to veterinary medical education: time commitment, financial commitment, peer reaction, faculty expertise and interest, and resource identification. Each of these challenges has been addressed as needed, primarily through education of faculty participants and interested onlookers. The time commitment is considerable in the planning stages; since the design is novel, most pieces need to be created *de novo*. Relationships need to be identified and developed; resources need to be identified, tested and procured; faculty development must occur; Problem-Based Learning cases need to be written, learning issues identified, and assessment methods developed; surveys and expert consultations must be conducted to prepare clinical skills lists; learning tools must be procured, designed, built, and/or co-ordinated; learning tool protocols must be written and assessment means created; and finances must be justified and acquired. When considering the means to an end, an optimistic (and therefore often rewarding) view is that if the end is worthy and justified, the means are achievable and will materialise. Perhaps behind this theory is that those working toward the end sincerely believe in its merit and thus work diligently to make the means arise! For some this might mean writing program grants, for others it means telling our compelling story to interested parties, and for others still it might mean establishing relationships and networks among those who might appreciate our goals and/or benefit from them.

Peer reaction to the plan has been mixed. The most striking observation is that most negative reactions stem from ignorance or misinformation; when the majority of peers are well informed about the plan, intentions, methods and diligence with regard to assessment, they are impressed and often ask to participate. The plan presents a 'new way'; this will always evoke some concern from those invested in the 'old way'. The plan *in toto* will not work in every location, because resources, society, faculty, students, and facilities may be different enough to preclude exact replication. The WesternU-CVM plan approaches veterinary medical education in an evidence-based manner; as outcomes data are collected, analysed and published, the plan will be modified, and this process will continue into the future. Others who are delivering veterinary medical education in this same evidence-based way will maintain quality programs of a variety of designs fitting with the needs of the times.

Since this approach is innovative in many different ways, few educators are experienced in the various methods we propose. Some educators may be reluctant to participate due to their perception of inexperience, or may participate and gradually revert to more traditional methods of education. For other educators, the freedom for creativity will lead to new advances. Lifelong learning must be an expectation of educators for themselves; the program at WesternU-CVM presents opportunities for educators to fulfil this lifelong mission.

Perhaps the most misunderstood component of our curriculum is best described in a commonly heard statement: "You can't teach surgery [or physiology or pharmacology or anaesthesia] with a set of plastic models!" The faculty of WesternU-CVM agree entirely. Every learning tool will have its place, and that includes plastic models, computer simulations, live simulations, cadaver exercises and living animal exercises. The needs of the curriculum will define what learning tools are developed and procured. Every learning tool will have proper expectations associated with it; every learning tool cannot 'teach' every component of every skill or concept; every learning tool may impact on various curricular goals. The selection of learning tools must weigh risks and benefits to the student, to the curriculum, to the animals, to the faculty. In veterinary academia, more emphasis must be placed on defining and designing learning tools that are creative, diverse, and considerate of all curricular goals.

Humans are a creative species. We have made tremendous achievements in medicine, physics, engineering, and art. Educators can make achievements as profound in the educational arena as well. Why should a learning challenge be handled any differently than a disease challenge? Identify the problem, brainstorm various creative solutions, apply them, gather data, modify our actions and reassess the problem. This process must be on-going - a constant evolution. Society is at a stage where eliminating the harmful use of animals in education is not only achievable, but doing so will result in superior learning. Only the future will determine what we have done right and what we have done wrong, but let us not be caught doing nothing.

Lives of great men (and women*) all remind us
We can make our lives sublime,
And, departing, leave behind us
Foot prints on the sands of time.

Let us, then, be up and doing,
With a heart for any fate;
Still achieving, still pursuing,
Learn to labour and to wait.

Henry Wadsworth Longfellow

*Authors' addition

References

1. Pritchard, W.R., Future directions for veterinary medicine. 1988, PEW National Veterinary Education Program, Institute of Policy Sciences and Public Affairs: Durham, NC, USA

2. Gogne, R.M., L.J. Briggs, and W.W. Wager, Principles of Instructional Design. 3rd ed. 1988, New York: Holt, Rinehart and Winston, Inc.

3. Johnson, A.L. and J.A. Farmer, Evaluation of traditional and alternative models in psychomotor laboratories for veterinary surgery. Journal of Veterinary Medical Education, 1989. 16(1): p. 11-14.

4. Nilson, L.B., Teaching at its best: A research-based resource for college instructors. 1997, Anker Publishing Co.: Bolton, MA, USA

5. Distlehorst, L. and R. Robbs, A comparison of problem-based learning and standard curriculum students: Three years of retrospective data. Academic Medicine, 1998. 10: p. 131-137.

6. Norman, G.R. and H.G. Schmidt, The psychological basis of problem-based learning: a review of the evidence. Academic Medicine, 1992. 67(9): p. 557-565.

7. Savery, J.R. and T.M. Duffy, Problem based learning: An instructional model and its constructivist framework. Educational Technology, 1995. 35(5): p. 31-37.

8. Kelson, A., Assessment drives the curriculum. Seminar course - Essentials of PBL: Tutor training, problem design and assessment. 2001. Santa Barbara, CA, USA.

9. Blackwood, C.C., Applying self-directed learning principles in the technical training of a high-risk industry, in Overcoming Resistance to Self-Direction in Adult Learning. New directions for adults and continuing education. Hiemstra, R. & Brockett, R.G., Eds. 1994, Jossey-Bass: San Francisco, CA, USA.

10. Paul, E.S. and A.L. Podberscek, Veterinary education and students' attitudes towards animal welfare. Veterinary Record, 2000. 146: p. 269-272.

11. Self, D.J., et al., Study of the influence of veterinary medical education on the moral development of veterinary students. Journal of the American Veterinary Medical Association, 1991. 198: p. 782-787.

12. Self, D.J., et al., Clarifying the relationship of veterinary medical education and moral development. Journal of the American Veterinary Medical Association, 1996. 209: p. 2002-2004.

Biographies

Lara Marie Rasmussen

Lara Marie Rasmussen completed an undergraduate Bachelors of Science degree in Biological Sciences and Policy Studies at the University of California (Davis) in 1989. She went on to receive a Doctor of Veterinary Medicine degree from UC Davis as well in 1993. A portion of her surgical training was accomplished during a summer surgical course at Washington State University. Her interest in small animal surgery as a career took her through a small animal internship at South Shore Veterinary Associates in Massachusetts and a three-year small animal surgery residency at the University of Minnesota. She later received Diplomate status in the American College of Veterinary Surgeons. Her beliefs about the inappropriate and detrimental use of animals in education were challenged at every stage of her educational experience, yet she prevailed and now succeeds as a board-certified surgeon. She spent one year as a clinical instructor at Washington State University in the surgery department, and then went into private referral practice with Veterinary Referral Services in Spokane, Washington. In 1999, she was recruited to develop and direct the surgery and clinical skills program at the new veterinary school in Southern California (Western University of Health Sciences, College of Veterinary Medicine.) The program will involve the non-detrimental use of animals and will incorporate extensive live animal experiences that benefit the animals involved. Dr. Rasmussen's approach to this new curriculum will be to capitalise on the wealth of education science available, and to require student mastery of skills rather than simple exposure to skills.

Shirley D. Johnston

Dr. Johnston is Founding Dean of the 28th College of Veterinary Medicine in the United States, at Western University of Health Sciences. She was educated at the University of Washington, Seattle (BS Zoology), Washington State University, Pullman (DVM), and the University of Minnesota (PhD, Theriogenology); and is a diplomate of the American College of Theriogenologists. Her career has focused on teaching and clinical research in canine and feline reproduction. She has lectured widely, authored more than 80 refereed publications, and is senior author of *Canine and Feline Reproduction*, W.B. Saunders, 2001. She was Director of Graduate Studies and Associate Dean for Academic Affairs at the University of Minnesota College of Veterinary Medicine, and Chair of the Department of Veterinary Clinical Sciences at Washington State University. She was president of the American College of Theriogenologists (1989), and is currently the president of the Executive Committee of the International Congress on Animal Reproduction.

Gary R. Johnston

Dr. Johnston is Professor of Radiology at the College of Veterinary Medicine, Western University of Health Sciences, California. He was educated at the University of Washington, Seattle (BA Zoology), Washington State University, Pullman (DVM) and the University of Minnesota (MS, Veterinary Radiology), and is a diplomate of the American College of Veterinary Radiologists. His career has focused on teaching and clinical research in veterinary radiology, with emphasis on the canine and feline urogenital systems. He has served as head of the Division of Radiology and Director of Graduate Studies for Veterinary Surgery, Radiology and Anesthesiology at the College of Veterinary Medicine, University of Minnesota, and Professor, Department of

Veterinary Comparative Anatomy, Pharmacology and Physiology, Washington State University College of Veterinary Medicine, Pullman, WA. At both institutions he established the veterinary nuclear pharmacy, and was responsible for initiating radioactive iodine therapy for feline hyper-thyroidism.

R. Ashley Robinson

Dr. Robinson is Associate Dean for Preclinical Programs and Professor of Veterinary Epidemiology at the College of Veterinary Medicine, Western University of Health Sciences, Pomona, California. He was educated at the University of Sydney, Australia (BVSc) and the University of Minnesota, St. Paul, MN (MPH and PhD), majoring in veterinary microbiology and epidemiology. In a career in veterinary epidemiology spanning three decades at the University of Minnesota College of Veterinary Medicine, he mentored more than 100 graduate students from five conti-nents, educated with excellence, published hundreds of papers, and lectured nationally and inter-nationally on infectious disease epidemiology and zoonotic diseases. His last international assignment was as Senior Veterinary Liaison for a Middle East Regional Co-operation Project in Amman, Jordan, sponsored by Tufts University School of Veterinary Medicine.

Lara Marie Rasmussen, DVM, MS
Diplomate, American College of Veterinary Surgeons
Assistant Professor

R. Ashley Robinson, DVM, MPH, PhD
Associate Dean

Gary R. Johnston, DVM, MS
Diplomate, American College of Veterinary Radiology
Professor

Shirley D. Johnston, DVM, PhD
Diplomate, American College of Theriogenology
Dean

College of Veterinary Medicine
Western University of Health Sciences
309 East 2nd Street
Pomona, CA 91766
USA

www.westernu.edu

Communicating author (L. M. Rasmussen):

tel: +1 909 469 5668
fax: +1 909 469 5635
e-mail: lmrasmussen@westernu.edu

part c **alternatives file**

The *Alternatives File* presents information on over 500 products, divided into 10 chapters according to discipline. Individual entries for alternative products are included alphabetically under the appropriate medium:

SOFTWARE
VIDEO
MODELS, MANNEKINS, SIMULATORS
WORLD WIDE WEB

Apparatus for self-experimentation are listed under MODELS, MANNEKINS, SIMULATORS. Each alternative is also listed in the comprehensive *Product Index* at the end of the book.

Please note that InterNICHE does not develop or sell these alternatives - readers should contact producers or distributors directly if interested in their products. Some are also available for trial through the various alternatives loan systems that exist across the world (see *Part D - Further Resources* or the InterNICHE website at www.interniche.org).

The disciplines chosen for inclusion in the *Alternatives File* reflect the areas where harmful animal use is widespread and where replacement is needed (see *Introduction*). In order to focus on state-of-the-art alternative methods that are pedagogically suitable for replacement, all slides and charts have been excluded. 16mm films have also been excluded, as they are seldom available today; some, however, have been digitised or transferred on to video and are therefore included under their new medium.

Full details about the products were sought from all producers in order to provide informative descriptive texts and accurate product specifications. Much of the information was derived from company websites and from on-line and printed catalogues. Some was written specifically for this book, and may include details of producers' development plans for translated versions and new products. In most cases the individual entries have been checked and approved by the relevant producers. Note that the descriptive texts for each alternative are not InterNICHE reviews.

The prices of products are referred to in the national or international currency used by the producers or distributors, and units of measurement are also kept to those provided. When measurements of products are included, these refer to length (L), width (W), height (H), diameter (D) and weight (Wt). The use of the term 'format' for videos refers to both standard (e.g. PAL or NTSC) and format (e.g. VHS); potential buyers of videos should ensure that they order the correct standard. The 'system requirements' described for software are in general those higher than the following minimum system requirements: for PC (IBM compatible): Windows 3.1, 100 MHz processor, 8 MB RAM, and VGA display with 256 colours and screen resolution of 640 x 480 pixels; for Macintosh: OS 7.0, 68040 Processor or Power Mac, 8 MB RAM, and display with 256 colours and screen resolution of 640 x 480 pixels; a soundcard, videocard, and at least 4X CD–ROM drive are required for many multimedia software products. To confirm all system requirements, and for any questions about compatibility, please contact the producers.

The authors have done their best to ensure the quality and accuracy of the information provided. InterNICHE cannot, however, guarantee the quality of individual products, nor be held responsible for any errors or omissions in the information presented. The network also cannot advise on the degree of ethical responsibility taken by producers, such as the ethical or harmful use of animals for the production of some alternatives, nor on their commitment to alternatives in all fields. However, all the alternatives described can replace harmful animal use within education; and furthermore, InterNICHE encourages the ethical production of alternatives (see *Appendix*).

Users of this information should be aware of the changes that may take place over time. In particular this will include the marketing or sharing of new products, upgrades, withdrawals, and price changes. Readers are encouraged to visit the websites of producers or to otherwise contact them for the latest information.

1. Anaesthesia & Critical Care

SOFTWARE

ACLS Simulator 2002

Anesoft *ACLS Simulator 2002* is a real-time simulator that provides the ability for all physicians and nurses to practice the management of cardiac arrest. The treatment protocols in this course are based on the ACLS guidelines published in the 2000 *American Heart Association Textbook of Advanced Cardiac Life Support*. It incorporates two modules - *Rhythm*, for ECG rhythm recognition (also available on-line free of charge - see under WORLD WIDE WEB) and *Pulse*, a real-time megacode simulator. It is an easy-to-use package that contains the most recent American Heart Association algorithms, medications and dosages. A colourful graphic interface, automated record-keeping and an on-line help system create a unique and realistic training environment. Interpret the ECG, assess the patient, control the airway, breathing and circulation, defibrillate and administer cardiac medications. One must act quickly in this real-time simulation or the patient's condition will deteriorate. Topics cover: 20 simulated cases, ventricular fibrillation, ventricular tachycardia, asystole, pulseless electrical activity, supraventricular tachycardia, atrial fibrillation, atrial flutter, AV blocks, paediatric advanced life support (PALS).

Medium: CD-ROM
System requirements: Windows only, with Internet Explorer 4.01 or higher or Netscape 4.x
Price: US$69.00 (single licence), US$399.00 (network licence - up to 10 concurrent users on one network), US$1,199.00 (departmental licence - up to 60 concurrent users)
Source: Anesoft Corporation

Anaesthesia of Rats

This interactive program teaches students the basic skills of anaesthetics and consists of 5 sections, each containing digital video: *Introduction, Phases, Injection anaesthesia, Inhalation anaesthesia, Combined injection/inhalation anaesthesia*. It succeeds in simulating the complex technique of anaesthetics, using the features of modern computers and a mathematical model which describes the concentration of an anaesthetic drug in the major compartments of the body (blood and target tissues). All parameters involved can be changed and the effects can be viewed and diagnosed using digital video. This allows many different situations and stages of the process to be studied, including effects of anaesthesia on reflexes (which can be tested after a variable period of time), mucous colour, muscle tonus and pupil size. The anaesthetic drug and its concentration (dosage) and factors like body weight, gender, and route of administration (inhalation or injection) can be set as well. Basic information on physiological parameters (heart rate, respiration and blood pressure) is also provided.

Medium: CD-ROM
System requirements: Windows only - Win95/98/2000
Price: €250.00
Source: BSL

Anaesthesia vol. 1 and 2

Anaesthesia, volumes 1 and 2 (combined), consists of the digitised images (in JPEG format) from the original British Laboratory Animal Veterinary Association (BLAVA) 35mm slide set, and an additional 150 or so images (200 in all) of assorted anaesthetic topics, primarily dealing with small mammal anaesthesia, together with equipment, drugs etc., and some large animal illustrations. Part of the *Digital Materials for Trainers* series.

Medium: CD-ROM
System requirements: Windows 95 and higher, Macintosh OS 8.6 and higher; QuickTime 5 (included)
Price: £5.00 / US$10.00 (plus £5.00 / US$10.00 postage for 1-10 disks)
Source: University of Newcastle upon Tyne

Anaesthesia vol. 3

A second collection of 200 anaesthesia digitised images (in JPEG format), including a series of illustrations of epidural anaesthesia in the dog, anaesthetic induction in the dog, and assorted equipment, drugs, etc. Part of the *Digital Materials for Trainers* series.

Medium: CD-ROM
System requirements: Windows 95 and higher, Macintosh OS 8.6 and higher; QuickTime 5 (included)
Price: £5.00 / US$10.00 (plus £5.00 / US$10.00 postage for 1-10 disks)
Source: University of Newcastle upon Tyne

Anaesthetic Case Simulation

Anaesthetic Case Simulation (labrador ovariohysterectomy and cat spay) covers anaesthetic preparation, drugs for induction, inhalational agents, flowmeters, and recovery. Includes instructional, self-testing and decision-making components.

Year of production: 2001
Medium: CD-ROM
System requirements: Windows only - Win98/NT; 16 MB RAM, 64k colour display
Price: Free site licence, only available to Associate Members of CLIVE consortium
Source: CLIVE

Anesthesia Simulator 2002

The *Anesthesia Simulator* is a real-time graphical simulator that reproduces the anaesthesia environment on a computer screen. Mathematical models of physiology and pharmacology predict the simulated patient's response to your management while an automated record-keeping system summarizes the case and an on-line consultant provides immediate management suggestions. It includes 72 cases with general anaesthetic problems, and cardiac, neuro, trauma, obstetric and pediatric cases and dozens of anaesthetic emergencies. Topics cover: air embolism, anaphylaxis, bronchospasm, carcinoid, diabetic ketoacidosis, difficult airway, intracranial hypertension, latex allergy, pheochromocytoma, preeclampsia, venous air embolism.

Medium: CD-ROM
System requirements: Windows only, with Internet Explorer 4.01 or higher or Netscape 4.x
Price: US$199.00 (single licence), US$699.00 (network licence - up to 10 concurrent users on one network), US$1,999.00 (departmental licence - up to 60 concurrent users)
Source: Anesoft Corporation

Critical Care Simulator 2002

The *Critical Care Simulator* is an exciting real-time graphical simulator that reproduces patient care in an Intensive Care Unit or Emergency Room. 20 different critically ill patients are presented and you must manage the airway, ventilation, fluids and medications to improve the simulated patient's condition. Optimise the patient's haemodynamic state with invasive monitoring and vasoactive infusions. Many emergency situations will occur requiring rapid diagnosis and proper treatment to avoid disaster. An on-line expert help system is available and an automated record-keeping system provides a detailed chart for the case. Topics cover: anaphylaxis, bronchospasm, cardiac tamponade, chest trauma, difficult airway, drug overdose, head injury, heart failure, myocardial ischemia, pneumothorax, pulmonary emboli.

Medium: CD-ROM
System requirements: Windows only, with Internet Explorer 4.01 or higher or Netscape 4.x
Price: US$99.00 (single licence), US$499.00 (network licence - up to 10 concurrent users on one network), US$1,499.00 (departmental licence - up to 60 concurrent users)
Source: Anesoft Corporation

Digital Materials for Trainers On-Screen Collection

All of the digitised images (in JPEG format) from Disks 1-5 of the *Digital Materials for Trainers* series at a resolution optimised for screen display. If one only wishes to use the material for computer-based presentations, this is a convenient mean of accessing the images. Contains: *Anaesthesia vol. 1 and 2, Anaesthesia vol. 3, Minor Procedures vol. 1, Health and Welfare vol. 1, Surgery vol. 1* (see individual titles for full description).

Medium: CD-ROM
System requirements: Windows 95 and higher, Macintosh OS 8.6 and higher; QuickTime 5 (included)
Price: £5.00 / US$10.00 (plus £5.00 / US$10.00 postage for 1-10 disks)
Source: University of Newcastle upon Tyne

GOLEM

This interactive multimedia software simulator has been designed as a clinical physiological trainer to help improve diagnostic and therapeutic decisions in real critical clinical disorders. It integrates blood circulation, respiration control, kidney function, body fluid volume and osmotic homeostasis, acid-base and electrolyte balance, and control of glycaemia, along with the regulatory influence of relevant hormones and the influence of some therapeutic procedures. By imitating the real biological original in various pathological states with sufficient fidelity, it allows substitution of real experiments performed on animals with computer simulated situations. Its theoretical basis relies upon the mathematical expression of the internal environment homeostasis, which includes 39 non-linear differential equations, with 89 input and 179 output variables.

Language: English, Czech; other language versions can be developed as the program may be distributed with source code
Medium: CD-ROM
System requirements: Windows only - Win98/2000/NT/XP; Pentium processor 133 MHz, 32 MB RAM; Control Web Run Time software required (distributed by Moravian Instruments - http://www.mii.cz; special version distributed free of charge with GOLEM)
Price: Freeware
Source: Dr. Jirí Kofránek (Charles University, Czech Republic)

Laboratory Animals Anaesthesia

These CD-ROMs from the *Digital Materials for Trainers* series contain QuickTime movies illustrating some anaesthetic techniques for use in small mammals. They can be played as stand alone movie files, or can be launched in a web-browser (Netscape is much faster than Explorer) using the home page (Home.htm) included on the CD. There is no sound track, and the movies are captioned to emphasise essential points. They can be used for teaching purposes, but if anyone wishes to edit the content and recaption into another language, please contact the source.

The titles available are:
- *Small Mammal Anaesthesia*
- *Laboratory Animals Anaesthesia - Small Mammals Part 2*
- *Laboratory Animals Anaesthesia - Anaesthesia of the Cat and Dog*
- *Clinical Veterinary Anaesthesia and Neutering - under production*

Language: English; others (Spanish, Italian, French and German) under production
Medium: CD-ROM (ISSO 9660 format)
System requirements: Windows 95 and higher, Macintosh OS 8.6 and higher; QuickTime 5 (included)
Price: Each program £5.00 / US$10.00 (plus £5.00 / US$10.00 postage for 1-10 disks)
Source: University of Newcastle upon Tyne

Laboratory Animals Anaesthesia, Surgery and Perioperative Care

This double CD-ROM from the *Digital Materials for Trainers* series contains interactive course notes on anaesthesia (CD 1) and surgery (CD 2). They can be used to support training and provide veterinary students with a basic introduction to anaesthesia, surgery and perioperative care. Copies of the notes can be printed, but when viewed on screen (using Acrobat Reader), links are included for accessing illustrations, QuickTime movie clips and additional text information.

Language: English; others (Spanish, Italian, French and German) under production
Medium: CD-ROM
System requirements: Windows 95 and higher, Macintosh OS 8.6 and higher; QuickTime 5 (included)
Price: £5.00 / US$10.00 (plus £5.00 / US$10.00 postage for 1-10 disks)
Source: University of Newcastle upon Tyne

ResusSim Inhospital

ResusSim Inhospital is a new state-of-the-art problem-based PC simulator of basic and advanced life support (ALS). An overview picture shows the emergency situation on the PC screen. The students can interact directly with the members of the emergency medical team and the patient by clicking on them. They also have access to more than 160 different investigations and treatments, including a wide range of drugs, different defibrillators (both manual and AED's), all common airway techniques, ventilation, and chest compression. In the simulator, the students are confronted with a wide variety of realistic cases (12 patients in the Basics Edition, 28 in Standard, 45 in Professional and 50 in the multiuser version), followed by a thorough evaluation of the treatment given along with suggestions for improvements. In this way, they can practice their diagnostic and therapeutic algorithms and strategies in an easily accessible, safe environment. The scenarios develop differently from time to time and the patients vary in difficulty in order to stimulate recurrent use. The program complies with the International Guidelines 2000, and can be customised to as many different levels as needed using different user profiles.

Medium: CD-ROM
System requirements: Windows only – Win95/98/2000/NT4.0/ME, Pentium 133 MHz (300 MHz recommended), 16 MB RAM (64 MB recommended), 140 MB HDD
Price: Single user: 618.75 DKK / ~ €82.91 / ~ US$78.12 (Basics Edition); 1268.75 DKK / ~ €170.02 / ~ US$160.19 (Standard Edition); 2337.50 DKK / ~ €313.24 / ~ US$295.13 (Professional Edition). Multiuser or network licence prices available upon request. A demo version (in English) is downloadable free of charge from the website
Note: 1. Additional cases will be made available on the internet (free of charge for the Professional Edition).
2. An older program – *ResusSim 98* – was developed by Sophus Medical in several languages (Danish, English, French, Italian, Norwegian) and in several local editions (European/UK, French, Italian, Australian/New Zealand, Southern African), each containing the relevant local policy statements and guidelines of the national Resuscitation Councils for that region; being far less advanced than the next generation (*ResusSim Inhospital* and *ResusSim Prehospital*), at the time of publication it is to be phased out by the producers
Source: Sophus Medical A/S

ResusSim Prehospital

This is a state-of-the-art problem-based PC simulator of advanced prehospital care. On the PC screen, an overview picture of the situation (either at the scene of the accident or inside the ambulance) is shown. The students can interact directly with the rescuers and the patient by clicking on them, and can even decide who should do what ('Crew Resource Management'). Students also have access to more than 160 different investigations and treatments including a wide range of drugs, different defibrillators (both manual and AED's), all common airway techniques, ventilation, and chest compression. In the simulator, the users are confronted with a wide variety of realistic cases (12 patients in the Basics Edition, 28 in the Standard Edition, 45 in the Professional and the multiuser version), followed by a thorough evaluation of the treatment given along with suggestions for improvements. This way, they can practice their diagnostic and therapeutic algorithms and strategies in an easily accessible, safe environment. The scenarios develop differently from time to time and the patients vary in difficulty in order to stimulate recurrent use. Cases include: airway problems (aspiration, allergies etc.), acute myocardial infarction, anaphylaxis, apoplexy, asthma & status asthmaticus, atrial fibrillation, cardiac arrest (variations of ventricular fibrillation, ventricular tachicardia, supraventricular tachycardia, electro-mechanical dissociation and asystole), cervical injuries, chronic obstructive pulmonary disease, epilepsy, gastric ulcer, hyperglycaemia, hypoglycaemia, hypothermia, internal bleeding, intoxications (drug overdoses and alcohol), pulmonary oedema, malignant hypertension, pneumonia, supraventricular tachycardia, vasovagal response. *ResusSim Prehospital* can be customised to fit each user's training needs.

Language: English, German (the latter can be purchased on-line from the German Red Cross, http://www.drk.de)
Medium: CD-ROM
System requirements: Windows only – Win95/98/2000/NT4.0/ME, Pentium 133 MHz (300 MHz recommended), 16 MB RAM (64 MB recommended), 140 MB HDD
Price: Single user: 618.75 DKK / ~€82.91 / ~ US$78.12 (Basics Edition); 1268.75 DKK / ~€170.02 / ~ US$160.19 (Standard Edition); 2337.50 DKK / ~ €313.24 / ~ US$295.13 (Professional Edition). Multiuser or network licence prices available upon request. A demo version (in English) is downloadable free from the website

Note: 1. Additional cases will be made available on the internet (free of charge for the Professional Edition).
2. An older program – *ResusSim 98* – was developed by Sophus Medical in several languages (Danish, English, French, Italian, Norwegian) and in several local editions (European/UK, French, Italian, Australian/New Zealand, Southern African), each containing the relevant local policy statements and guidelines of the national Resuscitation Councils for that region; being far less advanced than the next generation (*ResusSim Inhospital* and *ResusSim Prehospital*), at the time of publication it is to be phased out by the producers
Source: Sophus Medical A/S

Sedation Simulator 2002

The *Sedation Simulator* is the perfect program for radiologists, oral surgeons, endoscopists, surgeons and nurses to review the management of conscious sedation. Administer a variety of sedative agents, monitor the simulated patient and manage a number of emergency scenarios. 36 different patients are presented and you must manage the airway, ventilation, fluids and medications. Many emergency situations will occur requiring rapid diagnosis and proper treatment to avoid disaster. An on-line expert help system is available and an automated record-keeping system provides a detailed chart for the case. Topics cover: agitation, anaphylaxis, apnea, bradycardia, bronchospasm, cardiac arrest, hypertension, hypotension, myocardial ischemia, and tachycardia.

Medium: CD-ROM
System requirements: Windows only, with Internet Explorer 4.01 or higher or Netscape 4.x
Price: US$99.00 (single licence), US$499.00 (network licence - up to 10 concurrent users on one network), US$1,499.00 (departmental licence - up to 60 concurrent users)
Source: Anesoft Corporation

SimBioSys ABG

SimBioSys ABG is a structured, interactive course on the interpretation of arterial blood gases and acid-base disorders, designed for beginners and experts alike. At its heart is *SimBioSys*, a simulation engine which uses mathematical models of the heart, vessels, lungs, kidney, and their neural control. The program includes 48 cases, known and unknown, covering all of the blood gas derangements likely to be seen in clinical practice. Interactive physiology exercises and experiments increase the users' understanding of the topics presented. At the same time, their knowledge is tested throughout the program with section quizzes and case interpretation quizzes. Moreover, the users can create their own cases along with a quiz and patient history for each. Pulmonary physiology topics include: hypoxia, oxygen-haemoglobin dissociation, anatomic and alveolar dead space, shunt, ventilation-perfusion mismatch, A-a gradient, venous admixture, physiological dead space measurements, and carbon dioxide transport in the blood. Acid-base concepts include: carbon-dioxide reactions, hydrogen and hydroxide ions, pH, strong ion difference, base excess, blood bicarbonate, blood protein dissociation, metabolic compensation, respiratory compensation, anion gap, and diseases that can affect acid-base balance. *SimBioSys ABG* dynamically illustrates important concepts and principles that are difficult to learn through static pictures.

Medium: CD-ROM
System requirements: Windows only - Win3.1/95; 486/66 MHz processor (Pentium recommended), 16 MB RAM, 12 MB HDD space
Price: US$74.00 (single user licence); site licence price on request
Source: Critical Concepts

 Simbiosys ACLS

This interactive program teaches the American Heart Association (AHA) Advanced Cardiac Life Support (ACLS) guidelines in a clear and concise manner as it follows your every intervention. At its heart is *SimBioSys*, a simulation engine which uses mathematical models of the heart, vessels, lungs, kidney, and their neural control. *SimBioSys ACLS* allows you to gauge how well you know and adhere to AHA standards; it scores you on how well you followed them. It offers extensive help which can teach you about the protocols and guide you through each case. Or it can give you advice when you get stuck. In addition, *SimBioSys ACLS* offers two modes: test and practice. In practice mode, you are able to use every resource that *SimBioSys ACLS* has to offer while test mode restricts the amount of on-line help available. *SimBioSys* patients are not like the pre-scripted cases you find in most ACLS programs. The treatment of real patients is a complicated matter. They may change from one condition to another without warning. Over 55 cases include: ventricular fibrillation, asystole, ventricular tachycardia, atrial flutter, atrial fibrillation, supraventricular tachycardia, pulseless electrical activity, bradycardia (including 2nd and 3rd degree heart blocks), hypotension, shock, and pulmonary oedema.

Medium: CD-ROM
System requirements: Windows only - Win3.1/95/98; 486/66 MHz processor (Pentium recommended), 16 MB RAM, 12 MB HDD space
Price: US$89.00 (single user). Free demo downloadable from website
Note: This product has *not* been updated for the new AHA ACLS Guidelines (2000)
Source: Critical Concepts

 Simbiosys Clinics v2

This program is an interactive learning tool for critical care, allowing the user to explore human physiology in a clinical setting and replacing an animal or a patient in illustrating pathophysiology. At its heart is *SimBioSys*, a simulation engine which uses mathematical models of the heart, vessels, lungs, kidney, and their neural control. Diagnostic procedures including a physical exam, lab tests, ECG's, radiographs and echocardiographs can be performed, as well as interventions such as administering drugs and fluids, controlling the mechanical ventilator, or placing various catheters. The *SimBioSys* simulator updates the computerised patient's physiology with every move as if it were a real patient. The full program contains 11 cases - one normal patient and 11 critically ill ones. The normal patient can be used as a baseline for understanding important medical concepts. Resources include: ventilator with 7 settings, lab measurements, 12-lead ECGs, physical exam, X-rays, echocardiograms, catheters, chest tubes, 62 different drugs and fluids, and monitor.

A Student Edition is also available, but it only contains 4 patient cases and it does not support echocardiograms, X-rays, flow sheet, and 12-lead ECGs.

Medium: CD-ROM
System requirements: Windows 3.1/95 with 486/66 MHz processor and math coprocessor; Macintosh OS 7.5 with Power PC; 16 MB RAM and 4 MB HDD space
Price: US$79.00 (Student Edition); US$195.00 (full version); prices are for single user licence; site licence price on request. Free demo downloadable from website
Source: Critical Concepts

UMedic

The *UMedic* computer assisted instruction system provides a comprehensive cardiology curriculum for medical students and physicians, and programs are now being developed in oncology and neurology. The system may be used by self-learners, an instructor in a classroom, may stand alone, be linked to *Harvey* (see under MODELS, MANNEKINS, SIMULATORS) and/or used with standardised patients. A database automatically analyses learner performance. The programs feature full motion video and high fidelity audio and are compatible with current multimedia PCs or laptop computers. The first 5 programs cover normal and the 4 valve lesions and emphasise pathophysiology and basic bedside skills. The second series of 5 programs cover coronary disease, congestive failure and hypertension and emphasise common management problems. Basic content of each program: the history, bedside findings presented by an instructor on videos using *Harvey, the Cardiology Patient Simulator* (including: general appearance, blood pressure, arterial and venous pulses, precordial movements, auscultation), diagnosis, laboratory data (including: CBC & blood chemistries, ECGs, X-rays, real time echo dopplers, anigograms and other imaging techniques), treatment (including videos of interventional therapy/surgery), pathophysiology, discussions (including: key teaching points and remediation, case reviews by authoritative cardiologists).

Medium: CD-ROM
System requirements: Windows only - Win95 or later; 200 MHz Pentium processor, 32 MB RAM, minimum 25 MB HDD space, 12X CD-ROM drive or faster, 16-bit colour SVGA display, Windows compatible 16-bit sound device, 2 multimedia speakers (headphones are advised for optimal fidelity of heart sounds and murmurs)
Price: US$3,600.00 per series
Source: University of Miami School of Medicine

Virtual Anesthesia Machine

The *Virtual Anesthesia Machine* program simulates the inner workings of an anaesthesia machine and ventilator - the complex machinery in which oxygen, nitrous oxide and anaesthetics mix to render patients insensitive to pain during surgery and other procedures. The designers' goal is to increase patient safety by arming the next generation of anaesthetists with a clear understanding of the flow of gas within the equipment and the consequences of machine malfunctions or user actions on pressures, flows, and volumes and composition of gases in the anaesthesia machine. The

Virtual Anesthesia Machine depicts lungs, dials, gas canisters, pipes, ventilator settings and anaesthetic agents. Colour-coded circles flow through the pipes to represent molecules of oxygen, carbon dioxide, air, volatile anaesthetics and nitrous oxide. Dials can be adjusted, valves opened and closed, and rates and directions of gas flow changed. Just as significantly, users are allowed to adjust the controls improperly - for example, excessively inflating the lungs - and therefore can learn from their mistakes. Equipment faults also can be simulated.

Language: English, Spanish, German; other languages to be added in the future
Medium: Downloadable from website
System requirements: Windows 95/98/2000/NT, Macintosh
Price: Freeware
Source: http://www.anest.ufl.edu/vam (University of Florida, USA)

Virtual Ventilator

A 32-bit application designed for Windows that attempts to combine the simplicity of a static model with the advantage of an immediate user feedback to provide students with a realistic model/simulation of connecting their patients to a mechanical ventilator. The main screen is a depiction of a ventilator bellows, several ventilator controls, and several digital/analog displays. The patient's weight, lung compliance and status (normal or with various degrees of lung pathology) can be set by the student, and so can the size of the ventilator bellows and its functional parameters (fixed or variable inspiration : expiration ratio, dynamic or static inspiratory time). The simulation allows students to change the patient's ventilation parameters and observe the effect of these on the ventilator itself and on the patient they are ventilating. The breadth of different physiological conditions that the student may experience exceeds what may be achieved in a single live animal laboratory experience.

Medium: 3.5" disk
System requirements: Windows only - Win95 or later, with any Pentium processor
Price: Cost price
Note: Version 1.2 currently available; version 2.0 (with several enhancements to the user interface and to the simulations) under production
Source: Dr. R.D. Keegan (Washington State University, USA)

When contacting producers and distributors,
please cite *from Guinea Pig to Computer Mouse*

VIDEO

Canine Cardio-Pulmonary Resuscitation

This video presents the fundamentals of canine cardio-pulmonary resuscitation (CPR) by demonstration and discussion of the signs and forms of cardiac arrest; traditional treatment for CPR; external/internal cardiac massage and administering of drugs during CPR.

Format: VHS NTSC
Running time: 19.15 mins.
Price: US$95.00; other formats available at additional cost
Source: Michigan State University

General Anesthesia in the Dog

Presents physical examination for anaesthesia, checking the anaesthesia system, IV catheter for placement, induction, intubation, maintenance, and recovery from anaesthesia.

Year of production: 1985
Format: VHS NTSC
Running time: 31 mins.
Price: US$71.00
Source: Texas A&M University

Monitoring General Anaesthesia in the Dog and Cat for Veterinary Nurses

This video program describes monitoring in the dog and cat, but not anaesthetics. Nurses are shown how to monitor from initial induction, through maintenance, right to the end of recovery. Simple monitoring aids are shown along with a few of the more sophisticated ones. Intubation in an emergency is demonstrated, but obviously the nurse needs to practice intubation in order to become sufficiently skilled to save lives. The accompanying workbook provides a glossary, questions and answers, and much background data putting monitoring into the broad context of anaesthesia.

Year of production: 1987
Format: VHS PAL
Running time: 40 mins.
Price: £30.00 (excl. VAT and postage)
Source: Royal Veterinary College

 # MODELS, MANNEKINS, SIMULATORS

 ### Advanced Airway 'Jerry' K-9 CPR Mannekin

A full size K-9 mannekin approximating a 60-70 lbs dog, with working lungs and pulse, designed to perform endotracheal placement, compressions, mouth-to-snout resuscitation, splinting and bandaging. It has a realistic airway, and representations of the trachea, oesophagus, and epiglottis, disposable and cleanable parts, and realistic features. Accessories included: carrying case with kneeling pad, endotracheal tube, syringe, brush, 5 disposable lungs and demo leash.

Medium: Mannekin
Price: US$1,395.00 (Item #505)
Note: Additional disposable lungs are available at US$66.00 (packs of 24 - Item #102) or at US$198.00 (packs of 72 - Item #103)
Source: Rescue Critters

 ### Ceeper Dog

A great alternative to 'Jerry', designed to simulate compressions, splinting, and bandaging. It approximates a 40-50 lbs dog and has working lungs and mouth-to-snout capabilities, as well as disposable and cleanable parts. The fur is completely removable for machine washing. Accessories included: carrying bag and 5 disposable lungs.

Medium: Mannekin
Price: US$295.00 (Item #707)
Note: 1. Femoral pulse feature can be added for only an additional $25.00 (Item #708); **2.** Additional disposable lungs are available at US$66.00 (packs of 24 - Item #102) or at US$198.00 (packs of 72 - Item #103) (*CeePeR Dog* uses the same lungs as '*Jerry*')
Source: Rescue Critters

Critical Care 'Fluffy' Cat CPR Mannekin

This realistic full-size cat mannekin has a realistic airway, with representations of trachea, oesophagus, epiglottis, tongue, articulated jaw, and working lungs. She is designed for the CPR or anaesthesia trainee to perform mouth-to-snout rescue breathing and/or endotracheal tube placement and manual ventilation, and chest compressions while appreciating an artificial pulse. She can assist with learning exercises in cat restraint, bandaging, and intravenous access (several vein practice sites). Accessories included: carrying case, artificial training blood, IV reservoir, IV holder, 5 disposable lungs, endotracheal tube, syringe, and grooming brush.

Medium: Mannekin
Price: US$795.00 (Item #210)
Note: 1. Additional disposable lungs are available at US$38.40 (packs of 24 - Item #203) or at US$115.20 (packs of 72 - Item #204) **2.** Additional disposable intermediate training jugular & cephalic veins (good for 1-3 sticks or 1 catheter placement) are available at US$10.00 each (Item #409)
Source: Rescue Critters

 ## Critical Care 'Jerry' K-9 CPR Mannekin

A full size K-9 mannekin approximating a 60-70 lbs dog, which has all the features of the *Advanced Airway 'Jerry' K-9 CPR Mannekin* and of the *K-9 IV Trainer* arm in one 'body', plus jugular vascular access and the ability to aspirate air and fluid from the thoracic cavity to simulate trauma. It features a realistic airway, representations of trachea, oesophagus, and epiglottis, working lungs and artificial pulse, and is designed to perform endotracheal placement, compressions, mouth-to-snout resuscitation, splinting and bandaging. It has disposable and cleanable parts, and realistic features, coming with a bonus item: a full *K-9 IV Trainer* in its own carrying case. Accessories included: carrying case with kneeling pad, endotracheal tube, syringe, brush, 5 disposable lungs and demo leash.

Medium: Mannekin
Price: US$1,995.00 (Item #110)
Note: 1. Additional disposable lungs are available at US$66.00 (packs of 24 - Item #102) or at US$198.00 (packs of 72 - Item #103) **2.** Additional disposable beginner training jugular & cephalic veins (good for 75-100 sticks) are also available at US$10.00 each (Item #408)
Source: Rescue Critters

 ## ECS (Emergency Care Simulator)

Emergency medicine involves quick and confident thinking - decisive action can be the difference between life and death. METI created the *Emergency Care Simulator* (ECS) especially to support emergency care scenarios; the ECS has a broad range of capabilities that empower EMT's, paramedics, and ER clinicians. One key feature the ECS offers is portability, meaning this simulator can open up the classroom to real-life situations. Emergency scenarios don't usually happen in 'ideal' places. Training first responders to cope under any circumstance, in any environment fine-tunes their skills and ultimately saves more lives. The ECS offers much of the same technology as the *HPS (Human Patient Simulator* - see its description for more details), but optimises emergency scenarios to expose students to the most complicated and high-risk situations. The technology allows instructors to reinforce life-saving skills with a whole new level of realism, creating a more confident, sharp-minded first responder.

Medium: Simulator
Price: On request (see website for regional distributors)
Source: METI

 ### 'Fluffy' Cat CPR Mannekin

A realistic cat with working lungs and pulse, designed to perform compressions, mouth-to-snout resuscitation, splinting and bandaging. Has disposable and cleanable parts, and realistic features. Accessories included: carrying case and 5 disposable lungs.

Medium: Mannekin
Price: US$295.00 (Item #202)
Note: Additional disposable lungs are available at US$38.40 (packs of 24 - Item #203) or at US$115.20 (packs of 72 - Item #204)
Source: Rescue Critters

 ### Harvey

Harvey, a Cardiology Patient Simulator (CPS), is a life-size mannekin capable of simulating 27 conditions (2 normal conditions and 25 cardiovascular diseases). Each cardiac condition is integrated with a slide program that can be projected at the simulator's 'bedside'. This program sequentially presents the patient's history and physical examination, laboratory data, medical and surgical treatment options, and information about the pathology and epidemiology of the patient's disease state. The CPS is complete with carotid, brachial, radial and femoral pulses, venous pulsations, precordial movements, respiration, blood pressure and auscultation in the four classic acoustic areas flawlessly reproduced. Adjunctive ECG's, X-rays, and other data are also supplied. Individual students or small groups may learn without an instructor by using the CPS with self-assessment slides or the *UMedic* system (see under SOFTWARE).

Medium: Simulator
Price: US$80,000
Source: University of Miami School of Medicine

HPS (Human Patient Simulator)

The *Human Patient Simulator (HPS)* - a computer-model-driven, full-sized mannekin - delivers hands-on experience in true-to-life scenarios that swiftly change to meet instructors' goals. The ultra sophisticated and highly versatile *HPS* blinks, speaks and breathes, has a heartbeat and a pulse, and accurately mirrors human responses to such procedures as CPR, intravenous medication, intubation, ventilation, and catheterisation. It contains a profound array of intricately programmed systems - cardiovascular, pulmonary, pharmacological, metabolic, genitourinary (male and female), and neurological - which make it an easily controlled teaching laboratory where students can practice again and again. Important features and procedures available include: reactive eyes for neurological assessment, realistic airway, carotid, brachial, radial, femoral, popliteal and pedal pulses, thumb twitch, pneumothorax decompression, independent chest excursion, pericardiocentesis and peritoneal lavage.

Medium: Simulator
Price: On request (see website for regional distributors)
Source: METI

 Intubation Model

In co-operation with the Federal Centre for Health Education in Cologne, Germany, a practice model has been developed which makes it possible to learn how to intubate under realistic conditions. In its design and construction special importance has been attached to natural size relations and anatomical features to develop a functional model. If intubation is performed incorrectly, e.g. too great a pressure is exerted through the laryngoscope on the upper incisors, an acoustic signal sounds. Upon completion of intubation the correct position of the tube can be checked by listening to the respiratory sounds with a stethoscope lateral to the left and right wall of the thorax. The basic model has a separate larynx with removable tongue (in two parts); one part of the lower jaw can be disassembled into 5 parts. Carrying case included. H25 cm, W71 cm, D42 cm, Wt 15.2 kg.

Medium: Mannekin
Price: On request, from regional distributors
Source: Contact Marcus Sommer Somso Modelle for regional distributors (CLA Medien und Lehrmittel catalogue ref. CLA 8)

 'Jerry Jr.' First Aid Trainer

A plush mannekin specifically designed to perform first aid skills needed for Pet First Aid classes. It approximates a dog of under 30 lbs and can simulate compressions, emergency muzzling, splinting, and bandaging. Sold in 4-packs, with carrying bag included. A perfect addition to Rescue Critters' *'Jerry'* and *'Fluffy'* for students to do hands-on training.

Medium: Mannekin
Price: US$210.00 per pack of 4 (Item #303)
Source: Rescue Critters

    ## 'Jerry' K-9 CPR Mannekin

Approximating a 60-70 lbs dog, this mannekin has working lungs designed to perform compressions and mouth-to-snout resuscitation, a working pulse, legs designed to splint and bandage, disposable and cleanable parts, and realistic features. Accessories included: carrying case with kneeling pad, brush, 5 disposable lungs and demo leash.

Medium: Mannekin
Price: US$895.00 (Item #101)
Note: Additional disposable lungs are available at US$66.00 (packs of 24 - Item #102) or at US$198.00 (packs of 72 - Item #103)
Source: Rescue Critters

    ## K-9 Intubation Trainer

K-9 mannekin head mounted on base, realistic airway, representations of trachea, oesophagus, and epiglottis present. Has working lung to determine correct endotracheal placement with pass/fail feature, has disposable and cleanable parts, and realistic features. Accessories included: carrying case, endotracheal tube, syringe.

Medium: Mannekin
Price: US$495.00 (Item #606)
Source: Rescue Critters

    ## PediaSim

Children are not small adults. And the nuances of paediatric care cannot be adequately learned on small mannekins hooked up to adult simulation programs. There are minute but crucial differences that make pediatric medicine uniquely challenging - distinctions in anatomy, reactions to drugs, types of injuries and underlying physical conditions. Just as the *HPS (Human Patient Simulator)* relies on highly precise computer modeling of human physiology and pharmacology, the *PediaSim* operates on the basis of delicately calibrated mathematical equations that mirror the parameters and responses of the young patient. With METI's flexible 'plug-and-play' system design, the *PediaSim* can interface with any HPS model as an accessory, or be purchased as a stand-alone simulator. For more details, see *HPS (Human Patient Simulator)*.

Medium: Simulator
Price: On request (see website for regional distributors)
Source: METI

 Pet First Aid Trainer Kit for Kids

Includes one 'Jerry Jr.' plush mannekin, a basic pet first aid kit with pouch, and the Rescue Critters' 'Pet First Aid for Kids' book. This 28-page book was written with kids in mind and is suitable for ages 8 and over. It covers safety, preparedness, CPR, rescue breathing, and basic pet first aid. Children and adults are both highly encouraged to participate learning pet first aid skills together. Carrying case included.

Medium: Mannekin
Price: US$59.95 (Item #1020)
Source: Rescue Critters

 Sanitary CPR Dog

The CPR Dog comes in two versions, Basic and Advanced, both including a soft carrying case, 6 muzzles, 10 nosepieces with a one-way valve, and one lower disposable airway. The muzzles may be disinfected and reused, while the nosepieces and lower airways are disposable. In addition to practice in assisted breathing, students may practice the appropriate rate, pressure, and position of cardiac massage, and co-ordinate the respiratory and cardiovascular functions. For more advanced training, an IV can be established as well as placement of an endotrachial tube. The Advanced CPR Dog is connected to a small box that shows a green light when the correct ventilation pressure is applied; a blue light indicates correct position for cardiac massage, a white light indicates correct pressures, and an audible beep and a red light indicates excessive pressure. A visible chest rise appears when correct ventilations are applied.

Medium: Mannekin
Price: US$595.00 (Basic Sanitary CPR Dog); US$995.00 (Advanced Sanitary CPR Dog); US$47.25 (pack of 6 replacement muzzles); US$35.00 (pack of 10 disposable lower airway); US$75.00 (pack of 10 disposable nosepieces)
Source: Nasco

 Veterinary Intubation Simulator

This is a mannekin of the head and neck of a dog in dorsal recumbency; it is silicon rubber built at scale 1:1 by moulding on the cadaver of an adult Doberman Pinscher. The core of the simulator is made from polyurethane foam. The use of silicon rubber ensures stability and flexibility of flews, tongue, soft palate, and epiglottis as well as their return to original shape. The size of the simulator was chosen for didactic reasons, because the dimensions of giant breeds were seen as non-representative due to the perceived ease of their intubation. Special attention was focussed on realistic quality of reproduction. Designed to improve teaching and training of students in practising intratracheal intubation and to diminish avoidable encumbrance of patients in veterinary curriculum, this model offers the possibility to repeat anatomical knowledge without waste of time, to practice intratracheal intubation under supervision with the realistic possibility to fail and to simulate different positions of epiglottis and soft palate as well.

Medium: Mannekin
Price: €3,000.00
Source: Prof. Wolfgang Künzel (University of Veterinary Medicine Vienna, Austria)

 WORLD WIDE WEB

 RHYTHM 2000

http://www.anesoft.com/rhythm/rhythm.html
Anesoft Corporation, USA

2. Anatomy

SOFTWARE

Anatomia Canis

This multimedia program comes in two parts. *Part I: Extremitas cranialis* contains 45 mins. of video accompanied by sound recording, and approximately 200 stills with detailed labels displaying anatomical information about the anatomical dissection of the dog's forelimb. *Part II: Extremitas caudalis* details the dissection of the dog's hind limb.

Language: Hungarian, English, German
Year of production: 1999
Medium: CD-ROM
System requirements: Windows 95/98, MPEG1 player, DirectX 7; Pentium I with 233 MHz processor (Pentium II with 450 MHz processor recommended), 32 MB RAM, SVGA (800 x 600, colour 24-bit), 12X CD-ROM drive, soundcard, video drive
Price: €60.00 (whole program, parts I and II)
Source: Kisállatklinika

Annelids

This program explores the biology and natural history of segmented worms, presenting features that annelids share with all animals as well as distinctive characteristics found only in phylum *Annelida*. This interactive overview of the three largest annelid classes teaches students the importance of oligochaetes, the different body plans of polychaetes, and the actual medical uses of leeches.

Medium: CD-ROM
System requirements: Windows 95 with Pentium processor and 16 MB RAM; Macintosh OS 7.5.1 with 12 MB RAM
Price: US$129.95
Source: CyberEd; PLATO Learning (UK)

Arthropods

Why can tiny ants carry such large objects? *Arthropods* provides answers to students' major questions about insects, spiders, crustaceans, and other organisms with jointed legs. Arthropods are the most diverse animals on the planet in terms of both species diversity and sheer numbers. Full-colour photographs, detailed illustrations, and enlightening animations depict the biology of these unique and fascinating animals.

Medium: CD-ROM
System requirements: Windows 95 with Pentium processor and 16 MB RAM; Macintosh OS 7.5.1 with 12 MB RAM
Price: US$129.95
Source: CyberEd; PLATO Learning (UK)

 BioLab: Frog

An engaging, interactive lab which provides vivid coverage of frog external and internal anatomy. Students perform virtual dissections on-screen, guided by a series of questions to ensure their understanding. As the student dissects the frog, the software identifies and explains the function of each internal organ. Includes virtual labs on breathing rate, the alimentary canal, heart rate and muscle contraction. Also available as part of the *BioLab Virtual Lab Series Package* from Carolina Biological Supply.

Medium: CD-ROM
System requirements: Windows 95, Macintosh OS 7.5, or later
Price: Carolina Biological Supply: US$49.00 (single CD-ROM), US$209.00 (lab pack of 5), US$369.00 (lab pack of 10), US$899.00 (lab pack of 30); Neo/Sci: US$59.95 (single CD-ROM), US$199.95 (lab pack of 5)
Source: Carolina Biological Supply; Neo/Sci

 BioLab: Invertebrates

A series of interactive, virtual dissection labs which provide detailed anatomical coverage of 3 key invertebrates: earthworm, crayfish and starfish. Students are guided through each lab with a series of questions to ensure their comprehension. Includes *Survey of Invertebrates*, with images and taxonomy of several additional specimens, as well as an interactive *Invertebrate Comparison*. Also available as part of the *BioLab Virtual Lab Series Package* from Carolina Biological Supply.

Medium: CD-ROM
System requirements: Windows 95, Macintosh OS 7.5, or later
Price: Carolina Biological Supply: US$49.00 (single CD-ROM), US$209.00 (lab pack of 5), US$369.00 (lab pack of 10), US$899.00 (lab pack of 30); Neo/Sci: US$59.95 (single CD-ROM), US$199.95 (lab pack of 5)
Source: Carolina Biological Supply; Neo/Sci

Biolab: Pig

A realistic software which provides an in-depth interactive dissection of the foetal pig. It includes extensive coverage of the digestive, respiratory, urogenital, endocrine and skeletal systems. Also includes a series of mini-labs providing thorough coverage of the effects of exercise on carbon dioxide levels and heart rate, muscle contraction, kidney function and hormone balance. Also available as part of the *BioLab Virtual Lab Series Package* from Carolina Biological Supply.

Medium: CD-ROM
System requirements: Windows 95, Macintosh OS 7.5, or later
Price: Carolina Biological Supply: US$49.00 (single CD-ROM), US$209.00 (lab pack of 5), US$369.00 (lab pack of 10), US$899.00 (lab pack of 30); Neo/Sci: US$59.95 (single CD-ROM), US$199.95 (lab pack of 5)
Source: Carolina Biological Supply; Neo/Sci

 Biolab Virtual Lab Series Package

Special package including all 4 programs in the *BioLab* series - *BioLab Pig*; *BioLab Frog*; *BioLab Invertebrates*; and *BioLab Fly* (see descriptions under individual titles).

Medium: CD-ROM
System requirements: Windows 95, Macintosh OS 7.5, or later
Price: US$147.00 (individual package); US$627.00 (lab pack of 5); US$1,107.00 (lab pack of 10); US$2,697.00 (lab pack of 30)
Source: Carolina Biological Supply

 [The] Biology of Frogs

This program is packed with information on frogs - from their diversity and life cycles to their anatomy and physiology. Using engaging graphics, animations, stereo sound and the 3D frog named Figaro, it features an interactive dissection unit which covers external anatomy, internal organs, skeletal system, muscular system, and nervous system, as well as units on frog ecology, evolution, and conservation. Includes a glossary of terms and a testing section that gives feedback and explanations of answers.

Year of production: last revision 1999
Medium: CD-ROM
System requirements: Windows only - Win95/98/NT4; Pentium I 133 MHz, 32 MB RAM, 24X CD-ROM drive
Price: US$64.95
Source: Carolina Biological Supply

Bird Anatomy II - Surface Anatomy of Birds

This program is a multimedia approach to the study of the biology, behaviour, flight, and anatomical structure of birds, that works interactively with the laser videodisc *Encyclopedia of Animals, Volume 4, Birds 1* from Pioneer Electronics (USA). Incorporating stunning graphics, animations, and bird sounds, along with clear, concise text, the stack explains complex anatomical information by linking bird anatomy to the explanatory text and video segments of actual bird behaviour in the field. This approach is particularly effective when applied to dynamic concepts such as flight, where detailed anatomical drawings of wing structures are linked to the video segment showing birds in flight.

Year of production: 1993
Medium: 3.5" disk; laser videodisc
System requirements: Macintosh; laser videodisc player and video monitor (for laser videodisc)
Price: US$85.00 (four 3.5" disks and user's guide); US$99.95 (Pioneer laser videodisc)
Note: The distribution of the laser videodisc from Pioneer Electronics (USA) is limited to the USA; at the time of publication it is still in stock but production has ceased, and there are no plans to migrate its content to DVD format
Source: Yale University Press; Pioneer Electronics (USA) (for laser videodisc)

Birds: Characteristics & Adaptations

More than a program full of pretty pictures, this CD-ROM explores the evolution, structure, and adaptations of birds in an extensive and insightful manner. Excellent narratives and sound effects that will keep the viewer's interest are incorporated with numerous photographs, drawings, detailed illustrations and animations.

Medium: CD-ROM
System requirements: Windows 95 with Pentium processor and 16 MB RAM; Macintosh OS 7.5.1 with 12 MB RAM
Price: US$89.95 (+ US$22.49 upgrade)
Source: CyberEd; PLATO Learning (UK)

CALVE

CALVE (Computer Aided Learning in Veterinary Education) is a project comprising 40 interactive programs, developed at Massey University, New Zealand, to assist the learning of veterinary anatomy. These programs have mostly been created in HyperCard and SuperCard and are only available for use on the Macintosh platform. Titles available include:

Anatomy and Histology:
- *Anatomy Q on CUE.* Quiz template with flexible format, using pictures and digital movies. Ten questions on each of: Rodents and lagomorphs; Equine larynx; Anatomy of the trout;

Equine abdominal organs; Ruminant nose and olfaction; Quadrupedal mechanics; Canine oropharynx using endoscopy; Sheep foetal membranes; Bovine female reproductive organs; Canine stomach, using fluoroscopy; The ear, using museum models; Cat features; Horse hoof.

- *Canine Cardiography*. A fluoroscopic movie using intravascular contrast material and the use of a museum vascular cast.
- *Cow's Teats*. Histology of the papillary duct.
- *Cyberbrain*. Digital movies and quizzes from cyberspace about the brain of animals.
- *Digital Navigator*. Clinical and functional anatomy of the distal forelimb of the horse.
- *Discovering Bones*. An atlas of bone structure and growth.
- *Gracilis, the Racing Greyhound*. Topographical and clinical anatomy of the musculoskeletal system.
- *Head to Head*. Identification of structures in the heads of the horse, ox and dog. Quizzes.
- *HorseTrek*. Exploring the upper digestive and respiratory systems of the horse.
- *Inguinal Canal of the Horse*. The layers of the abdominal wall.
- *Joint Structure*. General features, mechanics and histology of the synovial joint.
- *Klikakat*. The only cat ever to be controlled by a mouse. Topographical views of feline anatomy.
- *Lymph Trails*. An animated demonstration of lymph structures and pathways in the dog.
- *Muscles of the Bovine Carcass*. Three-dimensional locations of muscles in export cuts.
- *Pig Head Tomography*. Interactive magnetic resonance imaging.
- *Ramifications*. Topography, clinical aspects and histology of the reproductive tract of the ram.
- *Right on the Head*. NMR and X-ray CT images of the head of dog and cat, with interpretation.
- *Scrotocat*. A gross and histological view of the wall of the scrotum and its contents.
- *Sheepscan*. X-ray computed tomography of the cranial abdominal region.
- *Skeledog Axial*. Anatomy and disorders of the vertebrae and ribs.
- *Skeledog Joints*. The different limb joints of the dog in diagrams and fluoroscopic movies.
- *Skeledog Limbs*. Anatomy of the limb bones of the dog.
- *Topocow*. Exploring the depths of the bovine abdomen in 3D.
- *Topodog*. Canine topographical anatomy quizzes.
- *Topohen*. Avian topographical and postmortem anatomy quizzes.
- *Toposheep*. Anatomy of thoracic and abdominal organs with fluoroscopic and virtual reality movies.
- *Vertebrae!* General features, regional differences and development.

Embryology:

- *Embryology Part 1*. The first 50 days of the embryonic pig.
- *Embryology Part 2*. The folding of the trilaminar embryonic disk.
- *Embryology Part 3*. Anatomy of a 6 mm pig embryo, using histological sections.
- *Morphogenic Processes*. Animations to show cellular interactions in development.
- *Spot the Difference*. Differentiation of male and female tracts.
- *Tutorials in Embryology*. 14 topics covering much of a veterinary embryology course, with speech and animations, created in Audiograph

Physiology:

- *Alive and Beating*. Studying the heart of the normal living dog with several clinical imaging methods.
- *Antlers*. Animation of the annual cycle of the fastest growing mammalian organ.
- *Bovicycle*. Ovarian blood flow, hormones and cyclical changes in the cow.
- *Muscles, Molecules and Movement*. Anatomy and mechanics of muscle tissue.
- *SimPharlap*. Animated gaits of the horse.

Medium: CD-ROM (under production)
System requirements: Macintosh OS only - Power Macintosh
Price: €20.00 (the whole series on one CD-ROM)
Source: Prof. Alexander S. Davies (Massey University, New Zealand)

[The] Canine Abdomen

This course is designed for veterinary students, nurses and clinicians who wish to gain a greater understanding of the anatomy of the canine abdomen. The program describes the abdominal wall, including its blood and nerve supply. It shows the embryological development of the abdominal organs and explains the anatomical relationships and blood supply of the major organs and structures. The material is presented using interactive questions, animations and high quality photographs.

Year of production: 1999
Medium: CD-ROM
System requirements: Windows only - Win95 and later; 16 MB RAM, 64k colour display
Price: £58.00; for departmental licence please contact CLIVE. Free site licence available to Associate Members of CLIVE consortium
Source: CLIVE. Available for purchase from Scottish Knowledge

Canine Osteology: An Interactive Atlas and Quiz

This is an interactive computer program principally designed for teaching osteology of the canine to first year veterinary students. The program presents full colour digital images of the canine skeleton and a list of structures present in each image. Using a mouse, listed structures may be identified by graphic highlighting. Major articulations of the skeleton are presented and supplemented with digitised radiographic images. Selected clinical conditions involving bones and joints are also included. *Canine Osteology Quiz* is a companion program which allows users to test their proficiency in canine osteology. The quiz uses digitised photographic images to randomly generate test questions on various anatomic structures.

Language: English; Spanish translation under production
Medium: CD-ROM
System requirements: Any Macintosh; Windows version under production
Price: US$65.00
Source: University of California (UC Davis)

When contacting producers and distributors,
please cite *from Guinea Pig to Computer Mouse*

Cat Dissection Laboratory

Every major system of the cat (skeletal, muscular, nervous, digestive, circulatory, reproductive, respiratory and more) is presented in 80 brilliant dissections, each micro-surgically prepared to show details beyond the capabilities of even the most talented student. Every 3D image shows true anatomical relationships better than using models or computer simulations. The program has a lecture mode, allowing you to guide your class; a tutorial mode, for the student that wants study on their own; and a quiz mode, allowing you to give real Lab Practical type exams without the inconvenience and expense.

Language: English, Spanish
Medium: CD-ROM
System requirements: Windows only; Windows 95/98/ME/NT/2000; Pentium processor, 16 MB RAM, 1024 x 768 resolution SVGA colour monitor, 24-bit colour, minimum 2 MB of video memory, soundcard, speakers
Note: 1. In order to view the 3D features of this program, the NEOTEK Base System is required. This includes: a video processor (to be placed between the computer and the monitor) and power supply, a pair of liquid crystal glasses, a sampler CD with excerpts from some of the most popular NEOTEK modules, a user manual and installation guide; **2.** Two similar programs from NEOTEK - *DogLab* and *HorseLab* - are currently under production
Price: US$85.00 (CD-ROM); $295.00 (Base System); US$95.00 (extra pair of liquid crystal glasses); US$850.00 (lab pack of 10 extra pairs of liquid crystal glasses); US$395.00 (wireless upgrade kit); US$195.00 (extra pair of wireless glasses); US$1,590.00 (lab pack of 10 extra pairs of wireless glasses)
Source: NEOTEK

 CatWorks

This highly interactive program was designed for the advanced life science student who needs detailed experience in mammal dissection. It offers an opportunity to perform exciting, highly accurate, electronic dissections of the common house cat. Through the use of special cursors and buttons, the user is able to 'dissect' nearly all areas of the cat's anatomy. Digitised images and real-life schematics, as well as QuickTime movies showing selected portions of actual dissections along with voice descriptions of the procedures being performed, present the user with a wide range of information that is keyed to a glossary with pronunciations, on-line quizzes, lab practicals and in-depth histology sections.

Medium: CD-ROM
System requirements: Windows 9x/NT/2000/XP, Macintosh PPC; 32 MB RAM
Price: US$79.95 (individual copies); US$159.95 (5 user licence); US$559.95 (10 user licence)
Source: Science Works

When contacting producers and distributors, please cite *from Guinea Pig to Computer Mouse*

Cnidarians

Cnidarians are an ancient yet successful group of animals that include colourful corals, strange sea anemones, and elegant jellyfish. Detailed graphics and a comprehensive narration allow students to discover the unique characteristics of this phylum. Creative animations and illustrations engage students to learn about the unusual strategies the members of this phylum use to eat, move, reproduce, and survive. Colourful interactive modules give students a chance to review their knowledge of Cnidarians in a stimulating manner.

Medium: CD-ROM
System requirements: Windows 95 with Pentium processor and 16 MB RAM; Mac OS 7.5.1 with 12 MB RAM
Price: US$129.95
Source: CyberEd; PLATO Learning (UK)

Comparative Anatomy: Mammals, Birds and Fish

This software includes: introduction, organisation of the organism, orientation to cells, tissues and organs, musculoskeletal system, circulatory system, nervous system, integumentary system, urinary system, digestive system, respiratory system, reproductive system.

Medium: CD-ROM
System requirements: Windows 95 or later, with Pentium processor; Macintosh Power with 24 MB RAM; thousands of colours or greater, 800 x 600 screen resolution
Price: US$65.00
Source: University of California (UC Davis)

CompuSeries

The *Compu* series is a set of 6 interactive menu-driven programs covering the rat, the frog, the rabbit, the pigeon, the cockroach and the earthworm. Each simulates the process of dissection of the animal concerned but can also be used as a complete teaching aid. They feature experiments, dissection, detailed examination and animated sequences to explain the working of organs. The subject matter is provided in text form with extended visual presentations. The programs simulate the process of dissecting a prepared specimen, including the choice of organ for dissection, location of the dissection point, the act of dissecting the organ, and transfer to the tray for detailed examination/observation of the animated sequence to study the function of the organ.

Language: English; *Compurat* and *Compufrog* also available in German and French
Medium: Sent on request via e-mail
System requirements: MS-DOS
Price: Freeware; however, donations are welcome to help upgrade the programs in the series
Source: Blue Cross of India

DigiDiss

A series of interactive multimedia programs developed by the Zoology Department of Göteborg University and marketed by DigiDiss Education AB. The company aims to offer a broad spectrum of programs for digital dissection of various animals - invertebrates, amphibians, mammals and birds. The *DigiDiss* modules use interactive simulation and video illustration which pedagogically demonstrate the dissection process step by step. They include animations of the heart, kidney and liver, as well as 3D models of the whole animal, the skeleton and the heart. Information on phylogeny, taxonomy and the proper use of dissection tools is also presented. The programs currently available are: *Digital Rat, Dissection of the Shark, Dissection of the Crayfish*. Also available is a program describing the fresh water fishes in Sweden and their natural habitat, with a Histology module which illustrates and explains the 40 histological specimens included in the basic zoology course at Göteborg University. Other programs, each presenting a separate animal, are under production.

Language: Swedish, English
Medium: CD-ROM
System requirements: Windows 95/98/NT/2000, Macintosh OS up to 9.1
Price: each program SEK 2,600.00 / €280.00 / US$271.00 (incl. VAT, for 15 licences)
Source: DigiDiss Education AB

 Digital Frog 2

This fully interactive program integrates a complete spectrum of multimedia technologies - full-motion (and full-screen) video, animation, sounds, narration, in-depth text and still images - to provide students with an excellent tool for learning about frog anatomy, physiology and ecology. The 'Dissection' module allows students to perform an entire frog dissection. They can make cuts with a 'digital scalpel' and then see the actual cuts with full-screen videos. The 'Anatomy' module, with its animation, movies, photographs and in-depth text, seamlessly linked to the dissection, provides a close-at-hand research as students work through the dissection. At the same time, the detailed animations (including 3D) and interactions allow students to see how the frog's body works - from blood pumping through the heart, to joints that can be built up and moved by the user. Human anatomy comparisons highlight differences between frogs and humans. The 'Ecology' section rounds out the educational experience by giving students insight into species diversity, frog calls, behaviour and the life cycle. The program also has an integrated dictionary with more than 3,000 definitions and over 700 pronunciations.

Medium: CD-ROM
Year of production: 2001
System requirements: Windows 95/98/NT, with Pentium I 180 MHz processor (Pentium II recommended), 32 MB RAM, 16-bit colour monitor; Macintosh OS 8.6 with Power PC 180 MHz, 20 MB RAM; QuickTime 4; sound card recommended

Price: US$85.00 (Home Version - CD only); US$99.00 (Home Schooling Edition - Home Version with workbook); US$155.00 (Single Educational Version - 1 CD); US$170.00 (Single Educational Version with workbook); US$425.00 (lab pack Educational Version - 5 CDs and workbook); US$599.00 (lab pack of 10); US$699.00 (lab pack of 15); US$899.00 (lab pack of 30); US$599.00 (Network of 10); US$899.00 (Building Site Licence - unlimited). Special District price offers available on the website
Source: Digital Frog International

Dissections CD-ROMs

A series of 6 CD-ROMs exploring the anatomy, the habits and the habitat of 6 animals commonly used for dissection - the frog, the crayfish, the perch, the grasshopper, the starfish, and the earthworm. Full-screen photographs, movies, and sound enable students to view organisms first hand without actually dissecting them. Users will discover how these creatures live in their respective environments and how their bodies help them survive. The programs also show instructionally-sound dissection procedures as they explore each animal's systems. The *External Anatomy* module gives details about each creature's body and appendages. The *Internal Anatomy* module covers systems such as the digestive, circulatory, nervous, and reproductive, as well as individual organs.

Medium: CD-ROM
System requirements: Windows (all versions); Macintosh OS 7.1 and above, with 5 MB RAM
Price: US$25.00 (each title, single user); US$200.00 (lab pack of 10 copies of an individual title); US$140.00 (complete set of 6 titles); US$1,200.00 (lab pack of 10 complete sets)
Source: CLEARVUE/eav

DissectionWorks

This innovative package of 5 programs was developed by master science teachers taking advantage of the latest technology, and represents a truly workable alternative to classroom dissection. The series includes 5 commonly studied animals: the crayfish, the earthworm, the perch, the frog and the foetal pig. Each animal (program) contains detailed schematics of the major body systems, information on organ function and structure, and review questions. Multimedia CD-ROM versions offer digital video and audio segments. Digitised photos of real animals with detailed diagrams give this program the 'feel' that many science teachers are looking for. The students perform all aspects of dissection, from pinning the specimen to a dissection tray, to removing and labeling parts.

Medium: CD-ROM
System requirements: Windows 9x/NT/2000/XP, Macintosh PPC; 32 MB RAM
Price: Individual programs on CD-ROM - US$59.95 (single user), US$229.95 (5 user licence), US$399.95 (10 user licence); complete set of 5 programs on one CD-ROM (Deluxe version) - US$199.95 (single user), US$799.95 (5 user licence), US$1,399.95 (10 user licence)
Source: Science Works

DryLab³ᴰ Crayfish

Eight chapters covering each system and including 68 virtual dissections for a basic but complete coverage of this specimen. Limb regeneration, moulting and the unique mating behaviour of the crayfish are presented in fine detail. The program contains an interactive 2D dissection, a non-interactive 2D dissection video, 3D pictures, and 3D quizzes. The 3D portion can be operated in tutorial mode with narration, or lecture mode with the teacher providing the narrative. Includes Quiz Mode for Lab Practical type exams.

Language: English; translations into Spanish, French and German under production
Medium: CD-ROM. See also *DryLab*^Web *Dissections On-Line* under WORLD WIDE WEB
System requirements: Windows only; Windows 95/98/ME/NT/2000; Pentium processor, 16 MB RAM, 1024 x 768 resolution SVGA colour monitor, 24-bit colour, minimum 2 MB of video memory, soundcard, speakers
Note: 1: In order to view the 3D features of this program, the NEOTEK *Base System* is required. This includes: a video processor (to be placed between the computer and the monitor) and power supply, a pair of liquid crystal glasses, a sampler CD with excerpts from some of the most popular NEOTEK modules, a user manual and installation guide; **2:** the original 2D editable version of this program (*DryLab*^Plus *Crayfish*), for use without the NEOTEK *Base System*, is produced by Duncan Software and distributed by Tangent Scientific
Price: US$149.00 (CD-ROM); $295.00 (*Base System*); US$95.00 (extra pair of liquid crystal glasses); US$850.00 (lab pack of 10 extra pairs of liquid crystal glasses); US$395.00 (wireless upgrade kit); US$195.00 (extra pair of wireless glasses); US$1,590.00 (lab pack of 10 extra pairs of wireless glasses)
Source: NEOTEK

 DryLab³ᴰ Earthworm

Eight chapters presenting the various features of an earthworm from a general overview to the microscopic detail. Also showing the difficult-to-see movement of the lateral setae and illustrating its peristaltic movement. The program contains an interactive 2D dissection, a non-interactive 2D dissection video, 3D pictures, and 3D quizzes. The 3D portion can be operated in tutorial mode with narration or lecture mode with the teacher providing the narrative. Includes Quiz Mode for Lab Practical type exams.

Language: English; translations into Spanish, French and German under production
Medium: CD-ROM. See also *DryLab*^Web *Dissections On-Line* under WORLD WIDE WEB
System requirements: See under *DryLab*³ᴰ *Crayfish*
Price: US$149.00. See also under *DryLab*³ᴰ *Crayfish*
Note: See under *DryLab*³ᴰ *Crayfish*
Source: NEOTEK

When contacting producers and distributors,
please cite *from Guinea Pig to Computer Mouse*

DryLab³ᴰ Fetal Pig

Ten chapters covering each major anatomical system and totaling 100 virtual dissection images. Shows difficult procedures such as the nervous system dissection and features specimens at eight different stages of gestation. Inlcudes an interactive 2D dissection, a non-interactive 2D dissection video, 3D pictures, and 3D quizzes. The 3D portion can be operated in tutorial mode with narration or lecture mode with the teacher providing the narrative. Includes Quiz Mode for Lab Practical type exams.

Language: English; translations into Spanish, French and German under production
Medium: CD-ROM. See also *DryLab^Web Dissections On-Line* under World wide web
System requirements: See under *DryLab³ᴰ Crayfish*
Price: US$149.00. See also under *DryLab³ᴰ Crayfish*
Note: See under *DryLab³ᴰ Crayfish*
Source: NEOTEK

DryLab³ᴰ Frog

Eight chapters and 95 virtual dissections cover the frog from egg to adult, male and female. Contains an interactive 2D dissection, a non-interactive 2D dissection video, 3D pictures, and 3D quizzes. The 3D portion can be operated in tutorial mode with narration or lecture mode with the teacher providing the narrative. Includes Quiz Mode for Lab Practical type exams.

Language: English; translations into Spanish, French and German under production
Medium: CD-ROM. See also *DryLab^Web Dissections On-Line* under World wide web
System requirements: See under *DryLab³ᴰ Crayfish*
Price: US$149.00. See also under *DryLab³ᴰ Crayfish*
Note: See under *DryLab³ᴰ Crayfish*
Source: NEOTEK

DryLab³ᴰ Perch

Eight chapters covering each anatomical system, as well as functional aspects such as mobility, buoyancy and predator protection. Includes 65 virtual dissection images providing for a traditional approach to this specimen, an interactive 2D dissection, a non-interactive 2D dissection video, 3D pictures, and 3D quizzes. The 3D portion can be operated in tutorial mode with narration or lecture mode with the teacher providing the narrative. Includes Quiz Mode for Lab Practical type exams.

Language: English; translations into Spanish, French and German under production
Medium: CD-ROM. See also *DryLab^Web Dissections On-Line* under World wide web
System requirements: See under *DryLab³ᴰ Crayfish*
Price: US$149.00. See also under *DryLab³ᴰ Crayfish*

Note: See under *DryLab³ᴰ Crayfish*
Source: NEOTEK

DryLab³ᴰ Rat

Nine chapters covering the external and internal anatomy of the rat - male, female, and pregnant female - as well as the differences between adult and foetal skeletal systems. Over 70 virtual 2D interactive and non-interactive dissection pictures and video, 3D rotating views of the appendix, stomach, lungs and heart, and 3D quizzes. The 3D portion can be operated in tutorial mode with narration or lecture mode with the teacher providing the narrative. Includes Quiz Mode for Lab Practical type exams.

Language: English; translations into Spanish, French and German under production
Medium: CD-ROM. See also *DryLab^Web Dissections On-Line* under WORLD WIDE WEB
System requirements: See under *DryLab³ᴰ Crayfish*
Price: US$149.00. See also under *DryLab³ᴰ Crayfish*
Note: See under *DryLab³ᴰ Crayfish*
Source: NEOTEK

DryLab^Plus Crayfish

Using full-colour, high-resolution images, full-motion video, sound, text and an easy-to-use, flexible interface, this program gives students the opportunity to study both the appendages and the internal anatomy of the crayfish without having to put on gloves. They can choose various views of a specimen. Each picture is accompanied by teacher's notes, anatomical features are highlighted, and full-motion videos offer detailed insight into difficult to show concepts or topics. Once the student has mastered the anatomical features, they can move on to the interactive dissection, where they must choose the correct instrument for each step and then perform all of the steps necessary in proper sequence. The crayfish serves as an excellent example to show just what is meant by the term homologous organs. Includes a comprehensive on-line 13-step dissection, over 50 high-resolution, reproducible images and almost 200 questions. The content (photos, movies, test questions, music, pronunciations, and text) can be edited by the teacher.

Medium: CD-ROM. See also *DryLab^Web Dissections On-Line* under WORLD WIDE WEB
System requirements: Windows only (all versions); 486/33 MHz processor or better; 16 MB RAM; sound card 16-bit recommended
Price: US$125.00 (single); US$249.00 (pack of 5); US$449.00 (pack of 10)
Note: A full 3D version of this program (*DryLab³ᴰ Crayfish*) is produced and distributed by NEOTEK
Source: Tangent Scientific

DryLab^Plus Earthworm

Study both the external and internal anatomy of the earthworm from a general 'overview' right down to microscopic detail of each system. Watch videos of difficult to see concepts like the movement of the lateral setae, the peristaltic movement of the worm or the surprisingly common invasion of a circulatory or excretory parasite. Participate in an interactive 9 step dissection. Includes over 90 images, slides, diagrams and more than 500 questions. For more general features see *DryLab^Plus Crayfish*.

Medium: CD-ROM. See also *DryLab^Web Dissections On-Line* under WORLD WIDE WEB
System requirements: Windows only (all versions); 486/33 MHz processor or better; 16 MB RAM; sound card 16-bit recommended
Price: US$125.00 (single); US$249.00 (pack of 5); US$449.00 (pack of 10)
Note: A full 3D version of this program (*DryLab^3D Earthworm*) is produced and distributed by NEOTEK
Source: Tangent Scientific

DryLab^Plus Fetal Pig

An expert dissection thoroughly investigates the complex internal and external anatomy of the foetal pig. Difficult dissections like the nervous system are here in full view - up close and without the fumes - as well as detailed diagrams, slides and pictures (over 100) of specimens at 8 different stages of gestation. Also includes over 400 questions. For more general features see *DryLab^Plus Crayfish*.

Medium: CD-ROM. See also *DryLab^Web Dissections On-Line* under WORLD WIDE WEB
System requirements: Windows only (all versions); 486/33 MHz processor or better; 16 MB RAM; sound card 16-bit recommended
Price: US$125.00 (single); US$249.00 (pack of 5); US$449.00 (pack of 10)
Note: A full 3D version of this program (*DryLab^3D Fetal Pig*) is produced and distributed by NEOTEK
Source: Tangent Scientific

DryLab^Plus Frog

An exciting investigative journey using over 100 incredible high-resolution photographs, comprehensive illustrations, complete interactive dissection video, sound and text. After mastering the external features of the frog, students will then move on to study the circulatory, digestive, muscular, nervous, respiratory, skeletal and urogenital systems. They can see frog development from a 1-hour old fertilised egg to a young frog using an incredible morphing movie, study the lens and pupil of the eye with extraordinary clarity or compare the male and female urogenital system in brilliant detail. For more general features see *DryLab^Plus Crayfish*.

Medium: CD-ROM. See also *DryLab*^{Web} *Dissections On-Line* under WORLD WIDE WEB
System requirements: Windows only (all versions); 486/33 MHz processor or better; 16 MB RAM; sound card 16-bit recommended
Price: US$125.00 (single); US$249.00 (pack of 5); US$449.00 (pack of 10)
Note: A full 3D version of this program (*DryLab*^{3D} *Frog*) is produced and distributed by NEOTEK
Source: Tangent Scientific

DryLab^{Plus} Perch

More than 50 high-resolution images and outstanding videos offer students a comprehensive look at the external and internal features of this bony fish. Demonstrates such things as mobility, buoyancy and protection as students make their way through the 15-step dissection. Approximately 200 questions are included. For more general features see *DryLab*^{Plus} *Crayfish*.

Medium: CD-ROM. See also *DryLab*^{Web} *Dissections On-Line* under WORLD WIDE WEB
System requirements: Windows only (all versions); 486/33 MHz processor or better; 16 MB RAM; sound card 16-bit recommended
Price: US$125.00 (single); US$249.00 (pack of 5); US$449.00 (pack of 10)
Note: A full 3D version of this program (*DryLab*^{3D} *Perch*) is produced and distributed by NEOTEK
Source: Tangent Scientific

DryLab^{Plus} Rat

Male, female and pregnant female are studied in this comprehensive look at the internal and external anatomy of the rat, including a close look at the adult and foetal skeletal systems. A simple, easy to use interface incorporates over 130 pictures and diagrams, and approximately 500 questions. Full motion video enhances the step by step dissection (over 35 steps) and provides a 3D look at the appendix, stomach, lungs and heart. For more general features see *DryLab*^{Plus} *Crayfish*.

Medium: CD-ROM. See also *DryLab*^{Web} *Dissections On-Line* under WORLD WIDE WEB
System requirements: Windows only (all versions); 486/33 MHz processor or better; 16 MB RAM; sound card 16-bit recommended
Price: US$125.00 (single); US$249.00 (pack of 5); US$449.00 (pack of 10)
Note: A full 3D version of this program (*DryLab*^{3D} *Rat*) is produced and distributed by NEOTEK
Source: Tangent Scientific

[The] Earthworm

The Earthworm introduces the anatomical structures and functions of the common earthworm - the perfect start to an understanding of invertebrate anatomy. Topics cover: digestive, nervous, circulatory and reproductive systems. A cross-sectional view is provided. Activities include identifying parts of the earthworm represented by computer graphics, referencing a database to find information, and answering questions in a multiple choice quiz. A Teacher's Guide provides additional activities.

Medium: CD-ROM
System requirements: DOS, Windows, Macintosh
Price: US$59.95 (single user); US$129.95 (lab pack of 5); US$279.95 (lab pack of 15); US$429.95 (lab pack of 25); US$595.95 (building licence)
Source: Ventura Educational Systems

Earthworm Dissection

This audiovisual software provides a detailed review of the earthworm's digestive, circulatory, excretory, nervous and reproductive systems. It combines graphic video of the earthworm in its natural habitat with vivid dissection footage featuring the circular and longitudinal muscles in action. Stimulating colour animation depicts even hard-to-see anatomical details. Also includes a self test for assessment and an illuminating trivia section.

Medium: CD-ROM
System requirements: Windows 95 or later, PowerMac 7.5 or later; 16 MB RAM
Price: US$69.95 (single); US$314.95 (lab pack of 5)
Source: Neo/Sci

Equine Osteology: An Interactive Atlas and Quiz

An interactive computer program principally designed for teaching the osteology of the equine thoracic and pelvic limbs to first year veterinary students. The program presents full colour digital images of the equine appendicular skeleton and a list of structures present in each image. Using a mouse, listed structures may be identified by graphic highlighting. Major articulations of the equine appendicular skeleton are presented and supplemented with digitised radiographic images. *Equine Osteology: A Quiz on the Thoracic and Pelvic Limbs* is a companion program which allows students to test their proficiency in equine limb osteology. The quiz uses digitised photographic images to randomly generate test questions on various anatomical structures.

Medium: CD-ROM
System requirements: Macintosh only
Price: US$65.00
Source: University of California (UC Davis)

[The] Fetal Pig

This program provides a comprehensive investigation of anatomical structures and biological functions common to mammals, making an excellent alternative to dissection. Textual information is dynamically linked to detailed, colourful graphics and digitally photographed images. Activities include an identification game, an anatomical probe and multiple choice quiz. Topics covered: superficial, skeletal and deep views, heart and arteries, venous, respiratory, digestive, nervous, and urogenital (male and female) systems. A Teacher's Guide provides additional activities.

Medium: CD-ROM
System requirements: Windows, Macintosh
Price: US$59.95 (single user); US$129.95 (lab pack of 5); US$279.95 (lab pack of 15); US$429.95 (lab pack of 25); US$595.95 (building licence)
Source: Ventura Educational Systems

Fetal Pig Dissection

This interactive program provides graphic overview of the pig's digestive, urogenital, respiratory, circulatory and nervous systems. Fascinating videoclips are complemented by colour animation and photographic enlargements which provide reinforcement of key points and depiction of hard-to-see structures. The fully interactive CD-ROM allows students to proceed at their own pace and includes self-assessment and review capabilities. Also features an audio-enhanced dictionary of anatomical terms.

Medium: CD-ROM
System requirements: Windows 95 or later, PowerMac 7.5 or later; 16 MB RAM
Price: US$99.95 (single); US$449.95 (lab pack of 5)
Source: Neo/Sci

Frog Dissection Laboratory

With the success of the *CatLab* (*Cat Dissection Laboratory*), NEOTEK has produced the same comprehensive treatment of the frog, and with the classic approach used in most texts and lab manuals. All major systems are covered in appropriate detail, including: skeletal, muscular, nervous, digestive, circulatory, respiratory and reproductive. Most students will never successfully see details like the central nervous system of the frog without a lot more time, equipment and experience than they have available. Now, with micro-surgically prepared dissections they can see what the book is talking about with real specimens, not just computer cartoons.

Language: English; translations into Spanish, French and German under production
Medium: CD-ROM
System requirements: Windows only; Windows 95/98/ME/NT/2000; Pentium processor, 16 MB RAM, 1024 x 768 resolution SVGA colour monitor, 24-bit colour, minimum 2 MB of video memory, soundcard, speakers
Note: 1. In order to view the 3D features of this program, the NEOTEK Base System is required. This includes: a video processor (to be placed between the computer and the monitor) and power supply, a pair of liquid crystal glasses, a sampler CD with excerpts from some of the most popular NEOTEK modules, a user manual and installation guide; **2.** Two similar programs from NEOTEK - *DogLab* and *HorseLab* - are currently under production
Price: US$85.00 (CD-ROM); $295.00 (Base System); US$95.00 (extra pair of liquid crystal glasses); US$850.00 (lab pack of 10 extra pairs of liquid crystal glasses); US$395.00 (wireless upgrade kit); US$195.00 (extra pair of wireless glasses); US$1,590.00 (lab pack of 10 extra pairs of wireless glasses)
Source: NEOTEK

[The] Heart in Depth

This program is for those looking for the classic university approach to the human heart. It includes 30 3D gross anatomy dissections intended for the anatomy and physiology student that wants the same level of understanding achieved in the lab.

Language: English; translations into Spanish, French and German under production
Medium: CD-ROM
System requirements: Windows only; Windows 95/98/ME/NT/2000; Pentium processor, 16 MB RAM, 1024 x 768 resolution SVGA colour monitor, 24-bit colour, minimum 2 MB of video memory, soundcard, speakers
Note: In order to view the 3D features of this program, the NEOTEK Base System is required. This includes: a video processor (to be placed between the computer and the monitor) and power supply, a pair of liquid crystal glasses, a sampler CD with excerpts from some of the most popular NEOTEK modules, a user manual and installation guide
Price: US$85.00 (CD-ROM); $295.00 (Base System); US$95.00 (extra pair of liquid crystal glasses); US$850.00 (lab pack of 10 extra pairs of liquid crystal glasses); US$395.00 (wireless upgrade kit); US$195.00 (extra pair of wireless glasses); US$1,590.00 (lab pack of 10 extra pairs of wireless glasses)
Source: NEOTEK

Injection and Dissection of the Chick

See description of this title under VIDEO.

Language: French
Year of production: Original film made in 1965
Medium: CD-ROM (MPEG4 format)
System requirements: Windows Media 7 (or Windows Player 6.4 for WinNT4 and Win95)
Price: Individual use: €15.00 (Europe), €30.00 (rest of the world); Institutional use: €30.00 (Europe), €45.00 (rest of the world)
Note: The original title of this program is *Injection et dissection du poussin*
Source: SFRS

Injection and Dissection of the Frog

See description of this title under VIDEO.

Language: French
Year of production: Original film made in 1965
Medium: CD-ROM (MPEG4 format)
System requirements: Windows Media 7 (or Windows Player 6.4 for WinNT4 and Win95)
Price: Individual use: €15.00 (Europe), €30.00 (rest of the world); Institutional use: €30.00 (Europe), €45.00 (rest of the world)
Note: The original title of this program is *Injection et dissection de la grenouille*
Source: SFRS

Invertebrates Zoology: Multimedia Lab Assistant

Authored by Dr. Tom Carefoot of the University of British Columbia, *Invertebrate Zoology* represents years of research and travel throughout the globe and covers 10 major phyla on 3 CD-ROMs: *Porifera*, *Platyhelminthes*, *Echinodermata*, *Annelida*, *Onychophora*, *Cnidaria*, *Nematoda*, *Chordata*, *Mollusca*, *Arthropoda*. Covered in each phylum are important life functions such as nutrition, gas exchange, excretion, locomotion, and reproduction, dealt with informatively and interactively. The program features thousands of brilliant colour photographs of marine, freshwater, and terrestrial invertebrates, along with hundreds of 2D and 3D animations illustrating feeding, locomotory, defensive, reproductive, and many other behaviours. Some 150 videoclips (total 25 mins.) show animals moving, burrowing, catching prey, copulating and feeding. Text and voiceover explanations are included throughout. Also included are 6 major interactive experiments: nematocyst discharge, pedicellariae activity, herbivore grazing, starfish as keystone predators, and polychaete, commensals, and clownfish defence from their anemone hosts, as well as dozens of other interactive exercises and 200 quizzes.

Medium: CD-ROM
System requirements: Windows 95 or later, with Pentium processor and sound card; Macintosh OS 7.5 or later with PowerMac (minimum 125 MHz) and audio speakers or headphones; 16 MB RAM, 8X CD-ROM drive, sound card, QuickTime 2.1
Price: US$179.00 (single), US$369.00 (Labpack of 5); Site licence: US$619.00 (10 CD pack), US$1,119.00 (20 CD pack), US$1,499.00 (30 CD pack)
Source: Tangent Scientific

[A] Journey through a Sheep Using X-ray Tomography

Adapted from the book 'An atlas of X-ray tomographic anatomy of the sheep' by A. S. Davies, K. L. Garden, M. J. Young and C. S. W. Reid (1987), Science Information Publishing Centre, DSIR, Wellington, New Zealand, this program consists of 122 plates of transverse tomographic slices of a living sheep, annotated and explained. It either plays as an animated sequence over a selected range of slices, or searches for nominated structures. It is intended to enhance the topographic study of living ruminants by relating the size, shape and position of organs to superficially palpable features, and will therefore reduce the need for dissection.

Medium: CD-ROM (under production)
System requirements: Windows, Macintosh
Price: €20.00
Source: Prof. Alexander S. Davies (Massey University, New Zealand)

 [The] Languedoc Scorpion (*Buthus occitanus*)

See description of this title under VIDEO.

Language: French, English, Portuguese, Spanish
Year of production: Original film made in 1966
Medium: CD-ROM (MPEG4 format)
System requirements: Windows Media 7 (or Windows Player 6.4 for WinNT4 and Win95)
Price: Individual use: €15.00 (Europe), €30.00 (rest of the world); Institutional use: €30.00 (Europe), €45.00 (rest of the world)
Note: The original title of this program is *Le Scorpion languedocien - Buthus occitanus*
Source: SFRS

 Learning About Insects

This comprehensive interactive multimedia presentation discusses in detail insect body structure and function, life cycle, and defences against enemies. The program features outstanding and intricate live action cinematography, including a slow motion sequence of a grasshopper jumping. It explains the three body sections found on all adult insects, as well as the insect's common compound eye and the different kinds of mouths found in the insect world, while looking at several different kinds of wing and leg designs and how each affects the movement of insects. The program also shows and explains the three stages of the insect life cycle, offering time-lapse cinematography of a larva building its cocoon, rare footage of an insect laying eggs, and several insects in the act of defending themselves. Finally, it reviews many defense mechanisms and demonstrates three defence techniques in which insects change their appearances.

Medium: CD-ROM
System requirements: Windows, Macintosh
Price: US$145.00, US$435.00 (lab pack of 5), US$725.00 (network)
Source: Queue

Learning All About Animals

This interactive multimedia program examines animals and animal classification with tutorials, audio narration, and stunning photographs. The program teaches the characteristics which distinguish plant from animal, and one animal from another. Each program provides a framework to classify organisms by the hierarchy of classification. Detailed descriptions of the characteristics, lifestyles, and environments of simple animals, worms, molluscs, spiny-skinned animals, joint-legged animals, fish, amphibians, reptiles, birds, and mammals are provided. Students will learn about the interdependence of life forms, adaptation, migration, learned and instinctive behaviour, evolution, and social structure of animal groups. Students will study natural selection; animal self-protection by movement, teeth and tails; and the balance of nature. The programs offer a comprehensive basic vocabulary and taxonomy of biology, defining each word with precise, self explanatory illustrations. Areas covered in this illustrated dictionary are: Protozoans, Sponges and Coelenterates, Flatworms and Echinoderms, Molluscs and Miscellaneous Groups, Arthropods (except Insects), Insects, Lower Chordates, Fishes, Amphibians, Birds, Reptiles and Mammals.

Medium: CD-ROM
System requirements: Windows, Macintosh
Price: US$75.00, US$225.00 (lab pack of 5), US$375.00 (network)
Source: Queue

 Learning All About Dissection

This interactive multimedia program contains exciting photographs, drawings, narration, and loads of information concerning dissection studies of 5 animals: earthworm, crayfish, fish, frog, and foetal pig. A great introduction to dissection and an overview of dissection as a scientific tool that can supplement or replace classroom dissections. Includes the habitat; skeleton; sense organs; brain; appendages; and locomotion, digestion, circulation, and reproduction of each one.

Medium: CD-ROM
System requirements: Windows, Macintosh
Price: US$95.00, US$285.00 (lab pack of 5), US$475.00 (network)
Source: Queue

 [The] Marine Life Series

A comprehensive series of 4 programs, suitable for comparative anatomy and marine biology studies. Graphically illustrated lessons present basic information on the topic. A database of structures and functions is linked to the graphic, which allows students to investigate the parts of the animal and to retrieve information about the biological structures and their functions. Researchers from marine biology centres in San Diego, California, provided some of the information presented in this program. Quizzes generate multiple choice or true and false questions based on the lessons. A Teacher's Guide provides additional activities. All 4 programs are included on one CD-ROM: 1. *Anatomy of a Fish* covers the external, internal, and skeletal structures of a bony fish; 2. *Anatomy of a Shark* presents the external, internal, and skeletal structures of the shark; 3. *The Life Cycle of a Sea Lamprey* presents the life cycle and anatomy of the sea lamprey; 4. *Marine Invertebrates* presents information on the sponge, sea anemone, clam, and starfish.

Medium: CD-ROM
System requirements: DOS, Windows, Macintosh
Price: US$59.95 (single user); US$129.95 (lab pack of 5); US$279.95 (lab pack of 15); US$429.95 (lab pack of 25); US$595.95 (building licence)
Source: Ventura Educational Systems

 Mollusks

Vibrant photographs and original 3D artwork reveal the biology of the molluscs in outstanding detail. Detailed animations show processes as they really occur in the 'soft bodied' animals. From unique evolutionary adaptations of the four major classes to in-depth examinations of unifying organ systems and body structures, the program provides a comprehensive study of these remarkable creatures.

Medium: CD-ROM
System requirements: Windows 95 with Pentium processor and 16 MB RAM; Macintosh OS 7.5.1 with 12 MB RAM
Price: US$119.95
Source: CyberEd; PLATO Learning (UK)

 Normal Ear of Dogs and Cats

An introduction to the anatomy, physiology and microbiology of the ear in dogs and cats. It is extracted from the CD-ROM program *Otitis in Dogs and Cats* and is aimed at pre-clinical students. Includes a 'fly-through' movie down the ear canal and into the tympanic bulla of a dog, reconstructed from serial MRI and CT scans.

Medium: Downloadable from website
System requirements: Windows only (all versions)
Price: Freeware
Source: CLIVE

Ocean Life Series

This highly acclaimed series offers "the most complete multimedia reference on marine life" available on CD-ROM. It includes 5 titles, available on separate CD-ROMs: *Caribbean, Great Barrier Reef, Hawaiian Islands, The Eastern Pacific, Western Pacific (2ⁿᵈ ed)*. They contain stunning photography and underwater video, covering hundreds of species of fish with comprehensive text, range maps, photographs, movies, and interactive morphology sections. The CD also provides text search capabilities and a visual index. In addition, text files and photographs may be exported for use in student reports or classroom presentations.

Medium: CD-ROM
System requirements: Windows, Macintosh
Price: US$49.95 (each title), US$149.95 (lab pack of 5 - same title)
Source: Queue

Operation: Frog (Deluxe)

Based on the popular *Operation: Frog* and *BioLab: Frog* products, this new teacher-developed program gives students the possibility to perform informative dissections, guiding them through comprehensive pre-lab instructions, lab simulations and post-lab reinforcements. Using full-colour photography and video, students learn the physiology of amphibians dissecting their external features and mouth, as well as the digestive, respiratory, circulatory, reproductive and skeletal systems.

Year of production: 1998
Medium: CD-ROM
System requirements: Windows (all versions), with 486/66 MHz processor; Macintosh OS 7.1 and later, with 68040 processor and 16 MB RAM.
Price: US$59.95 (Teacher Pack - 2 CD-ROMs and Teacher's Guide); US$139.80 (lab pack of 5); US$359.45 (lab pack of 15); US$658.95 (Super Pack of 30)
Source: Scholastic

When contacting producers and distributors,
please cite *from Guinea Pig to Computer Mouse*

[The] Paramecium – Morphology and Biology

See description of this title under VIDEO.

Language: French
Year of production: Original film made in 1968
Medium: CD-ROM (MPEG4 format)
System requirements: Windows Media 7 (or Windows Player 6.4 for WinNT4 and Win95)
Price: Individual use: €15.00 (Europe), €30.00 (rest of the world); Institutional use: €30.00 (Europe), €45.00 (rest of the world)
Note: The original title of this program is *La Paramécie - Morphologie et biologie*
Source: SFRS

ProDissector

ProDissector is a professionally prepared series of interactive, multimedia CD-ROMs that uses award winning technology to present digital dissection of commonly used laboratory animals in the instruction of biological sciences. At the time of printing, only one program is available (*Frog*), but the series will include *Cat, Gorilla, Fish, Invertebrates, Fetal Pig* and others. *ProDissector* uses digital images of actual animal anatomy which has been photo-retouched, sequentially layered and critically aligned to present accurate, detailed dissections of each animal. Each CD-ROM contains animal anatomy, organ systems and a self-test. In the Anatomy section, students use opacity buttons to transition from 2D opaque images into 3D transparent views of anatomical structures, which are highlighted, identified and defined. In the Systems section, students view a series of QuickTime movies that present physiological processes associated with major organ systems. Each movie is narrated and important terms are listed so students can obtain additional information.

Year of production: 2002
Medium: CD-ROM
System requirements: Windows 95/98/NT with Pentium II processor or better; Macintosh OS 8.0 or later with PowerPC or better; QuickTime 4.0; 20MB RAM, 800 x 600 screen resolution (thousands of colours)
Price: (For *Frog*): US$40.00 (single CD, home schooling); US$50.00 (single CD, educational price); US$400.00 (lab pack of 10); US$700.00 (lab pack of 20); US$900.00 (server licence). All prices excl. postage
Source: Schneider & Morse Group

Protozoa

Protozoa is a graphically illustrated program designed to help students understand the basic life suporting processes found in 4 typical micro-organisms. The product is designed for introductory level biology students and focuses on the structures and functions found in euglena (flagellate protozoans), amoeba (ameboid protozoans), paramecium (ciliated protozoans), and plasmodium (spore-forming protozoans). In addition, the program features a unit on *Malaria Cycle*, which explains how this deadly disease is transmitted by mosquitoes. Biology teachers will find that it is easy to focus the attention of students on learning the names of microstructures as well as the related life-supporting functions of these structures using this program. The Windows version also has a microscope simulation.

Medium: CD-ROM
System requirements: DOS, Windows, Macintosh
Price: US$59.95 (single user); US$129.95 (lab pack of 5); US$279.95 (lab pack of 15); US$429.95 (lab pack of 25); US$595.95 (building licence)
Source: Ventura Educational Systems

[The] Rat - A Functional Anatomy

This is a comprehensive teaching and learning resource that provides a detailed study of the functional relationship between organ systems in the rat, from gross morphology to microscopic detail. It has 3 parts: *An introduction to the rat, Classification of the vertebrates, A functional anatomy*. The latter gives the option to explore each of the major organ systems from an anatomical, physiological or histological perspective. The CD-ROM contains over 50 mins. of video including footage of the live animal and dissection technique, audio introductions to all sequences, over 100 histological slides that can be viewed at range of magnifications, diagrams, animations and text to provide a rich learning environment through which to study mammalian biology.

Year of production: 1998
Medium: CD-ROM
System requirements: Windows only - Win95/98/NT with DirectX software; Pentium 166 MHz, 16 MB RAM (32 MB recommended), 16-bit sound card
Price: £50.00 (excl. VAT)
Source: University of Portsmouth

Rat Dissection / Anatomy Resource Digital Video

This 318 MB digital video (MPEG format) contains over 2,000 still, high quality video frames and over 500 dissection sequences. The rat (either male or female) can be viewed from two angles (above and side) and a full dissection is illustrated, including: examination of the external features; dissection and study of the abdominal structures (gastrointestinal, urinary and reproductive systems) and structures in the thoracic cavity and neck region; and exposure, removal and examination of the brain. 300 (unlabelled) histology images showing up to 4x magnification of cellular detail are included along with some diagrams.

Medium: Downloadable from website
System requirements: MPEG player
Note: 1. The original video was developed to be used with the interactive software *The Rat Stack* (see separate entry), using high quality laser videodisc technology which is now almost completely out of date. However, the

181 **C**

digital version of the original video, which is up to date but provided in a single video stream, is free to download, and the use of excerpts or images is permitted for educational purposes. Users may download and make use of images or video sequences providing it does not infringe the moral copyright, as per UK law, of the authors as credited on the front of the video. The digital video is not as high quality as the original laser disc video, which was part of the now unavailable multimedia program *FARID - Functional Anatomy of the Rat (Interactive Dissection)*. Anyone wishing to re-code a program of interactive software using this video will almost certainly be given permission, but please contact the author for this permission in writing. The material is offered as it is, and no technical support is provided; **2.** *The Rat Dissection / Anatomy Resource Digital Video* and the original *Rat Anatomy Resource Disc* are dedicated to Graham Irving
Price: Freeware
Source: Dr. Megan Quentin-Baxter (University of Newcastle, UK)

[The] Rat Stack

The Rat Stack is an interactive CAL program which provides a realistic learning alternative to performing a rat dissection. *The Rat Stack* contains over 300 low resolution (72 dpi) images and 30,000 lines of data and programming code. The rat (either male or female) can be viewed from two angles (above and side) and a full dissection is illustrated, including: examination of the external features; dissection and study of the abdominal structures (gastrointestinal, urinary and reproductive systems) and structures in the thoracic cavity and in the neck region; and exposure, removal and examination of the brain. 300 (unlabelled) histology images showing up to 4x magnification of cellular detail are included along with some diagrams. Annotations appear on the computer screen to identify every structure in the dissection. Questions are automatically generated around the image on the screen; for incorrect answers *The Rat Stack* can show students where the structure is located, or students can attempt questions again.

Medium: Downloadable from website
System requirements: Any Macintosh computer with HyperCard 2.0 or 2.2 Player
Price: Freeware
Note: The program was developed to be used with the video *Rat Dissection / Anatomy Resource Digital Video* (see separate entry), using high quality laser videodisc technology which is now almost completely out of date. However, the program is up to date and is free to download, and the use of the program is permitted for educational purposes. The program was part of the now unavailable multimedia program *FARID - Functional Anatomy of the Rat (Interactive Dissection)*. Anyone wishing to re-code a program of interactive software using this material will almost certainly be given permission, but please contact the author for this permission in writing. The material is offered as it is, and no technical support is provided
Source: Dr. Megan Quentin-Baxter (University of Newcastle, UK)

Small Animal Ultrasound on CD-ROM

This CD-ROM brings along the critical element of real-time viewing of sonograms in small animal practice. It reveals anatomical structures exactly as they are seen via sonography on examination – providing a realistic approach to learning ultrasound in veterinary practice, as well as a superb method for confirming clinical diagnosis. The disk contains approximately 100 sonographic images, including normal and abnormal anatomy.

Year of production: 1997
Medium: CD-ROM
System requirements: Windows 95, Macintosh OS 7; Quick Time (included); 16 MB RAM
Price: US$150.00
Source: Lippincott Williams & Wilkins

Sponges

An interactive program that explores the structure and life of these primitive and peculiar animals. Pop-up graphics illustrate the characteristics that classify sponges as animals as well as the qualities that make them unique. Intriguing animations show how sponge cells relate to one another and how entire colonies of sponges relate to other organisms. Students will absorb the vividly presented information about sponge anatomy and reproduction. Easy to use tutorials reinforce the student's comprehension of the program.

Medium: CD-ROM
System requirements: Windows 95 with Pentium processor and 16 MB RAM; Macintosh OS 7.5.1 with 12 MB RAM
Price: US$99.95
Source: CyberEd; PLATO Learning (UK)

Unicellular Organisms

See description of this title under VIDEO.

Language: French, German
Year of production: Original film made in 1998
Medium: CD-ROM (MPEG4 format)
System requirements: Windows Media 7 (or Windows Player 6.4 for WinNT4 and Win95)
Price: €15.24 (individual use), €30.49 (institutional use)
Note: This program is distributed by SFRS in France only; its French title is *Organismes cellulaires*; the original German title is *Einzeller*
Source: SFRS

Vertebrate Dissection Guides Series

As a companion set to *The Rat - A Functional Anatomy*, a series of *Vertebrate Dissection Guides* are also available, either on video or on CD-ROM. Each program explores the anatomy and dissection techniques of a vertebrate commonly used at undergraduate level: *The Dogfish*, *The Frog* and *The Pigeon*. They all feature up to an hour of high quality video material. Included within each program are sections exploring the external features, initial dissection techniques, digestive, circulatory and urogenital systems, the brain and the skeleton. High quality macro photography is supplemented with graphic overlays and 3D computer animations to provide a comprehensive educational resource.

Year of prodution: 1999
Medium: CD-ROM
System requirements: Windows only - Win95/98/NT; 16-bit sound card
Price: £40.00 per program (incl. VAT)
Source: University of Portsmouth

Veterinary Anatomy Courseware

This instructional software is authored by faculty and students at the University of Minnesota for use as independent study material by veterinary students. The following is a listing of courseware that can be downloaded free of charge for educational purposes from the website: *Gross anatomy (Autonomic nervous system tutor, Canine bones, Canine muscle groups, Canine planar anatomy atlas, Cranial nerve reference, Gaits, Head anatomy, Horse teeth and age, Ungulate anatomy)*, *Microanatomy (Endocrine, GI-related organs, Glands, Immune system, Kidney, Ovary, Testis, Tubular organs, Histology courseware, Problem-solving in histology)*, *Developmental anatomy (Placental images, Embryology tutor - cardiovascular, genital and urinary systems, nervous system and special senses)*, *Radiographic anatomy (Small animal, Equine)*, *Neuroanatomy (Basic eye tutor, Canine brain atlas, Cranial nerve nuclei, Neuroembryology, Spinal cord tutor)*.

Medium: Downloadable from website
System requirements: Most of the courseware was written in HyperCard or SuperCard and runs only on Macintosh computers. *Histology courseware, Placental images* and *Radiographic anatomy* run on both Mac and Windows 95
Price: Freeware
Source: University of Minnesota

Veterinary Neurosciences

This program provides students with an interactive neuroanatomical atlas. Structures of the canine brain can be examined in high-resolution, 8-bit colour, myelin stained, transverse sections. Analogous gross sections of the sheep brain are instantly available with the click of a button. A variety of additional gross views are also provided. Both histological and gross views have inter-active highlighting labels which allow the student to learn over 100 structures by either directly clicking on the image or on the structure's name in a text list. A 'Find' command gives instant access to a particular structure. Nine additional modules present the major somatosensory, motor and visual pathways. A series of colour graphics trace the names and locations of the neural tracts and relay nuclei from the origin to the termination of each pathway. The modules are fully integrated with the atlas providing access to histological or gross views of any point along the pathway.

Medium: CD-ROM
System requirements: Macintosh only - Macintosh Power PC with 24 MB RAM, thousands colours or greater, 800 x 600 screen resolution
Price: US$65.00
Source: University of California (UC Davis)

Veterinary Radiographic Anatomy: Canine, Feline and Equine

This program was developed to help teach basic veterinary radiographic anatomy to veterinary students and practitioners. There are over 130 canine, feline and equine radiographs with a complete index to facilitate easy reference. The radiographs may be viewed sequentially or in a random manner. Overlays are used to identify important anatomical features of normal anatomy. A self-test quiz is provided with each radiographic view to teach mastery of the material.

Medium: CD-ROM
System requirements: Windows 95 or above with Pentium processor; Macintosh Power PC with 24 MB RAM; thousands of colours or greater, 800 x 600 screen resolution
Price: US$65.00
Source: University of California (UC Davis)

Veterinary Ultrasonography: Small Animal Abdomen

This program was developed to help teach the basic principles of small animal ultrasonography to veterinary students and practitioners. There are 70 cases grouped by organ system to facilitate easy reference. The cases may be viewed sequentially or in a random manner. Overlays are used to identify important ultrasonographic features of normal anatomy and illustrate major pathological conditions. Common ultrasound artifacts may be studied as a group or accessed using linked text from other parts of the program. A multiple choice quiz is provided to teach mastery of the material.

Medium: CD-ROM
System requirements: Windows 95 or above with Pentium processor; Macintosh Power PC with 24 MB RAM; thousands of colours or greater, 800 x 600 screen resolution
Price: US$65.00
Source: University of California (UC Davis)

Veterinary Virtual Museum

This database of images relevant to veterinary anatomy contains assorted digitised images that to date include: cat, chicken, dog, dolphin, emu, ferret, fur seal, guinea pig, horse, ostrich, ox, possum, pig, rabbit, red and sika deer, salmon, sea lion, sheep, trout, turkey, turtle and whale. At present containing nearly 400 records, it has an unlimited ability to expand. The fields set for users to search include: species (common categories such as ruminant, rodent and carnivore, combined with common names in English such as red deer, rat and turtle), code number, description (often referring to labels on the image), names of creators, reference to book specimen, journal article as applicable, date of creation and modification of entries. The images range from radiographs and other medical images such as X-ray and NMR digital tomography, to digital photographs of dissections, models, casts, skeletons, histological sections. Some records contain multiple images; for example, radiographs accompanied by colour overlays to explain skeletal structure at various angles. The result of a search appears as a series of thumbnail images that, when selected, are shown as full screen pictures with descriptions.

Medium: CD-ROM (under production)
System requirements: Windows, Macintosh
Price: €20.00
Note: copies will be available at cost early in 2003. The images will be free of copyright provided acknowledgement is given to the creators. It is hoped the database will grow as others contribute to it, and that in this way it will become a truly international resource
Source: Prof. Alexander S. Davies (Massey University, New Zealand)

[The] Virtual Heart

Totally involving the user in exploring the unique functionality of this organ, *The Virtual Heart* combines realistic images with stunning interactive 3D control of dissected and non-dissected hearts. Users can view the heart from almost any angle, and with a click of the mouse get information about any visible stucture, including the internal chambers. Additional features include digital video of conventional and Doppler ultrasonic scans, waveform tracings and audio of normal and abnormal heart sounds, views of common cardiac pathologies, an animation of the cardiac cycle, microscopic and EM images of cardiac tissue, radiographs and an annotated ECG.

Language: English; Spanish translation under production
Medium: CD-ROM
System requirements: Macintosh Power PC with 24 MB RAM, thousands colours or greater, 800 x 600 screen resolution. Windows version under production
Price: US$65.00
Source: University of California (UC Davis)

VisiFrog

VisiFrog introduces the frog's anatomical structures and biological functions through computer graphics, digital images, sound, and textual information. It offers a comprehensive overview of vertebrate anatomy, covering: the external surface (dorsal), the musculature (dorsal and ventral), the skeleton, the heart and arteries, the venous, digestive, respiratory, nervous, and urogenital (male and female) systems. Colour diagrams allow students easy access to a complete description while exploring anatomical structures and functions. The 'digital image' option allows students to move from colour diagrams to images of an actual frog, while the quiz component reinforces terminology and skills in a challenging and fun game format.

Medium: CD-ROM
System requirements: DOS, Windows, Macintosh
Price: US$59.95 (single user); US$129.95 (lab pack of 5); US$279.95 (lab pack of 15); US$429.95 (lab pack of 25); US$595.95 (building licence)
Source: Ventura Educational Systems

 VIDEO

 [The] Anatomy of the Cat

This video features an in-depth look at a mammal usually covered in more advanced classes. All major organ systems are thoroughly investigated, and each system can be viewed and discussed separately.

Year of production: 1991
Format: VHS NTSC
Running time: 85 mins.
Price: US$89.95
Note: This title is also available as part of *Vertebrate Anatomy Set* and *Animal Anatomy Set*
Source: Carolina Biological Supply (check website for country distributors)

[The] Anatomy of the Crayfish

An excellent introduction to the anatomy of this crustacean, covering all its organs and systems. Each individual system can be viewed and discussed separately. Includes teacher's manual.

Year of production: 1991
Format: VHS NTSC
Running time: 20 mins.
Price: US$39.95
Note: This title is also available as part of *Invertebrate Anatomy Set* and *Animal Anatomy Set*
Source: Carolina Biological Supply (check website for country distributors)

 [The] Anatomy of the Earthworm

Annelids are important in evolution because of their segmentation. This video covers the structure and function of all major organ systems in the earthworm - a representative annelid - and each individual system can be viewed and discussed separately. Includes teacher's manual.

Year of production: 1991
Format: VHS NTSC
Running time: 15 mins.
Price: US$89.95
Note: This title is also available as part of *Invertebrate Anatomy Set* and *Animal Anatomy Set*
Source: Carolina Biological Supply (check website for country distributors)

 Anatomy of the Equine Hoof and Innervation of the Forelimb

This video consists of 4 parts. Part 1 - *The Hoof* - explains the anatomy of the horse's foot and the biomechanics of the actions of the structures within it. Part 2 - *Nerves and Nerve Blocks* - demonstrates the problems of a lame horse and describes the innervation of the forelimb and the technique of nerve blocking various parts of the limb. Part 3 - *Bone* - explains the bone structure and function as an internal support system and mineral store. Part 4 - *Joints* - describes the different kinds of joint and their formation during embryological development.

Year of production: 1993
Format: VHS PAL
Running time: 45 mins.
Price: £30.00 (excl. VAT and postage)
Source: Royal Veterinary College

[The] Anatomy of the Fetal Pig

In this video the pig is discussed as a representative mammal, and all major organs and systems are thoroughly covered. Each individual system can be viewed and discussed separately. Includes teacher's manual.

Year of production: 1990
Format: VHS NTSC
Running time: 62 mins.
Price: US$69.95
Note: This title is also available as part of *Vertebrate Anatomy Set* and *Animal Anatomy Set*
Source: Carolina Biological Supply (check website for country distributors)

 [The] Anatomy of the Freshwater Mussel

Freshwater mussels are excellent examples of molluscs. This video provides an introduction to the structure and function of the organs and systems in this ancient phylum. Includes teacher's manual.

Year of production: 1991
Format: VHS NTSC
Running time: 13.30 mins.
Price: US$39.95
Note: This title is also available as part of *Invertebrate Anatomy Set* and *Animal Anatomy Set*
Source: Carolina Biological Supply (check website for country distributors)

 [The] Anatomy of the Frog

This video thoroughly covers all of the major organ systems of the frog, and each individual system can be viewed and discussed separately. Freshly dissected and injected specimens are used. Includes teacher's manual.

Year of production: 1990
Format: VHS NTSC
Running time: 45 mins.
Price: US$69.95
Note: This title is also available as part of *Vertebrate Anatomy Set* and *Animal Anatomy Set*
Source: Carolina Biological Supply (check website for country distributors)

[The] Anatomy of the Grasshopper

This video is designed to facilitate a study of the anatomy of the grasshopper as a representative arthropod and insect. Each individual system can be viewed and discussed separately.

Year of production: 1991
Format: VHS NTSC
Running time: 16 mins.
Price: US$39.95
Note: This title is also available as part of *Invertebrate Anatomy Set* and *Animal Anatomy Set*
Source: Carolina Biological Supply (check website for country distributors)

 ## [The] Anatomy of the Perch

This video provides an in-depth look at a typical bony fish. All major organ systems are thoroughly covered, and each individual system can be viewed and discussed separately. Includes teacher's manual.

Year of production: 1991
Format: VHS NTSC
Running time: 25 mins.
Price: US$39.95
Note: This title is also available as part of *Vertebrate Anatomy Set* and *Animal Anatomy Set*
Source: Carolina Biological Supply (check website for country distributors)

 ## [The] Anatomy of the Shark

This video covers the dissection of the spiny dogfish, which illustrates the anatomy of a cartilaginous fish. All major organ systems are thoroughly covered, and each individual system can be viewed and discussed separately. Includes teacher's manual.

Year of production: 1991
Format: VHS NTSC
Running time: 56 mins.
Price: US$69.95
Note: This title is also available as part of *Vertebrate Anatomy Set* and *Animal Anatomy Set*
Source: Carolina Biological Supply (check website for country distributors)

When contacting producers and distributors,
please cite *from Guinea Pig to Computer Mouse*

[The] Anatomy of the Starfish

This video covers the structure and function of the organs and systems in this representative of the phylum Echinodermata. Includes teacher's manual.

Year of production: 1991
Format: VHS NTSC
Running time: 16 mins.
Price: US$39.95
Note: This title is also available as part of *Invertebrate Anatomy Set* and *Animal Anatomy Set*
Source: Carolina Biological Supply (check website for country distributors)

 [The] Animal Anatomy Set

Contains 5 videos on invertebrate anatomy and 5 videos on vertebrate anatomy, available separately or as combined sets. The *Invertebrate Anatomy Set* includes the crayfish, the earthworm, the freshwater mussel, the grasshopper and the starfish. The *Vertebrate Anatomy Set* includes the cat, the foetal pig, the frog, the perch and the shark. More details under each individual title.

Format: VHS NTSC
Running time: See individual titles
Price: US$180.00 *(Invertebrate Anatomy Set)*; US$305.00 *(Vertebrate Anatomy Set)*; US$485.00 *(Animal Anatomy Set)*
Source: Carolina Biological Supply (check website for country distributors)

 Annelids

This program shows the pumping heart of the earthworm, and its life cycle, *Tubifex* worms boring their way through the bottom of ponds, and the unique adaptations that allow these worms, the clam worms and the leeches to survive in their environments. Also features a clam worm close up and witnesses the commensal relationship between leeches and their prey.

Format: VHS NTSC
Running time: 10 mins.
Price: US$60.00
Source: CLEARVUE/eav

When contacting producers and distributors, please cite *from Guinea Pig to Computer Mouse*

Arthropods

Illustrates the numbers and species diversity of this phylum. Explains the function of the exoskeleton, jointed appendages, segmentation, and other arthropod features.

Format: VHS NTSC
Running time: 13 mins.
Price: US$60.00
Source: CLEARVUE/eav

 Biological Dissection Series

These programs focus on the exploration of animal organisms in the context of their environment without sacrificing the detail necessary to get the most out of this method of teaching anatomy and physiology. *Part 1* includes an introduction to dissection, and dissections of an earthworm and a crayfish. *Part 2* features dissection of the perch and the frog.

Format: VHS NTSC, PAL
Running time: 32 mins. (*Part 1*); 36 mins. (*Part 2*)
Price: US$40.00 (each part, NTSC); US$76.00 (*Part 1* + *Part 2*, NTSC); for PAL standard, price on application
Source: CLEARVUE/eav

 [The] Biology of Annelids

Phylum *Annelida* is made up of segmented worms divided into three classes: *Oligochaetes* (earth worms and aquatic worms such as *Tubifex*), *Polychaetes* (*Nereis* and thousands of other species that live in almost all marine habitats), and leeches. Their segmented bodies, similar internal anatomy (seen in action through revealing new micro/macro imaging techniques), and developmental stages unite these diverse worms.

Year of production: 2000
Format: VHS NTSC
Running time: 15 mins.
Price: US$55.00
Note: This title will also be available as part of a series on DVD in 2003; contact BioMEDIA Associates for more details
Source: eBioMEDIA

[The] Biology of Arthropods

The arthropods are armoured creatures with jointed legs, which have developed elaborate behaviour patterns that assure survival. They are also the most successful phylum in the animal kingdom - phylum *Arthropoda*. This program explores the major classes of arthropods through dramatic photography of living examples: the Crustaceans (including all major crustacean groups); the Arachnids (including whipscorpions, scorpions, spiders, ticks and mites); and the Uniramians (including centipedes, millipedes, and insects). The program highlights important details of structure and behaviour, incorporating both familiar and unusual examples (such as forehead mites and barnacles) that will serve as memorable insights into arthropod biology.

Year of production: 2001
Format: VHS NTSC
Running time: 25 mins.
Price: US$55.00
Note: This title will also be available as part of a series on DVD in 2003; contact BioMEDIA Associates for more details
Source: eBioMEDIA

 [The] Biology of Chordates

Phylum *Chordata* evolved in ancient seas over 510 million years ago as shown by fossils (*Pikaia*) discovered in the Burgess Shales. The unique features of this group: a supporting rod (notochord), a hollow dorsal nerve cord, post-anal tail and pharyngeal gills are investigated in modern animals - tunicates, lancelets (*Branchiostoma* or *Amphioxus*), hagfish, cartilagenous fish and the other groups of vertebrates. Key adaptations leading to the diversification and proliferation of the modern vertebrate groups, from fish to mammals, are explored through fossil evidence, living examples and animation.

Year of production: 2001
Format: VHS NTSC
Running time: 18 mins.
Price: US$55.00
Note: This title will also be available as part of a series on DVD in 2003; contact BioMEDIA Associates for more details
Source: eBioMEDIA

 [The] Biology of Cnidarians

This video program presents a remarkable series of observations on *Hydra*, one of the 'classical organisms of biology', including habitat, structure, feeding, nematocyst discharge, locomotion (by looping) and its sexual and asexual reproductive strategies. *Obelia* illustrates the two-stage cnidarian life cycle, with asexually-reproducing polyps and free swimming sexual medusae, a characteristic shared by most members of Class *Hydrazoa*. The beautiful jellyfish of Class *Scyphozoa* pulse or drift through the open sea. Members of Class *Anthozoa*, sea anemones, hug the intertidal rocks trapping crabs and other small animals. Corals, their warm sea relatives, create one of the oldest and richest ecosystems on earth - the coral reef.

Year of production: 1998
Format: VHS NTSC
Running time: 16 mins.
Price: US$55.00
Note: This title will also be available as part of a series on DVD in 2003; contact BioMEDIA Associates for more details
Source: eBioMEDIA

 ## [The] Biology of Echinoderms

These animals have spiny skins, internal skeletons and elaborate hydraulic systems used in locomotion and food getting - and they all live in the sea. Examining echinoderm lifestyles shows that seastars (Class *Asteroidea*) are predators, brittle stars and basket stars (Class *Ophiuroidea*) are detritus feeders, urchins and sand dollars (Class *Echinoidea*) are herbivores, sea cucumbers (Class *Holothuoidea*) feed on detritus and plankton.

Year of production: 2001
Format: VHS NTSC
Running time: 15 mins.
Price: US$55.00
Note: This title will also be available as part of a series on DVD in 2003; contact BioMEDIA Associates for more details
Source: eBioMEDIA

 ## [The] Biology of Flatworms

Flatworms, with their three clearly defined cell layers and bilateral symmetry, represent an important advance in early animal evolution. This program provides detailed observations on structure, behaviour and life cycles of planarians and other free-living flatworms, some so small they can only be studied with a microscope (Class *Turbellaria*). It examines the bizarre life cycles of flukes (class *Trematoda*) and tapeworms (class *Cestoda*) with revealing shots of these parasites at home in the organs of their vertebrate hosts.

Year of production: 2001
Format: VHS NTSC
Running time: 16 mins.
Price: US$55.00

Note: This title will also be available as part of a series on DVD in 2003; contact BioMEDIA Associates for more details
Source: eBioMEDIA

 [The] Biology of Molluscs

The phylum *Mollusca* is filled with wonderfully adapted soft-bodied creatures that make up four major classes. Class *Polyplacophora* (with detailed observations on chitons), Class *Gastropoda* (snails, limpets, nudibranchs, and slugs), Class *Pelecypoda* (clams and mussels), and Class *Cephalopoda* (squid and octopus). In each group the emphasis is on: structure, behaviour, larval development, and the kinds of adaptations that allow these amazing creatures to live in virtually all aquatic habitats.

Year of production: 2001
Format: VHS NTSC
Running time: 15 mins.
Price: US$55.00
Note: This title will also be available as part of a series on DVD in 2003; contact BioMEDIA Associates for more details
Source: eBioMEDIA

 [The] Biology of Nematodes, Rotifers, Bryozoans and some Minor Phyla

A video program which presents observations and up-to-date information on round worms including a number of important human parasites. 13 common rotifer species illustrate this diverse group of microscopic animals. *Bryozoans* have evolved remarkable filter-feeding strategies that are observed in freshwater and marine species. Gastrotrichs, tardigrades (water bears), nemerteans, and a recently discovered phylum, *Gnathostomulida*, acquaint students with many of the lesser-known branches of animal life.

Year of production: 1998
Format: VHS NTSC
Running time: 18 mins.
Price: US$55.00
Note: This title will also be available as part of a series on DVD in 2003; contact BioMEDIA Associates for more details
Source: eBioMEDIA

When contacting producers and distributors, please cite *from Guinea Pig to Computer Mouse*

Cnidarians

A comprehensive and up-to-date treatment of the phylum *Cnidaria* (*coelenterata*), this program discusses the two basic body forms of cnidarians, polyps and jellyfish (medusas), after which it presents three classes of cnidarians. Students see the structure of a hydra, how gastrodermal cells digest food, and how stinging cells and nerve cells work. The segment on jellyfish includes an excellent animated life cycle and demonstrates how sense organs work. Finally, students discover how anemones eat, and learn about two principal types of corals: soft corals and stoney reef-builders.

Format: VHS NTSC, PAL
Running time: 27 mins.
Price: US$75.00 (NTSC); for PAL standard, price on application
Source: CLEARVUE/eav

 Dissection and Anatomy of the Brain

In this program, a sheep brain is used to explore the anatomy of a brain very similar in form and function to that of the human. Dr. Tom Quinn, Professor of Anatomy at Creighton University School of Medicine, performs the dissection while simultaneously narrating, identifying each structure - including the 12 cranial nerves - and explaining their function in the living organism. Accompanying the program is a set of review questions and a list of terms.

Format: VHS NTSC
Running time: 22.16 mins.
Price: US$107.00
Source: Denoyer Geppert International

 Dissection and Anatomy of the Eye

In this program, Dr. Tom Quinn, Professor of Anatomy at Creighton University School of Medicine, systematically dissects a beef eye, while simultaneously narrating and comparing it with the Denoyer Geppert *Giant Eye in Bony Orbit* model. The latter also serves as the basis for a demonstration of the extraocular muscles. Anatomical terminology is made meaningful by Dr. Quinn's literal translations. A set of review questions and a list of terms accompanies the program.

Format: VHS NTSC
Running time: 15.44 mins.
Price: US$107.00
Source: Denoyer Geppert International

Dissection Techniques - Introduction and Muscles

A method to begin the dissection and identification of canine muscles. Comments are made on techniques and useful instruments.

Year of production: 1975
Format: VHS NTSC, PAL
Running time: 24 mins.
Price: US$50.00
Source: University of California (UC Davis)

 Dissection Techniques - Peripheral Cutaneous Nerves

Views and techniques of dissection are presented to expose nerves and related structures in the dog.

Year of production: 1975
Format: VHS NTSC, PAL
Running time: 15 mins.
Price: US$50.00
Source: University of California (UC Davis)

 Dissection Video Series

A set of 7 high quality videos that illustrate the start-to-finish dissections of some standard lab study animals (cat, crayfish, earthworm, foetal pig, frog, perch, starfish). Using the most up-to-date equipment and techniques, the videos follow every step of the dissection process, as well as the organisation of most lab manuals, and therefore can be used as replacements for live animal dissections. They are extremely detailed and are accompanied by printed scripts with numbered frame references and a complete glossary. Especially difficult-to-locate anatomical structures are identified by graphics and pointers.

Format: VHS NTSC
Running time: Approx. 30 mins. each
Price: US$70.00 (each title); US$465.00 (complete series of 7 titles)
Source: CLEARVUE/eav

 Dissection Videos

This series shows each and every step of the dissection process using the most up-to-date equipment and techniques. Each video features full close-up photography and a narrative that

197 C

follows the organisation of most basic laboratory manuals. Helpful graphics and pointers make it easier for students to identify anatomical structures, particularly those that may be difficult to locate in an actual specimen. Each video comes with a written dissection manual. Titles include:

- *Cat Dissection* (39 mins.)
- *Clam Dissection* (7 mins.)
- *Crayfish Dissection* (14 mins.)
- *Dogfish Dissection* (25 mins.)
- *Earthworm Dissection* (13 mins.)
- *Fetal Pig Dissection* (32 mins.)
- *Frog Dissection* (26 mins.)
- *Grasshopper Dissection* (8 mins.)
- *Perch Dissection* (12 mins.)
- *Rat Dissection* (30 mins.)
- *Sheep Brain Dissection* (22 mins.)
- *Sheep Eye Dissection* (15 mins.)
- *Sheep Heart Dissection* (14 mins.)
- *Starfish Dissection* (8 mins.)

Format: VHS NTSC
Running time: See individual titles above
Price: US$55.00 (*Grasshopper, Perch, Starfish*); US$64.50 (*Cat, Fetal Pig, Frog*); US$65.00 (*Clam*); US$69.00 (*Crayfish*); US$75.00 (*Earthworm*); US$99.00 (*Sheep Brain, Sheep Eye, Sheep Heart*); US$135.00 (*Dogfish, Rat*); US$259.00 (*Economy Dissection Video Set: Earthworm, Frog, Fetal Pig, Cat*)
Source: Ward's Natural Science

 Fetal Pig Dissection & Anatomy

Stunning video serves as a superb resource for the study of the foetal pig. Excellent for use as a pre-lab prep, lab manual supplement, post-lab review or as an alternative to dissection. Includes sections on external anatomy; dissection techniques; nervous, respiratory, circulatory and urogenital systems; and the mouth cavity.

Format: VHS NTSC
Running time: 26 mins.
Price: US$79.95
Source: Neo/Sci

 Frog Dissection and Anatomy

Vivid photography provides an excellent source of pre-lab prep, post-dissection review, or as a viable alternative to dissection. Includes sections on terms of orientation, external anatomy; major muscles; digestive, respiratory, circulatory and urogenital systems; and the anatomy of the brain.

Format: VHS NTSC
Running time: 46 mins.
Price: US$79.95
Source: Neo/Sci

Injection and Dissection of the Chick

This film presents the dissection of a chick circulatory system (initial dissection, ligatures, injection of the arterial system with lead chromate).

Language: French
Year of production: 1965
Format: VHS PAL, SECAM, NTSC. Also available on CD-ROM (see under Software)
Running time: 15 mins.
Price: Individual use: €15.00 (Europe), €30.00 (rest of the world); Institutional use: €30.00 (Europe), €45.00 (rest of the world); the NTSC format is available at an additional cost of €15.00
Note: The original title of this program is *Injection et dissection du poussin*
Source: SFRS

Injection and Dissection of the Frog

This film presents the dissection of a frog circulatory system (initial dissection, ligatures, injection of the arterial system with lead chromate).

Language: French
Year of production: 1965
Format: VHS PAL, SECAM, NTSC. Also available on CD-ROM (see under Software)
Running time: 15 mins.
Price: Individual use: €15.00 (Europe), €30.00 (rest of the world); Institutional use: €30.00 (Europe), €45.00 (rest of the world); the NTSC format is available at an additional cost of €15.00
Note: The original title of this program is *Injection et dissection de la grenouille*
Source: SFRS

When contacting producers and distributors,
please cite *from Guinea Pig to Computer Mouse*

Innervation of Superficial Structures of the Head

Dissections and comments on techniques needed to expose nerves and the structures of the head which they supply.

Year of production: 1975
Format: VHS NTSC, PAL
Running time: 26 mins.
Price: US$50.00
Source: University of California (UC Davis)

 [The] Invertebrate Anatomy Set

See *Animal Anatomy Set.*

 Kingdom *Protista*

Surveys the microscopic world, including characteristics of primitive and complex algae, amoebae, paramecia, and many more. Provides an overview of microstructures as well as locomotion and eating habits.

Format: VHS NTSC
Running time: 20 mins.
Price: US$40.00
Source: CLEARVUE/eav

 Laboratory Dissection Video Series

Excellent step by step close-up photography of 7 classic dissections, partly captioned, partly unlabelled for quiz and review. The programs contain 22-32 frames; each frame appears on-screen for 50-60 secs., but can be held longer. There is no audio. Titles include: *Clam* (catalogue ref. FV-1351V), *Crayfish* (FV-1353V), *Earthworm* (FV-1352V), *Fetal Pig* (FV-1357V), *Fish* (FV-1355V), *Frog* (FV-1356V), *Grasshopper* (FV-1354V).

Format: VHS NTSC
Running time: 30 mins. each
Price: US$29.95 (individual titles, with guide); US$149.95 (full set of 7 videos - catalogue ref. FV-1352X)
Source: Educational Images

[The] Languedoc Scorpion (*Buthus occitanus*)

This film presents some aspects of the biology of *Buthus occitanus*, the yellow scorpion, also named 'Languedoc' because of its habitat: anatomy, hole digging, predation and feeding, moulting, coupling, reproduction, etc.

Language: French, English, Portuguese, Spanish
Year of production: 1966
Format: VHS PAL, SECAM, NTSC. Also available on CD-ROM (see under SOFTWARE)
Running time: 17 mins.
Price: Individual use: €15.00 (Europe), €30.00 (rest of the world); Institutional use: €30.00 (Europe), €45.00 (rest of the world); the NTSC format is available at an additional cost of €15.00
Note: The original title of this program is *Le Scorpion languedocien - Buthus occitanus*
Source: SFRS

[The] Paramecium - Morphology and Biology

The paramecium is a ciliated protozoan living in fresh water, often found in ponds and pools. The morphology and biology of *Paramecium caudatum* is studied *in vivo* through contrast interference, using histology and electron microscopy data: cortical and internal organisation, locomotion, feeding, division and conjugation.

Language: French
Year of production: 1968
Format: VHS PAL, SECAM, NTSC. Also available on CD-ROM (see under SOFTWARE)
Running time: 28 mins.
Price: Individual use: €15.00 (Europe), €30.00 (rest of the world); Institutional use: €30.00 (Europe), €45.00 (rest of the world); the NTSC format is available at an additional cost of €15.00
Note: The original title of this program is *La Paramécie - Morphologie et biologie*
Source: SFRS

Preparation of the Labyrinth of the Small-Spotted Dogfish

In this dissection, the chondrocranium of the dogfish is cleaned from the skin and adhering muscles from above. By cautiously working with a scalpel, thin superficial layers of the cartilage are cut away until the holes of the 3 semicircular ducts are exposed. The rest of the preparation is done by means of pointed steel forceps which are used for cutting or breaking the cartilage away. In the final sequence, the results of the preparation are displayed: the 3 semicircular ducts together with 3 ampullae and the utriculus in their natural spatial arrangement.

Language: German
Year of production: 1985
Format: VHS PAL, SECAM, NTSC
Running time: 12 mins.
Price: €25.05
Source: IWF Wissen und Medien gGmbH

 ## [The] Rat: A Practical Dissection Guide

A highly professional full colour video of a practical dissection of rat. The video is divided into 5 sections: preparation for the dissection and dissection instruments; external features; abdominal dissection showing the gastro-intestinal and urino-genital tracts; thoracic dissection; exposure, removal and dissection of the brain. Where there are significant differences between male and female rats, dissection of both is shown. Videoclips are punctuated with stills which are annotated to highlight important structures. An accompanying commentary describes the functional anatomy of the structures in view.

Format: VHS PAL, NTSC
Running time: 20 mins.
Price: £50.00 (incl. postage)
Source: Sheffield BioScience Programs

 ## Shark Dissection & Anatomy

Perfect for use as a guide to dissection or for pre-lab preparation, post-lab review, or as a viable alternative to dissection. Vivid video includes sections on external anatomy and the skin; dissection techniques; nervous, circulatory, excretory and reproductive systems; and the mouth cavity.

Format: VHS NTSC
Running time: 26 mins.
Price: US$79.95
Source: Neo/Sci

When contacting producers and distributors, please cite *from Guinea Pig to Computer Mouse*

Surgical Anatomy: Left Caudal Lobectomy in the Dog

The identification of anatomic landmarks to be noted during the surgical procedure of left caudal lobectomy. The dissection of this fresh cadaver displays the appropriate thoracotomy and approach to the caudal lobe of the left lung through the 7th intercostal space.

Year of production: 1982
Format: VHS NTSC, PAL
Running time: 9 mins.
Price: US$50.00
Source: University of California (UC Davis)

 Surgical Anatomy: The Canine Ventral Neck

The canine ventral neck is examined by dissection of a fresh cadaver. The approaches are caudal, beginning at the thyroid and midventral between the bodies of the mandible. Emphasis is on the identification of anatomical structures, including the oesophagus, trachea, larynx, thyroid, jugular vein, geniohyoidius muscle, cricoid cartilage, vagosympathic trunk, and lymph nodes.

Year of production: 1982
Format: VHS NTSC, PAL
Running time: 27 mins.
Price: US$50.00
Source: University of California (UC Davis)

 Unicellular Organisms

Unicellular algae and unicellular animal organisms were among the first forms of life on Earth. However, they already possessed specialised structures for locomotion, metabolism, defence and reproduction. This video uses the paramecium and the euglena to illustrate the structure and the life pattern of these minute organisms.

Language: French, German
Year of production: 1998
Format: VHS PAL, SECAM. Also available on CD-ROM (see under SOFTWARE)
Running time: 20 mins.
Price: €15.24 (individual use), €30.49 (institutional use)
Note: This program is distributed by SFRS in France only; its French title is *Organismes cellulaires*; the original German title is *Einzeller*
Source: SFRS

[The] Vertebrate Anatomy Set

See *Animal Anatomy Set*.

 Vertebrate Dissection Guides Series

This series of videos includes 4 titles: *The Rat, The Dogfish, The Frog and The Pigeon*. See description under SOFTWARE version of this series.

Year of prodution: 1992
Format: VHS PAL, NTSC
Running time: 38 - 56 mins.
Price: £40.00 per program (incl. VAT)
Source: University of Portsmouth

When contacting producers and distributors,
please cite *from Guinea Pig to Computer Mouse*

MODELS, MANNEKINS, SIMULATORS

 Amoeba Model

This is a *Bobbitt* model clearly showing all the important features of the amoeba. It is mounted on a 15 x 18" base, and comes with a manual.

Medium: Model
Price: US$170.00; see website for country distributors
Source: Carolina Biological Supply (catalogue ref. WW-56-4100)

 Amoeba Model, Deluxe

The 1,000x model is sectioned to reveal the various structures of an amoeba, including the nucleus, food and contractile vacuoles, fat droplet, and cytoplasm. It also features extended pseudopods re-creating natural movement. The model is mounted on a base and comes with a manual identifying 12 features. Size: 21"L x 11"W x 3¾"H.

Medium: Model
Price: US$169.95
Source: Ward's Natural Science (catalogue ref. 81 V 5195)

 Amoeba Proteus Model

Enlarged approximately 1,000x linearly, and modelled in 'SOMSO-Plast'. A small pseudopod can be opened up showing the structure after electronmicroscopic magnification. Adapted to the most modern standards of research. On a base with explanatory notes. Separates into 2 parts. H8 cm, W48 cm, D31 cm, Wt 1.8 kg.

Medium: Model
Price: On request, from regional distributors
Source: Contact Marcus Sommer Somso Modelle for regional distributors (catalogue ref. ZoS 101)

Ant Model

Formica polyctena - the worker red forest ant modelled at the scale of 30:1 in 'SOMSO-Plast'. In one piece, on a stand with base. H16 cm, W11 cm, D18 cm, Wt 600 g.

Medium: Model
Price: On request, from regional distributors
Source: Contact Marcus Sommer Somso Modelle for regional distributors (catalogue ref. ZoS 49/27)

 ## Aphid Model

Macrosiphum rosae - the wingless rose aphid, modelled at the scale of approximately 80:1 in 'SOMSO-Plast'. In one piece, on a stand with base. H16 cm, W24 cm, D18 cm, Wt 600 g.

Medium: Model
Price: On request, from regional distributors
Source: Contact Marcus Sommer Somso Modelle for regional distributors (catalogue ref. ZoS 49/22)

 ## Barkbeetle Model

Approximately 40x enlarged, and modelled in 'SOMSO-Plast'. Magnified and true to detail representation of the big Spruce barkbeetle with 8 teeth (*Ips typographus*). In one piece. On a stand with base. H17 cm, W32 cm, D18 cm, Wt 800 g.

Medium: Model
Price: On request, from regional distributors
Source: Contact Marcus Sommer Somso Modelle for regional distributors (catalogue ref. ZoS 47/5)

 ## Beaver Skull Model

Made from castor fibre, with natural casting in 'SOMSO-Plast', with movable and removable mandible. Wt 300 g.

Medium: Model
Price: On request, from regional distributors
Source: Contact Marcus Sommer Somso Modelle for regional distributors (catalogue ref. ZoS 53/20)

Bee Head Model

The head of *Apis mellifica*, modelled from nature at the scale of 50:1, in 'SOMSO-Plast'. The mouth parts adapted for chewing and licking are shown. Upper jaw movable to demonstrate its function. Separates into 2 parts. On a stand with base. H34 cm, W18 cm, D19 cm, Wt 800 g.

Medium: Model
Price: On request, from regional distributors
Source: Contact Marcus Sommer Somso Modelle for regional distributors (catalogue ref. ZoS 48/1)

Bee Hind Legs Model

A functional model, enlarged many times, in 'SOMSO-Plast'. It illustrates the following functions: brushing of the bee's body with the pollen combs, patting down the pollen masses at the outside of the tibia, and a movable joint between tibia and planta. On a stand with base. H34 cm, W18 cm, D18 cm, Wt 1 kg.

Medium: Model
Price: On request, from regional distributors
Source: Contact Marcus Sommer Somso Modelle for regional distributors (catalogue ref. ZoS 47/2)

Bone Clones Skulls

Bone Clones is a series of skulls skillfully cast by Kronen Osteo from the best original skulls available for each of the animals depicted. The materials of the finished skulls are of the highest quality resin, to capture the best original detail and to make them resistant to chipping and breakage. Careful attention is paid to the finished product from preparing the original skull to the finishing process, in order to achieve a skull or skeleton that is difficult to distinguish from a real one. Kronen Osteo also does replicas of various other animal bones and teeth, as well as custom casting.

- **Birds Skulls:** *Gymnogyps califonianus* (California condor), *Corvus brachyrhynchos* (crow), *Corvus corax* (raven), *Haliaeetus leucocephalus* (bald eagle), *Falco peregrinus* (peregrine falcon), *Buteo jamaicensis* (red-tail hawk), *Bubo virginianus* (great horned owl), *Pelecanus erythrorhynchos* (American white pelican), *Spheniscus magellanicus* (Magellan penguin), *Dryocopus pileatus* (pileated woodpecker)

- **Cats Skulls:** *Felis catus/domesticus* (common house cat), *Panthera leo* (African lion), *Panthera onca* (jaguar), *Panthera pardus* (African leopard), *Panthera tigris altaica* (Siberian tiger), *Acionyx jubatus* (cheetah)

- **Dogs Skulls:** *Canis familiaris* (Airdale, English bulldog, Great Dane, Saluki, Saint Bernard), *Canis lupus* (Siberian wolf), *Canis dirus* (dire wolf), *Chrysocyon brachyurus* (maned wolf), *Crocuta crocuta* (hyena)

- **Marine Mammals Skulls:** *Tursiops truncatus* (dolphin), Enhydra lutris (sea otter), *Phoca vitulina* (harbor seal), *Odobenus rosmarus* (walrus), *Pseudorca crassidens* (false killer whale)

- **Other Skulls:** *Pteropus poliocephalus* (fruit bat), *Desmodus rotundus* (vampire bat), *Mustela nigripes* (black-footed ferret), *Phascolartos cinereus* (koala), *Cynocephalus variegatus* (flying lemur)

- **Primates Skulls:** *Pan troglodytes* (chimpanzee), *Hylobates lar* (gibbon ape), *Gorilla gorilla* (gorilla), *Pongo pygmaeus* (orangutan), *Papio sphinx* (mandrill baboon), *Lemur catta* (ring tail lemur), *Sanginus oedipus* (tamarin)

Medium: Model
Prices: US$49.00 - US$490.00, depending on model
Source: Kronen Osteo

 Bony Fish Model

The carp - *Cyprinus carpio* - in 'SOMSO-Plast', modelled from life in natural size. Intestines, air-bladder and testicles are removable. Separates into 4 parts. On a stand with base and explanation. H35 cm, W49 cm, D15 cm, Wt 1.6 kg.

Medium: Model
Price: On request, from regional distributors
Source: Contact Marcus Sommer Somso Modelle for regional distributors (catalogue ref. ZoS 105)

 Brains of Vertebrates Models Series

New edition, in 'SOMSO-Plast', covering the following 8 models (many times enlarged): 1. River lamprey (*Lampetra fluviatilis*); 2. Dogfish (*Scyliorhinus caniculus*); 3. Trout (*Salmo trutta fario*); 4. Frog (*Rana esculenta*); 5. Alligator (*Alligator mississippiensis*); 6. Dove (*Columba livia domestica*); 7. Rabbit (*Oryctolagus cuniculus*); 8. Dog (*Canis lupus familiaris*). In one piece. Each model individually on a stand with base. Weight of the series: 1.6 kg.

Medium: Model
Price: On request, from regional distributors
Source: Contact Marcus Sommer Somso Modelle for regional distributors (catalogue ref. ZoS 55)

 Breeding Pig (Dam) Model

A model based on a breeding pig from the Bavarian State Institute for Animal Breeding in Grub. Approximately ½ natural size, in 'SOMSO-Plast'. One side shows the skin, the other side shows the muscular system. The model is mounted on a base which can be pulled out and is detachable in two halves through the median line. After separating both halves of the body, the left side shows the thoracic and abdominal cover, while the right one shows the thoracic and abdominal organs. The left half of the head shows the muscular system, the main blood vessels and glands (the parotid gland can be removed) as well as the auricular cartilage and the left foreleg (both removable). The model separates altogether into 17 parts: the right and left halves of body, left half of head, parotid gland, left foreleg, half of lungs, heart (2), liver, stomach (2), pancreas, small intestine, large intestine, renal fat and half of uterus. H48 cm, W102 cm (length of the model), D26 cm, Wt 21 kg.

Medium: Model
Price: On request, from regional distributors
Source: Contact Marcus Sommer Somso Modelle for regional distributors (catalogue ref. ZoS 18/1)

Bullfrog Junior

Scaled-down somewhat from the *Great American Bullfrog*, this just-over-life-size vinyl-plastic replica of an adult female bullfrog portrays the same ten organ systems found in its big sister, but with fewer numbered features (but still over 100) and no detachable parts. The accompanying key also includes a fully-labeled illustration of the reproductive system of a male frog. Overall dimensions: 43 x 30 x 10 cm.

Medium: Model
Price: US$398.00
Source: Denoyer Geppert International

Butterfly Head Model

The head of *Pieris brassicae*, modelled from nature at the scale of 50:1, in 'SOMSO-Plast'. The proboscis is shown stretched out and coiled. Separates into 5 parts. On a stand with base. H82 cm (with antennae), W18 cm, D25 cm, Wt 900 g.

Medium: Model
Price: On request, from regional distributors
Source: Contact Marcus Sommer Somso Modelle for regional distributors (catalogue ref. ZoS 48/2)

Carabus Head Model

The head of *Carabus auratus*, enlarged 50x linearly, in 'SOMSO-Plast'. Lower jaw, lower lip and both antennae are removable for demonstration purposes. Simplified facet structure. Separates into 6 parts. On a base. H40 cm, W40 cm (with antennae 69 cm), D26 cm, Wt 2.7 kg.

Medium: Model
Price: On request, from regional distributors
Source: Contact Marcus Sommer Somso Modelle for regional distributors (catalogue ref. ZoS 48)

 ## Chimpanzee Skeleton

Natural cast of the bones of an approximately 12 year-old *Pan troglodytes* adult male, in 'SOMSO-Plast'. Showing life-size all the anatomical details of the bone structure. Skull with removable vault and mandible. Joints mounted and movable, upper and lower extremities removable. The right and left foot can be detached from the leg and are also available separately, as are the skull and the pelvis. Mounted upright on a stand. H90 cm, W82 cm, D40 cm, Wt 10.3 kg.

Medium: Model
Price: On request, from regional distributors
Source: Contact Marcus Sommer Somso Modelle for regional distributors (catalogue ref. ZoS 53/110)

 ## Clam Model

This is a *Bobbitt* model with an open dissection showing clam anatomy in detail. It is mounted on a 8 x 15" base.

Medium: Model
Price: US$262.50; see website for country distributors
Source: Carolina Biological Supply (catalogue ref. WW-56-4379)

 ## Clam Model

View the intricate details of a typical *Pelecypod mollusc*, enlarged approximately 5x and highlighted with various colours to show the circulation patterns and all other major organ systems. The model is mounted on a base and includes a key identifying 53 structures. Size: 15"L x 8"W x 6"H.

Medium: Model
Price: US$262.50
Source: Ward's Natural Science (catalogue ref. 81 V 5173)

Clonorchis Model

With digestive and reproductive systems enlarged 30x, these two durable urethane models in one set allow a better view of the minute details of the liver fluke. Featuring exquisite colouring highlighting the internal structures, they are ideal supplements to microscope slide study of the organism. The ventral and dorsal dissections each measure 20" long and 4" wide. The 2 models are mounted on a common base. Includes a key identifying 20 structures. Size: 12"W x 24"H x 2"D.

Medium: Model
Price: US$285.00
Source: Ward's Natural Science (catalogue ref. 81 V 0040)

 Cockroach Head Model

The head of *Periplaneta americana*, modelled from nature at the scale of 50:1, in 'SOMSO-Plast'. The upper jaw and maxillae are movable and mounted to demonstrate the function. Separates into 3 parts. On a stand with base. H41 cm, W27 cm, D18 cm, Wt 1 kg.

Medium: Model
Price: On request, from regional distributors
Source: Contact Marcus Sommer Somso Modelle for regional distributors (catalogue ref. ZoS 48/6)

 Compound (Facet) Eye Model

Enlarged approximately 200x, in 'SOMSO-Plast'. Showing the delicate histological structure. In one piece, on a stand with base. H33 cm, W29 cm, D18 cm, Wt 900 g.

Medium: Model
Price: On request, from regional distributors
Source: Contact Marcus Sommer Somso Modelle for regional distributors (catalogue ref. ZoS 49)

 Cow Model

Approximately ⅓ natural size model, in 'SOMSO-Plast'. Median section, divisible in two halves. The left side shows the hide, the right side shows the surface muscular system. The right foreleg with shoulder-blade and the biceps of the thigh are removable. The udder shows suspension, network of blood and lymphatic vessels. The organs are detachable as follows: lungs, heart (2), small and large intestine, ruminant stomach, uterus and half of the udder. Altogether 11 parts.

Mounted on a removable base with rollers. Showing the paunch puncture. H54 cm, W85 cm, D25 cm, Wt 16.8 kg.

Medium: Model
Price: On request, from regional distributors
Source: Contact Marcus Sommer Somso Modelle for regional distributors (catalogue ref. ZoS 1)

 ## Crayfish Model

Astacus astacus - the crayfish - showing structure of the body and anatomy of a male animal, linearly enlarged 3x, in 'SOMSO-Plast'. Life-like model that shows on the left side the differentiated external limbs, and on the right side the internal structure of the crayfish. Movable claws are detachable to demonstrate the position of the internal organs. Separates into 13 parts. On a stand with base. H28 cm, W82 cm, D29 cm, Wt 4 kg.

Medium: Model
Price: On request, from regional distributors
Source: Contact Marcus Sommer Somso Modelle for regional distributors (catalogue ref. ZoS 118)

 ## Crayfish Model

The seemingly simple crayfish is more complex than it appears. This two-model set containing one sagittal section and one cross section, both enlarged 4x clearly shows the inner workings and intricate anatomy of a crayfish, including all major organ systems and appendages. Both models are mounted on a common wooden base. Includes a key identifying 122 structures.
Size: 30"L x 12"W x 2½"H.

Medium: Model
Price: US$400.00
Source: Ward's Natural Science (catalogue ref. 81 V 5174)

 ## Domestic Hen Model

Natural size, in 'SOMSO-Plast', and modelled from a natural skeleton. One side shows the feathers, and the other shows the organs. By a simple operation the torso can be taken from the feathers to show the muscular system. The internal organs are detachable as follows: left lung, part of the liver, stomach. Altogether in 5 parts, with a base. H49 cm, W45 cm, D26 cm, Wt 2.4 kg.

Medium: Model
Price: On request, from regional distributors
Source: Contact Marcus Sommer Somso Modelle for regional distributors (catalogue ref. ZoS 26)

Earthworm Model

This is a *Bobbitt* model with a dissection of the anterior portion showing the digestive, circulatory, nervous and reproductive systems. A cross-section of the 22nd segment is shown. The model is mounted on a 56 x 15 cm base.

Medium: Model
Price: US$435.75; see website for country distributors
Source: Carolina Biological Supply (catalogue ref. WW-56-4367)

 Earthworm Model

Lumbricus terrestris - the earthworm - enlarged 25x, in 'SOMSO-Plast'. The model shows the front third of the body with a cross section in relief. To see the inside of the stomach the intestine can be removed, also exposing all the sexual organs. Finally the seminal vesicles can be removed to show the testes and funnels of sperm ducts. Separates into 3 parts, on a stand with base and explanatory notes. H25 cm, W53 cm, D14 cm, Wt 2.2 kg.

Medium: Model
Price: On request, from regional distributors
Source: Contact Marcus Sommer Somso Modelle for regional distributors (catalogue ref. ZoS 108)

 Earthworm Set Model

This is a *Bobbitt* model showing the earthworm's internal organs and male and female reproductive systems. It is mounted on a 12 x 30" base, and comes with a manual.

Medium: Model
Price: US$385.00; see website for country distributors
Source: Carolina Biological Supply (catalogue ref. WW-56-4360)

When contacting producers and distributors,
please cite *from Guinea Pig to Computer Mouse*

Fetal Pig Model

This is a *Bobbitt* model at 2x life size. A separate piece shows the internal organs (heart, lungs, stomach, liver, and intestines) along with the basic pattern of the blood supply. It is mounted on a sturdy base.

Medium: Model
Price: US$675.00; see website for country distributors
Source: Carolina Biological Supply (catalogue ref. WW-56-5781)

 Fetal Pig Model

Cast from an actual specimen, all of the intricate structural detail usually only seen on a real dissected specimen can clearly be seen on this life-size model of a nearly full-term foetal pig. Features all internal organs and major arteries and veins found along the body cavity, head and neck. In addition, the heart, lungs, stomach, liver, and intestines are removable as a single unit so students can study the deeper organs and vasculature. One kidney is sectioned to show renal circulation. Made of a unique material for flexibility and durability, the model has look and feel of a real specimen, and is hand painted to match real dissection specimens. Comes with a key identifying over 100 structures. Size: 20"L x 8"W x 3½"H.

Medium: Model
Price: US$325.00
Source: Ward's Natural Science (catalogue ref. 81 V 2003)

 Flea Model

Ctenocephalides felis - the cat flea, modelled in 'SOMSO-Plast' at the scale of approximately 70:1, being 18 cm long from head to tip of abdomen and 22.5 cm high, including the stretched legs. In one piece, on a stand with base. H25 cm, W12 cm, D18 cm, Wt 500 g.

Medium: Model
Price: On request, from regional distributors
Source: Contact Marcus Sommer Somso Modelle for regional distributors (catalogue ref. ZoS 49/32)

 Fly Head Model

Head of *Musca domestica*, modelled from nature at the scale of 50:1, in 'SOMSO-Plast'. In one piece, on a stand with base. H27 cm, W18 cm, D20 cm, Wt 700 g.

Medium: Model
Price: On request, from regional distributors
Source: Contact Marcus Sommer Somso Modelle for regional distributors (catalogue ref. ZoS 48/4)

 Fly Model

Musca domestica - the common housefly - modelled at the scale of 30:1 in 'SOMSO-Plast'. Supplied on a stand with base. H23 cm, W22 cm, D26 cm., Wt 500 g.

Medium: Model
Price: On request, from regional distributors
Source: Contact Marcus Sommer Somso Modelle for regional distributors (catalogue ref. ZoS 49/31)

 Frog Lab

Developed in partnership with the Smithsonian Institution, the innovative *Frog Lab* allows students to mould their own 'frogs' using the easy-to-prepare materials included. Ready to dissect in just 15 mins., the resulting 'specimens' look and feel like the real thing. Students will even dissect and explore the 11-piece plastic skeletal and organ system - complete with lungs, heart and other organs. Includes comprehensive, fully illustrated teacher and student guides with step by step instructions, activities, detailed reference information and plastic dissection equipment.

Medium: Model
Price: US$24.95 (individual set - 3 specimens/1 mould); US$99.95 (class set - 9 specimens/3 moulds); US$9.95 (refill for 3 additional specimens)
Source: Neo/Sci

 Frog Model

This is a *Bobbitt* model showing a ventral dissection of the bullfrog. Half the lower jaw is removed, and the digestive system is spread to reveal deeply lying organs. The circulatory and reproductive (female) systems are shown in detail. It is mounted on 16 x 21" base, and comes with a manual.

Medium: Model
Price: US$345.00; see website for country distributors
Source: Carolina Biological Supply (catalogue ref. WW-56-4900)

Frog Models

The meticulous detail and incredible realism of both life-size *Rana catesbiana* models (male and female) are extraordinary; even the structures of the inner mouth are shown. Cast from actual specimens, they feature over 50 details from the digestive, circulatory, musculatory, and reproductive systems, colourfully yet subtly painted to realistically show all major structures. Each comes with a key identifying 45 structures. Made of a unique material for flexibility and durability. Size: female 14"L x 6"W x 2"H; male 13"L x 6"W x 2½"H.

Medium: Model
Price: US$112.00 (each)
Source: Ward's Natural Science (catalogue ref. 81 V 2000, male; 81 V 2001, female)

 Gnat Head Model

Head of a female gnat, *Culex pipiens*, modelled from nature, at the scale of 80:1, in 'SOMSO-Plast'. The long stylets, consisting of the labrum (upper lip), the paired mandibles (maxillae), the paired maxillae (mandibles) and the hypopharynx can be put together to demonstrate the function of the stylets. In one piece, on a stand with base. H40 cm, W18 cm, D45 cm, Wt 800 g.

Medium: Model
Price: On request, from regional distributors
Source: Contact Marcus Sommer Somso Modelle for regional distributors (catalogue ref. ZoS 48/3)

 Grasshopper Model

This is a *Bobbitt* model showing a lateral dissection of the female grasshopper, with external anatomy and major systems presented. It is mounted on a 7 x 24" base, and comes with a manual.

Medium: Model
Price: US$360.00; see website for country distributors
Source: Carolina Biological Supply (catalogue ref. WW-56-4555)

When contacting producers and distributors,
please cite *from Guinea Pig to Computer Mouse*

Grasshopper Model

Sectioned medially and dissected in detail, this 6x enlarged model of a female grasshopper shows all the major organ systems, colourfully illustrated for up-close view of anatomy. The one-piece, rotatable model is mounted on a stand and includes a key identifying 57 structures. Size: 23"L x 9 ½"W x 9"H.

Medium: Model
Price: US$360.00
Source: Ward's Natural Science (catalogue ref. 81 V 4064)

 Great American Bullfrog

This is a twice life-size vinyl-plastic replica of a sexually mature female bullfrog, *Rana catesbeiana*. Ten organ systems are faithfully portrayed, including a removable highly-detailed 3-chambered heart, which divides into anterior and posterior halves. Multi-level dissections expose all the viscera, the buccal cavity, the musculature of the hind leg, the brain and nervous system, the eye and optic nerve, the ear and all the bones. Half of the mandible, tongue, and glottis remove as a unit for detailed study. Strategic cutaways reveal the bronchi of the lung, stomach rugae, and the lumen of the large intestine. The model includes even such fine points as internal nares, vomerine teeth, eustachian tube, and the nictitating membrane of the eye. More than 175 hand-numbered features are identified in the accompanying key, which also illustrates the male reproductive system. Overall dimensions: 53 x 38 x 10 cm.

Medium: Model
Price: US$648.00
Source: Denoyer Geppert International

 Green Hydra Model

Colourfully illustrated and enlarged approximately 30x, the median longitudinal section clearly displays the external and internal structure, budding, spermary, and an ovary. The nematocyst 'harpoons' are extended to demonstrate how prey is captured. The model is mounted on a base. Size: 4½"L x 6"W x 10¼"H.

Medium: Model
Price: US$189.00
Source: Ward's Natural Science (catalogue ref. 81 V 4793)

Head of a Venomous Snake Model

The head of *Vipera berus* (adder, common viper) enlarged approximately 15x, in 'SOMSO-Plast'. This model illustrates very clearly the general construction of the head of a snake, the venom apparatus and the distinguishing characteristics of an adder. Not detachable, on a stand with base. H39 cm, W49 cm, D26 cm, Wt 1.7 kg.

Medium: Model
Price: On request, from regional distributors
Source: Contact Marcus Sommer Somso Modelle for regional distributors (catalogue ref. ZoS 115)

 Headlouse Model

Peaculus humanus, var. *capitis*, modelled to a scale of approximately 70:1 in 'SOMSO-Plast'. 20 cm long from head to tip of abdomen and 16 cm wide across the legs. In one piece, on a stand with base. H17 cm, W20 cm, D16 cm, Wt 400 g.

Medium: Model
Price: On request, from regional distributors
Source: Contact Marcus Sommer Somso Modelle for regional distributors (catalogue ref. ZoS 49/20)

 Hearts of Vertebrates Models Series

Separable models, in 'SOMSO-Plast'. The internal structure is shown in all its detail, and the direction of the blood flow is marked. Altogether 7 models, in natural size and slightly enlarged from natural size, individually mounted on a stand with base: 1. Fish (*Esox lucius*), 2. Frog (*Rana esculenta*), 3. Tortoise (*Emys orbicularis*), 4. Crocodile (*Crocodylus niloticus*), 5. Bird – Golden Eagle (*Aquila chrysaetos*), 6. Dog (*Canis lupus familiaris*), 7. Human being (*Homo sapiens*). 14 parts in total. Weight of the series: 2.9 kg.

Medium: Model
Price: On request, from regional distributors
Source: Contact Marcus Sommer Somso Modelle for regional distributors (catalogue ref. ZoS 54/1)

 Honeybee Brain Model

The brain of *Apis mellifera*, at the scale of 50:1, made in special plastic and in two versions: with or without transparent capsule. The capsule can be opened and the complete brain removed to study its posterior and inferior aspects. Parts shown: ocelli, mushroom body, optical neuropile, antennal lobes, dorsal lobes and the suboesophageal ganglion. Part of the protocerebrum can be removed to see the structures underneath. On a stand with base. H23 cm, W18 cm, D18 cm, Wt 0.83 kg.

Medium: Model
Price: On request, from regional distributors
Source: Contact Marcus Sommer Somso Modelle for regional distributors (catalogue ref. ZoS 47/3 - with capsule, and ZoS 47/4 - without capsule)

 Honeybee Model

Apis mellifica - the honeybee - enlarged approximately 25x, in 'SOMSO-Plast'. On the model one leg is removable to show the pollen basket with the collected pollen at the back. In addition the honey vesicle in connection with a piece of intestine and vesicle of droppings is removable to show the underlying sting apparatus and the venom bladder. Altogether in 3 parts. On a stand with base. H50 cm, W47 cm, D15 cm, Wt 1.8 kg.

Medium: Model
Price: On request, from regional distributors
Source: Contact Marcus Sommer Somso Modelle for regional distributors (catalogue ref. ZoS 47/1)

 Hydra Model

Model of hydra, the fresh water polyp, enlarged approximately 30x, in 'SOMSO-Plast'. The anatomy of hydra is shown in longitudinal section, with the entoderm, mesoglea, ectoderm, male and female egg-cells, buds and mouth opening. On a supplementary model enlarged approximately 200x, the microscopic structure of the wall of the body near the stomach and intestine is shown, including various types of cell (nematoblasts, musculo-epithelial cells, sense cells, interstitial cells and the nerve network). In one piece, on a base, and with explanatory notes. H46 cm, W39 cm, D33 cm, Wt 2.1 kg.

Medium: Model
Price: On request, from regional distributors
Source: Contact Marcus Sommer Somso Modelle for regional distributors (catalogue ref. ZoS 106)

When contacting producers and distributors,
please cite *from Guinea Pig to Computer Mouse*

Hydra Set Model

This is a set of 3 *Bobbitt* models showing the anatomy of hydra in detail. The set is mounted on a 16 x 21" base, and comes with a manual.

Medium: Model
Price: US$300.00; see website for country distributors
Source: Carolina Biological Supply (catalogue ref. WW-56-4212)

 Individual MI-OWN Frog Models

MI-OWN Frog models permit safe, humane, inexpensive, accurate and individual frog dissection. Each frog is life size (8"H) and has 22 removable parts. They are washable, reusable, unbreakable, and require no glue, magnets or 'Velcro'. The model comes with a reproducible student worksheet set, a teacher's guide and a key card.

Medium: Model
Price: US$41.95 (individual models); US$224.75 (box of 12 models)
Source: Hubbard Scientific

 Model of Middle and Inner Ear of the Horse

This is an enlarged decomposable polyester cast of middle and inner ear of the horse to demonstrate tympanic cavity, auditory ossicles, osseus and membranous labyrinth.

Medium: Model
Price: €350.00
Source: Prof. Wolfgang Künzel (University of Veterinary Medicine Vienna, Austria)

 Model of the Hoof

This is an enlarged decomposable polyester cast of the hoof for a better understanding of the surface of the corium and the epidermal horn layers.

Medium: Model
Price: €300.00
Source: Prof. Wolfgang Künzel (University of Veterinary Medicine Vienna, Austria)

Mosquito Model

Culex pipiens, enlarged at the scale of 50:1, in 'SOMSO-Plast'. Separates into 7 parts. On a base which can be pulled apart. H60 cm, W75 cm, D65 cm, Wt 3.1 kg.

Medium: Model
Price: On request, from regional distributors
Source: Contact Marcus Sommer Somso Modelle for regional distributors (catalogue ref. ZoS 48/5)

Paramecium Model

This is a *Bobbitt* model demonstrating the basic features of ciliate anatomy. It is mounted on 9 x 23" base, and comes with a manual.

Medium: Model
Price: US$200.00; see website for country distributors
Source: Carolina Biological Supply (catalogue ref. WW-56-4180)

Paramecium Model

Enlarged approximately 1,600x, in 'SOMSO-Plast', this model shows the cell inventory of a protozoa: macro- and micronucleus, contractile vacuoles, cytostome with membranellae, myonemes and food vacuoles, and the formation of the endo- and ectoplasm and the network of neuronemes. A detailed block shows the structure of the pellicle of the ectoplasm, and the position and order of the trichocysts and a range of cilia in typical order. Separates into 2 parts, on a stand with base and explanatory notes. H61 cm, W39 cm, D26 cm, Wt 2.7 kg.

Medium: Model
Price: On request, from regional distributors
Source: Contact Marcus Sommer Somso Modelle for regional distributors (catalogue ref. ZoS 107)

Paramecium Model

This representation of a widely studied protist is enlarged 1,500x and sectioned to show its inner anatomy. It features the nucleus, oral groove, contractile vacuole, intercilliary fibrils, and more, as well as discharged trichocysts. The model is mounted on a base and includes a manual identifying 29 structures. Size: 19"L x 6"W x 3"H.

Medium: Model
Price: US$200.00
Source: Ward's Natural Science (catalogue ref. 81 V 5194)

Perch Model

This is a *Bobbitt* model demonstrating the perch's internal organs in a spread dissection. A portion of the skull is removed to show the semicircular canals and brain. It is mounted on 10 x 24" base, and comes with a manual.

Medium: Model
Price: US$305.00; see website for country distributors
Source: Carolina Biological Supply (catalogue ref. WW-56-4755)

 Perch Model

Cast from an actual specimen, this life-size model clearly shows over 50 exterior and interior anatomical details. Every major body system is included: digestive; circulatory, with major arteries and veins; respiratory; muscular; and reproductive. A cut-out dorsal view of the brain is also featured, displaying the optic nerves, olfactory tract, optic lobes, cerebellum, and associated cranial nerves. The model, hand painted for a realistic, detailed representation, is made from flexible, unbreakable materials and includes a key identifying all structures. Size: 12"L x 6"W.

Medium: Model
Price: US$118.00
Source: Ward's Natural Science (catalogue ref. 81 V 2008)

 Planarian Model

Cast in durable resin, 2 large and 2 small models on one raised-relief plaque illustrate the various structures of the organism. The larger models, each 18"L and 5"W, depict dorsal dissections of the nervous system and of the reproductive system, with a cross section of the digestive and excretory systems, enlarged 25x. The two smaller models show a whole worm with extended pharynx, along with a highly magnified flame cell. Each model is beautifully detailed and coloured so all important features are emphasised and easy to locate. The 4 models are mounted on one plaque. Comes with a key identifying 20 structures. Size: 18"W x 22"H.

Medium: Model
Price: US$399.00
Source: Ward's Natural Science (catalogue ref. 81 V 0020)

When contacting producers and distributors,
please cite *from Guinea Pig to Computer Mouse*

Planarian Set Model

This is a *Bobbitt* model with dorsal and ventral dissections, and an enlarged cross section showing internal anatomy. The dissections are mounted together on a 9 x 23" base, and come with a manual.

Medium: Model
Price: US$345.00; see website for country distributors
Source: Carolina Biological Supply (catalogue ref. WW-56-4230)

 Pregnant Cat Model

With over 100 anatomical details, this one-piece, life-size model, cast from an actual specimen, is a very realistic cat dissection model. Some of the structures featured include a cross-sectioned kidney showing the cortex and medulla, major arteries and veins, muscle groups of the fore and hind limbs, and the open uterus exposing a developing foetus. The model is so precise, even the open mouth cavity details the teeth and nasopharynx. Made of a unique material for flexibility and durability, the model has the look and feel of a real specimen, and is hand painted to match real dissection specimens. Includes a key identifying 136 structures. Size: 23"L x 10"W x 5".

Medium: Model
Price: US$399.00
Source: Ward's Natural Science (catalogue ref. 81 V 2005)

 Pregnant Shark Model

This life-size dissection model provides an exceedingly realistic representation of shark anatomy, clearly displaying over 100 anatomical details. Cast from a real specimen, it features a pup with yolk sac in the uterus. Also shows mouth and pharynx, dorsal view of the eyes, brain and cranial nerves, branchial circulation, ventral view of the viscera and circulatory vasculature, and the trunk musculature in lateral and cross-sectional views. Each model is made from unbreakable materials and is painted by hand to ensure the finest detail possible. Includes a key identifying 100 structures. Size: 19½"L x 7½"W x 3"H.

Medium: Model
Price: US$305.00
Source: Ward's Natural Science (catalogue ref. 81 V 2007)

When contacting producers and distributors,
please cite *from Guinea Pig to Computer Mouse*

Rat Brain Model

Scaled at 4.25:1, in 'SOMSO-Plast'. On a stand with base. H25 cm, L12 cm, D12 cm, Wt 0.3 kg.

Medium: Model
Price: On request, from regional distributors
Source: Contact Marcus Sommer Somso Modelle for regional distributors (catalogue ref. ZoS 55/9)

 Rat Model

Highly detailed and expertly prepared, this durable life-size model was patterned on an actual dissected rat. Made from unbreakable material and hand painted for accuracy, it features a number of detailed structures including a foetus in a partially dissected uterus and a sectioned kidney. Includes a key identifying over 50 structures. Size: 11½"L x 6½"W x 2¾"H.

Medium: Model
Price: US$164.00
Source: Ward's Natural Science (catalogue ref. 81 V 2009)

 Rat Model

This life-size, 4-piece model is mounted on a base and comes with a key identifying 25 structures. All the important structures are shown in the typical ventral dissection, including the heart, lungs, liver, stomach, and intestines, which can all be removed for closer examination. Size: 12"L x 6"W x 4"H.

Medium: Model
Price: US$169.00
Source: Ward's Natural Science (catalogue ref. 81 V 5036)

 Ruminant Stomach of the Cow Model

A one-third natural size model. Rumen and reticulum can be divided into 2 halves to show the relief of the mucous membrane of the stomach, omasum and abomasum can be opened up. Separates into 3 parts. On a stand and base. H35 cm, W28 cm, D18 cm, Wt 1.7 kg.

Medium: Model
Price: On request, from regional distributors
Source: Contact Marcus Sommer Somso Modelle for regional distributors (catalogue ref. ZoS 6/1)

Sea Anemone Model

This is a *Bobbitt* model of a sea anemone dissection showing the gullet and the system of mesenteries that supports the gullet and reproductive structures. The gastrovascular cavity, the mesenteric filament, and the acontia are also exposed. D23 cm x H25 cm.

Medium: Model
Price: US$240.00; see website for country distributors
Source: Carolina Biological Supply (catalogue ref. WW-56-4224)

 Shark Head Model

Life-size model of an anterior dissection of a shark head, from the pectoral fins forward, which clearly displays the circulatory system. The ventral and dorsal dissections show the detail in the gills and the branchial basket. In addition, the vasculature is highlighted in colour. The model is mounted and comes with a key identifying 48 structures. Size: 14"H on 9½"D base.

Medium: Model
Price: US$340.00
Source: Ward's Natural Science (catalogue ref. 81 V 5175)

 Shark Lab

Developed in partnership with the Smithsonian Institution, *Shark Lab* allows students to mould their own realistic 'sharks' in just 15 mins. using the easy-to-use materials included. Each of the 'specimens' feature detailed, 13-piece plastic skeletal and organ systems - ready to explore through dissection. Includes comprehensive, fully illustrated teacher and student guides with step by step instructions, activities and detailed reference information and plastic dissection equipment.

Medium: Model
Price: US$24.95 (individual set - 3 specimens/1 mould); US$99.95 (class set - 9 specimens/3 molds); US$9.95 (refill for 3 additional specimens)
Source: Neo/Sci

 Shark Model

This is a *Bobbitt* model showing a dissection of the anterior portion of the shark (from pectoral fins forward) and demonstrating major details of the circulatory system. Ventral and dorsal dissections show the major blood vessels of the regions.

Medium: Model
Price: US$340.00; see website for country distributors
Source: Carolina Biological Supply (catalogue ref. WW-56-4740)

 ## Skulls of Anthropoids Models Series

Developed in co-operation with the State zoological collection in Munich, the series comprises natural casts, in 'SOMSO-Plast', of either male or female anthropoids skull models. Lower jaws are movable and can be removed. Species included: Gorilla, Orang-Utan, Chimpanzee, Baboon, Gibbon, Rhesus-Ape, Tupaia, Howling Monkey.

Medium: Model
Price: On request, from regional distributors
Source: Contact Marcus Sommer Somso Modelle for regional distributors (catalogue ref. ZoS 50 - ZoS 53/7)

 ## Snail Model

This is an elementary Bobbitt model, greatly enlarged, with a sagittal dissection showing internal anatomy. It is mounted on a sturdy base, and comes with a manual.

Medium: Model
Price: US$220.00; see website for country distributors
Source: Carolina Biological Supply (catalogue ref. WW-56-4390)

 ## SOMSO Vertebrate Models

Vertebrate models available as special orders:

- *Bavarian Warmblut Mare Model* (catalogue ref. Zo 62/1)
- *Breeding Pig 'Ingrid' Model* (catalogue ref. Zo 66)
- *Carcass of a Bullock Model* (catalogue ref. Zo 50/6)
- *Carcass of a Pig Model* (catalogue ref. Zo 50/5)
- *East Fresian Breeding Bull Model* (catalogue ref. Zo 73)
- *Fresian Dutch Cow Model* (catalogue ref. Zo 71)
- *Horse Model* (catalogue ref. Zo 28)
- *Shorthorn-Bull 'Roan Sam' Model* (catalogue ref. Zo 74)

Descriptions not available.

Medium: Model
Price: On request, from regional distributors
Source: Contact Marcus Sommer Somso Modelle for regional distributors

Sponge Model

This raised-relief 10x model of *Scypha (Grantia)* details typical poriferan structure. It shows the canal system to make it easy to discern how oxygen is diffused through the body walls and a bud to demonstrate the process of asexual reproduction. The model is mounted on an integral base and comes with a key identifying 10 structures. Size: 5½"L x 4½"W x 13"H.

Medium: Model
Price: US$175.00
Source: Ward's Natural Science (catalogue ref. 81 V 5172)

 Starfish Model

This is a *Bobbitt* model of a starfish, greatly enlarged, showing internal and external anatomy. It is mounted on a base, and comes with a manual.

Medium: Model
Price: US$240.00; see website for country distributors
Source: Carolina Biological Supply (catalogue ref. WW-56-4300)

 Starfish Model

Asterias - the starfish - many times enlarged, in 'SOMSO-Plast'. The model shows in detail: 1. Complete arm with normal position of the organs (stomach, intestinal caeca, pyloric caica, ampullae); 2. Arm with ampullae, ring canal, Polian vesicles; 3. Skeleton of the arm with nervous system (nerve-ring and radial nerves); 4. Arm in transverse section (ambulacral system in cross-section). The cut surface shows the stomach, stone canal, axial organ and madreporite. In addition on the outside the podia, pedicellariae and optic organs are shown. Altogether in 3 parts. On a stand (from which it can be removed), and base. H31 cm, W53 cm, D35 cm, Wt 2.2 kg.

Medium: Model
Price: On request, from regional distributors
Source: Contact Marcus Sommer Somso Modelle for regional distributors (catalogue ref. ZoS 114)

When contacting producers and distributors,
please cite *from Guinea Pig to Computer Mouse*

Starfish Model

Lifesize and cast from an actual specimen, this durable, flexible, freestanding model shows all the intricate details of the starfish's surface structure as well as its internal anatomy. Three arms are dissected at various levels to show the digestive, reproductive, and water vascular systems; one arm is cross-sectioned to reveal the coelom. Hand painted for exceptional accuracy. Comes with a key identifying 25 structures. Size: 10" diameter.

Medium: Model
Price: US$125.00
Source: Ward's Natural Science (catalogue ref. 81 V 2004)

 ## Starfish Model (Introductory)

This raised-relief plaque model illustrates all the important components of the starfish. Three arms are dissected to varying depths to show digestive, reproductive, and water vascular systems. The central disk is also partly dissected to display the ring canal and madreporite. Features a key printed on the plaque, identifying 12 structures. Size: 22"W x 16"H.

Medium: Model
Price: US$53.00
Source: Ward's Natural Science (catalogue ref. 81 V 5179)

 ## Tapeworm (Beef / Unarmed) Head Model

Taenia saginata, enlarged many times, in 'SOMSO-Plast'. In one piece, on a base. H28 cm, W18 cm, D18 cm, Wt 900 g.

Medium: Model
Price: On request, from regional distributors
Source: Contact Marcus Sommer Somso Modelle for regional distributors (catalogue ref. ZoS 116/2)

When contacting producers and distributors,
please cite *from Guinea Pig to Computer Mouse*

Tapeworm (Pork/Armed) Head Model

Taenia solium, enlarged many times, in 'SOMSO-Plast'. In one piece, on a base. H28 cm, W18 cm, D18 cm, Wt 800 g.

Medium: Model
Price: On request, from regional distributors
Source: Contact Marcus Sommer Somso Modelle for regional distributors (catalogue ref. ZoS 116/1)

 Tapeworm Model Board

Enables comparison of the pork (armed) tapeworm, *Taenia solium*, with the beef (unarmed) tapeworm, *Taenia saginata*, both enlarged many times, in 'SOMSO-Plast'. The model illustrates: egg, cysticercus, some final segments in natural size, and enlarged segments in varying degrees of maturation. In one piece, on a base plate. H38 cm, W61 cm, D10 cm, Wt 3.1 kg.

Medium: Model
Price: On request, from regional distributors
Source: Contact Marcus Sommer Somso Modelle for regional distributors (catalogue ref. ZoS 116/3)

 Termite Model

Coptotermes acinaciformis - a soldier termite or 'white ant', modelled to the scale of 50:1 in 'SOMSO-Plast'. In one piece, on a stand with base. H24 cm, W10 cm, D10 cm, Wt 600 g.

Medium: Model
Price: On request, from regional distributors
Source: Contact Marcus Sommer Somso Modelle for regional distributors (catalogue ref. ZoS 49/14)

 Udder of the Cow Model

Natural size model, in 'SOMSO-Plast'. After Prof. Dr. Vollmerhaus and Prof. Dr. Waibl from the Institute of Veterinary Medicine, University of Munich. Detachable in 4 parts by a sagittal and vertical section. Showing the arteries, veins, lymphatic vessels and milk passages and the 4 glandular regions. Removable, on a stand with base. H35 cm, W39.5 cm, D28 cm, Wt 5.5 kg.

Medium: Model
Price: On request, from regional distributors
Source: Contact Marcus Sommer Somso Modelle for regional distributors (catalogue ref. ZoS 16)

Vineyard Snail Model

Helix pomatia - a crawling edible snail - enlarged approximately 6x, in 'SOMSO-Plast'. The right total view shows the shell, while the left one shows the opened snail. The lower portion of the shell as well as parts of the intestinal sac, the lungs and foot muscles are partly removed to show all important internal organs. The part lying between throat and small intestine of the intestinal canal can be removed. Therefore the cross genital apparatus can be seen completely. Separates into 4 parts. On a base. H28 cm, W68 cm, D45 cm, Wt 7.5 kg.

Medium: Model
Price: On request, from regional distributors
Source: Contact Marcus Sommer Somso Modelle for regional distributors (catalogue ref. ZoS 117)

 Water Flea Model

Daphnia pulex - the water flea, female animal with summer eggs, illustration ratio 200:1, in 'SOMSO-Plast'. This 35 cm tall transparent model shows, apart from typical characteristics such as rowing-antennae, two-leaf shell and turgor-legs, many structural details. The right side separates into the following parts: right shell half with second antenna, part of the right half of the body with the 5 turgor-legs as well as the median sectioned front third of the digestive tract; median sectioned two thirds at the back of the digestive tract, right ovary and two embryos. The model separates into 6 parts. On a stand with base. H50 cm, W42.5 cm, D35 cm, Wt 2.5 kg.

Medium: Model
Price: On request, from regional distributors
Source: Contact Marcus Sommer Somso Modelle for regional distributors (catalogue ref. ZoS 121)

 Water Frog Model

Rana esculenta, enlarged 4x, in 'SOMSO-Plast'. The dorsal side of the model is mounted on a base plate and shows an open ventral side of the male animal. The liver and gastro-intestinal tract are removable to show the position of the internal organs. The abdominal side of the urinary and genital organs of a female water frog are shown on a supplementary model for comparison purposes. Separates altogether into 3 parts. H39 cm, W62 cm, D12 cm, Wt 3.9 kg.

Medium: Model
Price: On request, from regional distributors
Source: Contact Marcus Sommer Somso Modelle for regional distributors (catalogue ref. ZoS 100)

Water Frog Model

Rana esculenta, enlarged 4x, in 'SOMSO-Plast'. The model shows a male water frog with extended legs and inflated vocal sacs. The view shows characteristics including colour and marking. Liver and gastro-intestinal tract are removable to show the position of organ systems. The hind legs can be removed at the thighs. The urinary and genital organs of a female water frog are shown on a supplementary model for comparison purposes. Separates into 5 parts. On a stand and base. H58 cm, W42 cm, D26 cm, Wt 3.9 kg.

Medium: Model
Price: On request, from regional distributors
Source: Contact Marcus Sommer Somso Modelle for regional distributors (catalogue ref. ZoS 100/1)

 Zoology Models

A set of 7 lightweight, full-colour dissection models shown in raised relief. Each markable model is constructed of durable vinyl, illustrates internal structures, biological functions, and comparative anatomy in great detail, and is capable of replacing the use of animal specimens in the classroom. This series of models makes a co-ordinated program for life sciences study, and with each comprehensive lesson plan, provides for both class and individual study. All models are 18" x 24" and come with a 3-ring notebook that includes instructor background information, student basic understandings, learner activities, a glossary, colour transparencies, blackline masters, and a key to model structures. The models can be purchased either separately or as a set.

- *Clam Model.* Shows exaggerated perspective of a mollusc gill structure as well as cut-away section of the shell, foot, and mantle to reveal internal organs. Two separate inset diagrams show the circulatory and nervous systems.

- *Crayfish Model.* A commonly dissected invertebrate, the crayfish is shown in 3D so learners can study the organs and structure of an animal with an exoskeleton. This colourful model illustrates the special adaptations the crayfish has for life under water, with an inset of the gill structure.

- *Earthworm Model.* Classical relief of the anterior portion of the earthworm showing the internal organs and systems representative of primitive invertebrates. The inset clearly illustrates the body in cross section.

- *Fetal Pig Model.* This model illustrates a dissected portion of the abdominal and thoracic organs. The male reproductive system is shown ventrally, and a dorsal view allows examination of the female reproductive organs as well as the brain, muscles, and nervous system. Inset diagram outlines the circulatory system.

- *Frog Model.* The anatomy of all frog organs and systems is presented in ventral and dorsal dissected views. Abdominal organs expose a representation of the female reproductive organs from the left, while the male is shown on the right. A separate inset details the structure of a frog's 3-chambered heart.

- *Grasshopper Model.* A representation of an insect, this model shows the wing and has a portion of the exoskeleton cut away to reveal the internal organs. The often studied mouth is shown in a separate inset, illustrating the frontal view of the head as well as dissected in magnified detail.

- *Perch Model.* Learners view the special adaptations aquatic vertebrate have for exchanging oxygen and carbon dioxide. Organ systems are graphically illustrated in 3D; two inset diagrams show gas exchange in the gills and complete skeletal system.

Medium: Model
Price: US$104.50 (individual models); US$614.00 (full set of 7 models)
Source: Nasco

WORLD WIDE WEB

Biology Lab Reviews: Rat and Frog Dissections

http://www.umanitoba.ca/faculties/science/biological_sciences/biolab.html
University of Manitoba, Canada

Brain Biodiversity Bank Atlases (Axolotl, Dolphin, Human, Sheep)

http://www.msu.edu/~brains/atlases
Michigan State University, USA

Cat Dissections On-Line

http://www.bhs.berkeley.k12.ca.us/departments/Science/anatomy/cat
Berkeley High School, USA

Clam, Squid, Earthworm, Crayfish Dissections

http://biog-101-104.bio.cornell.edu/BioG101_104/tutorials/animals.html
Cornell University, USA

Cockroach Dissection

http://www.ento.vt.edu/~carroll/insect_video_dissection.html
Virginia Tech, USA

Comparative Mammalian Brain Collections

http://brainmuseum.org
University of Wisconsin, Michigan State University, National Museum of Health and Medicine, USA

DryLab^{Web} Dissections On-Line

http://www.duncansoftware.com
Duncan Software, USA

Fetal Pig Dissection on the WWW

http://lakeview.esu7.org/science/fetal.html
Lakeview High School, USA

FlyBrain: An On-Line Atlas and Database of the *Drosophila* Nervous System

http://flybrain.neurobio.arizona.edu (University of Arizona, USA)
http://flybrain.uni-freiburg.de (University of Freiburg, Germany)
http://flybrain.nibb.ac.jp (National Institute for Basic Biology, Japan)

Frog Dissection

http://www.aa.psu.edu/div/mns/biology/Frog/frogtable.htm
Penn State Altoona Biology, USA

Froguts.com

http://www.froguts.com

High Resolution Mouse Brain Atlas

http://www.hms.harvard.edu/research/brain
Harvard Medical School, USA

NetFrog, The Interactive Frog Dissection, An On-Line Tutorial
http://curry.edschool.virginia.edu/go/frog
The Curry School of Education, University of Virginia, USA

Sheep Brain Dissection Guide
http://academic.uofs.edu/department/psych/shee
University of Scranton Neuroscience Program, USA

Sheep Brain Dissection - The Anatomy of Memory
http://www.exploratorium.edu/memory/braindissection/index.html
Exploratorium Museum, USA

Veterinary Anatomy at the University of Minnesota
http://vanat.cvm.umn.edu
University of Minnesota, USA

Virtual Cat Anatomy
http://learning.mgccc.cc.ms.us/science/cat/sld001.htm
Mississippi Gulf Coast Community College, USA

Virtual Fetal Pig Dissection
http://www.whitman.edu/offices_departments/biology/vpd
Whitman College, USA

Whole Frog Project (including the Interactive Frog Dissection Kit)
http://www-itg.lbl.gov/ITG.hm.pg.docs/Whole.Frog
Lawrence Berkeley National Laboratory, USA

3. Biochemistry & Cell Biology

SOFTWARE

Biochemical Simulations

Traditional laboratory classes in biochemistry frequently fail in two of their major objectives: providing data for interpretation, because the students' results are too scattered to be amenable to useful interpretation; and providing experience in planning and designing experiments, because of the constraints of class time. The programs on this disk are intended to supplement or replace laboratory classes, although of course for those who intend to progress to careers in experimental science real hands-on work is essential. There are relatively extensive screens to explain the theory at each stage of the simulation exercises, and you may find these programs useful for students to use for self-paced learning to ensure that they understand the topics, as well as part of a formal practical class. Specimen class worksheets for each simulation are included on the disk. There are 5 simulation exercises on the disk: *Enzyme assay, Urea synthesis in liver cells, Peptide sequence, Oxygen electrode studies,* and *Radio-immunoassay of oestradiol.*

Year of production: 2001 latest revision
Medium: CD-ROM
System requirements: Windows (all versions)
Price: £25.00 within EU; for orders outside the European Union, add £5.00 to cover air mail postage; if paying other than in £, please convert at the current rate of exchange and then add 10% to cover bank charges. This includes a site licence for as many copies as are required within a single purchasing institution, including installation on a local network
Source: Dr. David A. Bender

Cell Biology

This program gives students a solid foundation in the basics of cell biology. It covers cell structure and function, cell cycle, cell division, mitosis and meiosis, membranes, and cell motility. The CD-ROM contains an audiovisual presentation, with the text linked to a complete 24-volume student encyclopaedia, a 150,000-word dictionary, and a glossary of important words. Also includes many multiple choice questions.

Year of production: 1995
Medium: CD-ROM

System requirements: MS-DOS 5.0 or later (MS-DOS version does not support sound play), Windows (all versions), Macintosh OS 7 or later
Price: US$140.00
Source: Nasco

[The] Cell Is A City

While everyone recognises the 3D nature of gross anatomy, the 3D structure of the cell itself often gets overlooked and misunderstood. This new CD from the authors of the classic 'Atlas of the Cell' uses the NEOTEK virtual reality system to show the cell in its true 3D form, and, like other NEOTEK modules, it also uses only actual electron micrographs of real cells, not computer generated images or drawings.

Language: English; translations into Spanish, French and German under production
Medium: CD-ROM
System requirements: Windows only; Windows 95/98/ME/NT/2000; Pentium processor, 16 MB RAM, 1024 x 768 resolution SVGA colour monitor, 24-bit colour, minimum 2 MB of video memory, soundcard, speakers
Note: In order to view the 3D features of this program, the NEOTEK Base System is required. This includes: a video processor (to be placed between the computer and the monitor) and power supply, a pair of liquid crystal glasses, a sampler CD with excerpts from some of the most popular NEOTEK modules, a user manual and installation guide
Price: US$149.00 (CD-ROM); $295.00 (Base System); US$95.00 (extra pair of liquid crystal glasses); US$850.00 (lab pack of 10 extra pairs of liquid crystal glasses); US$395.00 (wireless upgrade kit); US$195.00 (extra pair of wireless glasses); US$1,590.00 (lab pack of 10 extra pairs of wireless glasses)
Source: NEOTEK

Cell Processes

A series of interactive exercises on osmosis, diffusion, cell size, cell crenation and others, which explores the basics of cell processes (cellular respiration, photosynthesis, passive and active transport, mitosis, cytokinesis and cancer) through use of a narrated, step by step tutorial featuring stunning illustrations, animations and micrographs. The program features a unique assessment section - complete with practice and test modes - which automatically grades and tracks student comprehension. A detailed teacher's resource section also allows the user to create customised tutorials, tests and presentations as well as print colour illustrations of cell processes for use as handouts, tests or overhead transparencies.

Medium: CD-ROM
System requirements: Windows 95 or later, Power Mac 8.1 or later; 32 MB RAM
Price: US$99.95 (single); US$299.95 (lab pack of 5); US$699.95 (library pack of 20); US$499.95 (network version); US$139.95 (*Cell Processes* Curriculum Pack: CD-ROM plus *Exploring Cell Processes Laboratory Investigation Kit* - See under MODELS, MANNEKINS, SIMULATORS)
Source: Neo/Sci

Cell Structure & Function

Interactive virtual lab investigations exploring the intricate cell structure of plants and animals using microscope slide preparation and observation techniques. A comprehensive, narrated tutorial section - featuring stunning illustrations, animations and micrographs - provides a step by step overview of cell theory; animal and plant cell organelles; cell specialisation; and the chemistry of cells. Also included is a unique assessment section - complete with practice and test modes - which automatically grades and tracks student comprehension. A detailed teacher's resource section also allows the user to create customised tutorials, tests and presentations as well as print colour illustrations of cell organelles for use as handouts, tests or overhead transparencies.

Medium: CD-ROM
System requirements: Windows 95 or later, Power Mac 8.1 or later; 32 MB RAM
Price: US$99.95 (single); US$299.95 (lab pack of 5); US$699.95 (library pack of 20); US$499.95 (network version)
Source: Neo/Sci

Cellular Respiration

Gain insight into the vital biological process of converting food into a source of energy that can be used by the cell. Eye-catching animations and special effects depict important processes that take place during cellular respiration. Includes detailed diagrams, photographs and electron micrographs. Examines among other things: ATP, ADP, oxidation-reduction reactions, glycolysis, anaerobic respiration, lactate fermentation, alcoholic fermentation, aerobic respiration, the mitochondria, the formation of acetyl CoA from pyruvic acid, the Krebs cycle, and the electron transport chain. Interactive tutorials utilise a 'hands-on' instructional approach that stimulates learning, while the 'jump-to' outline provides a quick review of specific topics.

Medium: CD-ROM
System requirements: Windows, Macintosh (all versions)
Price: Single user - £100.00 / ~ US$155.00 (excl. VAT), £117.50 / ~ €200.00 (incl. VAT); 10 user network or 5 user multipack - £300.00 / ~ US$465.00 (excl. VAT), £352.50 / ~ €600.00 (incl. VAT); 15 user network or 10 user multipack - £500.00 / ~ US$775.00 (excl. VAT), £587.50 / ~ €1000.00 (incl. VAT); 30 user network or 15 user multipack - £700.00 / ~ US$1085.00 (excl. VAT), £822.50 / ~ €1400.00 (incl. VAT). Prices incl. VAT apply to orders from the European Economic Area, prices excl. VAT apply to orders from the rest of the world
Source: AVP

When contacting producers and distributors,
please cite *from Guinea Pig to Computer Mouse*

Cellular Respiration

A highly interactive menu-driven program based on a series of experiments which may be performed on isolated rat liver mitochondria *in vitro* and designed to teach, by investigation, the important principles of cellular respiration. *Introduction* uses text and high-resolution colour graphics to provide tutorial support for students and describes the structure and function of mitochondria, glycolysis, the TCA cycle and oxidative phosphorylation. *Methods* covers the experimental apparatus used to measure mitochondrial oxygen consumption and ATP formation, the principles of using an oxygen electrode, the techniques used to isolate and prepare a viable mitochondrial suspension, and an explanation of how to take measurements from the program display and calculate ADP : O and respiratory control ratios. The *Experiments* section allows students to obtain data from a series of experiments in which different respiratory substrates or electron donor systems are used. The effects of inhibitors and de-coupling agents are also demonstrated. An interactive on-screen facility allows students to define and calculate gradients from the display and to calculate P : O ratio and ACR.

Medium: 3.5" disk; CD-ROM
System requirements: MS-DOS
Price: £120.00 (departmental multiuser/network licence; includes documentation - program manual and, where appropriate, student's workbook and tutor's notes - and postage)
Source: Sheffield BioScience Programs

 Electron Micrography PhotoCD

Ninety-seven stunning images by electron micrograph of internal cell structures, cell processes and other microscope structures. The images can be printed out, included in projects or the production of worksheets.

Medium: CD-ROM
System requirements: Windows (all versions); Macintosh (all versions); Acorn. PhotoCD access software, or software like CorelDraw, Quark Express, Pagemaker, or ProArtisan 2, Revelation, Impression (Acorn)
Price: Single user - £42.54 / ~ US$65.94 (excl. VAT), £49.98 / ~ €85.00 (incl. VAT). Prices incl. VAT apply to orders from the European Economic Area, prices excl. VAT apply to orders from the rest of the world
Source: AVP

 Enzyme Kinetics

There are many laboratory experiments which students can usefully do in enzyme kinetics, but there is seldom time available for more than a few. This program allows the student to plan and interpret the realistic results very rapidly from a wide range of simulated enzyme-catalysts reactions. It includes suggested preliminary lab work, finding the optimum pH, varying the temperature, incubation time, enzyme and substrate concentrates.

Medium: 3.5" disk
System requirements: MS-DOS; Acorn
Price: Single user - £32.50 / ~ US$50.38 (excl. VAT), £38.19 / ~ €65.00 (IncVAT); network version (MS-DOS version only) - £81.00 / ~ US$125.55 (excl. VAT), £95.18 / ~ €162.00 (incl. VAT); site licence - £97.50 / ~ US$151.13 (excl. VAT), £114.56 / ~ €195.00 (incl. VAT). Prices incl. VAT apply to orders from the European Economic Area, prices excl. VAT apply to orders from the rest of the world
Source: AVP

Explorations in Cell Biology and Genetics

Interactive animations explain vital cellular structures and processes in a dramatic new way. Engage in a thought-provoking investigation of relevant subjects like mitosis and topical issues like DNA fingerprinting. Contents: *How proteins function: haemoglobin; Cell size; Active transport; Cell-cell interactions; Mitosis: regulating the cell cycle; Cell chemistry: thermodynamics; Enzymes in action: kinetics; Oxidative respiration; Photosynthesis; Exploring meiosis: Down syndrome; Constructing a genetic map; Heredity in families; Gene segregation within families; DNA fingerprinting: You be the judge; Reading DNA; Gene regulation; Making a restriction map.*

Medium: CD-ROM
System requirements: Windows; Macintosh (all versions)
Price: Single user - £36.59 / ~ US$56.71 (excl. VAT), £42.99 / ~ €73.00 (incl. VAT). Prices incl. VAT apply to orders from the European Economic Area, prices excl. VAT apply to orders from the rest of the world
Source: AVP

GET*it Biochemistry

One of four CD-ROMs in this innovative series, GET*it Biochemistry covers basic chemical concepts, molecular structure, enzymes and biochemical reactions, glycolysis, the citric acid cycle, chemiosmosis, oxidative phosphorylation, fermentation, photophosphorylation, the Calvin-Benson cycle, C_4 photosynthesis and crassulacean acid metabolism, and a guide to biological terminology. It features more than 750 topics, minicourses that guide students through topic areas, interactive self-quizzing with more than 600 true-false questions, advanced hypertext navigation, extensive index function, hundreds of original illustrations, photos and animations, narration and spoken pronunciations of terms.

Medium: CD-ROM
System requirements: Windows 3.1/95/98/NT, 486 processor (Pentium or better recommended) with 16 MB RAM or better and Super VGA monitor; Macintosh OS 7.0 or better, 68040 or better with 24 MB RAM (32 MB recommended) and 8-bit colour monitor (16-bit or 24-bit recommended)
Price: US$14.95
Source: Sinauer Associates

GET*it Cell Biology

One of four CD-ROMs in this innovative series, *GET*it Cell Biology* covers the eukaryotic cell, transport and the plasma membrane, the nucleus, the cytoskelelton, the extracellular matrix, the endomembrane system, animal cell junctions, mitosis, meiosis, the cell cycle, cancer, and a guide to biological terminology. It features more than 750 topics, minicourses that guide students through topic areas, interactive self-quizzing with more than 600 true-false questions, advanced hypertext navigation, extensive index function, hundreds of original illustrations, photos and animations, narration and spoken pronunciations of terms.

Medium: CD-ROM
System requirements: Windows 3.1/95/98/NT, 486 processor (Pentium or better recommended) with 16 MB RAM or better and Super VGA monitor; Macintosh OS 7.0 or better, 68040 or better with 24 MB RAM (32 MB recommended) and 8-bit colour monitor (16-bit or 24-bit recommended)
Price: US$14.95
Source: Sinauer Associates

GET*it Molecular Biology

One of four CD-ROMs in this innovative series, *GET*it Molecular Biology* covers molecular structure, DNA replication, the flow of genetic information, regulation of prokaryotic gene expression, regulation of eukaryotic gene expression, RNA processing in eukaryotes, basic gene splicing, immunoglobulins, the immune responses, the generation of antibody diversity, cancer, some classic experiments in biology, and a guide to biological teminology. It features more than 750 topics, minicourses that guide students through topic areas, interactive self-quizzing with more than 600 true-false questions, advanced hypertext navigation, extensive index function, hundreds of original illustrations, photos and animations, narration and spoken pronunciations of terms.

Medium: CD-ROM
System requirements: Windows 3.1/95/98/NT, 486 processor (Pentium or better recommended) with 16 MB RAM or better and Super VGA monitor; Macintosh OS 7.0 or better, 68040 or better with 24 MB RAM (32 MB recommended) and 8-bit colour monitor (16-bit or 24-bit recommended)
Price: US$14.95
Source: Sinauer Associates

Inside the Cell

Explores the microscopic world of cells and their components with detailed drawings as well as actual electron micrographs of cells. Students learn about the prokaryotic and eukaryotic cell, the basic differences between plant and animal cells, and the organelles of plant and animal cells. Special effects and animations are used to visually portray how a plasma membrane, Golgi complex, and other organelles function. Interactive tutorials provide plenty of practice identifying organelle structures and functions, and an on-line glossary makes for easy learning of biology.

Medium: CD-ROM
System requirements: Windows (all versions); Macintosh (all versions)
Price: Single user - £85.00 / ~ US$131.75 (excl. VAT), £99.88 / ~ €170.00 (incl. VAT); 10 user network or 5 user multipack - £260.00 / ~ US$403.00 (excl. VAT), £305.50 / ~ €520.00 (incl. VAT); 15 user network or 10 user multipack - £430.00 / ~ US$666.50 (excl. VAT), £505.25 / ~ €860.00 (incl. VAT); 30 user network or 15 user multipack - £600.00 / ~ US$930.00 (excl. VAT), £705.00 / ~ €1200.00 (incl. VAT). Prices incl. VAT apply to orders from the European Economic Area, prices excl. VAT apply to orders from the rest of the world
Source: AVP

Introduction to Cell Biology (v2.0)

This package, developed at the Welsh School of Pharmacy (UK), comprises 3 separate modules which together provide an introduction to cell structure and function. 1. *The eukaryote cell* - makes extensive use of 3D graphics and animations in explaining the structure and function of typical animal and plant cells and their organelles; 2. *Prokaryote/eukaryote differences* - compares and contrasts the features found in the eukaryote and prokaryote cell and discusses examples from different kingdoms of the classification system; 3. *Animal tissue structure* - explores the differentiation of the cell into specific animal cell and tissue types, providing an introduction to the following tissue types: epithelial tissues, glandular epithelia, exocrine glands, endocrine glands, connective tissues, smooth, heart and skeletal muscle, and neurone structure.

Medium: CD-ROM
System requirements: available in Windows and web/intranet versions. The Windows version (compatible with Windows 95/98/NT) is supplied on a CD-ROM Installation disk and can be installed to a local hard disk or network drive; requires a PC with minimum 100 MHz Pentium processor, 8 MB RAM and a VGA monitor capable of displaying 16-bit colour at 640 x 480 resolution. The web version is supplied on a CD-ROM Installation disk for installation to a web server and runs on PC clients only; requires a 200 MHz Pentium processor with 32 MB RAM and a Super VGA monitor capable of displaying 16-bit colour at 800 x 600 resolution; it is compatible with both Netscape Navigator 4.x and Internet Explorer 4 or better and requires Java and JavaScript to be enabled on browsers
Price: £220.00 (excl. VAT at 17.5% for UK and EU orders, and £20.00 handling charge)
Source: COACS

Investigation of Gluconeogenesis

A realistic experimental simulation aimed at undergraduate students of biological science and allied subjects, replacing a class that required the use of freshly killed rats to study the effect of starvation on induction of gluconeogenic enzymes. This program reflects as accurately as possible the procedures used in 'wet' practicals. Video sequences of an actual experiment are included. The data are taken from past student practicals. Important points are explained with animation of the pathways of gluconeogenesis and self-testing questions. Drag and drop simulates manipulation of kidney tissue sections on-screen while washing, weighing and incubating them. Measurements are made of glucose synthesis from different substrates in slices from fed and starved rats. Numerical results of the experiment differ with each run-through so that results copied from one will not score in another.

Year of production: 1998
Medium: CD-ROM
System requirements: Windows only (all versions); 16 MB RAM , 64k colour display
Price: £49.50 + VAT (Blackwell Science Ltd); £58.00 (Scottish Knowledge plc); for departmental licence please contact CLIVE. Free site licence available to Associate Members of CLIVE consortium
Source: CLIVE. Available for purchase from Blackwell Science Ltd in Europe, and from Scottish Knowledge plc in The North American Free Trade Association (Canada, Mexico, the USA), The Gulf Cooperation Council (Kuwait, Saudi Arabia, Bahrain, Qatar, the United Arab Emirates and the Sultanate of Oman), The Association of South East Asians Nations (Brunei, Cambodia, Indonesia, Laos, Malaysia, Myanmar, Philippines, Singapore, Thailand and Vietnam). Purchasers elsewhere may buy from either distributor

Learning All About Cells & Biology

This generously illustrated interactive multimedia program examines theories about the origins of living things, their characteristics, and cell structures. Topics include: one-celled and multicellular organisms; respiration, metabolism, and reproduction; chemical elements of living matter, structure and function of cell organelles, photosynthesis, and more.

Medium: CD-ROM
System requirements: Windows, Macintosh
Price: US$95.00 (single), $285.00 (lab pack of 5), US$475.00 (Network)
Source: Queue

Learning More About Cells

This interactive multimedia presentation with live video features a complete review of living cells, with spectacular photo-micrography of cells dividing, amoebae 'running', and single-celled animals 'eating'. The program thoroughly explains cell structure, the differences between animal and plant cells, and photosynthesis. The program also includes a complete review of mitosis, the process by which genetic information is passed on during cell division, giving students a clear explanation of all five phases of mitosis. Incredible time-lapse photomicrography captures the duplication of chromosomes and the whole mitosis process. Incorporating the most recent biological thought and theory, this dynamic program, with outstanding cinematography, traces the early evolution of life. Starting from a barren planet, the program shows the different stages of cellular evolution, from primitive bacteria to blue/green algae to complex multicellular organisms. Highlights include a unique time-lapse sequence following the development of a single-celled egg into a tadpole.

Medium: CD-ROM
System requirements: DOS 5.0+, Windows, Macintosh; sound blaster or compatible card
Price: US$125.00 (single), US$375.00 (lab pack of 5), US$625.00 (network)
Source: Queue

Plant & Animal Mitosis & Meiosis

This software features dozens of dual-magnification images providing a detailed overview of mitosis and meiosis in both plants and animals. Includes stunning microphotography, complemented by authoritative reference text. Mitotic stages are represented by magnified images which allow students to observe clear cytological detail in the onion root tip and whitefish blastodisc. Meiosis is illustrated using the lily and grasshopper testis.

Medium: CD-ROM
System requirements: Windows 95 or later, Power Mac 8.1 or later; 32 MB RAM
Price: US$59.95 (single); US$179.95 (lab pack of 5); US$419.95 (library pack of 20); US$299.95 (network version)
Source: Neo/Sci

UNDERSTAND! Biochemistry

This interactive computer program covers all basic cell chemistry through enzymology, bioenergetics, metabolism, macromolecular structure, assembly and modification, the flow of genetic information, signal transduction, and molecular biology techniques. It features over 120 original animations, over 900 original illustrations, 25 3D interactive molecular models, graphics for over 100 macromolecules, 60 minicourses covering an entire 2-semester course, interactive, self-quizzing multiple choice questions, advanced hypertext navigation, extensive index function, web links to useful and effective web sites, and true voice pronunciation for over 400 terms.

Medium: CD-ROM
System requirements: Windows 95/98/NT, Pentium processor with 24 MB RAM and Super VGA monitor; Macintosh OS 7.61 minimum, Power PC with 24 MB RAM
Price: US$34.95 (Student Version); US$150.00 (Instructor's Version); US$299.99 (Computer lab pack Site Licence first 10 computers), US$27.00 (additional computers); US$695.00 (Multiple-User Network Site Licence first 15 users), US$75.00 (additional 5 users)
Source: Sinauer Associates

UNDERSTAND! Biology: Molecules, Cells & Genes

This interactive computer program covers all basic cell biology, molecular biology, and genetics in 41 minicourses. It allows students to take an active role in learning biology through exciting and relevant visuals that show not just the theory, but the actual processes. Includes classic experiments, terminology, development, cancer, an extensive library of spoken pronunciations for terms, covering over 1,700 topics in basic cell chemistry through DNA, gene expression and regulation, gene splicing, and immunology. Contains more than 100 original animations, 800 pieces of original art, 17 video microscopy sequences, more than 125 micrographs, advanced hypertext navigation, extensive index function and interactive self-quizzing. The Instructor's Version provides a lecture organiser which allows the customisation of the program's art, animations, and videos according to each teacher's lecture sequence.

Medium: CD-ROM
System requirements: Windows 95/98/NT, Pentium processor with 24 MB RAM and Super VGA monitor; Macintosh OS 7.61 minimum, Power PC with 24 MB RAM
Price: US$29.95 (Student Version); US$125.00 (Instructor's Version); US$249.95 (Computer lab pack Site Licence first 10 computers), US$21.00 (additional computers); US$400.00 (Multiple-User Network Site Licence first 15 users), US$50.00 (additional 5 users)
Source: Sinauer Associates

Virtual Physiochemistry Lab

This software introduces students to a physiochemical laboratory environment and allows them to perform uric acid analysis experiments. The first segment of the program introduces students to the primary equipment used (spectrophotometer) and discusses the principle upon which it is based. The *Lab* segment allows students to test different serum samples by mixing them with various chemical reagents. Pre-programmed values allows a variance in absorbance readings. Analysis of the results obtained is performed in the third segment of the program from which diagnosis can be made.

Year of production: 2000
Medium: CD-ROM
System requirements: Windows only - Win95/98/ME/2000/NT/XP, Media Player 7 with Codecs; Pentium I processor (200 MHz), 32 MB RAM, 8 MB graphics card
Price: US$20.00 (student licence); US$150.00 (institution licence - 10 users). Prices excl. postage
Source: Saints Web Design

Visualizing Cell Processes

One DVD containing the whole series of 5 programs available on VHS (see video version of this title). A comprehensive program for teaching, learning, and understanding cell biology. The DVD includes menu access to 52 narrated modules that together define life at the cell level. DVD resolution is twice that of VHS, offering remarkable observations of living cells and beautifully crafted graphics that allow students to visualise and understand cell functions. Video sequences can be examined frame by frame at high resolution, and the action can be slowed or sped up, offering unparalleled opportunities for analysis and discussion. The DVD includes integrated study guides for each of the 52 narrated modules with each module broken down into concept-based learning bits. The illustrated glossary contains over 500 entries creating a comprehensive concept vocabulary for cell biology. The *Learning Guide* includes 14 printable posters summarising each major cell process (mitosis, Krebs cycle, DNA replication, etc.), self-tests, and extended resources that integrate the latest discoveries and applications of cell biology.

Year of production: 2003
Medium: DVD
Price: US$850.00 (individual user); US$1295.00 (network licence)
Source: eBioMEDIA

VIDEO

Cell Division: Mitosis and Cytokinesis

After distinguishing mitosis (nuclear division) from cytokinesis (cell division), this video shows several live animal (newt lung) cells undergoing mitosis, and a 3D animation illustrates how the mitotic spindle is assembled. All phases of mitosis are shown and discussed in detail. The relationship between cell division and morphogenesis is introduced by showing several single-celled organisms that differentiate into complex shapes after every division. Other types of cells remain together after division to form simple multicellular organisms. These two abilities are required for embryogenesis. Two examples (in frogs and zebrafish) show how repeated cycles of cell division and differentiation transform the ball of cells created by these divisions into recognisable embryos. Embryonic development and cell growth are also covered, while meiosis, the process whereby the cell nucleus divides to form sex cells, is graphically depicted. Accompanied by Instructor's Guide.

Year of production: 1999
Format: VHS NTSC, PAL
Running time: 20 mins.
Price: US$60.00
Source: Cytographics, Neo/SCI

Cell Processes

Featuring living plant and animal cells photographed in the laboratory of Prof. Jeremy Pickett-Heaps at The University of Melbourne, Australia, this video introduces students to the relationship between internal structures within cells and the processes that enable life to continue, minute to minute, generation to generation. Brilliant, microscopic footage, time-lapse photography and graphic animations complement the video sequences and provide detailed explanations on topics such as mitosis, diffusion, cell size, cell division, photosynthesis, cellular respiration, sectioning and visualising cells directly. All these are introduced with familiar organisms. The microscopical images of organelles and cellular activity are drawn from a wide variety of cells. They are remarkably vivid and will stimulate students' imagination. Accompanied by Instructor's Note.

Year of production: 2001
Format: VHS NTSC, PAL
Running time: 25 mins.
Price: US$60.00
Source: Cytographics, Neo/SCI

CELLebration

Sponsored by the American Society for Cell Biology, this video is a collection of footage of sequences filmed by active researchers in cell biology. A wide variety of microscopic and imaging techniques (including DIC, fluorescence, and time-lapse) have been used to capture these extraordinary events. This video will be appropriate for introductory biology courses to demonstrate how alive cells are, as well as for upper-level students who are interested in the details of cellular phenomena.

Year of production: 1995
Format: VHS NTSC
Price: US$85.00
Source: Sinauer Associates

Cytology and Histology

The cell's organelles and their functions are highlighted through histological photomicrographs to show location of the various structures in different tissues. Each photomicrograph is identified in relation to tissue type, location and function. These are carefully selected colour slides of nervous, epithelial, muscular, connective and other tissues taken with both light and electron microscopes. An excellent collection, especially for pre-clinical and medical technology students.

Format: VHS NTSC
Running time: approx. 23 mins.
Price: US$79.95
Source: Educational Images

[The] Dynamics and Mechanics of Mitosis

This colourful and dramatic video reveals the events of mitosis at a level of detail usually seen only in research laboratories. Every time a living cell divides, it undergoes the process of mitosis during which dozens - sometimes hundreds - of jumbled chromosomes are individually organised into the metaphase configuration; then the chromosomes split and are separated into two equal groups with absolute fidelity. How this extraordinary process is accomplished is still poorly understood. This video shows in several types of living cells how the spindle machinery becomes organised and how the chromosomes attach and respond to it. The video includes two Appendices. The first analyses mitosis in a classical system, the diatom cell; not only are these spindles uniquely well organised, but the mitotic cycle is precisely integrated with the major morphogenetic events inside the cell that accompany every cell division. The second Appendix demonstrates several types of experiments on living cells which illustrate why the mechanisms involved in chromosome movement are so difficult to define and understand. Accompanied by Instructor's Guide.

Year of production: 2002
Format: VHS NTSC, PAL
Running time: 26 mins. (*The Dynamics and Mechanics of Mitosis*); 16 mins. (*Mitosis in Diatoms*); 18 mins. (*Experiments on Mitotic Cells*)
Price: US$85.00
Source: Cytographics, Sinauer Associates

[An] Introduction to Cells

A beautifully executed introduction, with difficult concepts slowly added to a framework of simpler ones. The film is perfect for the new biology student, and has 6 parts, each containing an average of 75 frames: 1. *Cell growth and development* - the cell as the basic building block of life, whose function is defined in the nucleus; 2. *Within the nucleus* - the nucleus as a library; 3. *Regeneration* - why some simple organisms can regenerate while others can only reproduce; 4. *The genetic code* - the books of the nuclear library are the chromosomes, and the chemical coding lies inside the genes; 5. *DNA, RNA and proteins* - passing on the genetic information, the role of amino acids; 6. *Why each of us is different* - inheritance, dominant versus recessive genes.

Format: VHS NTSC
Running time: approx. 66 mins.
Price: US$99.95
Source: Educational Images

[An] Introduction to the Living Cell

Take a visual tour of the living cell and learn why all organisms rely on cells to grow, reproduce, and generate energy. Discover how subcellular organelles work together to meet the continuously changing needs of the cell. Full-motion computer animation, art, and microscopic images help describe the wondrously complex and dynamic world of the living cell.

Format: VHS NTSC
Running time: 30 mins.
Price: US$39.95
Source: Carolina Biological Supply

 [The] Isolation and Metabolism of Mitochondria

The first part of the program demonstrates the isolation of mitochondria in a sample of minced homogenised liver from a freshly-killed rat. The experiment demonstrates the crucial conditions of homogenisation and the subjection of the homogenate to several stages of increasing centrifugation; the result is the separation of successively lighter organelles and debris. The second part of the experiment is devoted to measuring the uptake of oxygen. The reaction vessel contains a reaction medium, mitochondria, a substrate such as succinic acid, and ADP. All air above the medium is excluded by means of a perspex stopper. As the oxygen in the solution is consumed by the reactions in the mitochondria, the fall in the oxygen concentration is recorded on the chart-recorder. As other substances are introduced via a small hole in the perspex stopper, their effects on the reactions are recorded.

Format: VHS NTSC
Running time: 15 mins.
Price: US$59.95
Source: Films for the Humanities and Sciences (United States and Canada only)

 [A] Journey through the Cell

This set of 2 videos takes students on an incredible journey into the world of the cell. Combining live-action video, colourful computer graphics, animation, and interviews with scientists, these programs introduce students to ideas which are central to understanding cells and their profound role in the living world. *Part One* provides a virtual journey through the cell, where viewers become familiar with cells and their properties. Describes and shows examples of cells of many shapes and sizes; explores the structure and functions of different types of cells. Compares plant and animal cells; emphasises cells as the basic building blocks of all organisms; describes the organisation of cells and the formation of tissues, organs, and systems; and concludes with an overview of the organelles and their functions. *Part Two* examines three main activities of the cell: energy storage and release, protein synthesis, and cell reproduction. Students take a closer look at important organelles such as mitochondria and chloroplasts, and the roles they play in cell metabolism. Covers proteins, amino acids, ribosomes, DNA, RNA, genes, chromosomes, transcription, and translation. Mitosis is clearly defined and illustrated. The set includes 2 videos and 2 teacher's guides which include key terms and concepts, previewing and post-viewing questions, and reproducible activity sheets.

Year of production: 1996
Format: VHS NTSC
Running time: 50 mins.
Price: US$119.95 (set of 2 videos)
Source: Nasco

Living Cells - Structure and Diversity

This video introduces students to a variety of cell types, the major sub-cellular components (organelles) and some important cellular activities such as mitosis and cell-division. Real time and time-lapse video microscopy are used to reveal mitochondria, Golgi bodies and microtubules in living cells. Subjects covered include: the cell membrane, nucleus and nucleolus, endoplasmic reticulum, microtubules and the microtubule cytoskeleton, mitosis and cytokinesis, the actin cytoskeleton, streaming, cleavage, flagella and cilia, contractile vacuoles, cell walls, turgor pressure and growth. Accompanied by Instructor's Guide.

Year of production: 1996
Format: VHS NTSC, PAL
Running time: 36 mins.
Price: US$60.00
Source: Cytographics, Sinauer Associates

Visualizing Cell Processes

This series of 5 videos which appeared in 1995 in laser videodisc and video formats has been updated in 2001 with new animations and expanded content. Each video program is a series of short, narrated, full-motion modules that describe an essential process of cell biology. All programs are closed-captioned. Teaching guides and samples can be downloaded from the website.

- *Cells and Molecules.* Modules: A variety of cells; Cell organisation; Overview of organic molecules; Prokaryotic cells; The evolution of eukaryotic cells

- *Cell Movement and Transport.* Modules: Structure and behaviour of the plasma membrane; Osmosis; Transport proteins; Phagocytosis; Pinocytosis; Receptor mediated endocytosis; Golgi function; Lysosomes and hydrolytic digestion; Microtubules; Cilia; Actin and myosin motor proteins

- *Photosynthesis and Cellular Respiration*. Photosynthesis modules: Chloroplast structure; Light trapping by chlorophyll; Light-dependent reactions of photosynthesis; The light independent reactions of photosynthesis. Respiration modules: Glycolysis and fermentation; Mitochondrion structure; Aerobic respiration; Krebs cycle; Electron transport chain; ATP synthesis

- *DNA Replication, Mitosis and Cell Reproduction*. Modules: Mitosis: chromosome condensation; Mitosis: stages; Cytokinesis; Meiosis; Nucleotide structure and bonding; Replication enzymes; Replicating the strands; The twisting problem; Proof reading and repair

- *The Genetic Code and Its Translation*. Modules: The protein nature of life; Protein structure; Transcription, translation and protein synthesis; Gene regulation in prokaryotes; Classes of eukaryote DNA; Exons and introns; Mutations; Renegade DNA - the viruses

Year of production: Revised 2001
Format: VHS NTSC
Running time: 15 mins. (each program)
Price: US$60.00 (each title); US$295.00 (whole series of 5 tapes). Plus applicable taxes and postage
Source: eBioMEDIA

Models, Mannekins, Simulators

Exploring Cell Processes

This laboratory investigation kit allows teachers to conduct several activities designed to compare plant and animal cells, illustrating cell structure and processes to include mitochondria, cell membranes, DNA and RNA identification, osmosis, plasmolysis, and more. Using no actual materials, but just simulations, it helps identifying and comparing organelles in plant and animal cells, relating their structure to their specific function. In the process, the class learns how to make observations and comparisons, analyse data, relate cause and effect, and make inferences. The kit also allows students to construct models of cells to simulate the semipermeable nature of plasma membrane, to predict the effect of exposing model cells to hypertonic, hypotonic and isotonic solutions, and to observe the genetic material in a rapidly dividing plant tissue (e.g. root tips).

Medium: Simulator
Price: US$52.95 (class size - 40 students); US$139.95 (*Cell Processes* Curriculum Pack: Lab Kit plus *Cell Processes* CD-ROM - see under SOFTWARE)
Source: Neo/Sci

4. Clinical Skills & Surgery

SOFTWARE

Animal Health and Welfare Images vol. 1

Includes digitised images (in JPEG format) from the original British Laboratory Animal Veterinary Association (BLAVA) 35mm slide set, plus another 100 or so images (200 in all), and provides a series of illustrations of animals with normal and abnormal clinical appearance. Part of the *Digital Materials for Trainers* series.

Medium: CD-ROM
System requirements: Windows 95 and later, Macintosh OS 8.6 and later; QuickTime 5 (included)
Price: £5.00 / US$10.00 (plus £5.00 / US$10.00 postage for 1-10 disks)
Source: University of Newcastle upon Tyne

Consequences of the Isolated Vesico-Ureteral Reflux in the Ewe Foetus

See description of this title under VIDEO.

Language: French, English
Year of production: Original film made in 1979
Medium: CD-ROM (MPEG4 format)
System requirements: Windows Media 7 (or Windows Player 6.4 for WinNT4 and Win95)
Price: Individual use: €15.00 (Europe), €30.00 (rest of the world); Institutional use: €30.00 (Europe), €45.00 (rest of the world)
Note: The original title of this program is *Conséquences du reflux vésico-urétéral isolé chez le foetus de brebis*
Source: SFRS

Digital Materials for Trainers On-Screen Collection

See under 'Anaesthesia & Critical Care'.

Fracture Game 2000

This is an interactive program that is educational in general, however, its main purpose is to be a ready reference for fracture management in small animals. A practitioner, resident, intern, or student that has a fracture presented to them can go to this program and follow down the algorithmic orthopaedic tree until they find a similar fracture. Using the interactive process, they can determine the best treatment for that specific fracture. The program involves all bones of the dog and cat, and consists of 189 fracture cases, 719 illustrations and photos, 1,302 radiographs, and 270 MB of knowledge. In this game, for each case the users can practice their reduction skills by bringing each fragment, one at a time, from the pre-operative radiograph into reduction until they have reconstructed the entire bone.

Medium: CD-ROM
System requirements: Windows with 486 or faster processor, Macintosh with Power Mac or later; 16 MB of RAM; web browser (e.g., Netscape 3.0 or later, or Internet Explorer 3.0 or later)
Price: US$50.00 (MSU student rate - accepted only if MSU Student ID is being sent by fax); US$75.00 (intern / resident / student rate - proof of status required); US$125.00 (veterinarian / institution)
Source: Michigan State University

[A] Guide to Lizards

This program is the first in the *Exotics* series from The Royal Veterinary College. It is aimed at veterinary surgeons and nurses in practice who have little or no experience of dealing with these animals. It contains important background information on husbandry and handling, along with core material on diagnosing and dealing with disease. The CD-ROM also includes accessible and well-illustrated reference material and essential tools for use in practice.

Year of production: 1999
Medium: CD-ROM
System requirements: Windows only - Win95/98/NT/XP; Pentium processor, 32 MB RAM, sound card and 64k video display
Price: £49.50 (excl. VAT and postage)
Source: Royal Veterinary College

[A] Guide to Snakes

A *Guide to Snakes* is the second in the *Exotics* series from The Royal Veterinary College. The program provides veterinary surgeons, students and nurses with a comprehensive guide to the care and treatment of snakes. It gives clear and practical advice through the use of text, graphics, photographs, video and interactive case challenges. The CD–ROM also includes accessible and well-illustrated reference material and essential tools for use in practice.

Year of production: 2000
Medium: CD-ROM
System requirements: Windows only - Win95/98/NT/XP; Pentium processor, 32 MB RAM, sound card and 64k video display
Price: £49.50 (excl. VAT and postage)
Source: Royal Veterinary College

Laboratory Animals Anaesthesia, Surgery and Perioperative Care

See under 'Anaesthesia & Critical Care'.

Practical Animal Handling - 1. Small Mammals

This CD-ROM is part of the *Digital Materials for Trainers* series and contains QuickTime movies prepared from the video program *Practical Animal Handling*, produced and distributed by the British Veterinary Association Animal Welfare Foundation (see under VIDEO). It features expert veterinary staff demonstrating the correct procedures for handling small mammals for clinical examination and medication. Its aim is to show that the primary consideration should be for the welfare of the animal. The movies can be played as stand alone movie files, or can be launched in a web-browser (Netscape is much faster than Explorer) using the home page included on the CD-ROM. There is no sound track, the movies are captioned to emphasise essential points. They can be used for teaching purposes, but if anyone wishes to edit the content and recaption in a language other than English, they should contact the source.

Medium: CD-ROM (ISSO 9660 format)
System requirements: Windows 95 and later, Macintosh OS 8.6 and later; QuickTime 5 (included)
Price: £5.00 / US$10.00 (plus £5.00 / US$10.00 postage for 1-10 disks)
Source: University of Newcastle upon Tyne

Surgery vol. 1

Digitised images (JPEG format) from the original British Laboratory Animal Veterinary Association (BLAVA) 35mm slide set, plus over 100 more (150 in total) illustrating gowning, gloving, instruments etc., plus the postscript images (and an explanation) of how to tie an Aberdeen knot. Part of the *Digital Materials for Trainers* series.

Medium: CD-ROM
System requirements: Windows 95 and later, Macintosh OS 8.6 and later; QuickTime 5 (included)
Price: £5.00 / US$10.00 (plus £5.00 / US$10.00 postage for 1-10 disks)
Source: University of Newcastle upon Tyne

Surgical Skills vol. 1 and 2

Surgical Skills, vol. 1 and 2 (combined), is part of the *Digital Materials for Trainers* series and contains QuickTime movies illustrating some basic surgical techniques - handling instruments and suturing, scrubbing, gowning and gloving. The movies can be played as stand alone movie files, or can be launched in a web-browser (Netscape is much faster than Explorer) using the home page included on the CD-ROM. There is no sound track, the movies are captioned to emphasise essential points. They can be used for teaching purposes, but if anyone wishes to edit the content and recaption in a language other than English, they should contact the source.

Language: English; others (Spanish, Italian, French and German) under production
Medium: CD-ROM
System requirements: Windows 95 and later, Macintosh OS 8.6 and later; QuickTime 5 (included)
Price: £5.00 / US$10.00 (plus £5.00 / US$10.00 postage for 1-10 disks)
Source: University of Newcastle upon Tyne

 VIDEO

 Bone Marrow Aspiration - Bovine and Canine

Demonstrations of how to perform bone marrow aspirations from the ribs of a cow and a dog. Reference is made to the adaptability of such a technique on a horse.

Year of production: 1976
Format: VHS NTSC, PAL
Running time: 16 mins.
Price: US$50.00
Source: University of California (UC Davis)

 Canine Castration (Orchidectomy)

Routine open and close castration is described in the dog. Techniques for surgical excision of the canine testicle are described and thoughts on current techniques as related to post-operative complications are also discussed.

Format: VHS NTSC
Running time: 14.50 mins.
Price: US$95.00; other formats available at additional cost
Source: Michigan State University

 Canine Stifle Surgery

Shows the clinical and radiological features of developmental and traumatic conditions of the stifle. Discusses methods of treatment and illustrates surgical technique with the aid of diagrams, bone specimens and film taken during operations. Workbook includes equipment list and questions and answers.

Year of production: 1985
Format: VHS PAL
Running time: 65 mins.
Price: £30.00 (excl. VAT and postage)
Source: Royal Veterinary College

 Castration of the Cat

Description not available.

Year of production: 1996
Format: VHS NTSC, PAL
Running time: 10 mins.
Price: US$50.00
Source: University of California (UC Davis)

 Castration of the Dog

Two techniques for castration of the dog are demonstrated.

Year of production: 1992
Format: VHS NTSC, PAL
Running time: 22 mins.
Price: US$50.00
Source: University of California (UC Davis)

Catheterization Techniques - Venous and Arterial

Percutaneous catheterisation technique is demonstrated on the canine cephalic vein, saphenous vein, jugular vein, femoral artery and anterior tibial artery. Surgical cutdowns are demonstrated on the jugular vein, femoral artery and carotid artery. The program emphasises and demonstrates aseptic preparation of the catheterisation site and maintenance procedures for indwelling catheters. Common problems regarding positioning and placement of indwelling catheters are also addressed.

Year of production: 1979
Format: VHS NTSC, PAL
Running time: 42 mins.
Price: US$50.00
Source: University of California (UC Davis)

 ## Clinical Examination of the Eye of the Dog and Cat

Demonstrates a thorough clinical examination using light illumination, PLRs, tonometry, gonioscopy, ophthalmoscopy (direct and indirect). Gives reasons for ophthalmoscopy: ocular disease (traumatic, infectious and hereditary) and systemic disease. Shows normal variations and abnormalities in the appearance of the fundus.

Year of production: 1992
Format: VHS PAL
Running time: 45 mins.
Price: £30.00 (excl. VAT and postage)
Source: Royal Veterinary College

 ## Consequences of the Isolated Vesico-Ureteral Reflux in the Ewe Foetus

This film explores, through an experimental study performed on an animal, the relationships between renal dysplasia and the vesico-ureteral reflux - two conditions often associated in children. Contents include: *Purpose of the research; Experimental protocol; Surgical operation on the ewe foetus to create the vesico-ureteral reflux; Analysis of the animals born at term (0 to 6 months); Conclusions.* Media include: real views, cinemicrography, animation, slides and photographs.

Language: French, English
Year of production: 1979
Format: VHS PAL, SECAM, NTSC. Also available on CD-ROM (see under SOFTWARE)
Running time: 10 mins.

Price: Individual use: €15.00 (Europe), €30.00 (rest of the world); Institutional use: €30.00 (Europe), €45.00 (rest of the world); the NTSC format is available at an additional cost of €15.00
Note: The original title of this program is *Conséquences du reflux vésico-urétéral isolé chez le foetus de brebis*
Source: SFRS

 DASIE Video

This film is a demonstration of aseptic draping, incision, performing an intestinal anastomosis, and multiple layer wound closure on a *DASIE Surgical Model* (see under MODELS, MANNEKINS, SIMULATORS). It is intended as a self study tool or for pre-laboratory viewing by the student.

Format: VHS PAL
Running time: 37 mins.
Price: US$25.00 each (excl. postage)
Source: DASIE International

 Dehorning the Mature Goat

This program demonstrates the removal of horns, using two techniques. The first technique is by use of the embryotomy wire, the second by use of a hacksaw. Post-operative bandaging of the head is demonstrated.

Format: VHS NTSC
Running time: 18.44 mins.
Price: US$95.00; other formats available at additional cost
Source: Michigan State University

 Early-Age Neutering: A Practical Guide for Veterinarians

This instructional video - produced jointly by AVAR (Association of Veterinarians for Animal Rights) and the University of California at Davis, School of Veterinary Medicine - demonstrates some useful techniques for veterinarians for neutering male and female puppies and kittens from 6 to 16 weeks of age or before sexual maturity. It also provides valuable information about the veterinarian's role in helping to reduce the number of unwanted cats and dogs in our society. The techniques shown in the video are meant to augment basic surgery skills by providing tips and encouragement for the veterinarian who has not performed surgery on small animals, as well as to provide information about the safety and benefits of pre-pubertal surgery.

Language: English; Spanish translation under production
Year of production: 2000
Format: VHS NTSC, PAL

Running time: 19 mins.
Price: US$15.00; videos ordered through the AVAR may also be borrowed for up to 2 weeks with a US$20.00 cheque made payable to the AVAR, US$15.00 of which will be refunded when the video is returned
Source: AVAR; University of California (UC Davis)

Endoscopic Examination of the Stomach of the Dog and Cat

Deals with the indications for endoscopic examination. Shows the components of a flexible endoscope and how to handle and control it. Shows how to examine the normal stomach, and stomach abnormalities, removal of foreign bodies and biopsy technique.

Year of production: 1992
Format: VHS PAL
Running time: 50 mins.
Price: £30.00 (excl. VAT and postage)
Source: Royal Veterinary College

Exploratory Celiotomy

This program presents a step by step demonstration for incision and exploration of the canine abdomen. The surgery is supported by a review of the corresponding anatomy.

Year of production: 1984; revised 1996
Format: VHS NTSC, PAL
Running time: 43 mins.
Price: US$50.00
Source: University of California (UC Davis)

Feline Perineal Urethrostomy - Including Castration

After a brief demonstration of castration techniques, the surgery is achieved by a single midline incision ending just below the anal ring. The dissection of the urethra and the creation of the stoma are detailed. Post-operative care and possible complications are indicated.

Year of production: 1983
Format: VHS NTSC, PAL
Running time: 23 mins.
Price: US$50.00
Source: University of California (UC Davis)

Gastrotomy and Enterotomy in the Dog

This program presents the specific procedures and does not include the opening or closure of the surgical site. During the surgery, a review of the corresponding anatomy is illustrated.

Year of production: 1984
Format: VHS NTSC, PAL
Running time: 33 mins.
Price: US$50.00
Source: University of California (UC Davis)

 [The] Initial Evaluation and Management of the Ill Neonatal Foal

Presents a description of the physical examination of the newborn foal and outline of procedures performed in the initial evaluation including: venipuncture, blood culture, blood gas analysis, naso-gastric intubation, jugular vein catheterisation, nasal oxygen administration, transtracheal wash and establishing an initial database.

Year of production: 1989; revised 1991
Format: VHS NTSC, PAL
Running time: 59 mins.
Price: US$50.00
Source: University of California (UC Davis)

 Mandibular and Sublingual Salivary Gland Excision

Step-by-step procedures are demonstrated for canine neck dissection and surgery for salivary gland excision. The anatomy of the region is reviewed and supported with illustrations.

Year of production: 1984
Format: VHS NTSC, PAL
Running time: 29 mins.
Price: US$50.00
Source: University of California (UC Davis)

 Nephrotomy and Cystotomy in the Dog

The program presents 2 canine abdominal surgical procedures. The first, a nephrotomy, demonstrates an incision and exploration of the left kidney as approached through an already prepared midline laparotomy. The pertinent anatomy is reviewed with illustrations. The cystotomy shows the bladder exteriorised caudally from within the same midline incision. The frequency of calculi and specific closure sutures for the bladder are noted.

Year of production: 1984; revised 1996
Format: VHS NTSC, PAL
Running time: 30 mins.
Price: US$50.00
Source: University of California (UC Davis)

 ## Open Heart Surgery in the Dog

Describes basic methods for performing open heart canine surgery and demonstrates techniques of cannulation, cardiac open heart surgery bypass, and prosthetic valve placement.

Format: VHS NTSC
Running time: 18.00 mins.
Price: US$95.00; other formats available at additional cost
Source: Michigan State University

 ## Ovariohysterectomy in the Dog

A basic demonstration of technique, stressing anatomical structures. Comparative illustrations of anatomy highlight the similarities and differences between the bitch and the queen.

Year of production: 1986
Format: VHS NTSC, PAL
Running time: 42 mins.
Price: US$50.00
Source: University of California (UC Davis)

 ## Percutaneous Renal Biopsy: The Ishizaki Technique

Presents a discussion of the objectives and methods of renal biopsy, and evaluation of each; comparison of the various instruments used including the Ishizaki Technique and discussion of the advantages offered by the latter; and demonstration of the procedure first using an embalmed kidney, then on living dogs.

Year of production: 1982
Format: VHS NTSC, PAL
Running time: 24 mins.
Price: US$50.00
Source: University of California (UC Davis)

Practical Animal Handling - 1. Small Mammals

A video program produced and distributed by the British Veterinary Association Animal Welfare Foundation (BVA AWF), which features expert veterinary staff demonstrating the correct procedures for handling small mammals for clinical examination and medication. Its aim is to show that the primary consideration should be for the welfare of the animal. The content reminds professionals of the different approaches to handling 7 representative species of small mammals (mouse, rat, hamster, gerbil, rabbit, guinea pig and ferret), assisting in the training of new staff, students and veterinary nurses by demonstrating techniques which limit stress to the patient. Holding, lifting, and examining each species is shown in close-up, along with how to present each of the common injection sites. An additional section considers the handling of young and old animals.

Format: VHS PAL
Running time: 15 mins.
Price: Free of charge (UK); postage costs (elsewhere)
Note: A digitised version of this program is available on CD-ROM from Prof. Paul Flecknell at the University of Newcastle upon Tyne
Source: BVA Postal Bookshop

 Small Animal Bandaging Techniques

This program describes and illustrates proper application of bandages and casts commonly used for dogs and cats.

Year of production: 1994
Format: VHS NTSC, PAL
Running time: 36 mins.
Price: US$50.00
Source: University of California (UC Davis)

 Small Bowel Resection and Anastomosis in the Dog

This program emphasises the specific procedure and does not include the standard opening and closure of the surgical site.

Year of production: 1984
Format: VHS NTSC, PAL
Running time: 30 mins.
Price: US$50.00
Source: University of California (UC Davis)

Splenectomy

Description not available.

Year of production: 1992
Format: VHS NTSC, PAL
Running time: 12 mins.
Price: US$50.00
Source: University of California (UC Davis)

 Surgical Instruments and Their Use

The basic surgical instruments for veterinary surgery are introduced and their design described. The proper methods for handling these tools are illustrated using both *in vivo* and tabletop examples.

Year of production: 1985
Format: VHS NTSC, PAL
Running time: 33 mins.
Price: US$50.00
Source: University of California (UC Davis)

 Suture and Suturing

Suture materials are examined in detail, as are the needles to be used in various applications. Suture patterns are illustrated both in computer graphic sequences and *in vivo* on the dog.

Year of production: 1987
Format: VHS NTSC, PAL
Running time: 27 mins.
Price: US$50.00
Source: University of California (UC Davis)

 Thoracotomy for Lung Lobe Excision in the Dog

Lobectomy in the dog is demonstrated within an already open and prepared surgical site. The surgery is accompanied by a review of the appropriate thoracic anatomy.

Year of production: 1984
Format: VHS NTSC, PAL

Running time: 17 mins.
Price: US$50.00
Source: University of California (UC Davis)

Thoracotomy for Pyloromyotomy in the Dog

Demonstration of an approach through the canine chest wall for the purpose of exploring the pylorus. The surgery is supported with a review of corresponding anatomy.

Year of production: 1984
Format: VHS NTSC, PAL
Running time: 19 mins.
Price: US$50.00
Source: University of California (UC Davis)

Transposition of the Canine Parotid Duct

Clinical manifestations of the 'canine dry eye' are explained and illustrated in the living dog. A test to determine surgical candidacy is demonstrated. Surgical anatomy is reviewed and the surgical process is observed. A post-operative patient exhibits dramatic results at two weeks after surgery.

Year of production: 1981
Format: VHS NTSC, PAL
Running time: 23 mins.
Price: US$50.00
Source: University of California (UC Davis)

When contacting producers and distributors,
please cite *from Guinea Pig to Computer Mouse*

MODELS, MANNEKINS, SIMULATORS

Abdominal Opening and Closure Trainer

Simulator for the training of laparotomy, laparoscopy, and wound closure. A strong frame carries a pad which simulates the central line of the abdominal wall. Pushing hard against the pad from below is an inflated balloon. The pad contains the layers of skin, fat, linea alba and peritoneum. During a procedure of laparotomy the trainee opens the abdominal wall through the various layers showing that the balloon is not damaged in the process. Both Hassan technique and the Verres needle technique can be carried out. Suturing is possible at different levels - fascial, subdermal and final closure.

Medium: Simulator
Price: On request from regional distributors (see website)
Source: Limbs & Things

Arthroscopic Model of the Wrist

Consists of a plastic hand in which the carpal bones, the radius and the ulna, together with the carpal disk and the intra-articular ligaments are visible. On the extensor side of the hand, there are two points of access to the inner cavity of the joint: a radiodorsal opening and an ulnodorsal one. The carpal disk can be attached to the ulna and the carpal ligaments on both the flexor and extensor sides, and can be exchanged or replaced as required. H48 cm, W26 cm, D10 cm, Wt 1.2 kg.

Medium: Simulator
Price: On request, from regional distributors
Source: Contact Marcus Sommer Somso Modelle for regional distributors (CLA Medien und Lehrmittel catalogue ref. CLA 16)

Arthroscopy Model of the Knee Joint

Natural size model made of synthetic smooth cutaneous and muscular covers (kept in place by four synthetic screws) in which the bones of the knee joint are embedded. The anterior outer cover has four access points to the articular internal area - two lateral, one central and one medial. There is also one lateral and one medial access opening to the posterior recess. The Hoffa's fat body is shown and can be taken off and replaced by an adhesive catch. The internal and external menisci are anchored by plug-in threads and can be easily exchanged and replaced. The ligamentous apparatus, i.e. the lateral ligaments and the cruciate ligaments, are represented nearly true-to-nature. An easy exchange of the ligaments is possible because of the screw and plug-in joints. The patellar ligament is shown and the patella can be exchanged. After removal of the cutaneous-muscular covers one can use the bones with the ligaments as a functional knee-joint model. The mounting support at the thigh is suitable for mounting in an operating vice. H16 cm, W17 cm, D53 cm, Wt 2.5 kg.

Medium: Simulator
Price: On request, from regional distributors
Source: Contact Marcus Sommer Somso Modelle for regional distributors (CLA Medien und Lehrmittel catalogue ref. CLA 10)

 ## Arthroscopy Model of the Shoulder Joint

Comprises a soft skin and muscle covering in which the joint is embedded, complete with its ligamental connections and capsule. This makes it possible to simulate operations in many ways, on the shoulder joint, on the biceps tendon and on the joint capsule, including the rotator cuff. The shoulder joint can also be used as a functional joint at lectures after the skin and muscle covering has been removed. H41 cm, W31 cm, D29 cm, Wt 2.5 kg.

Medium: Simulator
Price: On request, from regional distributors
Source: Contact Marcus Sommer Somso Modelle for regional distributors (CLA Medien und Lehrmittel catalogue ref. CLA 15)

 ## Balloon Harvesting Saphenous Vein Dissection Trainer

This model is very important for professional education and demonstration purposes. This schematic model offers gel-filled saphenous and perforating veins; held within a tunnel as if created by the use of a vein harvesting balloon. The space is cushioned by connective tissue, fat and skin. Entry ports are pre-formed; the veins are replaceable; all other parts are permanent or semi-permanent.

Medium: Simulator
Price: On request from regional distributors (see website)
Source: Limbs & Things

 ## Bladder Phantom for Endoscopy

Natural size, and made of plastic, this model comprises a trunk on a base, external female genitalia with urethra and elastic fastening closure for the bladder (removable inspection window and screw-fit closure cap). Six exchangeable parts demonstrating characteristic bladder diseases can be used to assess the changes to the bladder. For examination, the endoscope is inserted through the urethra via an elastic valve opening in the bladder. The following 6 pathological changes can be diagnosed: papillary bladder tumour, trabeculated bladder, broad-base bladder tumour, fibrinous cystitis, urinary calculus, and radiation cystitis. The examination routine can be checked by a second person through the inspection window. H23 cm, W37 cm, D27 cm, Wt 4.2 kg.

Medium: Simulator
Price: On request, from regional distributors
Source: Contact Marcus Sommer Somso Modelle for regional distributors (CLA Medien und Lehrmittel catalogue ref. CLA 6/6)

 ## Bovine Rectal Palpation Mannekin

A full size cow mannekin, with all necessary organs, a bovine foetus, and the ability for artificial insemination training. Currently in research and development.

Medium: Mannekin
Source: Rescue Critters

 ## Bowel for Anastomosis

Simulation of the human bowel, with soft, strong and very life-like lumen of varying sizes, providing an essential part of basic surgical skills training. The models are constructed entirely from non-biological materials; the inner mucosal layer is lightly bonded to the outer serosa muscular layer to simulate the feel and behaviour of real tissues. With these models extensive practice of anastomotic technique using sutures and stapling instruments is now possible in a clean environment. Each layer of the bowel is sufficiently strong to hold sutures and the whole range of end and cross stapling techniques. For simpler procedures a single layer bowel is provided. Available in 20mm and 30mm diameters.

Medium: Simulator
Price: On request from the regional distributors (see website)
Source: Limbs & Things

 ## Bronchoscopy and Anaesthesiology Trainer 'Broncho Boy II'

This is a teaching model for flexible fibre optic bronchoscopy, rigid bronchoscopy, fibre optic-guided naso- and orotracheal intubation, laryngoscopic intubation, and auto-fluorescent bronchoscopy. While retaining the life-like anatomical features of the original 'Broncho Boy', 'Broncho-Boy II' incorporates a number of innovations enabling its use in a variety of training settings. It comprises retroflexion and left-right rotation of the head for laryngoscopic, orotracheal and bronchoscopic intubation; an acoustic warning signal if excessive pressure exerted on upper teeth by rigid tube or laryngoscope; slightly widened and softer nasal passages for fibre-optic guided nasotracheal intubation; reduced danger of damage to sheath; interchangeable, membrane-connected balloons, enabling stethoscopic confirmation of endotracheal tube placement; new, spring-based supports for tracheobronchial tree which increase pliability and reduce the likelihood of bronchoscope damage; exchangeable fluorescent tracheobronchial system with 'cold' areas of reduced fluorescence for practising autofluorescent bronchoscopy. H25 cm, W70 cm, D38, Wt 11.5 kg.

Medium: Simulator
Price: On request, from regional distributors
Source: Contact Marcus Sommer Somso Modelle for regional distributors (CLA Medien und Lehrmittel catalogue ref. CLA 9/7)

Bronchoscopy Model 'Broncho Boy'

This model was designed initially to facilitate learning transoral and transnasal flexible fibre optic bronchoscopy. It may, however, be used for intubation with the rigid bronchoscope. A specially developed casting process has enabled exact reproduction of internal structures and contours of mucous membranes in nasal passages, pharynx and tracheobronchial system. Anatomical landmarks aid the trainee bronchoscopist in mastering problems of endoscopic orientation. For those experienced with the rigid bronchoscope and wishing to learn flexible endoscopy, practising with the 'Broncho Boy' model will greatly ease the change. The following characteristics typify this unique training model: integrated nasopharynx with tracheobronchial tree; extreme durability with softness and pliability due to the special synthetic substance used in moulds (with no risk of damage to the endoscope); removable sternum, enabling the trainee to check the position of the endoscope (the tracheobronchial tree allows penetration of light from tip of bronchoscope). It comprises the following components: 'Broncho Boy' model (complete model with nasopharynx and tracheobronchial tree with head and thorax), aluminium transport and storage suitcase, adjustable mounting base, lubricant spray, and instructions for use. H25 cm, W71 cm, D42 cm, Wt 14.8 kg.

Medium: Simulator
Price: On request, from regional distributors
Source: Contact Marcus Sommer Somso Modelle for regional distributors (CLA Medien und Lehrmittel catalogue ref. CLA 9)

Bronchoscopy Model - Fluorescing Tracheobronchial Tree with Regions of Reduced Fluorescence

A recent innovation for use with the 'Broncho Boy' Bronchoscopy Model is the auto-fluorescing endoscopic systems in conjunction with the Light Imaging Fluorescence Endoscope (LIFE Xillix / Olympus), or SAFE (1000 Pentax). The bronchial mucosa appears normal with conventional (white light) bronchoscopy, but on being illuminated in the fluorescent mode, emits a green image identical to that of normal mucosa. The trachea and left-sided bronchial branches appear normal in the fluorescence mode, but distinct areas of reduced fluorescence can be observed on the right-sided bronchial tree (upper lobe spur, middle lobe spur, right main bronchus and right bronchus 9/10 spur). Endoscopists using the LIFE-System or SAFE 1000 for the first time can practice switching from white light to fluorescent mode, and in the latter mode learn (light intensity) adjustment in addition to recognising areas of reduced fluorescence. The *Fluorescent Tracheobronchial Tree* can be added to each CLA 'Broncho Boy' with the catalogue numbers CLA 9 to CLA 9/7 or can be supplied additionally as the interchangeable lower part of the tracheobronchial tree. H17 cm, W15 cm, D4 cm, Wt 0.2 kg.

Medium: Simulator
Price: On request, from regional distributors
Source: Contact Marcus Sommer Somso Modelle for regional distributors (CLA Medien und Lehrmittel catalogue ref. CLA 9/8)

Bronchoscopy Model 'Sick Boy'

As the name implies, this model offers the trainee bronchoscopist the opportunity of visualising typical endoscopic pathology, as well as doing forceps biopsies of a right upper lobe lesion. It includes an adenoma, a tumour, and a mucous plug, which also presents the differential diagnosis of a perforated lymph node. As a training aid, it is meant to be used in conjunction with the 'Broncho Boy' model. A simple, but effective, locking device at the lower end of the trachea in all new 'Broncho Boy' models allows quick interchange of the normal tracheobronchial tree with the 'Sick' system. Comprises the following components: 'Broncho Boy' model (nasopharynx with interchangeable healthy and sick tracheobronchial tree integrated into head and thorax), aluminium transport and storage suitcase, adjustable mounting base, lubricant spray, instructions for use. H25 cm, W71 cm, D42 cm, Wt 15 kg.

Medium: Simulator
Price: On request, from regional distributors
Source: Contact Marcus Sommer Somso Modelle for regional distributors (CLA Medien und Lehrmittel catalogue ref. CLA 9/6)

Canine Foreleg

See *Canine Head* for general description.

Medium: Simulator
Price: US$295.00
Source: University of California (UC Davis)

Canine Head

The head and neck model consists of a sculpted mandrel containing channels for a simulated jugular vein covered with a moveable latex 'skin'. It can be used to teach advanced techniques such as placement of through-the-needle catheters, special procedures like the Seldinger (guide wire) technique for placement of multi-lumen and pulmonary artery catheters, and blood collection techniques with a syringe and needle, or through an existing catheter. An instructional video pertaining to the use of these models is included at no extra charge. Replacement skin and tubing is available; please call for price information.

Medium: Simulator
Price: US$450.00
Source: University of California (UC Davis)

 Canine Intestinal Anastomosis Model

Soft-tissue simulator providing the veterinary student with exposure to and practice with anastomosis procedure and suture technique. The model may be filled with user-supplied ingested material or implanted with foreign bodies. Durable and suitable for multiple procedures, with a replaceable intestinal insert. Supplied with storage case for ease of use in laboratory or classroom environments.

Medium: Simulator
Price: US$103.50 (*Canine Intestinal Anastomosis Model* – catalogue ref. #2530-1); US$37.25 (*Canine Replaceable Intestinal Insert* – catalogue ref. #1490)
Source: Pacific Research Laboratories

 Cannulation Pads

These training models allow for the withdrawal of mock blood and the insertion of a cannula; they also allow for the setting up of an IV drip and have the following features: the veins have a self-sealing mechanism and are designed for repeated use; the epidermis is washable and the blood vessels are replaceable; the vessels are designed to allow for a drip to be set up - they can be recharged with mock blood through a one-way valve; the pad is attached to the hand, arm or forearm using an elastic strap - a strong backing sheet prevents the needle from leaving the pad.

Medium: Simulator
Price: On request from regional distributors (see website)
Source: Limbs & Things

Catheterisation Model

Simulator with interchangeable male and female genital organs, as well as interchangeable bladder, in natural size, and made of special plastic. H23 cm, W43 cm, D46 cm, Wt 6 kg.

Medium: Simulator
Price: On request, from regional distributors
Source: Contact Marcus Sommer Somso Modelle for regional distributors (CLA Medien und Lehrmittel catalogue ref. CLA 7)

 ## Catheterisation Model (Male)

Ideal for demonstrating disposable and balloon catheters, as well as suprapubic aspiration, in male patients. It is made of special plastic and can be dismantled into two parts. Natural size, on a stand with base. H30 cm, W18 cm, D18 cm, Wt 0.9 kg.

Medium: Simulator
Price: On request, from regional distributors
Source: Contact Marcus Sommer Somso Modelle for regional distributors (CLA Medien und Lehrmittel catalogue ref. CLA 7/10)

 ## Custom Mannekins

Rescue Critters has made custom mannekins for several universities and companies, such as the University of California at Davis, and the Humane Society of the United States. If you have a special need for a veterinary training mannekin, a realistic animal for filming, or a special effect needing animatronic realistic animals, then enquiries are welcome. Several Rescue Critters artisans work in the special effects industry in Hollywood.

Medium: Mannekin
Source: Rescue Critters

 ## Cutdown Pad

The *Cutdown Pad* is a layered pad simulating the epidermis and subdermal layer with three single veins charged with mock blood. These are deep within the skin layers and only located by palpating the surface. Up to 10 or 12 cuts can be made on the pad thus making it a very useful and economical tool for training students in this emergency procedure. Cannulas can be inserted and veins ligated both distally and proximally. It is recommended that these are made good so that the next student may repeat the procedure without losing the contents from the veins.

Medium: Simulator
Price: On request from the regional distributors (see website)
Source: Limbs & Things

DASIE Surgical Model

DASIE (Dog Abdominal Surrogate for Instructional Exercises) consists of an outer laminated fabric and polyurethane cylinder containing two feet of polyurethane 'bowel'. The outer shell is useful for practising incisions and layered closure of surgical wounds. Multiple string 'vessels' embedded in the outer layer are the proper size for grasping with haemostats and practising ligation of small bleeders. The internal 'bowel' is useful for learning hollow organ surgery. This model is currently used in teaching laboratories throughout the world for psychomotor training in the basics of aseptic technique, instrument and tissue handling, and suture patterns encountered in surgical cases. Each model can be reused multiple times without loss of teaching value.

Medium: Simulator
Price: US$15.00 each (excl. postage)
Note: See also *DASIE Video* under VIDEO
Source: DASIE International

Equine Jugular Vascular Access Mannekin

A full size horse head for vascular training, designed to perform IV draw and injections. Currently in research and development.

Medium: Mannekin
Source: Rescue Critters

Female K-9 Urinary Catheter Training Mannekin

This mannekin replicates the female dog external and internal urogenital structures relevant to urinary catheterisation. Anatomically correct reproductions exist for the vulva, clitoral fossa, vaginal vault, urethral papilla, and urethral orifice enabling the learner to practice the complex skill of urinary catheterisation using visual or tactile cues. A fluid reservoir (representing the bladder) and a one-way valve (representing the urethral sphincter) allow positive feedback during the training exercises. This mannekin, in conjunction with appropriate preliminary skill acquisition, will be essential to the learning of this valuable skill without the detrimental use of animals. It allows the necessary repetition and the absence of negative consequences so critical to a successful learning experience. Future variations of this mannekin will address the skills of artificial insemination, vaginal pathology, and female cystic/urethral calculi management. Accessories included: carrying case, lubricating jelly, and catheter.

Medium: Mannekin
Price: US$425.00 (Item #910)
Source: Rescue Critters

 ## Hollow Organ Surgical Simulator

A reusable simulator for the practice of hollow organ closure which allows the student freedom to practice surgical skills at home or in class. The simulator is a collapsible, hollow laminated mould of the canine stomach (when viewed through a ventral midline abdominal approach), secured to a stow-away base with rubber feet to prevent slippage. The base and incorporated case are made of high-impact plastic to resist physical and moisture damage to the urethane-polymer mould, and the size of the simulator is approximately that of a ¾" professional video case, allowing easy storage and transport. ID Label and model-specific instructions are included.

Medium: Simulator
Price: US$35.00
Note: A range of accompanying video autotutorials is available from Educational Resources, The Ohio State University College of Veterinary Medicine (http://www.vet.ohio-state.edu)
Source: Dr. Daniel D. Smeak (The Ohio State University College of Veterinary Medicine, USA)

 ## Humane K-9 & Cat Trainer

These mannekins allow veterinary students, animal regulation officers, and shelter personnel to learn how to humanely euthanise both dogs and cats. It lets the individual learn these skills by repetitive practice in a non-stressful environment and ensure mastery of a skill before having to perform it. Currently in research and development.

Medium: Mannekin
Source: Rescue Critters

When contacting producers and distributors,
please cite from *Guinea Pig to Computer Mouse*

K-9 Breath Sounds Simulator

This simulator recreates actual breath sounds sampled from dogs. It is a full size K-9 mannekin with multiple sounder locations to be listened with a stethoscope. Currently in research and development.

Medium: Simulator
Source: Rescue Critters

 ## K-9 IV Trainer

Designed to perform IV draw and injections, with disposable and cleanable parts and realistic features. Accessories included: realistic K-9 forearm, ABS carrying case, IV pole, IV holder, 2 IV reservoir bags, and artificial training blood.

Medium: Mannekin
Price: US$425.00 (Item #404)
Note: Additional disposable cephalic veins are also available at US$7.50 each, either as beginner training veins (good for 75-100 sticks - Item #406) or as intermediate training veins (good for 1-3 sticks or 1 catheter placement - Item #407)
Source: Rescue Critters

 ## K-9 Ophthalmology Training Mannekins

Comprising a K-9 head with mounting base, this mannekin will have realistic K-9 eyes for ophthalmology training for both direct and indirect scoping, and will come with several pairs of eyes with different diagnoses. Currently in research and development.

Medium: Mannekin
Source: Rescue Critters

 ## K-9 Thoracentesis Mannekin

This special K-9 training mannekin, approximating a 60-70 lbs dog, allows for chest tube placement as well as the ability to aspirate air and fluid from the thoracic cavity to simulate emergency trauma. Incorporates anatomical landmarks to find key points for the learning process.

Medium: Mannekin
Price: US$975.00 (Item #925)
Source: Rescue Critters

K-9 & Cat Arrhythmia Simulator

This feature recreates arrhythmias for dogs and cats. The simulator can be added to any of Rescue Critters brand full size K-9 or cat mannekins at the time of purchase or be integrated into a previously purchased one. Currently in research and development.

Medium: Simulator
Source: Rescue Critters

 ## K-9 & Cat Heartbeat Simulator

This feature recreates heartbeats for dogs and cats. The simulator can be added to any of Rescue Critters brand full size K-9 or cat mannekins at time of purchase or be integrated into a previously purchased one. Heart sounds are listened to with a stethoscope. Currently in research and development.

Medium: Simulator
Source: Rescue Critters

 ## K-9 & Cat Nursing Mannekins

Life-like dog and cat nursing models. When the mother is not available, this model will deliver nursing formula to care for puppies and kittens in a natural manner. Realistic features. Multiple nipple locations for feeding incorporated. Currently in research and development.

Medium: Mannekin
Source: Rescue Critters

 ## K-9 & Cat Urinary Catheter Training Mannekins

Both dog and cat male/female urinary catheter models will be available. See *Female K-9 Urinary Catheter Training Mannekin* for description details.

Medium: Mannekin
Source: Rescue Critters

Koken Rabbit

This model of silicone, soft vinyl chloride and fur-like material is weighted to feel just like a real female New Zealand White (NZW) rabbit, and has been designed to be used for practical training in proper animal handling, peroral dosage, intravenous injection and blood collection from the auricular vein, orotracheal intubation and urine collection by urethral catheterisation. Its abdomen opens via flaps with Velcro strips, revealing a gel-filled pouch with a stomach inside. The model also features anatomically correct silicone replicas of the skull, pharynx, larynx, trachea, ears with veins, pelvis, perineum, and urethra, and is approximately 2.4 kg in body weight. It comes with artificial blood which can be drawn from the ear vein.

Medium: Mannekin
Price: £400.00 (excl. VAT)
Source: B&K Universal

Koken Rat

The *Koken Rat* is a life-size model of a rat, made of silicone and soft vinyl chloride, which gives it a texture similar to the live animal, much the same feel, and a similar weight (approximately 150 g). It has been designed to train students in rodent handling, oral intubation and venipuncture, and therefore contains anatomically correct replicas of the pharynx, oesophagus, trachea, stomach and ureter, as well as a replaceable tail, with one central and two lateral veins beneath a realistic skin. The tail can be used repeatedly for developing competence in intravenous injection technique and withdrawal of blood. Proper insertion of a needle into the tail vein is confirmed by the flow of imitation blood. As in real rats, the vein and skin close up after an injection. Its posture is similar to that which may be seen in a live rat. The dosage of a substance delivered by gavage can be confirmed through a transparent 'window' in the abdomen, which exposes the windpipe, the gullet and and the stomach.

Medium: Mannekin
Price: £105.00 (the *Koken Rat*); £29.14 (replacement tail); £7.46 (imitation blood 50 cc). Prices excl. VAT
Source: B&K Universal

When contacting producers and distributors,
please cite *from Guinea Pig to Computer Mouse*

Laparoscopic Cholecystectomy Model

Includes a realistic liver, gallbladder, cystic duct, stones, common bile duct, cystic artery, bile and connecting tissue. The hard plastic base includes both a rigid and flexible liver and a life-like moulded stomach. The gallbladder and related structures are one replaceable unit.

Medium: Simulator
Price: US$595.00 (catalogue ref. LC-10); US$475.00 (*Replaceable Gallbladder* – 10-pack, LC-20)
Source: Simulab Corporation

 Laparoscopic Nissen Fundoplication Model

Ideal for the practice of the gastroesophageal reflux procedure. Included with the reusable base with liver is a replaceable stomach, oesophagus, and connecting tissue.

Medium: Simulator
Price: US$725.00 (catalogue ref. LNF-10); US$480.00 (*Replaceable Fundus,* 10-pack – LNF-20); US$165.00 (*Replaceable Fundus, Crura, Omentum* – LNF-30)
Source: Simulab Corporation

 Life/form IV Arm

A special, extremely thin, synthetic skin, and rubber tubing with appropriately small lumen and thin walls. The cephalic and basilic vein are accessible, as well as the dorsal venous arch on the hand. Comes with 2 IV bags with clamps, one pint Life/form blood, and one winged infusion set.

Medium: Simulator
Price: US$245.00
Source: Nasco

 Life/form IV Demonstration Arm

An economical IV demonstration arm constructed of soft material with life-like veins in the skin surface that are visible and palpable. No internal tubing exists, but the skin can be punctured repeatedly. No blood to set up, no mess to clean up, and no leaking. However, no fluids should be injected into this arm. May be used in venipuncture practice when fluid return is not essential, and is suitable for allied IV demonstrations and practice (flexion, cleaning, and taping). Intramuscular injections can be practised in the deltoid region. The skin and underlying foam may be cut for suturing practice. Comes in 2 versions, with either white or black skin.

Medium: Simulator
Price: US$110.00
Source: Nasco

 Life/form IV Leg

A special, extremely thin, synthetic skin is paired with rubber tubing featuring a small lumen and thin walls. The greater and lesser saphenous veins are accessible, as well as the dorsal venous arch on the foot. Comes with 2 IV bags with clamps, one pint Life/form blood, one 3 cc syringe, one 22-gauge needle, and one winged infusion set.

Medium: Simulator
Price: US$245.00
Source: Nasco

 Life/form Suture Practice Arm

Made with a soft vinyl skin over a core of stitchable foam to provide a life-like suturing experience for students or a realistic suturing demonstration by an instructor. Realistic skin texture with wrinkles, pores, and visible fingerprints. Soft and pliable for easy sewing, the skin is tough enough that sutures will not pull out when tightened. The unit is provided with three 'wounds'. These 'wounds' can be sutured repeatedly until the skin around them is finally worn out; then, new 'wounds' can be cut. Although disposable, the arm provides hundreds of suturing experiences before wearing out. Conservatively, over one hundred cuts can be made on the trainer and each of these cuts can be sutured several times. *Life/form Suture Practice Arm* is complete with a starter suturing kit and instruction booklet. Includes a one-year warranty.

Medium: Simulator
Price: US$110.00
Source: Nasco

 'Lucky' the Horse Mannekin

'Lucky' is a new life-sized horse mannekin used to safely learn hands-on training of emergency search and rescue techniques. It has articulating limbs, a tail feature as an attachment point, realistic training weight and a height of 15 hands. It will accept standard horse harnesses, glides and gear. *'Lucky'* can be used in all weather, in mud or water, and is designed for training indoors or out. It is specifically designed to train emergency search and rescue techniques to fire and police departments, SAR units, military, government agencies, animal control, humane organisations, veterinarians and equine groups. *'Lucky'* comes with all accessories needed to assemble, and

carrying bag for connecting rods, knobs and washers. All components engineered to be rust proof.

Medium: Mannekin
Price: US$5,675.00 (item #750). Please contact the source for postage and handling charges; this item must be sent via freight; price does not include reusable crate used for both postage and storage
Source: Rescue Critters

 ## M.A.T. Trainer

The *Minimal Access Therapy (M.A.T.) Trainer* is a cost-effective, simple, practical endosurgery trainer. It is versatile, lightweight and is incorporated within a neat and strong carrying case. Inside this there is a plastic case suitable for wet and dry work. The foam latex cover represents the abdominal skin and it is supported by two removable arches. Trochar ports can be placed anywhere for entry and exit of scopes or instruments; two unique supporting jigs fit on to the base and receive Limbs & Things simulators. Assemblies for use in the M.A.T. *Trainer* include:

- *Large Surgical Dissection Pad.* This pad has a multitude of separate liquid filled vessels with alternating venous, arterial and bile liquid set in connective tissue and covered with simulated skin. It can be positioned within the M.A.T. *Trainer* using the jig or clips provided, and allows the practice of a large amount of incision, dissection, mobilisation, division and ligation. A fluid feed may be connected to any of the vessels to simulate fluid.

- *Small Surgical Dissection Pad.* Having the same format as the *Large Dissection Pad*, this product is designed to cater for incision, dissection, mobilisation, division and ligation - essential skills for any surgeon. The two surgical pads develop virtually every perception, dexterity and co-ordination skill needed by the endo-surgeon.

- *Ectopic Pregnancy Simulator.* This realistic simulation fills the gap in the requirements for gynaecological basic surgical skills training. It enables the practice of removing ectopic pregnancy using diathermy, laser and other electro-surgery techniques. It is an important part of basic surgical skills training, designed for use in the Limbs & Things M.A.T. *Trainer* and *Body Form* or other endoscopic trainers.

- *Gynae Dissection Pad.* The plane of dissection from the round ligament, through the broad ligament layers to the crossover point of the uterine artery and the ureter is represented many times. There is a multitude of dissection and suturing practice in this cleverly designed multi-use training pad. A fluid feed can be added to simulate flow through the vessels. An essential part of any gynaecological surgical training program. Ideal for two trainees to share on a course.

- *Surgical Gall Bladder Pad.* A single gall bladder, cystic duct and common bile duct on one pad is again attached to the variable slope jig using Velcro. This ingenious simulation caters for not only ligation of the cystic artery and cystic duct and removal of the gall bladder (chole-cystectomy), but also for cholangiogram catheter insertion. All vessels are fluid filled. A drip system may be added to provide fluid flow through the Luer lock which is attached to the cystic artery. There are 4 variations on the gall bladder available: 1. *Normal gall bladder;*

2. *Gall bladder with wide common bile duct and stone for exploration*; 3. *Gall bladder with short cystic duct*; 4. *Gall bladder with bifurcated cystic artery.*

Medium: Simulator
Price: On request from regional distributors (see website)
Source: Limbs & Things

 Nursing Doll

A standard nursing doll (catalogue ref. CLA 1) in natural size for nursing care which comprises the following parts: removable head, removable eyes, dentures and tracheostomy, thorax with chest wall and moving arms with infusion and injection pads, lower body with abdominal wall and artificial anus, injection pads in the buttocks, movable mounted legs with injection pads in the thigh, lung alveolus, stomach, intestines, detachable female and male genitalia with rectum and bladder. The joints are robust and they are able to reproduce practically all natural movements. Openings for inserting a PEG catheter and for suprapubic bladder puncture are provided. L178 cm, Wt 23 kg. Model CLA 2 has additional male genitalia with urinary bladder of 2 litres capacity and lungs with closure, for cleaning. Model CLA 3 has external female genitalia only and moving arms without infusion pads. Training applications include: handling of injured limbs, bandaging, stoma care, suprapubic puncture of the bladder, PEG catheter care, tracheostomy care, care of the eye and introduction of medications, care of the outer ear and introduction of medications, administration of enemas, urinary catheterisation (male and female), physical treatment (respiration, inhalation, oxygen treatment, resucitation), injections, infusions/transfusions and intravenous access, and rinsing (stomach lavage, and bladder, colon, colostomy and enterostomy irrigation).

Medium: Simulator
Price: On request, from regional distributors
Source: Contact Marcus Sommer Somso Modelle for regional distributors (CLA Medien und Lehrmittel catalogue ref. CLA 1, CLA 2, CLA 3)

 OGI Phantom

For upper gastrointestinal tract endoscopy training (esophagoscopy, gastroscopy, bulboscopy), and catheterisation of the major duodenal papilla by retrograde instillation of contrast medium into the pancreatic duct system (endoscopic retrograde cholangiopancreatography, ERCP). Natural size, made of special plastic. H35 cm, W98 cm, D32 cm, Wt 11 kg.

Medium: Simulator
Price: On request, from regional distributors
Source: Contact Marcus Sommer Somso Modelle for regional distributors (CLA Medien und Lehrmittel catalogue ref. CLA 4)

Pelviscopic Operations Model

Consists of a rigid plastic mass and corresponds to the actual size of a normal woman. It has been designed for the simulation of all pelviscopic operations. When using the stand, team operations can also be practised with ease using three apertures. H22 cm, W43 cm, D45 cm, Wt 6,5 kg (model without stand); H97 cm, W55 cm, D55 cm, Wt 8,5 kg (model with stand).

Medium: Simulator
Price: On request, from regional distributors
Source: Contact Marcus Sommer Somso Modelle for regional distributors (CLA Medien und Lehrmittel catalogue ref. CLA 14 - model without stand; CLA 14/1 - model with stand)

P.O.P. Trainer

The operation simulator with pulsatile organ perfusion (*P.O.P. Trainer*) simulates the blood supply of organs and organ complexes and was developed for the training of both minimally invasive and conventional surgery. It uses animal organs taken directly from the slaughterhouse during food production. The central artery of these organs/organ complexes is catheterised and connected to the pump of the *P.O.P. Trainer*, which is electronically controlled and maintains the pressure of the perfusion medium (coloured tap water). Nearly all operations (abdominal, thoracic, urological, vascular, gynaecological) can be carried out under quasi-real conditions. All technologies familiar from clinical work, such as high frequency lasers, ultrasound dissector, aquadissector etc., can be used. With the third generation of *P.O.P. Trainer*, even complex operations such as colorectal and antireflux procedures can be practised. Furthemore, all types of haemorrhages can be simulated, allowing the trainee to practice the management of bleeding complications. OPTIMIST also offers workshops and leasing arrangements

Medium: Simulator
Price: €5,959.00 (*P.O.P. Trainer*, including: 1 neutral-electrode, 5 neopren mats, 1 video operating instruction, 1 power conversion, 1 litre colouring fluid); €261.00 (leasing rate per day excl. insurance and transport); €574.00 (workshop day per participant, excl. insurance, transport and tutor's travel expenses, but incl. tutors, *P.O.P. Trainers* and training know-how, with calculation based on 12 participants). For prices of catheterised, chemically prepared, deep-frozen and vacuum-packed organs please contact source or check website
Source: OPTIMIST

When contacting producers and distributors,
please cite *from Guinea Pig to Computer Mouse*

PracticeRat

This simulator for learning and practising basic vascular and neurological microsurgical techniques is an integral part of the Sharpoint microsurgical training system (for other components see below, under Price). It mimics the properties of a rat's femoral vessels and sciatic nerve - appearance, consistency, tear characteristics and resistance to needle and blade passage. It is fully portable and available in several models: artery and vein; artery and vein with adventitia; artery and vein with adventitia and also with sciatic nerve. Provided access to a microscope is available, students can practice end-to-end and end-to-side anastomoses, interpositional vein grafts and nerve sutures. *PracticeRat* is also available with a pumping system controlled electronically by a built-in-digital-clock time slice method, so artificial blood can be pumped through the vessels with a pulsatile flow.

Medium: Simulator
Price: US$38.00 (*Basic Unit 100* - platform); US$70.00 (*Basic Unit 101* - 1 mm artery & vein only); US$82.00 (*Unit 102* - 1 mm artery & vein with adventitia); US$105.00 (*Basic Unit 103* - 1 mm artery & vein with adventitia and sciatic nerve); US$7.00 (*U Connector Tubing Set*); US$12.00 (250 ml artificial arterial/venous blood); US$8.80 (per box of *PracticePack* - latex membrane in frame with a blue background to help enhance microsurgical suturing skills); US$106.40 - US$228.65 (per box of *Nonsterile Laboratory Packs* - needles and suture materials); US$100.00 (VHS NTSC version of videofilm 'Microsurgical Repair of the Rat Sciatic Nerve') / US$112.50 (VHS PAL version, special order only); US$24.95 (*A Laboratory Manual for Microvascular and Microtubal Surgery*); US$19.95 (*Manual of Experimental Muscle Flap and Organ Transplantation Models in the Rat*)
Source: Surgical Specialties Corporation

 PVC-Rat

This model has been developed to master skills in microsurgery, and thus to replace live rats, commonly used in the training of microsurgical techniques. Made of soft plastic, it features a number of organs, blood vessels, and ducts from the abdominal and neck regions of the rat. All parts are rendered in exquisite detail, can be used many times, and can be replaced as necessary. The *PVC-Rat* gives the possibility to practice approximately 25 different microsurgical techniques (anastomoses, cannulations, transplantations of vessels and organs). It comes in a carrying case, together with a video user guide, several spare parts and *Remote* - a patient monitoring training computer program. Some parts of the model can easily be replaced, however blood vessels and ducts can be used many times. *Remote* comes on a CD-ROM (for Windows) and can be used in combination with the *PVC-Rat*. One can train the skills needed for patient monitoring during several (micro-)surgical techniques. During surgery, anaesthesia can be administered, the animal's temperature and breathing can be observed and controlled. When the exercise is finished, the software generates a full report, showing every event and status. Several cannulation and experimental techniques are explained in great detail in a series of 10 videos which go with the 'Manual of Microsurgery on the Laboratory Rat' (Elsevier Science Publishers B.V., Amsterdam).

Medium: Simulator
Price: €160.00 / US$160.00 (complete set of *PVC-Rat* in box, User's Guide on video included, *Remote* software for free); €25.00 / US$25.00 (separate *Remote* software on CD-ROM); €170.00 / US$168.00 (individual video in VHS PAL format), €215.00 / US$208.00 (individual video in VHS NTSC format), €1,475.00 / US$1,420.00 (set of 10 videos in VHS PAL format), €1,928.00 / US$1,872.00 (set of 10 videos in VHS NTSC format); €66.50 / US$66.50 (manual, 1990, 2ⁿᵈ reprint 2000). These prices do not include postage, handling and taxes
Source: Microsurgical Developments

 ## *Rhesus* Primate Mannekin

This *Rhesus* monkey will have femoral and saphenous venipuncture sites as well as a femoral pulse. Also the ability to perform endotracheal, nasal and gastric placement. Currently in research and development.

Medium: Mannekin
Source: Rescue Critters

 ## Sawbones Models

A range of more than 2,000 models and simulators, with a focus on orthopaedics, including over 200 veterinary (canine, equine and bovine) models. They comprise normal bones and simulations of various pathologies. The orthopaedic models, developed specifically for use in motor skills exercises where a realistic bone specimen is required, provide a working model for orthopaedic operations and to further develop orthopaedic surgical skills outside the operating room. Also available are soft tissue, endoscopy and endovascular models. Custom-made specimens such as those with pre-cut fractures, osteoporotic bones, specific pathologies and combination models can be provided on request. See on-line catalogue for more details.

Medium: Model; simulator
Price: Varies, depending on item (see website for more details)
Source: Pacific Research Laboratories

 ## Simulab Hernia Training Model

This unit allows for the practice of surgical mesh placement (ventral, direct and indirect) among other practices. The model includes iliac and pubic simulated bone structures, Cooper's ligament, fascia transversalis, external iliac vessels, inferior epigastric vessels and parietal peritoneum. It has realistic vessel, testicle and cord structures, with life-like synthetic tissue.

Medium: Simulator
Price: US$1,395.00 (catalogue ref. HTM-30)
Note: A laparoscopic hernia training model is under development
Source: Simulab Corporation

 ## Simulab Pop-Up Pelvic Trainer

A versatile collapsible pelvic trainer with multiple height adjustments and with both clear and opaque covers for trocar placement.

Medium: Simulator
Price: US$195.00 (catalogue ref. SPT-10)
Source: Simulab Corporation

 ## Simulab Tissue Models

- *Simulab GI Tissue*. Realistic simulation models including oesophagus, fundus, duodenum, small intestine, and large intestine. The complete digestive tract from oesophagus to descending colon is available now as one model; it can be insufflated and will retain fluid.

- *Simulab Breast Probe Model*. Simulated breast and axilla for probe equipment demonstration. Specially formulated simulated tissue reacts realistically to probe. A canal in the underside provides multiple locations for chip placement.

- *Simulab Tissue Suture Pads*. Allow multiple practice scenarios. Constructed from Simulab patented formulas, providing realistic life-like structures.

Medium: Simulator
Price: US$995.00 (*Complete Digestive Tract*, 15 feet / ca. 4.6m – catalogue ref. SDT-10); US$480.00 (*Replaceable Fundus*, 10-pack – LNF-20); US$400.00 (*Small Intestine*, 10-pack – SMI-10; *Large Intestine*, 10-pack – LGI-10); US$258.00 (*Breast Probe Model* – BPM-10); US$25.00 (*Tissue Suture Pad* – TSP-10)
Source: Simulab Corporation

When contacting producers and distributors,
please cite *from Guinea Pig to Computer Mouse*

Simulab Torso

Accepts most Simulab training models and provides a realistic laparoscopic experience by concealing the procedure from direct view.

Medium: Simulator
Price: US$625.00 (catalogue ref. ST-10)
Source: Simulab Corporation

 Simulator for Rectal Examination of Horses

This is a mannekin of a horse, built at scale 1:1 for teaching and training rectal examination with veterinary students before living animals become involved. The mannekin is in use at the University of Veterinary Medicine in Vienna (Austria), at the Clinic of Equine Medicine of the University of Bern (Switzerland) and at the University of Glasgow Veterinary School (UK). The mannekin is part artificial, to provide a realistic feel, and part slaughterhouse material. The artificial organs include the kidneys, the spleen, the suspensory renosplenic ligament, the aorta, the urinary bladder, the ovaries, the uterus, the deferent ducts, their mesenteries, and the vaginal rings. The intestines, taken from slaughterhouses, are fixed in a solution of Formalin and Tegodor, and then impregnated with polyethyleneglycol. Fittings are mounted at both ends of the intestine, so that it can be inflated to the required feel. The anus is built with a metal frame, which stretches a perforated rubber fold; this replaces the sphincter muscle and is attached to the artificial rectum.

Medium: Mannekin
Price: From €27,000 - €30,000, depending on individual orders
Source: Prof. Wolfgang Künzel (University of Veterinary Medicine Vienna, Austria)

 SIMUVIEW Suture Trainer

A two dimensional laparoscopic simulator that utilises Simulab's patented reflective image system. This system allows the user to perform laparoscopic training without setting up traditional videoendoscopic camera equipment. Other than hand instruments, no other equipment is required. The suture trainer is available in two different styles: a folding trainer that is designed to be collapsible for easy storage, or a rigid box trainer that is designed with clear sides and a cover that has a convenient carrying handle. Both styles come with a replaceable tissue suture pad.

Medium: Simulator
Price: US$295.00 (*Suture Trainer, rigid box* – catalogue ref. SST-10; *folding* – SST-20); US$25.00 (*Key Trainer* – SKT-10; *Tissue Suture Pad* – TSP-10); US$40.00 (*Small Intestine* – SMI-10; *Large Intestine* – LGI-10); US$48.00 (*Fundus Tissue*, LNF-20)
Source: Simulab Corporation

Skin Simulator Kit - Skin Pads and Lesions

Limbs & Things' unique skin simulation not only provides for incision, undermining, and suturing of wounds but responds and gives a life-like quality which is very important in the training process. The suturing system which has been designed, and which is constantly expanding, provides for training in a range of techniques which are needed daily during patient care. Products include:

- *Wound Closure Pad - Small/Large*
- *Double Sebaceous Cyst Pad*
- *Double Lipoma Pad*
- *Curettage* (removal of seborrhoeic keratoses using a curette), *Shave* (removal of compound naevi using a scalpel) and *Snip Pads* (removal of skin tags using toothed forceps)
- *Ring Block Injection Set*
- *Local Anaesthesia Pad*
- *Diagnostic Full Face with Lesions*

Medium: Simulator
Price: On request from regional distributors (see website)
Source: Limbs & Things

Skin / Suture Pattern Simulator

A reusable simulator for the practice of instrument handling skills, suture patterns, and intradermal suturing techniques, which allows the student freedom to practice surgical skills at home or in class. The simulator imitates the suturing qualities of dermal tissue, and consists of a flat laminated urethane-polymer mould positioned over, but not attached to, a mid-density foam core for support. The simulator mould is secured to a stow-away base with rubber feet to prevent slippage. The base and incorporated case are made of high-impact plastic to resist physical and moisture damage to the urethane-polymer mould, and the size of the simulator is approximately that of a ¾" professional video case, allowing easy storage and transport. ID label and model-specific instructions are included.

Medium: Simulator
Price: US$32.50
Note: A range of accompanying video autotutorials is available from Educational Resources, The Ohio State University College of Veterinary Medicine (http://www.vet.ohio-state.edu)
Source: Dr. Daniel D. Smeak (The Ohio State University College of Veterinary Medicine, USA)

When contacting producers and distributors,
please cite *from Guinea Pig to Computer Mouse*

Stomach and Duodenum Phantom

Natural size, and made of special plastic. For training of endoscopy. H12 cm, W36 cm, D27 cm, Wt 1.3 kg.

Medium: Simulator
Price: On request, from regional distributors
Source: Contact Marcus Sommer Somso Modelle for regional distributors (CLA Medien und Lehrmittel catalogue ref. CLA 4/1)

Surgical Training System (Aboud's Model)

Designed by Dr. Emad Aboud from the University of Arkansas for Medical Sciences in the USA, this new surgical system allows the simulation of live surgery, including bleeding, pulsation, softness of tissue, and the vascular tree. A specially prepared human cadaver (or part thereof) is connected to the device, which comprises a pump to provide pulsating pressure in the arteries and static pressure in the veins, artificial blood reservoirs, and tubing to connect the pump and the reservoirs to the specimen. The simulator can be used to learn and practice established procedures in general surgery and in vascular, endoscopic and micro-neurosurgery; to test or demonstrate new medical devices; to study the blood supply of various anatomical regions; and to practice venicannulation, venipuncture and the drawing of blood. The device is suitable for surgeons, residents, students and nurses, and is an innovative alternative to surgery training involving live animals. For more information contact Dr. Emad Aboud (University of Arkansas for Medical Sciences, Slot 507, Little Rock, AR 72205, USA, e-mail: aboud@swaida.com).

Medium: Simulator
Price: On request
Note: At present the University of Arkansas for Medical Sciences is seeking partners to produce this device
Source: University of Arkansas for Medical Sciences

Suture Trainer Arm

Made from polyurethane foam and silicone, this suture trainer arm has realistic skin and can be used over and over. Designed for both internal and external sutures with an indefinite shelf life.

Medium: Simulator
Price: US$29.95 (Item #909)
Source: Rescue Critters

Suture Trainer Skin Pad

A speciality of Soft Options Ltd. lies in the life-like simulation of skin and other anatomical structures (e.g. limbs, organs and blood vessels). Through many years experience in medical model making and within the film and television industries, Soft Options has gained the expertise to tailor-make products and R&D services to an individual customer's technical requirements and budget. This *Suture Pad* provides a highly realistic aid to teaching cutting and suturing and is as close as possible to the feel of living human or animal tissue. For medical and veterinary students it gives invaluable confidence and experience before tackling the real thing. The pad is 18-20 mm thick and is constructed from a number of different foams and elastomers, layered and bonded together to simulate accurately the epidermis, dermis and sub-dermis found in living tissue. It can be cut and sutured in any of these layers. The pad is robust and large enough to allow re-suturing of an incision, or for several incisions to be made. To provide additional learning experiences, it can also be made in a range of sizes and specifications to suit customer requirements; various pathological features such as warts, skin tags and sebaceous cysts can be added.

Medium: Simulator
Price: On request (£8.00 - £25.00 depending on size and features)
Source: Soft Options

Tower Trainer

This simulator has Simulab's patented 'SIMUVIEW' imaging system, which allows realistic portrayal, ideal for laparoscopic training in a 2D field without setting up traditional videoendoscopic camera equipment. Used primarily for dissection, suture and knot training, a removable cover conceals the subject from direct view. The adjustable periscope allows the user to sit or stand and may be modified to fit any height. The uppermost mirror simulates a video monitor, conveying a realistic replication of surgery, and manipulation of instruments. The viewing angle of the tissue pad may be altered and the simulated tissues are easily replaced. A removable lens magnifies the field of vision.

Medium: Simulator
Price: US$1,495.00 (*Tower Trainer* – catalogue ref. TPT-10); US$295.00 (*Liver Base Insert* – LCT-10); US$380.00 (*Replaceable Gallbladder* – 10-pack); US$25.00 (*Tissue Suture Pad* – TSP-10); US$40.00 (*Small Intestine* – SMI-10; *Large Intestine* – LGI-10); US$48.00 (*Fundus Tissue* – LNF-20)
Source: Simulab Corporation

Trauma Man Surgical Trainer

This is an anatomical human body form designed for students to practice several of the surgical procedures taught in surgical skills training. It is the only human patient simulator certified for use by the American College of Surgeons in the ATLS course. It consists of simulated human tissue structure made of an elastomeric composition designed specifically for surgical dissection, and allows the practice of surgical skills in at least three areas:

- Abdomen. Allows the practice of diagnostic peritoneal lavage. For this procedure, the *Trauma Man Surgical Trainer* features a simulated tissue structure including a skin layer, a subcutaneous fat layer, an anterior rectus sheath layer, a muscle layer, a posterior rectus sheath layer, an extraperitoneal layer, and a peritoneum layer. Underlying the tissue structure, the trainer includes simulated abdominal organs within an abdominal cavity. The organs and cavity can be filled with simulated bodily fluids (e.g. blood) to lend more realism to the practice procedure.

- Chest. Chest tube insertion and pericardiocentesis are procedures which can be performed on the trainer for this area. In addition to the simulated tissue structure on the exterior of the chest, the trainer includes additional tissue structure in the form of a layer of simulated tissue to mimic the intercostal muscle and the parietal pleura. To be more life-like, the trainer also includes airflow inside the pleura for a realistic response during a procedure plus inflatable lungs to simulate breathing, and ribs. For pericardiocentesis, a sternum, ribs, a heart and additional pericardium tissue structure are included. The heart and pericardium can be filled with simulated bodily fluids to mimic the real life procedure.

- Neck. Cricothyroidotomy is a procedure which can be performed on this part of the trainer. In addition to the simulated human tissue structure on the exterior of the neck, the trainer includes a simulated cricoid cartilage, thyroid cartilage, and cricothyroid ligament in this area. To be more life-like, the trainer also includes airflow in the trachea for a realistic response during a practice procedure.

Medium: Simulator
Price: On request
Source: Simulab Corporation

 ## Urological Examination Phantom for Endoscopic Operations

Transurethral operation techniques require extensive training. A practice phantom can support the learning process to a great extent. This model comprises a natural size trunk, made of special plastic with interchangeable genitalia, on a base with a water tray: male genitalia with urethra and interchangeable prostate and connection to the bladder; external female genitalia with urethra and connection to the bladder. The prostate capsule can be filled with natural or synthetic materials. The bladder is split and joined together with a sealing ring. The bladder incorporates 4 openings: the front connection to either the prostate or urethra; the top to take a bladder trocar or for drainage; the back wall for providing tissue, if necessary, for measuring pressure or the insertion of electrodes; an opening for the plug connector for draining the contents of the bladder with the pertinent shut-off and drain hose. All endoscopic operations can be practised on the phantom using ultrasound or lasers. The phantom is also suitable for various experimental examinations. For example, testing and assessing new methods in high frequency technology, pressure and flow measurements, testing new instruments etc. H28 cm, W45 cm, D36 cm, Wt 6.3 kg.

Medium: Simulator
Price: On request, from regional distributors
Source: Contact Marcus Sommer Somso Modelle for regional distributors (CLA Medien und Lehrmittel catalogue ref. CLA 6/4)

 Urological Practice Model

Made of special plastic, this model allows rectal examinations and palpation of the testicles to be learned under true-to-life conditions. Five different states of the prostate can be felt in the anus after insertion of the fingers: normal condition, beginning of carcinoma, widespread carcinoma, adenoma, and congestion. The different prostate models are mounted on a swivel plate so that the person investigating can feel the 5 different prostate changes in one operation. In testicle palpation, the testicles themselves, the epididymis and the spermatic cord can be felt. On one testicle, a hardening can be felt as in carcinoma of the testicle. Feeling of testicles can also be demonstrated to the lay person for early detection of cancer of the testicles. H34 cm, W52 cm, D30 cm, Wt 4.5 kg.

Medium: Simulator
Price: On request, from regional distributors
Source: Contact Marcus Sommer Somso Modelle for regional distributors (CLA Medien und Lehrmittel catalogue ref. CLA 6)

When contacting producers and distributors,
please cite *from Guinea Pig to Computer Mouse*

WORLD WIDE WEB

Principles of Surgery
http://cal.nbc.upenn.edu/surgery/
University of Pennsylvania School of Veterinary Medicine, USA

Web-Based Surgical Simulators and Medical Education Tools
http://synaptic.mvc.mcc.ac.uk/simulators.html
University of Manchester / Leeds General Infirmary / University of Leeds, UK

5. Embryology & Developmental Biology

SOFTWARE

Asterina gibbosa – The Egg, the Larva and the Metamorphosis of a Starfish

See description of this title under VIDEO.

Language: French
Year of production: Original film made in 1973
Medium: CD-ROM (MPEG4 format)
System requirements: Windows Media 7 (or Windows Player 6.4 for WinNT4 and Win95)
Price: Individual use: €15.00 (Europe), €30.00 (rest of the world); Institutional use: €30.00 (Europe), €45.00 (rest of the world)
Note: The original title of this program is *Asterina gibbosa - L'oeuf, la larve et la métamorphose d'une étoile de mer*
Source: SFRS

Biology of the Cuttlefish *(Sepia officinalis)*

See description of this title under VIDEO.

Language: French, English, Portuguese, Russian, Spanish
Year of production: Original film made in 1967
Medium: CD-ROM (MPEG4 format)
System requirements: Windows Media 7 (or Windows Player 6.4 for WinNT4 and Win95)
Price: Individual use: €15.00 (Europe), €30.00 (rest of the world); Institutional use: €30.00 (Europe), €45.00 (rest of the world)
Note: The original title of this program is *Biologie de la seiche (Sepia officinalis)*
Source: SFRS

CALVE

See description and details of this program under 'Anatomy'.

Development of the Amphibian Egg, as a Model of Vertebrate Embryology

This program will help students in biomedical sciences to understand the vertebrate 'building plan'. High-quality videos of a living embryo, together with animations of gastrulation and neurulation, as well as histological sections of embryos, make the morphological processes and aspects of vertebrate embryology very clear. The presence of self-tests will help the student to develop a solid understanding of the key concepts of vertebrate embryology. The content is presented to the students in a logical and intuitive style, enabling them to navigate freely without losing focus on the main storyline.

Language: Dutch, English; other languages possible
Year of production: 2002
Medium: CD-ROM; world wide web
System requirements: Windows 98/ME/2000/XP, Internet Explorer 5+, QuickTime 4, DirectX (newest version recommended); Pentium II with 450 MHz processor (or equivalent), 64 MB RAM, 8 MB video card, 16-bit sound card, high colour display with 800 x 600 24-bit resolution; 300 MB free on the HDD to copy the program (otherwise the movies won't run smoothly). An HTML 1.1 version is under construction at the time of publication
Price: €50.00
Source: University of Gröningen

Development of the Batrachian Egg

See description of this title under VIDEO.

Language: German, English
Year of production: Original film made in 1967
Medium: CD-ROM (MPEG4 format)
System requirements: Windows Media 7 (or Windows Player 6.4 for WinNT4 and Win95)
Price: Individual use: €15.00 (Europe), €30.00 (rest of the world); Institutional use: €30.00 (Europe), €45.00 (rest of the world)
Note: The French title of this program is *Développement de l'oeuf de batracien*
Source: SFRS

Embryology

Discover the major patterns of embryology with a fascinating look at chordate development of the frog and chick. The library of microscopic images included can be magnified, manipulated and measured - just like with a traditional microscope. Each image is accompanied by supporting reference text and callouts. The unique program can be operated in either tutorial or assessment mode. Includes stunning video footage of a developing human foetus.

Medium: CD-ROM
System requirements: Windows 95 or later, PowerMac 7.5 or later; 16 MB RAM
Price: US$59.95; US$179.95 (lab pack of 5); US$419.95 (library pack of 20); US$299.95 (network version)
Source: Neo/Sci

FlyCycle CD

This is a CD-ROM adaptation of the film *Fly Cycle: The Lives of a Fly, Drosophila melanogaster* (Sinauer Associates, 1996). Formatted for Macintosh and/or Windows processors, it includes 40 mins. of QuickTime movies, depicting details on the biology and life cycle of *Drosophila* - adult courting and mating, embryonic development, larval growth, imaginal disks and salivary glands, metamorphosis, and a gallery of mutants used in research. *FlyCycle CD* is designed to be used at a range of educational levels. At high school and introductory undergraduate levels, it can acquaint students with the fruit fly life cycle and a number of the mutants used in introductory courses. For more advanced undergraduates in developmental biology and genetics courses, and for graduate students beginning their research on *Drosophila*, the CD-ROM introduces the many specifics they will need to know, and techniques for examining the organism in detail. Included on the CD-ROM is the text to an accompanying 40-page booklet that can be used on the computer with convenient text hyperlinks, or printed out. The booklet presents information on each segment of the CD-ROM, a 'getting started' section for those who want to raise fruit flies, a list of suppliers, an annotated selected bibliography, and a glossary.

Year of production: 1998
Medium: CD-ROM
System requirements: Windows 95/NT with Pentium processor; Macintosh OS 7.0 or later with Power PC; 16 MB RAM (24 MB recommended)
Price: US$19.95
Source: Sinauer Associates

Foetal Development of the Rat

See description of this title under VIDEO.

Language: French, English, German, Portuguese, Russian, Spanish
Year of production: Original film made in 1964
Medium: CD-ROM (MPEG4 format)
System requirements: Windows Media 7 (or Windows Player 6.4 for WinNT4 and Win95)
Price: Individual use: €15.00 (Europe), €30.00 (rest of the world); Institutional use: €30.00 (Europe), €45.00 (rest of the world)
Note: The original title of this program is *Développement foetal du rat*
Source: SFRS

[The] Genesis of Monsters

See description of this title under VIDEO.

Language: French
Year of production: Original film made in 1974
Medium: CD-ROM (MPEG4 format)
System requirements: Windows Media 7 (or Windows Player 6.4 for WinNT4 and Win95)
Price: Individual use: €15.00 (Europe), €30.00 (rest of the world); Institutional use: €30.00 (Europe), €45.00 (rest of the world)
Note: The original title of this program is *La Genèse des monstres*
Source: SFRS

 Hatching Patterns in Cephalopods

See description of this title under VIDEO.

Language: French
Year of production: Original film made in 1987
Medium: CD-ROM (MPEG4 format)
System requirements: Windows Media 7 (or Windows Player 6.4 for WinNT4 and Win95)
Price: Individual use: €15.00 (Europe), €30.00 (rest of the world); Institutional use: €30.00 (Europe), €45.00 (rest of the world)
Note: The original title of this program is *Modes d'éclosion chez les céphalopodes*
Source: SFRS

 In Vitro **Development of a Viviparous Toothcarp**

See description of this title under VIDEO.

Language: French, English, Spanish
Year of production: Original film made in 1964
Medium: CD-ROM (MPEG4 format)
System requirements: Windows Media 7 (or Windows Player 6.4 for WinNT4 and Win95)
Price: Individual use: €15.00 (Europe), €30.00 (rest of the world); Institutional use: €30.00 (Europe), €45.00 (rest of the world)
Note: The original title of this program is *Développement in vitro d'un cyprinodonte vivipare*
Source: SFRS

Metamorphosis of Nudibranch Molluscs

See description of this title under VIDEO.

Language: French
Year of production: Original film made in 1980
Medium: CD-ROM (MPEG4 format)
System requirements: Windows Media 7 (or Windows Player 6.4 for WinNT4 and Win95)
Price: Individual use: €15.00 (Europe), €30.00 (rest of the world); Institutional use: €30.00 (Europe), €45.00 (rest of the world)
Note: The original title of this program is *Métamorphose des mollusques nudibranches*
Source: SFRS

Vade Mecum: An Interactive Guide to Developmental Biology

This is a CD-ROM that takes the student through the developmental cycles of several model organisms used in developmental biology and illustrates techniques used in studying these organisms. With over 130 interactive videos and 300 labeled photographs, the CD-ROM includes chapters on: the slime mould, *Dictyostelium discoideum*; planarian; sea urchin; the fruit fly, *Drosophila melanogaster*; chick; and amphibian. There is a chapter on the risks of ultraviolet radiation and its effects on sea urchin development. Within each chapter are embedded 'how-to' instructions on techniques used in studying the organisms, from obtaining gametes from a sea urchin to dissecting imaginal disks from a fruit fly larva. Where useful, colour-coding is superimposed on living embryos to illustrate positioning of different germ layers. Included is a complete set of cross-sections of a 33-hour chick embryo and whole mounts with definitions of terms on rollover. Several 'purely technique' chapters are included as well. One, on making the most of the microscope, includes a 'virtual microscope' which teaches how to achieve Köhler illumination, dark-field illumination and how to use polarising filters. Two other chapters illustrate, in a step by step manner, how to make microdissecting tools and how to do histological techniques for paraffin sections. For each chapter, there is a set of study questions and websites. Also included are slide shows on laboratory safety.

Year of production: 2000
Medium: CD-ROM
System requirements: Windows 95/98/NT or later, with Pentium II CPU 200 MHz or faster (Pentium III recommended), sound card, SVGA monitor, 16-bit colour (24-bit recommended); Macintosh 7600/132 (G3 recommended), OS 8.5 or later, thousands of colours; 64 MB of installed RAM (20 MB free RAM), 800 x 600 resolution (or greater), 8X CD-ROM drive; QuickTime 4.0 or higher (installer provided); internet connection and Netscape Communicator or Internet Explorer are optional
Price: US$29.95
Source: Sinauer Associates

VIDEO

Asterina gibbosa - The Egg, the Larva and the Metamorphosis of a Starfish

This video illustrates the embryonic and larval development of a starfish and the particularities of its metamorphosis, at egg level (high content of yolk uniformly distributed), at segmentation level and at larval (sedentary) level. The metamorphosis shows the formation of ambulacra, hydrophore canal, oral opening, etc. Some comparisons are made with the development of the sea urchin egg and its larva.

Language: French
Year of production: 1973
Format: VHS PAL, SECAM, NTSC. Also available on CD-ROM (see under SOFTWARE)
Running time: 12 mins.
Price: Individual use: €15.00 (Europe), €30.00 (rest of the world); Institutional use: €30.00 (Europe), €45.00 (rest of the world); the NTSC format is available at an additional cost of €15.00
Note: The original title of this program is *Asterina gibbosa - L'oeuf, la larve et la métamorphose d'une étoile de mer*
Source: SFRS

Behavioural Development in Puppies

Describes how puppy behaviour develops from birth to 7 weeks, outlining the stages in which each type of behaviour appears and disappears. Correlates the puppy's behavioural development with its physical development.

Year of production: English version 1985 (original French version 1983)
Format: VHS PAL
Running time: 43 mins.
Price: £30.00 (excl. VAT and postage)
Source: Royal Veterinary College

Biology of the Cuttlefish (*Sepia officinalis*)

The success of breeding in an aquarium allows the presentation of various aspects of cuttlefish biology: hatching after egg maturation, growth of the young with their locomotion system common to that of adults, homochromy and chromatic variations, predator behaviour. The adult cuttlefish - colour differences compared to the young, branchiogenic breathing mechanism, prey catching and ingestion mechanism, sexual behaviour (courtship, coupling and laying). Real views, macro and microcinematography.

Language: French, English, Portuguese, Russian, Spanish
Year of production: 1967
Format: VHS PAL, SECAM, NTSC. Also available on CD-ROM (see under SOFTWARE)
Running time: 26 mins.
Price: Individual use: €15.00 (Europe), €30.00 (rest of the world); Institutional use: €30.00 (Europe), €45.00 (rest of the world); the NTSC format is available at an additional cost of €15.00
Note: The original title of this program is *Biologie de la seiche (Sepia officinalis)*
Source: SFRS

 Development of the Batrachian Egg

This film presents a study made on triton (*Triturus alpestris*). After having seen the segmentation of the egg, one sees the gastrulation movements and the formation of the yolk. A schematic representation of a gastrula opened sagitally, then transversally, allows students to follow the development of the blastodermic layers up to neurulation. The last part of this film shows the neurulation and the modelling of embryo, with the formation of the branchiae and the lower limbs.

Language: German, English
Year of production: 1967
Format: VHS PAL, SECAM, NTSC. Also available on CD-ROM (see under SOFTWARE)
Running time: 15 mins.
Price: Individual use: €15.00 (Europe), €30.00 (rest of the world); Institutional use: €30.00 (Europe), €45.00 (rest of the world); the NTSC format is available at an additional cost of €15.00
Note: The French title of this program is *Développement de l'oeuf de batracien*
Source: SFRS

 [A] Dozen Eggs: Time-Lapse Microscopy of Normal Development

Sponsored by the Society for Developmental Biology, these research sequences use a wide variety of techniques for embryo preparation, optics, filming, and time compression. They range from a classic film made in the 1940s to sequences obtained using computer-enhanced video microscopy and digital image processing. The 12 organisms covered include many well-studied model systems as well as some less familiar ones: *Sea urchin development* (4.56 mins.); *Slime mould morphogenesis* (5.46 mins.); *Snail polar lobe formation* (2.47 mins.); *Meiotic blebbing in flatworms* (1.20 mins.); *Nematode development* (3.40 mins.); *Fruit fly embryogenesis* (5.56 mins.); *Ascidian embryogenesis* (2.35 mins.); *Frog gastrulation* (1.58 mins.); *Zebrafish development* (2.41 mins.); *Killifish deep cell migration* (2.48 mins.); *Chicken organogenesis* (1.57 mins.); *Mouse development to blastocyst* (2.05 and

1.48 mins.). The teacher's manual provides descriptions of embryo preparation, as well as diagrams for orientation. In addition, a list of references for each sequence provides more information on normal development of that organism, techniques for manipulating and filming the embryos, and the research program of the filmer.

Year of production: 1991
Format: VHS NTSC, PAL
Running time: Approx. 41 mins.
Price: US$60.00
Source: Carolina Biological Supply, Sinauer Associates

 Fly Cycle: The Lives of a Fly, *Drosophila melanogaster*

This 40-minute colour film depicts many of the intricacies of *Drosophila's* biology and life cycle, including detailed sequences on adult courting and mating, embryonic development, larval growth, imaginal disks and salivary glands, metamorphosis, and a gallery of mutants used in research. It can be used at the high school and introductory undergraduate levels to acquaint students with the life cycle and mutants. For more advanced undergraduates in developmental biology and genetics courses, and for graduate students beginning their research on *Drosophila*, the film introduces the many specifics they will need to know, and techniques for examining the organism in detail. *Fly Cycle* is accompanied by a booklet that presents information on each segment of the film, a 'getting started' section for those who want to raise fruit flies, a list of suppliers, an annotated selected bibliography, and a glossary. See also *FlyCycle CD* under SOFTWARE.

Year of production: 1996
Format: VHS NTSC
Price: US$100.00
Source: Sinauer Associates

 Foetal Development of the Rat

This film presents the morphological evolution of the foetus and foetal annexes of the rat during gestation, explaining step by step its various phases: differentiation, vascularisation, and interactions. Real views and macrocinematography.

Language: French, English, German, Portuguese, Russian, Spanish
Year of production: 1964
Format: VHS PAL, SECAM, NTSC. Also available on CD-ROM (see under SOFTWARE)
Running time: 18 mins.
Price: Individual use: €15.00 (Europe), €30.00 (rest of the world); Institutional use: €30.00 (Europe), €45.00 (rest of the world); the NTSC format is available at an additional cost of €15.00
Note: The original title of this program is *Développement foetal du rat*
Source: SFRS

From Egg to Tadpole: Early Morphogenesis in *Xenopus*

A dramatic video chronology of the tadpole's development. Using time-lapse photography to compress events that take hours or even days into mere seconds, it shows in vivid colour some of the major events of the embryogenesis in the African toad *Xenopus*. The spectacular video covers the initial cycle of cell division; gastrulation; neurulation; elongation of the embryo and its escape from the egg membrane; and the ultimate transformation of the simple embryo into a recognisable tadpole. Accompanied by Instructor's Guide.

Year of production: 1999
Format: VHS NTSC, PAL
Running time: 19.30 mins.
Price: US$60.00
Source: Cytographics, Neo/SCI, Sinauer Associates

[The] Genesis of Monsters

This video demonstrates that the large number of malformations seen spontaneously in humans and domestic animals can be reproduced in a bird embryo if one intervenes at an early stage, using precise experimental techniques. The similarity is striking and gives an explanation to the genesis of most malformations.

Language: French
Year of production: 1974
Format: VHS PAL, SECAM, NTSC. Also available on CD-ROM (see under Software)
Running time: 29 mins.
Price: Individual use: €15.00 (Europe), €30.00 (rest of the world); Institutional use: €30.00 (Europe), €45.00 (rest of the world); the NTSC format is available at an additional cost of €15.00
Note: The original title of this program is *La Genèse des monstres*
Source: SFRS

Hatching Patterns in Cephalopods

This film demonstrates that as well as the action exerted by the enzymatic hatching gland of cephalopod embryos, the mechanical action performed by them plays an important role in the process of hatching. An analysis of anatomical characteristics and behaviour of embryos (according to families and genres) in relation to the resistance conferred by their egg membranes is presented. Hatching in the octopus, cuttlefish, lesser cuttlefish and Mediterranean squid (*Octopus vulgaris, Rossin macrosoma, Sepiola, Sepia officinalis* and *orbignyana, Loligo vulgaris* and *Alloteuthis*). Media include real and underwater views, and macrocinematography.

Language: French
Year of production: 1987
Format: VHS PAL, SECAM, NTSC. Also available on CD-ROM (see under Software)
Running time: 16 mins.
Price: Individual use: €15.00 (Europe), €30.00 (rest of the world); Institutional use: €30.00 (Europe), €45.00 (rest of the world); the NTSC format is available at an additional cost of €15.00
Note: The original title of this program is *Modes d'éclosion chez les céphalopodes*
Source: SFRS

In Vitro Development of a Viviparous Toothcarp

Development from the first stages up to the term, in an appropriate culture medium, of the ovo-viviparous fish *Lebistes reticulatus* eggs. *In vitro* study of vascularisation and morphogenesis.

Language: French, English, Spanish
Year of production: 1964
Format: VHS PAL, SECAM, NTSC. Also available on CD-ROM (see under Software)
Running time: 18 mins.
Price: Individual use: €15.00 (Europe), €30.00 (rest of the world); Institutional use: €30.00 (Europe), €45.00 (rest of the world); the NTSC format is available at an additional cost of €15.00
Note: The original title of this program is *Développement in vitro d'un cyprinodonte vivipare*
Source: SFRS

Insect Metamorphosis

This program illustrates the dramatic changes that insects undergo during their life cycle, introducing the students to the 2 types of metamorphosis - incomplete and complete. Viewers will follow a praying mantis through 3 stages of incomplete metamorphosis: egg, nymph, and adult. A monarch butterfly is then shown going through the 4 stages of complete metamorphosis: egg, larva, pupa, and adult.

Format: VHS NTSC
Running time: 22 mins.
Price: US$60.00
Source: CLEARVUE/eav

When contacting producers and distributors,
please cite *from Guinea Pig to Computer Mouse*

Metamorphosis of Nudibranch Molluscs

This video presents a few examples of nudibranch molluscs metamorphosis and analyses the main processes leading from the veliger larva to the limaciform shell-less adult. Also included are metamorphosis modalities of two types of *Aeolidiidae* and of one pleurobranch. Morphological and anatomical changes include: cellular proliferation of the pallium, brain making, filiation of nudibranchs from related forms of pleurobranchs. In macro and microcinematography.

Language: French
Year of production: 1980
Format: VHS PAL, SECAM, NTSC. Also available on CD-ROM (see under Software)
Running time: 14 mins.
Price: Individual use: €15.00 (Europe), €30.00 (rest of the world); Institutional use: €30.00 (Europe), €45.00 (rest of the world); the NTSC format is available at an additional cost of €15.00
Note: The original title of this program is *Métamorphose des mollusques nudibranches*
Source: SFRS

 [The] Miracle of Life

This first filmed record of human conception won an Emmy Award as part of the acclaimed NOVA series. This 60-minute video takes an incredible voyage through the human body as new life begins. The camera follows the development of the single new cell into an embryo, then a foetus, until finally a baby is born.

Year of production: 1986
Format: VHS NTSC
Running time: 60 mins.
Price: US$22.95
Source: Nasco

When contacting producers and distributors, please cite *from Guinea Pig to Computer Mouse*

MODELS, MANNEKINS, SIMULATORS

 Barkbeetle Development Model

Approximately 40x enlarged, in 'SOMSO-Plast', this representation of the big Spruce barkbeetle with 8 teeth (*Ips typographus*), shows the following phases of development: egg, 2x young larva, full-grown larva, pupa and beetle. The models are cast in relief. Separates into 5 parts. On a base. H20 cm, W49 cm, D28 cm, Wt 1.7 kg.

Medium: Model
Price: On request, from regional distributors
Source: Contact Marcus Sommer Somso Modelle for regional distributors (catalogue ref. ZoS 47/6)

 Chicken: Germinal Disc of a Fertilised but Unincubated Egg

The model shows the germinal disk in the stage of yolk membrane formation - linearly enlarged 70x, in 'SOMSO-Plast'. In one piece, on a stand with base. H45 cm, W28 cm, D18 cm, Wt 1.4 kg.

Medium: Model
Price: On request, from regional distributors
Source: Contact Marcus Sommer Somso Modelle for regional distributors (catalogue ref. ZoS 103/1)

 Chicken's Embryo after ca. 20 Hours Incubation

This separable model shows a section of the membrane enlarged 56x linearly, in 'SOMSO-Plast'. Separates into 4 parts, on a stand with base. H41 cm, W28 cm, D18 cm, Wt 1.3 kg.

Medium: Model
Price: On request, from regional distributors
Source: Contact Marcus Sommer Somso Modelle for regional distributors (catalogue ref. ZoS 103/2)

When contacting producers and distributors,
please cite *from Guinea Pig to Computer Mouse*

Chicken's Embryo after ca. 33 Hours Incubation

Enlarged 53x linearly, in 'SOMSO-Plast'. A concentric part of the embryo can be removed from the yolk, Somites and chorda are visible through a ventral window. Separates into 2 parts, on a stand with base. H44 cm, W29 cm, D18 cm, Wt 1.4 kg.

Medium: Model
Price: On request, from regional distributors
Source: Contact Marcus Sommer Somso Modelle for regional distributors (catalogue ref. ZoS 103/3)

Chicken's Embryo after ca. 50 Hours Incubation

Enlarged 54x linearly, in 'SOMSO-Plast'. The embryo separated from the vitelline mass shows the changes of position caused by the bending of the neck and turning of the anterior body. In one piece, on a stand with base. H51 cm, W18 cm, D18 cm, Wt 900 g.

Medium: Model
Price: On request, from regional distributors
Source: Contact Marcus Sommer Somso Modelle for regional distributors (catalogue ref. ZoS 103/4)

Chicken's Embryo after ca. 4 Days Incubation

Enlarged 45x linearly, in 'SOMSO-Plast'. The embryo when opened on the right gives a general view of the detailed regions of the central nervous system and the structure of the cerebral nerves. In one piece, on a stand with base. H45 cm, W26 cm, D18 cm, Wt 1.4 kg.

Medium: Model
Price: On request, from regional distributors
Source: Contact Marcus Sommer Somso Modelle for regional distributors (catalogue ref. ZoS 103/5)

Development of the Frog

This series of models is in preparation for exemplary presentation of the development of a water frog (*Rana esculenta*). Individual models in proposed series: egg, ovum division, blastula, gastrula, 3 tadpole stages, frog. A basic set - egg, tadpole and frog - is to be offered in addition as a supplementary alternative at a later date.

Medium: Model
Price: On request, from regional distributors
Source: Contact Marcus Sommer Somso Modelle for regional distributors (catalogue ref. ZoS 61/1)

Equal Cell Division and the Formation of the Nuclear Membrane in the Branchiostoma Lanceolatum

Amphioxus - the lancelet - enlarged approximately 500x , in 'SOMSO-Plast'. 9 models (A-J) on stands with bases show the various stages in cell division, the formation of the blastula and original membrane. In one piece. Weight of the series: 1.9 kg.

Medium: Model
Price: On request, from regional distributors
Source: Contact Marcus Sommer Somso Modelle for regional distributors (catalogue ref. ZoS 58)

 ### Frog Development Set

This is a set of *Bobbitt* models comprising the 5 models from the *Frog Cleavage Set*, the 10 models from the *Frog Early Neural Tube Set*, and 5 additional models showing early larval development. The *Frog Cleavage Set* shows development from fertilisation to cleavage; the egg is shown in hemisection shortly after sperm entrance; the other models represent 2-, 4-, 8-, and 16-cell stages, and all are approximately 5" in diameter. The *Frog Early Neural Tube Set* traces development from blastula formation to neural tube formation; each is shown in hemisection, the germ layers are decorated with standard embryological colours, and each model is mounted on a base. Manuals are included.

Medium: Model
Price: $380.00 (*Frog Cleavage Set* - catalogue ref. WW-56-3028); US$600.00 (*Frog Early Neural Tube Set* - catalogue ref. WW-56-3029); US$1,625.00 (*Frog Development Set* - WW-56-3040); see website for country distributors
Source: Carolina Biological Supply

 ### Lancelet

Branchiostoma lanceolatum, enlarged approximately 150x , in 'SOMSO-Plast'. The 4 models (K-N) show the formation of the nuclear membrane in the larva of the lancelet and its final structure in longitudinal and cross section. Individually mounted on a stand with base. Weight of the series: 4.2 kg.

Medium: Model
Price: On request, from regional distributors
Source: Contact Marcus Sommer Somso Modelle for regional distributors (catalogue ref. ZoS 59)

WORLD WIDE WEB

Developmental Biology Cinema

http://sdb.bio.purdue.edu/dbcinema
Society for Developmental Biology, USA

FishScope: Developmental Biology of Fish

http://depts.washington.edu/fishscop
University of Washington, USA

6. Histology

SOFTWARE

Animal Cells & Tissues

Features a comprehensive set of interactive microscope slide images that offer a detailed view of the fascinating world of animal cells and tissues. These engaging images can be magnified, manipulated and measured - just like with a traditional microscope - and are accompanied by supporting text and videoclips. The program offers the flexibility to choose from either tutorial, assessment or lecture modes. Features dozens of magnifiable images of live and prepared specimen material which include invertebrates, insect structures, vertebrate tissues, frog development and human sex indicators (e.g. human male/female chromosomes), squamous epithelium, and peripheral blood film. Features video loops of *Hydra*, *Planaria* and *Daphnia*.

Medium: CD-ROM
System requirements: Windows 95 or later, PowerMac 7.5 or later; 16 MB RAM
Price: US$59.95 (single); US$179.95 (lab pack of 5); US$419.95 (library pack of 20); US$299.95 (network version)
Source: Neo/Sci

CALVE

See description and details of this program under 'Anatomy'.

Haematoxylin and Eosin - A Training Guide

This program provides an introduction to the histological preparation of biological materials and describes the chemical interactions associated with the common stain preparation - haematoxylin and eosin. Using a sample of rat gut the program describes the processes of dehydration, wax embedding, the use of the microtome, floating sections and staining procedures. A range of mammalian tissues are then investigated at low and high power.

Year of production: 1999
Medium: CD-ROM

System requirements: Windows only - Win95/98/NT; 16-bit sound card
Price: £40.00 (incl. VAT)
Source: University of Portsmouth

Histology: An Interactive Virtual Microscope

This two-volume computer program recreates the look and feel of a microscope in an intuitive, browser-based interface. Histology requires both an understanding of the cellular structure of organs and tissues and the ability to recognise tissues at the microscopic level. While extensive practice with the microscope is not essential in the modern health care setting, histology remains an image-intensive discipline. By presenting nested images at increasing magnification, *Histology: An Interactive Virtual Microscope* provides a sense of scale and proportion that cannot be achieved in a standard histology text or atlas. Moreover, the text descriptions and labeled images offer flexibility (students can study at any computer) and opportunities for small-group learning (several students can examine the images together), yet provide guidance for independent study.

Year of production: 2002
Medium: CD-ROM
System requirements: Windows 95/98/NT/2000/ME/XP, Macintosh OS 7 or later, Netscape Communicator 4.5 / Internet Explorer 5 or later (the latter recommended)
Price: US$39.95 (CD1 + CD2)
Source: Sinauer Associates

Histology Interactive

This program was designed to replace the conventional microscope as the tool for teaching histology. It provides an interactive interface that allows student to perform a practical whilst also getting theoretical feedback. The software contains slide displays coupled with identifiable characteristics of the tissues projected, and a voice commentary serves to supplement the practical with a theoretical foundation. Sketches of tissue and cell structure are used to highlight concepts not easily exhibited in the tissue section. Tissues are often displayed at various magnifications to identify their multifaceted characteristics. System overviews were produced as flow charts illustrating the hierarchy of tissues, organs and systems to allow students to obtain a holistic view of histology. The navigation menu is simple and always visible, and an auto-mode is incorporated into the navigation for revision purposes.

Year of production: 2000
Medium: CD-ROM
System requirements: Windows only - Win95/98/ME/2000/NT/XP, Media Player 7 with Codecs; Pentium I processor (200 MHz), 32 MB RAM, 8 MB graphics card
Price: US$25.00 (student licence); US$200.00 (institution licence - 10 users). Prices excl. postage
Source: Saints Web Design

Microanatomy of Insects

Learn about insect structure and function with this comprehensive set of interactive digital microscopic slide images. These fascinating images can be magnified, manipulated and measured - just like with a traditional microscope. Each image is accompanied by supporting reference text and callouts. Students will view the external and internal microanatomy of a host of insect types from 8 different orders. In the process, they will discover how insects walk, breathe, fly, see, sense and reproduce.

Medium: CD-ROM
System requirements: Windows 95 or later, PowerMac 7.5 or later; 16 MB RAM
Price: US$59.95 (single); US$179.95 (lab pack of 5); US$419.95 (library pack of 20); US$299.95 (network version)
Source: Neo/Sci

Microscopic Anatomy

This is an interactive cellular anatomy tutorial modeled after classroom exercises at a medical school level. Organised in 23 chapters covering all systems of the body, the program contains more than 1,200 digitised histological slides and electron micrographs and over 1,750 multiple choice test questions. The explanatory text leads the student in a logical sequence through the tutorial portion of the program. Students can quiz themselves and receive immediate feedback using the practice practical mode. Other features include: a narrated video describing the set-up and use of the microscope; zoom capabilities to double magnification (slides enlargeable to full screen, with references to degrees of magnification represented on each slide); and information conveniently organised by organ/organelle, species and preparation.

Medium: Internet, intranet, CD-ROM
System requirements: The CD-ROM version is optimised for Internet Explorer, but does not require installation; QuickTime is necessary to view the animations and hear sounds throughout the program; the internet version requires any computer running Internet Explorer 5.x or Netscape 4.5 and above, with JavaScript enabled; for specific system requirements for intranet systems, please contact the source
Price: Individual use: US$20.00 (6-month subscription for on-line version); US$35.00 (annual subscription for on-line version). Internet, intranet and CD-ROM annual institutional site licences on request
Source: Gold Standard Multimedia

When contacting producers and distributors,
please cite *from Guinea Pig to Computer Mouse*

VIDEO

 Basic Histological Techniques

Demonstrates the essential steps - fixation, embedding, sectioning, mounting and staining - required in the preparation of fresh animal tissue for viewing under the light microscope. Primary audience is first year medical and dental students, but the film is also suitable for sixth form (high school) students.

Year of production: 1987
Format: VHS PAL
Running time: 11 mins.
Price: £25.00 (different price for bulk copies and other standards and formats)
Source: Leeds University Television

 Haematoxylin and Eosin - A Training Guide

See description under SOFTWARE version.

Year of production: 1993
Format: VHS PAL, NTSC
Running time: 15 mins
Price: £40.00 (incl. VAT)
Source: University of Portsmouth

When contacting producers and distributors,
please cite *from Guinea Pig to Computer Mouse*

WORLD WIDE WEB

 Atlas of Histology

http://www.med.uiuc.edu/histo/medium/atlas/index.htm

University of Illinois at Urbana-Champaign College of Medicine, USA

 Electron Microscopic Atlas of Mammalian Tissues on the Internet

http://www.uni-mainz.de/FB/Medizin/Anatomie/workshop/EM/EMAtlas.html

Johannes Gutenburg University Mainz, Germany

 Histology Imagebase

http://numbat.murdoch.edu.au/histology/index_low.html

Murdoch University School of Veterinary Studies, Western Australia

 Histology Lab

http://cal.nbc.upenn.edu/histo/

University of Pennsylvania School of Veterinary Medicine, USA

 Histology Tutorial

http://www.medinfo.ufl.edu/year1/histo

University of Florida College of Medicine, USA

 HistoWeb

http://www.kumc.edu/instruction/medicine/anatomy/histoweb

Kansas University Medical Center, USA

 HistoWeb - An Interactive Digital Lab Guide for Histology

http://courses.usd.edu/anat521001/labguide.htm

University of South Dakota School of Medicine, USA

Internet Guide to Veterinary Microscopic Anatomy

http://www.vetmed.ufl.edu/sacs/histo/histoframes.htm
University of Florida College of Veterinary Medicine, USA

LUMEN Histology Slide Series

http://www.meddean.luc.edu/lumen/MedEd/Histo/frames/histo_frames.html
Loyola University Medical Education Network, USA

Veterinary Histology: Laboratory Exercises

http://classes.cvm.tamu.edu/vaph911/labtoc.htm
Texas A&M University College of Veterinary Medicine, USA

Virtual Slidebox

http://www.path.uiowa.edu/virtualslidebox
University of Iowa College of Medicine, USA

7. Pathology

SOFTWARE

NOAH'S ARKIVE

Originally named *The International Veterinary Pathology Slide Bank (IVPSB)*, this database was conceived in the early 1980's as a repository of slides contributed by individuals and institutions around the world. In 1986, the 3rd edition was the first to become available on laser videodisc format. Now in its 8th edition, the slides are currently being digitised into images for CD-ROM. The *Clinical Pathology, Ruminant,* and *WHEAL (Wildlife, Human, Exotic Animals, Avian, Laboratory Animals)* subsets are now available on CD-ROM. Additional subsets are in development; however, there is no projected time frame for availability of all of the planned subsets. The 7th edition of the *IVPSB* laser videodisc included approximately 30,000 still frame visuals of veterinary medicine (comprising normal breeds of animals, gross lesions, histopathology, normal histology, cytology and haematology, parasitology, poisonous plants, animals with/without clinical signs, schematics, radiographs, electron micrographs and techniques), 4,500 still images from the English videodisc *U.K. Path I,* 1,500 still images from the *Atlantic Veterinary College Histopathology* videodisc, and 70,000 frames of real time motion sequences of clinical neurology in the dog and cat. The visuals were donated by over 250 contributors representing 13 countries.

Medium: CD-ROM; laser videodisc
System requirements for CD-ROM subsets: Windows 95/98/2000/NT4.0/ME, with Pentium processor of at least 200 MHz; Macintosh computers may be utilised to open files in JPG, TXT, and PDF formats, but the searchable database is not supported at this time; also required is an image viewer capable of displaying JPG files, such as Microsoft Photoeditor (included with Microsoft Office 2000), Adobe Photoshop, Thumbs Plus, QuickTime, ACDSee, etc. Adobe Acrobat Reader is needed to open the image catalogues
System requirements for laser videodisc edition: PC compatible computer with 512 KB RAM Level I, III CAV disc; standard videodisc player (i.e. Pioneer LD-V4400); the videodisc player must be NTSC video format (not PAL or SECAM); the most stable and easiest configured system consists of a PC running Windows 95 and equipped with a Pioneer laser videodisc; software problems may be encountered with any other configuration
Price: US$50.00 (*Clinical Pathology* subset, on one CD-ROM); US$60.00 (*Ruminant* subset, on 2 CD-ROMs); US$70.00 (*WHEAL* subset, on 4 CD-ROMs); US$400.00 (7th edition laser videodisc)
Source: University of Georgia

Veterinary Clinical Pathology 2000

This case-oriented, autotutorial instructional program contains 52 interactive computerised lessons and has been developed for courses given to veterinary students, graduate students, technical staff and continuing education. Lessons are intended to provide practical diagnostic material in interactive ways to help develop veterinary diagnostic skills. Users obtain positive and negative feedback to their answers based on questions posed in the lessons. Material is both image (over 1,500) and text. Most programs are on clinical pathology topics while some lessons present gross or microscopic pathology. Descriptions of lessons are given in the *Companion Book* - approximately 300 pages, divided into three electronic files: *Hematology*, *Cytology* and *Chemistry*. Detailed materials include laboratory data and case presentations used in the initial question for each case.

Medium: CD-ROM
System requirements: Windows only
Price: US$29.00 (student rate - accepted only if student ID is being sent by fax); US$150.00 (single user); US$400.00 (site licence)
Source: Michigan State University

Veterinary Gross Pathology

The interactive lessons in this program present mainly gross pathology lesions used for diagnosis. Most of the 500 images have been used by the Department of Pathology at Michigan State University in preparing veterinary students to describe lesions and use them for gross pathology diagnosis. 11 lessons present gross pathology cases from 'food producing' animals, dogs and cats and laboratory animals (rabbits, rodents, primates, guinea pigs and hamsters). 'Food producing' animals is then divided into respiratory, gastrointestinal, systemic, musculoskeletal, liver and kidney, central nervous sytem, skin and reproductive. 3 other lessons were prepared for 2 lectures and one laboratory session.

Medium: CD-ROM
System requirements: Windows only
Price: US$20.00 (student rate - accepted only if student ID is sent by fax); US$45.00 (single user / veterinarian); US$125.00 (site / university licence)
Source: Michigan State University

Veterinary Neuropathology Modules

Designed as self-paced interactive neuropathology laboratories, each of these 9 modules covers a specific central nervous system disease or syndrome. Using a consistent interface, each module includes high-resolution, annotated images of gross pathological specimens, specially stained histological brain and/or spinal cord sections and in one module, QuickTime video of pathognomonic clinical signs is included. Animated 'helps' highlight key structures and guide the user through the disease process. Topics include nigropallidal encephalomalacia in the horse, feline infectious peritonitis, feline brain abscess, canine distemper virus, fibrocartilaginous embolisation in the dog, choroid plexus tumour and spinal cord trauma.

Medium: CD-ROM
System requirements: Windows 95 or greater with Pentium processor, Macintosh Power with 24 MB RAM, thousands of colours or greater, 800 x 600 screen resolution
Price: US$65.00
Source: University of California (UC Davis)

 ## Veterinary Systemic Pathology

These are individual interactive atlases covering the pathology of individual organ systems. Each comprehensive atlas consists of dozens of full-screen, high-resolution colour images of gross and histological speciments. Images are clearly labeled, and all are randomly accessible using a searchable index. The software covers pathology of 12 organ systems, including: *Cardiovascular pathology, Gastrointestional pathology, Neuropathology, Reproductive pathology (male and female), Tumour pathology, Musculoskeletal pathology, Hepatic and pancreatic pathology, Renal pathology, Lymphatic pathology, Dermopathology,* and *Pathology of the pregnant uterus.*

Medium: CD-ROM
System requirements: Windows 95 or greater with Pentium processor, Macintosh Power with 24 MB RAM, thousands of colours or greater, 800 x 600 screen resolution
Price: US$65.00
Source: University of California (UC Davis)

When contacting producers and distributors,
please cite *from Guinea Pig to Computer Mouse*

MODELS, MANNEKINS, SIMULATORS

Glanders in a Horse Model

Natural cast median section through the nose and throat cavities, and larynx, showing the form of the disease. In one piece, on a base plate. H33 cm, W10 cm, D8 cm,Wt 3.7 kg.

Medium: Model
Price: On request, from regional distributors
Source: Contact Marcus Sommer Somso Modelle for regional distributors (catalogue ref. Zo 89)

SOMSO Pathological Models

Through the use of natural castings, the SOMSO pathological models for domestic animal anatomy provide exact information for recognition of clinical pictures. Models available as special orders in the series:

- *Cow's Hoof with Foot Disease Model* (catalogue ref. Zo 85)
- *Cow's Mouth with Mouth Disease Model* (catalogue ref. Zo 84)
- *Cow's Tongue with Mouth Disease Model* (catalogue ref. Zo 86)
- *Pig's Hoof with Foot Disease Model* (catalogue ref. Zo 88)
- *Pig's Snout with Mouth Disease Model* (catalogue ref. Zo 87)

Descriptions not available.

Medium: Model
Price: On request, from regional distributors
Source: Contact Marcus Sommer Somso Modelle for regional distributors

---

When contacting producers and distributors,
please cite *from Guinea Pig to Computer Mouse*

WORLD WIDE WEB

[The] Museum of Human Disease

http://129.94.18.13/pathmus
University of New South Wales, Australia

PathWeb - The Virtual Pathology Museum

http://pathweb.uchc.edu
University of Connecticut, USA

[The] Urbana Atlas of Pathology

http://www.med.uiuc.edu/PathAtlasf/titlepage.html
University of Illinois College of Medicine at Urbana-Champaign, USA

Virtual Slidebox

http://www.path.uiowa.edu/virtualslidebox
University of Iowa College of Medicine, USA

WebPath - The Internet Pathology Laboratory for Medical Education

http://www-medlib.med.utah.edu/WebPath/webpath.html
Florida State University College of Medicine, USA

8. Pharmacology

SOFTWARE

Basic Psychopharmacology (v2.0)

This package, developed at the University of Galway (Republic of Ireland), introduces the student to psychopharmacology. It is divided into 3 subjects containing a total of 11 activity modules. The student first learns about the neuroscientific foundation of psychopharmacology (blood-brain barrier, drug entry into brain, electrophysiological mechanisms, biochemical mechanisms), then continues by considering some of the clinical applications of psychopharmacology (hypnotics, anxiolytics, antidepresssants, antipsychotics). In the final subject of the package, the student looks at research methods used in psychopharmacology, including laboratory techniques, use of animal models and their limitations, and some of the problems of clinical trials.

Medium: CD-ROM

System requirements: Available in Windows and web/intranet versions. The Windows version (compatible with Windows 95/98/NT) is supplied on a CD-ROM installation disk and can be installed to a local hard disk or network drive; requires a PC with minimum 100 MHz Pentium processor, 8 MB RAM and a VGA monitor capable of displaying 16-bit colour at 640 x 480 resolution. The web version is supplied on a CD-ROM installation disk for installation to a web server and runs on PC clients only; requires a 200 MHz Pentium processor with 32 MB RAM and a SVGA monitor capable of displaying 16-bit colour at 800 x 600 resolution; it is compatible with both Netscape Navigator 4.x and Internet Explorer 4 or better and requires Java and JavaScript to be enabled on browsers

Price: £220.00 (excl. VAT at 17.5% for UK and EU orders, and £20.00 handling charge per order)

Source: COACS

CardioLab - *In Vivo* Cardiovascular Pharmacology Simulator (v3.0)

This is a Windows program simulating chart recorder outputs of *in vivo* cardiovascular pharmacology experiments on anaesthetised (normal or reserpinised) and pithed animals. The simulated heart rate and blood pressure traces appear on screen and can be printed out. *CardioLab* allows 'administration' of the following drugs: 10 agonists - norepinephrine (noradrenaline), angiotensin, vasopressin, DMPP, epinephrine (adrenaline), tyramine, phenylephrine, B-HT 920, isoproterenol (isoprenaline), acetylcholine; 12 antagonists - hexamethonium, propranolol, prazosin, atropine, mepyramine, ranitidine, yohimbine, atenolol, nifedipine, phenoxybenzamine, cocaine, neostigmine. *CardioLab* can also mimic stimulation of vagal and sympathetic cardiac nerves.

Effects of blockers 'wear off' at a rate corresponding to their $t_{1/2}$. Tachyphylaxis is seen with relevant agonists. 'Overdoses' with agonists or blockers will 'kill' the preparation. Responses are subject to 'biological variation' and are influenced by cardiac compensatory reflexes if appropriate. The program even simulates the slow deterioration of a preparation which may 'die' unexpectedly after 6 hours of 'preparation time' (responses appear instantaneously but each represents about 3 mins. of 'preparation time'). *CardioLab* can provide 'unknown' drugs for characterisation by students.

Year of production: 1999
Medium: 3.5" disk; CD-ROM
System requirements: Windows (all versions)
Price: US$199.00 / £99.00 / €199.00; free demo downloadable fromwebsite
Source: Biosoft

Cat Nictitating Membrane

An interactive, menu-driven program which simulates experiments on the superior cervical ganglion-nictitating membrane preparation of the cat (*in vivo*) to teach the pharmacology of ganglionic transmission and sympathetically innervated smooth muscle. Tutorial sections combine text and high-resolution graphics to provide sufficient background detail for students to plan experiments. Animated sequences are used to demonstrate the stages of transmission at both the synapse and neuro-effector junction and to highlight possible sites of drug action. Drugs include: saline (vehicle control), acetylcholine, noradrenaline, atropine, phentolamine, propranolol, isoprenaline, hexamethonium, physiostigmine, nicotine (low and high dose), tyramine, and an unknown (which is randomly selected from the list above when the program is run). Students must decide which drug to administer - by close arterial injection - and the site of administration - either to the ganglion or the nictitating membrane. The pre-ganglionic nerves of the preparation are stimulated using parameters which evoke half-maximal contraction to observe effects of drugs which will relax the membrane. Simulated contractions of both ipsi- and contralateral nictitating membranes are displayed simultaneously in a form comparable to that of a chart recorder.

Medium: 3.5" disk; CD-ROM
System requirements: Windows only - Win95/98/NT4, 166 MHz Pentium processor with 32 MB RAM and 16-bit colour graphics
Price: £199.00 (departmental multiuser/network licence; includes documentation - program manual and, where appropriate, student's workbook and tutor's notes - and postage)
Source: Sheffield BioScience Programs

Finkleman Preparation

A computer simulation of the Finkleman preparation (isolated rabbit intestine). *Introduction* and *Methods* sections combine high-resolution graphics to describe the preparation and the apparatus, and to provide the background pharmacology. In the *Experiments* section, simulated rhythmic contractions, derived from experimental data, are presented on a chart recorder-like display on the monitor. The user can investigate the effects of adrenergic drugs (either alone or in certain pre-determined combinations), the effects of electrically stimulated sympathetic nerves, or the effects of a range of other drugs on the response to sympathetic nerve stimulation.

Medium: 3.5" disk; CD-ROM
System requirements: MS-DOS
Price: £120.00 (departmental multiuser/network licence; includes documentation - program manual and, where appropriate, student's workbook and tutor's notes - and postage)
Source: Sheffield BioScience Programs

Frog Rectus Abdominis Preparation

This program simulates the frog rectus abdominis preparation. The tissue can be exposed to drugs such as succinylcholine, acetylcholine, carbachol, atropine, potassium, dimethylphenylpiper-azinium (DMPP), methacholine, histamine, physostigmine, hexamethonium, tubocurarine, pancuronium, gallamine, fazadinium, decamethonium, edrophonium, atracurium, dantrolene, lignocaine and neostigmine at any concentration. Agonists can be added in the presence of an antagonist, and the order of addition and the concentration is entirely in the hands of the user. Drug effects can be reversed by washing as required. Output in the form of a simulated trace can be displayed on the screen or provided as a permanent record on a printer. Students can be asked to follow a schedule of drug administration fixed by the teacher and to observe and write-up effects produced in the normal way. Alternatively, students can design their own experiments to answer set questions or can learn using learn-by-discovery methods.

Year of production: 1996
Medium: 3.5" disk
System requirements: Windows only (all versions)
Price: £199.00 (multiuser, department licence for unlimited copies)
Source: PIDATA

Guinea Pig Ileum

A highly interactive computer program which simulates the transmurally stimulated guinea pig ileum preparation (*in vitro*) designed to teach the pharmacology of intestinal smooth muscle and the enteric nervous system. Students control the experiment using easy-to-use pull-down menus, while the program offers a stimulator (with on/off and control over voltage, frequency and duration of stimulation), a range of drugs (acetylcholine, clonidine, morphine, naloxone, phentolamine, atropine) which may be added to the organ bath in a range of doses; and a 'magic' wash facility which instantly removes all traces of added drugs. Simulated contractions of the gut are displayed in real time in a form comparable to that of a chart recorder. Drugs may be administered either alone or in any combination, and dose-response curves may be obtained.

Medium: 3.5" disk; CD-ROM
System requirements: MS-DOS
Price: £120.00 (departmental multiuser/network licence; includes documentation - program manual and, where appropriate, student's workbook and tutor's notes - and postage)
Source: Sheffield BioScience Programs

Guinea Pig Isolated Ileum (*In Vitro*)

This program accurately simulates laboratory experiments which investigate the effects of drugs on the *in vitro* guinea pig ileum. Drugs available for the ileum simulation include a dozen familiar agonists, which will contract the muscle, together with blockers of various sorts. It is possible to mimic experiments to identify an unknown compound. Random elements are incorporated into *Ileum* to simulate the inherent biological variability in the response to the same dose of agonist. *Ileum* can be used quantitatively or qualitatively and a permanent record of results is produced on a printer in the form of a 'chart trace' which can be measured and processed using the usual statistical procedures.

Year of production: 1995
Medium: 3.5" disk
System requirements: Windows only (all versions)
Price: £149.00 (multiuser, department licence for unlimited copies)
Source: PIDATA

Ileum - Isolated Guinea Pig Ileum Simulator

Ileum accurately simulates laboratory experiments which investigate the effects of drugs on the *in vitro* guinea pig ileum. Drugs available include: 12 familiar agonists, which will contract the muscle (acetylcholine, carbachol, angiotensin, histamine, potassium chloride, tetramethylammonium, furmethide, methacholine, vasopressin, barium chloride, hexyltrimethylammonium, dimethylphenylpiperazinium), and 6 antagonists/blockers (atropine, hexamethonium, papaverine, mepyramine, lignocaine, eserine). It is possible to mimic experiments to identify an unknown compound. Random elements are incorporated in *Ileum* to simulate the inherent biological variability in the response to the same dose of agonist. *Ileum* can be used quantitatively or qualitatively and a permanent record of results is produced in the form of a 'chart trace' on screen, which can be printed out and measured and analysed in the usual way.

Year of production: 1998
Medium: 3.5" disk; CD-ROM
System requirements: Windows (all versions)
Price: US$99.00 / £49.00 / €99.00; free demo downloadable fromwebsite
Source: Biosoft

Inflammation Pharmacology

This program simulates a range of experiments designed to demonstrate the action of inflammatory mediators and pharmacological agents on the *in vivo* inflammatory response in the anaesthetised rabbit, using data obtained from actual experiments. *Introduction* and *Methods* sections combine text and high-resolution graphics to describe the animal preparation, the methods employed to measure oedema formation and neutrophil accumulation, and to provide the student with the essential background information required to understand the inflammatory response. The *Experiments* section allows the user to study the effects of the following agents on oedema formation (and where appropriate on neutrophil numbers) in normal rabbits: 1. A range of direct mediators of increased microvascular permeability, either alone (dose-response relationships), in the presence of a vasodilator (PGE2) or with receptor antagonists; 2. A range of agents which cause inflammation principally via neutrophil accumulation, either alone (dose-response relationships), or in the presence of a vasodilator (PGE2); the effects of neutrophil depletion and the importance of adhesion molecules are also covered; 3. Non-steroidal (local and systemic effects) and steroidal anti-inflammatory agents. A section describing the results of selected experiments using sensitised rabbits is also included and covers the IgG (Reverse Passive Arthus response) and IgE response. Results are presented in graphical form either as bar charts or line graphs.

Medium: 3.5" disk; CD-ROM
System requirements: Windows only - Win95/98/NT4; Pentium processor with 16 MB RAM and 16-bit colour graphics
Price: £199.00 (departmental multiuser/network licence; includes documentation - program manual and, where appropriate, student's workbook and tutor's notes - and postage)
Source: Sheffield BioScience Programs

Isolated Vas Deferens Preparation

The isolated vas deferens can be used without electrical stimulation, adding drugs cumulatively into the tissue bath or washing out between application of appropriate concentrations. The latter, however, does not remove any antagonist present. Antagonists are applied via the bulk of the physiological saline and both agonists and antagonists can be removed from the bath. Antagonists may be easy, difficult or impossible to reverse, and may equilibrate with the tissue at different rates. Alternatively, electrical stimulation using trains of pulses at 5 Hz can be applied through hook electrodes to the whole vas deferens via the hypogastric nerve. This type of stimulation is pre-ganglionic and yields responses which are mainly noradrenergically mediated. Electrical stimulation of the epididymal portion of the vas deferens through transmural electrodes with similar trains yields responses which are noradrenergically mediated but originate from post-ganglionic sympathetic stimulation. Stimulation of the prostatic portion of the vas deferens through transmural electrodes with individual shocks delivered al 0.03 Hz yields responses with are wholly mediated by the non-adrenergic non-cholinergic (NANC) transmitter (probably ATP). Judicious use of these possibilities enables a great variety of experiments and investigations to be performed. Note however that the simulation keeps a record of the passage of 'laboratory time' and if excessively long experiments are attempted tissue sensitivity and performance may deteriorate sharply.

Year of production: 1995
Medium: 3.5" disk
System requirements: Windows only (all versions)
Price: £299.00 (multiuser, department licence for unlimited copies)
Source: PIDATA

Laboratory Preparations 1, 2

See description of this title under VIDEO.

Year of production: 1995
Medium: CD-ROM (MPEG format)
Price: Each volume £50.00 (UK Higher Education only); £125.00 (others)
Source: British Pharmacological Society

Langendorff Heart

A highly interactive program that simulates experiments which may be performed on an isolated perfused mammalian heart (Langendorff preparation). In the *Experiments* section, simulated data, derived from actual data, is presented on a screen display which emulates a chart recorder. Students 'design' experiments by choosing, from a menu, a range of pharmacological agents which may be administered either alone, or in combination with an antagonist or a potentiator. Each trace represents several minutes of recording and thus allows students to access a large amount of data in a short period of time. A facility to compare traces of 'drug X alone' with 'drug X + antagonist Y' or 'drug X + potentiator Z' is available. This allows easy visual comparison of qualitative effects, and more accurate measurements can be taken from the screen. The program covers: 1. Effects of drugs given either alone or in combination with a range of antagonists or potentiators – sympathomimetics, parasympathomimetics, cardiac glycosides, coronary vasodilators, adenosine, histamine, verapamil; 2. Effect of ions – high and low concentrations of calcium, potassium and sodium; 3. Effect of increasing pre-load on contractile (ventricular) force (Starling's law). The simulated responses (heart rate, ventricular force and coronary blood flow) are derived from actual experimental data and presented in high resolution colour graphics in a form comparable to that of a chart recorder. The program contains textual information describing the preparation and experimental method, and an editable on screen help facility allows teachers to tailor the information content of the program to specific groups of students.

Medium: 3.5" disk; CD-ROM
System requirements: Windows only - Win3.1/95/98/NT
Price: £199.00 (departmental multiuser/network licence; includes documentation - program manual and, where appropriate, student's workbook and tutor's notes - and postage)
Source: Sheffield BioScience Programs

MacPrac 2.2

This pharmacology program consists of a number of subprograms, including clearance, elimination, value of distribution, dosage of digoxin and blood pressure effects of catecholamines. Visuals are well-made and charts are easy to read. Instructors may add their own questions to student worksheets.

Medium: Sent by e-mail
System requirements: Macintosh
Price: US$50.00; demo version free
Source: Dr. Robert D. Purves (University of Otago, New Zealand)

MAXSIM (v4.1)

This program simulates drug absorption, distribution and elimination in detail. It uses both compartmental and physiologically-based pharmacokinetic models. *MAXSIM* is also used for simulating pharmacodynamics (direct and distributional/link models). Updates on the original *MAXSIM* include the pharmacokinetics of the placenta, uptake via the skin and lungs, and instructional programs in clinical pharmacology and toxicology.

Year of prodution: 1990
Medium: Sent by e-mail (with manual)
System requirements: MS-DOS, Windows 3.1/95/NT
Price: Freeware
Source: Johan Gabrielsson (AstraZeneca)

Microlabs for Pharmacologists - Animal Experiments without Experimental Animals

Microlabs is a series of computer-based modules with the primary aim of replacing animal use in education by simulating the effects of drugs on isolated tissues *in vitro* and the effects of drugs on whole animals *in vivo*. It allows the user to design experiments and reduce the use of animals by careful planning, to link animal behaviour to pharmacokinetics, to study the effect of drugs and 'unknowns' *in vivo* and *in vitro*, to get information about drugs, and to refine experiments under simulated conditions. Some of the programs available in the *Microlabs* package are: *Anaesthesia* of the rat; *Mouse behaviour* (an animation); *Heart rate and blood pressure in vivo*; *Guinea pig ileum in vitro* (simulating the effects of agonists and antagonists); *Vas deferens of the rat in vitro*; *Frog rectus abdominis in vitro*; *Phrenic nerve - diaphragm preparation in vitro*; *Sciatic nerve - anterior tibialis muscle preparation in vitro*; *Human case studies and pharmacokinetics*; *Animal behaviour* (digital video - on CD-ROM only - demonstrating drug induced behaviour in mice, rats and rabbits); and a *Drug list* linked to the program providing information about the drugs used.

Medium: 3.5" disk (MS-DOS version); CD-ROM (Windows version)
System requirements: MS-DOS, Windows 95/98; minimum 20 MB free memory on the HDD for the Windows version
Price: Cost price
Source: Dr. Henk van Wilgenburg (University of Amsterdam, The Netherlands)

Mouse Watch

This program is designed to train students to recognise different aspects of normal and drug induced mouse appearance, and to become consistent and reliable in their scoring of mouse behaviours. Students can see standard behaviours (e.g. walk, groom, stretch, lick etc.) and can then obtain a sequence of behaviours which can be scored using either the inbuilt scoring system or any available scoring system familiar to them. The sequence of behaviour can be repeated with the same behaviours in a different order to investigate reproducibility and standardisation of observational skills. Scored behaviour can be compared with actual behaviours so observational skills can be improved.

Year of production: revised 2002
Medium: CD-ROM; world wide web
System requirements: CD-ROM version Windows only; internet version both Windows and Macintosh
Price: £75.00 (UK Higher Education only); £250.00 (others); £950.00 (whole *Simulations Suite: Mouse Watch; Rat Blood Pressure; Simulated Anterior Tibialis - Sciatic Nerve Preparation; Simulated Vascular Rings; Simulated Water Maze*). Prices include full multiuser site licence for unlimited copies, tutor's guide, and telephone support. For internet version price please contact the source
Source: British Pharmacological Society

Neuromuscular Pharmacology

An interactive menu-driven program which simulates experiments performed on the sciatic nerve - anterior tibialis muscle preparation of the cat (*in vivo*) to illustrate the important differences in the pharmacological action of depolarising (e.g. decamethonium) and non-depolarising (e.g. d-tubocurarine) blocking agents. High-resolution graphic simulations of experimental results (muscle contractions) are presented, in accelerated time, on a scrolling display to simulate a chart recorder. Phase I of each experiment compares the action of the two types of neuromuscular blocking agents: after either intravenous or close arterial administration; in conjunction with anticholinesterase or a different competitive (non-depolarising or depolarising) blocker; and in response to tetanic stimulation or to acetylcholine administered by close arterial injection.

Phase II experiments compare the effects of 4 successive doses of decamethonium followed by the effects of tetanic stimulation and anticholinesterase. Information is included on the animal preparation, the method, and the clinical relevance of the different blocking agents. Each experiment has associated self-assessment questions with feedback.

Medium: 3.5" disk; CD-ROM
System requirements: Windows only - Win95/98/NT4, 166 MHz Pentium processor with 32 MB RAM and 16-bit colour graphics
Price: £199.00 (departmental multiuser/network licence; includes documentation - program manual and, where appropriate, student's workbook and tutor's notes - and postage)
Source: Sheffield BioScience Programs

PharmaCalc

This program lets you enter the pharmacokinetic parameters of a drug administered via IV bolus, IV infusion or extravascularly, then it calculates and draws the plasma concentration curve. The basis for the simulation is a one-compartment model with first-order elimination kinetics. It allows repeated and complex dosing schemes: loading and maintenance dose, missing dose, etc. It is possible to draw multiple curves in one graph for comparison, and to differentiate them by colour and line style. A therapeutic range can also be indicated. Drug parameters can be read in from a file, and new parameter sets can be saved into files. This allows to easily create a library of substances for quick reference, besides the program's own library of over 70 substances with pre-set parameters.

Medium: Downloadable from:
http://www.pharma.ethz.ch/biopharmacy/research/Simulation/pharmacalc.html
System requirements: Windows, Macintosh
Price: Freeware
Source: Institute of Pharmaceutical Sciences ETH

Pharmacodynamics Simulator

This program simulates an isolated guinea pig intestine in a bath, thus allowing the student to test the effect of some common drugs on it using a simulated output graph. The students can perform various experiments, and display the outcome on a graph for comparisons and manipulations. They are then requested to explain the results of the simulated laboratory environment.

Year of production: 1998
Medium: 3.5" disk; CD-ROM
System requirements: Windows only - Win95/98/2000/NT; 386 processor, basic video card
Price: On request
Source: Dr. Gabriel Shavit (Tel Aviv University, Israel)

Pharmacokinetics Simulations (v2.0)

The primary objective of this package, originally developed at the Washington State University (USA) and reprogrammed by PCCAL International (UK), is to teach the basic principles of pharmacokinetics through computer simulations. Simulation of the plasma concentration-time profile is a valuable tool to understand the basic pharmokinetic principles and to appreciate the interplay of various pharmokinetic parameters. The program allows the student to evaluate the impact of changing one or more pharmokinetic parameters on the concentration-time profile of the drug. The program covers: IV bolus and oral drug administration; constant rate and intermittent IV infusions; single and multiple drug administration; linear and non-linear drug elimination; one- and two-compartment pharmokinetic models.

Medium: CD-ROM
System requirements: Available in Windows and web/intranet versions. The Windows version (compatible with Windows 95/98/NT) is supplied on a CD-ROM installation disk and can be installed to a local hard disk or network drive; requires a PC with minimum 100 MHz Pentium processor, 8 MB RAM and a VGA monitor capable of displaying 16-bit colour at 640 x 480 resolution. The web version is supplied on a CD-ROM installation disk for installation to a web server and runs on PC clients only; requires a 200 MHz Pentium processor with 32 MB RAM and a Super VGA monitor capable of displaying 16-bit colour at 800 x 600 resolution; it is compatible with both Netscape Navigator 4.x and Internet Explorer 4 or better and requires Java and JavaScript to be enabled on browsers
Price: £240.00 (excl. VAT at 17.5% for UK and EU orders, and £20.00 handling charge per order)
Source: COACS

PharmaSim

This program is developed for teaching pharmacokinetics. It focuses on the simulation of drug plasma levels based on compartment models. It simulates one- and two-compartment models, IV bolus, IV infusion, and extravasal administration, linear and half-log plots, multiple doses and complex dosing schemes: loading and maintenance dose, missing dose, or change of parameters during treatment. The novel features of *PharmaSim* are the easy visualisation of curves and the high speed of the simulations. Students can change the value of a parameter with a scroll bar. The resulting change in display of the curves is almost immediate. This allows to visualise the effects of one parameter in a formula, a concept which was hard to illustrate so far. *PharmaSim* allows the user to easily create many different tutorials.

Medium: Downloadable from:
http://www.pharma.ethz.ch/biopharmacy/research/Simulation/pharmasim.html
System requirements: Windows, Macintosh
Price: Freeware
Source: Institute of Pharmaceutical Sciences ETH

PharmaTutor

PharmaTutor is an old graphic based interactive computer program designed to assist the teaching of an introductory course in pharmacology and physiology without the use of animal experiments. It consists of 5 parts, each one designed to be a self-contained practical class exercise that can be completed in relatively short time (20 to 25 mins.): 1. *Pharmacokinetic simulations* (IV injection, IV infusion, single oral dose, two-compartment model, renal insufficiency); 2. *Blood pressure and catecholamines*; 3. *Blood pressure and acetylcholine*; 4. *Smooth muscle in an organ bath*; 5. *Neuromuscular transmission* (including the effects of tubocurarine, suxamethonium and neostigmine in various combinations).

Year of production: 1987
Medium: Downloadable from:
http://www.pharma.ethz.ch/biopharmacy/research/Simulation/pharmatutor.html
System requirements: MS-DOS, Windows, Macintosh
Price: Freeware
Note: *PharmaTutor* was developed in 1986-1987, and has never been extended or revised. It is therefore out of date, particularly in regard to today's technical possibilities, but is still a useful program
Source: FFVFF

 Pictures Instead of Animals

This double CD-ROM is part of the *Digital Materials for Trainers* series and illustrates a variety of adverse drug reactions in laboratory animals. The material was originally produced on laser videodisc by Novartis plc (formerly Ciba Geigy plc), and then transferred on to CD-ROM with the support of the Doerenkamp-Zbinden Foundation. Thus the content has been provided in a more readily accessible format, although inevitably the quality of images is lower than on the original laser videodisc. The videoclips are numbered so that they correspond with the scheme used in the original brochure, which is included on the CD-ROM in various text formats. The program is supplied upon request to training establishments in the field of experimental biology for use solely as an instructional aid.

Medium: CD-ROM
System requirements: Windows 95 and later, Macintosh OS 8.6 and later; QuickTime 5 (included)
Price: £5.00 / US$10.00 (plus £5.00 / US$10.00 postage for 1-10 disks)
Source: University of Newcastle upon Tyne

 Rat Blood Pressure

This interactive program uses text, high quality colour graphics, animation and interactive questions to simulate a range of experiments demonstrating the effects of various pharmacological agents and procedures on the blood pressure (BP) and heart rate (HR) of the anaesthetised rat (*in vivo*). It comprises several sections: 1. *Introduction* - (UK) Home Office Licence requirements; 2. *Preparation* - anaesthesia/anaesthetisation, cannulation of trachea, jugular vein and carotid artery; 3. *Apparatus* - equipment used to maintain body temperature, BP and HR; 4. *Measurements* - describes how to take measurements from the simulated chart recorder and how to calculate mean BP and pulse pressure; 5. *Experiments* - provides typical data for 16 experiments: catecholamines, pressor agents, acetylcholine, ganglion stimulants, uptake 1-blockers, alpha-blockers, beta-blockers, adrenaline reversal, guanethidine, sympathetic nerve stimulators, depressor drugs, ganglion blockade, quantitative effects of alpha- and beta-blockade, reserpine, pithing. The stimulation can be applied to the vagus or pre- and post-ganglionically to the cardioaccelerator nerve.

Year of production: Revised 2002
Medium: CD-ROM; world wide web
System requirements: CD-ROM version Windows only; internet version both Windows and Macintosh
Price: £75.00 (UK Higher Education only); £250.00 (others); £950.00 (whole *Simulations Suite: Mouse Watch; Rat Blood Pressure; Simulated Anterior Tibialis - Sciatic Nerve Preparation; Simulated Vascular Rings; Simulated Water Maze*). Prices include full multiuser site licence for unlimited copies, tutor's guide, and telephone support. For internet version price please contact the source
Source: British Pharmacological Society

Rat Phrenic Nerve (*In Vitro*)

This program simulates the phrenic nerve - diaphragm preparation. The tissue can be exposed to drugs such as triethylcholine, 4-aminopyridine, succinylcholine, acetylcholine, carbachol, atropine, streptomycin, physostigmine, hexamethonium, tubocurarine, pancuronium, gallamine, fazadinium, decamethonium, choline, edrophonium, atracurium, dantrolene, lignocaine and neostigmine at any concentration and in any combination. The time sequence and order of addition is entirely in the hands of the user. Drug effects can be reversed by washing as required. Stimulation of the phrenic nerve can be turned off or applied at 0.05 Hz, 0.5 Hz or at 30 Hz for 5 secs. (tetanus). Output in the form of a simulated trace can be displayed on the screen or provided as a permanent record on a printer. Students can be asked to follow a schedule of drug administration fixed by the teacher and to observe and write-up effects produced in the normal way. Alternatively, students can design their own experiments to answer set questions or can learn about neuromuscular pharmacology using learn-by-discovery methods.

Year of production: 1995
Medium: 3.5" disk
System requirements: Windows only (all versions)
Price: £199.00 (multiuser, department licence for unlimited copies)
Source: PIDATA

When contacting producers and distributors, please cite *from Guinea Pig to Computer Mouse*

Respiratory Pharmacology

This highly interactive program uses pulmonary function data obtained from a guinea pig to teach the fundamental pharmacology of the airways. *Aims, Introduction* and *Methods* sections use a combination of text and high-resolution colour graphics to describe: the aims and objectives of the program; the structure of the airways, the physiological control of bronchial smooth muscle tone, airway smooth muscle receptor pharmacology, pathophysiology (asthma and COPD) and its treatment; the guinea pig preparation and the apparatus used to monitor airway function. *Experiments* is the main section and allows the student to select, from a menu, to study the effects of various mediators and inhibitory agents in the normal and allergen-sensitised animals. 1. Normal guinea pig: vehicle (0.9 ml saline); bronchoconstrictors (histamine: 3 single doses, +mepyramine, +indomethacin, +propranolol; acetylcholine: 3 single doses, +atropine, +indomethacin, +propranolol; bradykinin: 3 single doses, +indomethacin; vagal stimulation: low/high frequency stimulation, +atropine); bronchodilators (bombesin treated: single dose, +epinephrine, +mepyramine); 2. Allergen-sensitised guinea pig: histamine, +mepyramine; LTC4, +mepyramine, +montelukast; antigen (IV), +mepyramine, +mepyramine and montelukast. For each experiment the display shows simultaneous traces of resistance, dynamic compliance and blood pressure which are presented in a form similar to that in the Mumed recording system. Each set of data is accompanied by self-assessment questions which demand interpretation of experimental data presented to them, and an understanding of the underlying control mechanisms.

Medium: 3.5" disk; CD-ROM
System requirements: Windows only - Win95/98/NT4; Pentium processor with 16 MB RAM, 10 MB space available on HDD and 16-bit colour graphics
Price: £199.00 (departmental multiuser/network licence; includes documentation - program manual and, where appropriate, student's workbook and tutor's notes - and postage)
Source: Sheffield BioScience Programs

Selected Animal Tests in Pharmacology and Toxicology

This CD-ROM contains a selection of 7 historical German films featuring some experiments performed on animals in pharmacology and toxicology: *Muscarine poisoning and its reversal with atropine in the cat; Effects of morphine on dogs; Methods of validating systemic medication on small animals; Effects of anti-epileptics; Interaction of alcohol with another CNS depressant drug; Isolated atrial myocardium from guinea pig heart; Whole-body autoradiography (of a rat).*

Language: The films are silent; menus and subtitles are in English
Year of production: 1998
Medium: CD-ROM
System requirements: Windows 95 or later, Active Movie Mediaplayer; Pentium 160 MHz processor, 16 MB RAM, VGA graphics adapter (640 x 480) True Colour (24-bit), soundboard
Running time: 48 mins.
Price: €28.19
Source: IWF Wissen und Medien gGmbH

Simulated Anterior Tibialis - Sciatic Nerve Preparation

This program simulates the effects of various drugs on the skeletal muscles and motor nervous system of a laboratory animal. It can be used to teach the actions of depolarising and non-depolarising neuromuscular blockers, to teach about the interactions between drugs which affect transmission at the neuromuscular junction, to provide experience in the design of experiments, or to generate data for subsequent practice of data handling and data interpretation skills. A wide range of drugs which act at the neuromuscular junction can be injected (normally intravenously, but some also close intraarterially) and since this is an *in vivo* preparation they will only gradually wear off. Electrical stimulation can be applied at 0.05 Hz, 0.5 Hz, as a brief tetanus (at 30 Hz for 5 secs.), or switched off completely. The sequence and dose of drugs employed is entirely in the hands of the user. It is possible to move backwards and forwards in the experimental record to review results obtained previously in the current experiment. A great variety of experiments can be performed, tailored to the requirements of basic or advanced students. The simulation is embedded in an authorware teaching package providing pharmacological information about the systems involved.

Year of production: Revised 2002
Medium: CD-ROM; world wide web
System requirements: CD-ROM version Windows only; internet version both Windows and Macintosh
Price: £75.00 (UK Higher Education only); £250.00 (others); £950.00 (whole *Simulations Suite: Mouse Watch; Rat Blood Pressure; Simulated Anterior Tibialis - Sciatic Nerve Preparation; Simulated Vascular Rings; Simulated Water Maze*). Prices include full multiuser site licence for unlimited copies, tutor's guide, and telephone support. For internet version price please contact the source
Note: This program (without the authorware teaching package) is also available from PIDATA, on 3.5" disk, for Windows only (all versions); price £299.00 (multiuser, department licence for unlimited copies); year of production: 1996
Source: British Pharmacological Society

Simulated Vascular Rings Preparations

This flexible simulation allows students to perform experiments on 4 different preparations: the arterial ring with or without endothelium, the venous ring with endothelium and the arterial ring previously treated with endotoxin. These tissues can be exposed to various drugs, the sequence, doses and timing of administration are all in the hands of the user. A wide range of drugs which act on vascular muscle and/or the endothelium are available (noradrenaline, 5-HT, desmethylimipramine, acetylcholine, nitroprusside, clonidine, phenylephrine, nifedipine, etc.). A great variety of experiments can be performed, tailored to the requirements of basic or advanced students. A comprehensive tutor's guide provides examples of schedules, references and guidance for tutors. The simulation is embedded in an authorware teaching package providing pharmacological information about the systems involved.

Year of production: Revised 2002
Medium: CD-ROM; world wide web
System requirements: CD-ROM version Windows only; internet version both Windows and Macintosh

Price: £75.00 (UK Higher Education only); £250.00 (others); £950.00 (whole *Simulations Suite: Mouse Watch; Rat Blood Pressure; Simulated Anterior Tibialis - Sciatic Nerve Preparation; Simulated Vascular Rings; Simulated Water Maze*). Prices include full multiuser site licence for unlimited copies, tutor's guide, and telephone support. For internet version price please contact the source
Note: This program (without the authorware teaching package) is also available from PIDATA, on 3.5" disk, for Windows only (all versions); price £299.00 (multiuser, department licence for unlimited copies); year of production: 1995
Source: British Pharmacological Society

Simulated Water Maze

This program explains the importance of memory defects, illustrates different types of maze and gives a detailed description of the nature and use of a water maze. The integral simulation allows generation of data on the performance in the water maze of rats given various treatments (vehicle, scopolamine, neostigmine, physostigmine, hydergine or any of 6 unknowns). Groups of 6 rats are tested on each of 4 days and individual data on latency (time required to find refuge), path length (distance swum) and swim speed are presented. Help is given with interpretation and statistical analysis. Students are shown how to calculate means (+S.E.M.), simple and paired t-tests and how to apply non-parametric statistics (the rank test; Wilcoxin or Mann-Whitney).

Year of production: Revised 2002
Medium: CD-ROM; world wide web
System requirements: CD-ROM version Windows only; internet version both Windows and Macintosh
Price: £75.00 (UK Higher Education only); £250.00 (others); £950.00 (whole *Simulations Suite: Mouse Watch; Rat Blood Pressure; Simulated Anterior Tibialis - Sciatic Nerve Preparation; Simulated Vascular Rings; Simulated Water Maze*). Prices include full multiuser site licence for unlimited copies, tutor's guide, and telephone support. For internet version price please contact the source
Source: British Pharmacological Society

Simulations of Pharmacological Experiments on the Guinea Pig Ileum (v4.0)

This program, developed at the University of Bath (UK), covers basic receptor theory, including occupancy and how response size is related to occupancy. The user is introduced to dose-response curves through simulated experiments of the action of drugs on isolated guinea pig ileum. Dose-response curves found using a range of drugs and combinations of drugs are then compared in order to discuss: 1. Full and partial agonists; 2. Types of antagonism; 3. The use of agonists/antagonists to show the presence of different receptors. The aims of the package are as follows: the user should be able to design an experiment to find out the pharmacological properties of an unknown drug on the guinea pig ileum, i.e. to find out whether the drug is an agonist (full/partial) or an antagonist, and its possible sites of action (including receptors). Thus the user is required to demonstrate an understanding of experimental techniques, receptor theory and knowledge of the structure and pharmacology of the guinea pig ileum. The user will learn the structure and innervation of the guinea pig ileum; equations for occupancy and response; how to construct dose-response curves (experimental procedure and plotting of results); how to interpret dose-response curves and say whether a drug is an agonist (full/partial) or antagonist (if so, what type); what pA_2 is and how to find it; and how to use agonist/antagonist combinations to find out about receptors and sites of action.

Medium: CD-ROM
System requirements: Available in Windows and web/intranet versions. The Windows version (compatible with Windows 95/98/NT) is supplied on a CD-ROM installation disk and can be installed to a local hard disk or network drive; requires a PC with minimum 100 MHz Pentium processor, 8 MB RAM and a VGA monitor capable of displaying 16-bit colour at 640 x 480 resolution. The web version is supplied on a CD-ROM installation disk for installation to a web server and runs on PC clients only; requires a 200 MHz Pentium processor with 32 MB RAM and a SVGA monitor capable of displaying 16-bit colour at 800 x 600 resolution; it is compatible with both Netscape Navigator 4.x and Internet Explorer 4 or better and requires Java and JavaScript to be enabled on browsers
Price: £240.00 (excl. VAT at 17.5% for UK and EU orders, and £20.00 handling charge per order)
Source: COACS

Simulations of Pharmacological Experiments on the Rabbit Jejunum (v3.0)

This package, developed at the Welsh School of Pharmacy (UK), extends the work covered in the *Guinea Pig Ileum* package (see previous entry). The experimental section outlines the equipment and techniques used and explains the differences between the two tissues. The package provides a brief, overall review of the activities of the autonomic nervous system and proceeds to consider its specific activity in the rabbit jejunum. The significance of using rabbit jejunum tissue in demonstrating the activities of the autonomic nervous system is explained. The classification and mechanism of action of the sympathetic and parasympathetic receptors together with other receptor types found in the jejunum, such as histamine, 5-HT and adenosine is considered. A range of suitable agonists and antagonists are provided which permit the student to construct dose response curves which demonstrate the relative affinity of adrenergic agonists for specific adrenoceptors. The use of specific agonists and antagonists to differentiate between muscarinic and nicotinic receptors is explored. The activities of histamine, 5-HT and adenosine in the jejunum are demonstrated together with their specific antagonists.

Medium: CD-ROM
System requirements: Available in Windows and web/intranet versions. The Windows version (compatible with Windows 95/98/NT) is supplied on a CD-ROM installation disk and can be installed to a local hard disk or network drive; requires a PC with minimum 100 MHz Pentium processor, 8 MB RAM and a VGA monitor capable of displaying 16-bit colour at 640 x 480 resolution. The web version is supplied on a CD-ROM installation disk for installation to a web server and runs on PC clients only; requires a 200 MHz Pentium processor with 32 MB RAM and a SVGA monitor capable of displaying 16-bit colour at 800 x 600 resolution; it is compatible with both Netscape Navigator 4.x and Internet Explorer 4 or better and requires Java and JavaScript to be enabled on browsers
Price: £240.00 (excl. VAT at 17.5% for UK and EU orders, and £20.00 handling charge per order)
Source: COACS

Strathclyde Pharmacology Simulations

This package contains a suite of programs simulating pharmacological experiments on isolated tissues or whole animals.

- *The Virtual Cat.* Simulation of an anaesthetised cat experiment - a whole animal preparation which is used as a tool for screening the actions of pharmaceutical compounds on the cardio-vascular and skeletal muscle systems. The simulation displays the effects of drugs on the cat's blood pressure, heart rate, skeletal muscle and nictitating membrane contractions. Downloadable from:
  http://innovol.sibs.strath.ac.uk/physpharm/downloads/Cat_V251.exe

- *The Virtual Rat.* Simulation of the pithed rat experimental preparation for investigating the actions of drugs on the heart and cardiovascular system. 'Pithing' refers to the destruction of spinal cord pathways, severing all the nerve connections between the brain and the cardio-vascular system, simplify the interpretation of experimental results by removing the central baroreceptor reflexes. Downloadable from:
  http://innovol.sibs.strath.ac.uk/physpharm/downloads/RATCVS_V322.exe

- *The Virtual Twitch (Nerve-Muscle Preparation).* This is a simulation of the rat phrenic nerve - hemidiaphragm preparation, used to study the actions of neuromuscular blocking and reversal agents, and other drugs which affect neuromuscular transmission. The hemi-diaphragm is a large, focally innervated, respiratory skeletal muscle, composed of fast-type muscle fibres. Electrical stimulation of the phrenic nerve evokes fast, short-lasting muscl twitches. Downloadable from:
  http://innovol.sibs.strath.ac.uk/physpharm/downloads/TWITCH_v213.exe

- *The Virtual NMJ (Neuromuscular Junction Electrophysiology).* This is a simulation of an exper-iment recording the electrical potentials associated with neuromuscular transmission at the skeletal neuromuscular junction. The simulation allows you to observe the muscle action potential (AP) and endplate potentials (EPPs) evoked by either nerve stimulation or by direct current stimulation of the muscle fibre. The effects of a variety of drugs and of changes to ionic composition of the extracellular solution on the AP and EPPs can be studied. Downloadable from:
  http://innovol.sibs.strath.ac.uk/physpharm/downloads/nmj_v213.exe

Latest updates at the time of publication: 4 September 2001. Earlier MS-DOS versions of the software, are also available, and can be downloaded from:
http://innovol.sibs.strath.ac.uk/physpharm/downloads/dossims.exe

Medium: Downloadable from website
System requirements: MS-DOS (for earlier versions); Windows 3.11/95
Price: At the discretion of the author, the software is supplied free of charge to academic users and others working for non-commercial, non-profit making, organisations; commercial organisations may purchase a licence to use the software from the University of Strathclyde (contact the author for details)
Source: University of Strathclyde

Veterinary Guide to Poisonous Plants and Toxic Syndromes

Designed as a diagnostic tool for practitioners as well as veterinary students and residents, this interactive computer program contains hundreds of high-resolution colour photographs and nearly 15 mins. of digitised video segments showing clinical signs of various toxic syndromes involving poisonous plants. Each plant or syndrome is accompanied by botanical information for plant identification, plant distribution, poisonous principle, clinical signs, recommended diagnostic tests and suggested treatment modalities.

Medium: CD-ROM
System requirements: Windows 95 or above with Pentium processor; Macintosh Power PC with 24 MB RAM; thousands of colours or greater, 800 x 600 screen resolution
Price: US$65.00
Source: University of California (UC Davis)

Videoclips 1, 2, 3

See description of this series under VIDEO.

Year of production: 1995
Medium: CD-ROM (MPEG format)
Price: Each volume £50.00 (UK Higher Education only); £125.00 (others)
Source: British Pharmacological Society

When contacting producers and distributors,
please cite *from Guinea Pig to Computer Mouse*

VIDEO

 [The] Action of Drugs on Guinea Pig Ileum

The apparatus and procedure for testing the effect of various agonists and antagonists on an isolated strip of guinea pig ileum are demonstrated.

Year of production: 1996
Format: VHS PAL
Running time: 7 mins.
Price: £20.00 (different for bulk copies and other standards and formats)
Source: Leeds University Television

 [The] Action of Drugs on Skeletal Muscle

Demonstrates the action of various drugs and combinations of drugs on a rat diaphragm - phrenic nerve preparation and on a strip of frog rectus abdominus muscle.

Year of production: 1982
Format: VHS PAL
Running time: 15 mins.
Price: £25.00 (different for bulk copies and other standards and formats)
Source: Leeds University Television

 Experiments on the Isolated Heart of a Rabbit in the Langendorff Apparatus

An isolated, still beating heart is perfused with solutions of adrenalin, acetylcholine and verapamil. The alterations in contractility and heart rate are shown and discussed. Finally the cooling of the sinus node (primary pacemaker) and its typical reactions are demonstrated.

Language: German, English
Year of production: 1990
Format: VHS PAL, SECAM, NTSC
Running time: 13 mins.
Price: €25.05
Source: IWF Wissen und Medien gGmbH

Laboratory Preparations 1, 2

Using a mix of real dissection and diagrams, these video programs show how to set up more than 10 classical pharmacological preparations in laboratory practicals and feature details of the dissection and preparation of the tissue. They can be used in conjunction with computer based simulations so that students better appreciate the nature of the preparation which is being simulated. They are not concerned with the operation of the equipment, nor with the pharmacological properties of the preparations. *Laboratory Preparations 1:* Guinea pig isolated ileum; Rat vas deferens; Rat anococcygeus muscle; Rat phrenic nerve - diaphragm; Guinea pig isolated atria; Introduction to isometric / isotonic contractions. *Laboratory Preparations 2:* Guinea pig isolated trachea; Guinea pig isolated aorta; Rabbit isolated jejunum (Finkleman); Rat isolated perfused mesenteric bed; Measurement of blood pressure in anaesthetised animals; Injection techniques.

Year of production: 1995
Format: VHS PAL
Price: Each volume £25.00 (UK Higher Education only); £125.00 (others)
Source: British Pharmacological Society

 Nerve Physiology & Pharmacology

Video recordings of experiments explaining and demonstrating the effects of neurotransmitters and their antagonists on the autonomous system and the sympathetic system. The experiments illustrate the effects on the cat's nictitating membrane and the isolated heart and gut of a rat, and the output of various induced conditions in a tachograph. Clinical pictures of the human eye pupil after exposures to the substances discussed further demonstrate these effects. The film was intentionally produced without background narration, since it was demonstrated that students pay more attention when the explanation is given by the teacher, and not the video, but it does have text labels.

Year of production: 2000
Format: VHS PAL
Price: On request
Source: Dr. Gabriel Shavit (Tel Aviv University, Israel)

 Neuromuscular Blocking Agents

This video demonstrates the consequences of neuromuscular blockage in birds (chicken) and mammals (cat). It contrasts the effects produced by clinically useful drugs having different mechanisms of action. In addition, the antagonism on neuromuscular blockage by cholinesterase inhibition is demonstrated and the side effects that can develop with the use of such antagonists is emphasised.

Year of production: 1980
Format: VHS NTSC, PAL
Running time: 52 mins.
Price: US$50.00
Source: University of California (UC Davis)

Videoclips 1, 2, 3

The *Videoclips* series collects together short (1-5 mins.) videoclips showing various aspects of pharmacological topics. This material is designed for illustrating lectures or to be used as the starting point for tutorial teaching. It is collected from several sources, is of variable quality and some is clearly 'dated'. The material is not designed to be viewed by unsupervised students, or in a self-teaching context. *Videoclips 1*: Epilepsy; Myasthenia gravis; Hyperthyroidism. *Videoclips 2*: Rat and mouse drug-induced behaviours (including the 5-HT syndrome in the rat). *Videoclips 3*: Parkinson's disease; Alzheimer's disease; Morphine and naloxone in the rabbit.

Year of production: 1995
Format: VHS PAL
Price: Each volume £25.00 (UK Higher Education only); £125.00 (others)
Source: British Pharmacological Society

When contacting producers and distributors,
please cite *from Guinea Pig to Computer Mouse*

WORLD WIDE WEB

Cardiovascular and Autonomic Pharmacology On-Line
http://courses.washington.edu/chat543/cvans
University of Washington, USA

ExPharm
http://expharm.virtualave.net
Dr. R.Raveendran, JIPMER, Pondicherry, India

KinetiClass 5.0
http://cpharm.vetmed.vt.edu/Kineticlass5/default.htm
Prof. Jeff R. Wilcke, Virginia-Maryland Regional College of Veterinary Medicine,
Virginia Tech, USA

9. Physiology

SOFTWARE

ABASE: A Program for Teaching Acid Base Regulation

This exercise is designed to help students to integrate their knowledge about the components of acid base regulation by requiring them to make predictions about the effects of disturbances on 5 important variables. The program consists of 4 tutorial lessons and 7 problems.

Medium: 3.5" disk
System requirements: Macintosh
Price: US$375.00
Source: Rush Medical College

Animated Physiology

This computer animated organ physiology software covers the following topics: *Cardiovascular system* - capillary dinamics, cardiac excitation, cardiac cycle depicted with bar graphs, in real time and in detail, haemodynamics, laminar flow in vessels, flow in parallel and series vessels; *Kidney* - anatomy, filtration, reabsorption, secretion, clearance, water excretion and clearance, concentration-heat model, concentration locus - short and long versions; *Nervous system* - action and resting potential, membrane, neuromuscular junction and muscle, synaptic transmission; *Respiratory system* - respiratory mechanics. Each topical module (chapter) is a self-contained teaching unit (playing time 10-15 mins.). *Animated Physiology* supplements a wide variety of physiology textbooks and contains about 3 hours of animated instruction. It was developed to assist in teaching time-varying physiological events such as the movement of ions across the membrane, cardiac excitation and contraction, haemodynamics, the countercurrent multiplier, etc., which it presents in a dynamic way.

Language: English, Spanish
Year of production: 1995
Medium: 3.5" disk
System requirements: MS-DOS, Windows, PowerMac; Local Area Networks (LANs) compatible; 30 MB HDD
Price: US$100.00 (individual licence); US$350.00 (5-site licence; additional sites are $50.00 each); on-line demo available on website or can be requested on 3.5" disk (enclose full postal address and indicate the operating system)
Source: Didactic Systems

ArtMemW / ARTMEM

ArtMem for Windows (*ArtMemW*) and its DOS version (*ARTMEM*) are teaching programs designed to simulate an experiment to illustrate how membrane potentials are set up across biological and other membranes. This is mainly achieved by students exploring the response of an artificial ion-selective membrane to changes in salt solution concentrations across it. It would be a good first introduction to membrane potentials, prior to using the *MemPotW* or *MEMPOT* program, which deals with membrane potentials of simulated excitable biological cells.

Medium: 3.5" disk; CD-ROM
System requirements: DOS, Windows 95 and later, Macintosh with a fully compatible Windows/DOS emulation package
Price: US$395.00 (including Instructor's Manual, Student's Note and departmental site licence) for the first program, and US$200.00 each for either of the other two programs in the *Electrophysiology Software* series (*MemPotW* / *MEMPOT*, *MemCableW* / *MEMCABLE*). A special upgrade price from the DOS to the full Windows version is also available. Free demo version of each program is available and can be downloaded from website
Source: Prof. Peter H. Barry (University of New South Wales, Australia)

Blood Pressure Regulation

This self-supporting multimedia program is a realistic alternative for first year students in the biomedical sciences, which allows them to learn in an interactive and attractive way about key physiological aspects of blood pressure regulation in the rat. The use of high-quality video during surgery and experiments, together with a scientific research approach (*Introduction*, *Material and methods*, *Results*, *Discussion*), makes the program a worthwhile replacement for experiments on rats. Students are guided through every stage of real scientific animal experiments, asked to interpret the data, and draw conclusions. They follow the program individually, but it is possible for 2 students to work together.

Language: Dutch, English; other languages possible
Year of production: 2002
Medium: CD-ROM; world wide web
System requirements: Windows 98/ME/2000/XP, Internet Explorer 5+, QuickTime 4, DirectX (newest version recommended); Pentium II with 450 MHz processor, 64 MB RAM, 8 MB video card, 16-bit sound card, high colour display with 800 x 600 24-bit resolution; 300 MB free on the HDD to copy the program (otherwise the movies won't run smoothly). An HTML 1.1 version is under construction at the time of publication
Price: €50.00
Source: University of Gröningen

CALVE

See description and details of this program under 'Anatomy'.

Cardiac Muscle Practical Simulation

Investigation of the contractile responses of cardiac muscle (rate and force of contraction) when exposed to various agents, for example agonists and antagonists of the autonomic nervous system.

Year of production: 2000
Medium: CD-ROM
System requirements: Windows only - Win98/NT; 16 MB RAM, 64k colour display
Price: Free site licence, available to Associate Members of CLIVE consortium only
Source: CLIVE

Cardiovascular Laboratory

This interactive program on laser videodisc simulates a series of cardiovascular physiology experiments normally conducted by health science students. The experiments emphasise traditional physiology laboratory exercises, including: catheterisation of the left and right heart, autonomic control of the circulation, fibrillation and defibrillation, normal and abnormal cardiac cycle, positive pressure ventilation, a water manometer experiment, and euthanasia. A split screen shows actual polygraph recordings of blood pressures, ECG, blood flow, respiration, and heart rate in real time as a window insert simultaneously illustrates the experimental procedures or results associated with the recording, such as advancing a catheter, stimulating a nerve, or the fibrillating heart. An autonomic tutorial is also included. Each procedure is demonstrated on a dog that is anaethetised, intubated and prepared for recording of ECG, respiratory patterns, arterial and venous blood pressure, carotid artery flow and heart rate.

Medium: Laser videodisc; 3.5" disk (executable programs for IBM compatibles). Currently the author is developing a digital version of the program, which will include all the still images from the laser videodisc, and also a digital animation of the cardiac cycle and MPEG1 and MPEG2 digital versions of the motion video
System requirements: For single monitor with video overlay - IBM InfoWindows, IBM MMotion, Sony View, Visage, VideoLogic, FULD, Video Associates, Compuvid SchoolBoard (305-885-9155), and Matrox VGO-AT systems; for dual monitor - any computer monitor with a Pioneer LD-V6000, LD-V4200, or LD-V8000 laser videodisc player, a special version to run with Sony players; European Version - a special version of the programs to run on the Sony dual NTSC/PAL laser videodisc players; Dummy Videodisc - permits evaluation of the program logic and will run on any MS DOS computer, simulating actions of the laser videodisc player (downloadable from ftp://ftp.vetmed.auburn.edu/pub/branch - in the CVLab folder, CVL_E is the most recent version and CVLab.doc is a text description of the laser videodisc program)
Price: US$500.00 (one copy of laser videodisc and documentation; additional copies for use at the same site - US$200.00 each); US$50.00 (European version of programs for Sony Players); executable programs for IBM compatibles and authoring system - no charge
Source: Dr. Charles E. Branch (Auburn University, USA)

Cardiovascular Physiology Part I: Pressure / Flow Relations

This program is a tutorial exercise that uses a single circuit, parallel organ system circulatory model without reflexes to explore the student's knowledge of and ability to evaluate and/or calculate pressures, flows, and resistances in static and dynamic states. Postural changes are used as stimuli.

Medium: 3.5" disk
System requirements: MS-DOS
Price: US$75.00; US$100.00 (*Cardiovascular Physiology Parts I & II*); US$500.00 (*Cardiovascular Physiology Parts I & II, CIRCSIM, GASP*)
Note: The newest versions of Windows no longer support this DOS product. The authors are in the process of revising some of their programs, as well as developing some new ones. When these are ready, they will be available for free downloading from PERC's website (http://www.physiologyeducation.org)
Source: Rush Medical College

Cardiovascular Physiology Part II: Reflex

This program is a tutorial that deals with basic haemodynamics using a set of problems related to a single circuit, parallel organ system circulation. The reflex responses to postural changes, haemorrhage and exercise are explored.

Medium: 3.5" disk
System requirements: MS-DOS
Price: US$75.00; US$100.00 (*Cardiovascular Physiology Parts I & II*); US$500.00 (*Cardiovascular Physiology Parts I & II, CIRCSIM, GASP*)
Note: The newest versions of Windows no longer support this DOS product. The authors are in the process of revising some of their programs, as well as developing some new ones. When these are ready, they will be available for free downloading from PERC's website (http://www.physiologyeducation.org)
Source: Rush Medical College

Cardiovascular System / Autonomic Nervous System Tutor (v3.0)

This package, developed at the University of Aston (UK), is an interactive simulation of the effects of the main autonomic nerves and transmitters on the cardiovascular system of an anaesthetised animal. Questions are asked at each stage and progress is dependent upon correct answers being given - although correct answers and further information is provided if questions are answered incorrectly. The package is split into 4 areas: 1. *Introduction*; 2. *Experimental set-up* - outlines the methods used to anaesthetise and prepare a rat for injecting drugs, the methods used to record blood pressure and heart rate and the methods used for stimulating autonomic nerves in the laboratory; 3. *Parasympathetic nervous system* - is split into an introductory module, which guides the student through vagus nerve stimulation and injection of acetylcholine, and an extended module, which includes the use of blockers to distinguish receptor types; 4. *Sympathetic nervous system* - is again split into an introductory module, which includes injection of adrenaline and noradrenaline compared to stimulation of the cardiac nerve, and an extended module, which distinguishes between adrenoceptor types by the use of blockers. The results of all experiments are displayed as a trace of heart rate and blood pressure.

Medium: CD-ROM
System requirements: Available in Windows and web/intranet versions. The Windows version (compatible with Windows 95/98/NT) is supplied on a CD-ROM installation disk and can be installed to a local hard disk or network drive; requires a PC with minimum 100 MHz Pentium processor, 8 MB RAM and a VGA monitor capable of displaying 16-bit colour at 640 x 480 resolution. The web version is supplied on a CD-ROM installation disk for installation to a web server and runs on PC clients only; requires a 200 MHz Pentium processor with 32 MB RAM and a SVGA monitor capable of displaying 16-bit colour at 800 x 600 resolution; it is compatible with both Netscape Navigator 4.x and Internet Explorer 4 or better and requires Java and JavaScript to be enabled on browsers
Price: £220.00 (excl. VAT at 17.5% for UK and EU orders, and £20.00 handling charge per order)
Source: COACS

 ## Central 5-HT Transmission

This highly interactive program covers the physiological role of 5-hydroxytryptamine (5-HT) in the central nervous system and its clinical significance; 5-HT transmission: synthesis, storage, release, pre- and post- synaptic receptors, uptake and inactivation; 5-HT pathways: main sites of 5-HT pathways in the rat brain; 5-HT receptors - the families 5-HT1 to 5-HT7, their sub-types and transduction mechanisms; 5-HT drugs - their actions and clinical importance. The program assumes a basic knowledge of synaptic transmission, covered in another program, *Synaptic Transmission in the CNS*.

Year of production: Revised 2002
Medium: CD-ROM; world wide web
System requirements: CD-ROM version Windows only; internet version both Windows and Macintosh
Price: £75.00 (UK Higher Education only); £250.00 (others). Prices include full multiuser site licence for unlimited copies, tutor's guide, and telephone support. For internet version price please contact the source
Source: British Pharmacological Society

 ## Central Dopaminergic Transmission

This highly interactive program covers the physiological role and clinical significance of dopamine in the central nervous system; dopamine transmission: synthesis, storage, release, pre- and post-synaptic receptors, uptake and inactivation; central dopaminergic pathways in the rat brain; dopamine receptors (D1 and D2) - their sub-types and transduction mechanisms; dopaminergic drugs - their action and clinical importance. The program assumes a basic knowledge of synaptic transmission, covered in another program, *Synaptic Transmission in the CNS*.

Year of production: Revised 2002
Medium: CD-ROM; world wide web
System requirements: CD-ROM version Windows only; internet version both Windows and Macintosh
Price: £75.00 (UK Higher Education only); £250.00 (others). Prices include full multiuser site licence for unlimited copies, tutor's guide, and telephone support. For internet version price please contact the source
Source: British Pharmacological Society

Central Peptidergic Transmission

This highly interactive program covers the structure and physiological properties of neuropeptides; peptidergic transmission (synthesis, transport, release, postsynaptic action and inactivation); the major methods by which peptides are studied (immunohistochemical, radioimmunoassay and enzyme-linked immunoassay techniques) and drugs affecting peptide-mediated transmission. Each section describes principles and uses the opioids to illustrate them. The program assumes a knowledge of synaptic transmission covered in *Synaptic Transmission in the CNS*.

Year of production: Revised 2002
Medium: CD-ROM; world wide web
System requirements: CD-ROM version Windows only; internet version both Windows and Macintosh
Price: £75.00 (UK Higher Education only); £250.00 (others). Prices include full multiuser site licence for unlimited copies, tutor's guide, and telephone support. For internet version price please contact the source
Source: British Pharmacological Society

CIRCSIM: A Teaching Exercise on Blood Pressure Regulation

This is a simulated experiment based on a model of the baroreceptor reflex loop (*MacMan*; Dickinson *et al*). Users are required to make predictions about the effects of each of 8 experiments on 7 cardiovascular parameters before obtaining the actual results. Prediction errors then serve as triggers for discussion of the physiology involved.

Medium: 3.5" disk
System requirements: MS-DOS
Price: US$225.00; US$450.00 (*CIRCSIM* and *GASP*); US$500.00 (*CIRCSIM, GASP, Cardiovascular Physiology Parts I & II*)
Note: The newest versions of Windows no longer support this DOS product. The authors are in the process of revising some of their programs, as well as developing new ones. When these are ready, they will be available for free downloading from PERC's website (http://www.physiologyeducation.org)
Source: Rush Medical College

Circulatory System (Physiology Experiments)

Illustrates 4 short experiments. *Experiment A* shows cardiac output; total peripheral resistance; arterial mean blood pressure. *Experiment B* shows determinants of capillary pressure. *Experiment C* shows pressure gradients, volume rates of flow, and tube diameters. *Experiment D* shows flow through siphons.

Year of production: 2001
Medium: CD-ROM
System requirements: Windows only - Win95 and later; 16 MB RAM, 64k colour display
Price: Free site licence, available to Associate Members of CLIVE consortium only
Source: CLIVE

cLabs-Neuron

This program provides interactive computer animations and simulations for teaching basic neurophysiology. To facilitate independent student work, *cLabs-Neuron* is split into several applications. It introduces passive and active membrane properties and their electrical equivalents, and illustrates gating mechanisms of different types of ion channels. Relatively simple experiments can be done, for example with RC (resistor-capacitor) circuits or variable 'ionic' conductances. More complex laboratories are provided to examine voltage-dependent single-channel currents and to see them summing-up to whole-cell currents. Holding and command voltages as well as several neuron parameters (e.g. ionic concentrations) can be changed, and ion channel blockers (TTX, TEA) can be applied. The same can be done in a voltage-/current-clamp laboratory to examine the relationships between ionic kinetics and action potential generation on different types of neurons which are simulated with Hodgkin-Huxley (HH) type algorithms. Advanced students can make use of a 'neuron-editor' to change the neuron's parameters in order to attain specific dynamic properties.

Year of production: 2002
Medium: CD-ROM
System requirements: Windows only - Win95 and later, plus an internet browser (Internet Explorer 4 or later recommended); Pentium II processor, with 32MB RAM and monitor with at least 16-bit colours (high colour) and 1024 x 768 resolution
Price: €49.00 / US$45.00 (personal licence); €490.00 / US$450.00 (institute / school licence)
Source: Dr. Hans A. Braun (University of Marburg, Germany)

cLabs-SkinSenses

This interactive program provides a virtual laboratory equipped with realistic looking devices for extracellular action potential recordings from different types of mechano- and thermosensitive skin afferents. The students use an isolated piece of skin with 10 prepared single fibre afferents, whose characteristics are not presented. It is the students' task to find out which kind of sensory receptors innervate the afferents and what are the characteristics of these receptors. A mechano- and thermostimulator, an oscilloscope and a chart recorder are provided. The recordings (stimuli, firing rate and interspike intervals) can be stored in a 'data analysis lab' for a more detailed examination of the response characteristics. The program additionally provides interactive tutorials for teaching sensory physiology and allows play back of typical examples of original impulse recordings from real experiments. Moreover, the advanced student can work with recently published scientific simulations of intrinsically oscillating thermo- and electrosensitive neurons.

Year of production: 2002
Medium: CD-ROM
System requirements: Windows only - Win95 and later, plus an internet browser (Internet Explorer 4 or later recommended); Pentium II processor, with 32MB RAM and monitor with at least 16-bit colours (high colour) and 1024 x 768 resolution
Price: €49.00 / US$45.00 (personal licence); €490.00 / US$450.00 (institute / school licence)
Source: Dr. Hans A. Braun (University of Marburg, Germany)

Contraction Mechanism of the Frog Heart

This self-supporting multimedia program is a realistic alternative for first year students in the biomedical sciences, which allows them to learn in an interactive and attractive way about several physiological aspects that play an important role in the adequate functioning of the heart pump. The use of high-quality video during surgery and experiments, together with a scientific research approach (*Introduction, Material and methods, Results, Discussion*), makes this program a worthwhile replacement for experiments on frogs. Students are guided through every stage of real scientific animal experiments, asked to interpret the data, and draw conclusions. They follow the program individually, but it is possible for 2 students to work together.

Language: Dutch, English; other languages possible
Year of production: 2002
Medium: CD-ROM; world wide web
System requirements: Windows 98/ME/2000/XP, Internet Explorer 5+, QuickTime 4, DirectX (newest version recommended); Pentium II with 450 MHz processor, 64 MB RAM, 8 MB video card, 16-bit sound card, high colour display with 800 x 600 24-bit resolution; 300 MB free on HDD to copy the program (otherwise the movies won't run smoothly). An HTML 1.1 version is under construction at the time of publication
Price: €50.00
Source: University of Gröningen

When contacting producers and distributors,
please cite *from Guinea Pig to Computer Mouse*

Electrical Activity of the Isolated Nerve of a Batrachian

See description of this title under VIDEO.

Language: French, English
Year of production: Original film made in 1962
Medium: CD-ROM (MPEG4 format)
System requirements: Windows Media 7 (or Windows Player 6.4 for WinNT4 and Win95)
Price: Individual use: €15.00 (Europe), €30.00 (rest of the world); Institutional use: €30.00 (Europe), €45.00 (rest of the world)
Note: The original title of this program is *Activité électrique du nerf isolé de batracien*
Source: SFRS

Electrical Activity of the Myocardium and Transmembrane Ionic Currents

See description of this title under VIDEO.

Language: French
Year of production: Original film made in 1970
Medium: CD-ROM (MPEG4 format)
System requirements: Windows Media 7 (or Windows Player 6.4 for WinNT4 and Win95)
Price: Individual use: €15.00 (Europe), €30.00 (rest of the world); Institutional use: €30.00 (Europe), €45.00 (rest of the world)
Note: The original title of this program is *Activité électrique du myocarde et les courants ioniques transmembranaires*
Source: SFRS

Essentials of Human Physiology

This is an interactive multimedia learning and teaching resource that provides a complete, easy-to-use, up-to-date survey of the basic principles of human physiology and functional anatomy. Developed by the faculty in the Department of Physiology and Endocrinology at the Medical College of Georgia, it represents a breakthrough in human physiology education. The unique software combines descriptive text, full colour graphics and animations, clinical problems, full motion video, audio, and a self-testing question bank into the first fully integrated human physiology program. The 77 chapters are organised into 8 sections: *Membrane transport and bioelectric activity, Muscle physiology, Cardiac and circulatory physiology, Respiratory physiology, Endocrinology, Gastrointestinal physiology, Renal physiology, Brain function (nervous system)*. Other features include: 3,000 screens of comprehensive text supported by over 1,800 illustrations presented via split-screen, over 125 multimedia features, 32 correlative clinical cases, search capabilities, and a self-testing question bank containing over 850 questions with detailed explanations of all answers.

Medium: Internet, intranet, CD-ROM
System requirements: The CD-ROM version is optimised for Internet Explorer, but does not require instal-lation; QuickTime is necessary to view the animations and hear sounds throughout the program; the internet version requires any computer running Internet Explorer 5.x or Netscape 4.5 and above, with JavaScript enabled; for specific system requirements for intranet systems, please contact the source
Price: Individual use: US$20.00 (6-month subscription for on-line version); US$35.00 (annual subscription for on-line version). Internet, intranet and CD-ROM annual institutional site licences on request
Source: Gold Standard Multimedia

Experimental Study of Gastric Complex Motility in Sheep

See description of this title under VIDEO.

Language: French, English, Spanish
Year of production: Original film made in 1967
Medium: CD-ROM (MPEG4 format)
System requirements: Windows Media 7 (or Windows Player 6.4 for WinNT4 and Win95)
Price: Individual use: €15.00 (Europe), €30.00 (rest of the world); Institutional use: €30.00 (Europe), €45.00 (rest of the world)
Note: The original title of this program is *Étude expérimentale de la motricité du complexe gastrique chez le mouton*
Source: SFRS

Experiments in Human Neuro-Muscular Physiology (v2.0)

This package, developed at the University of Aston (UK), introduces the student to some of the apparatus (oscilloscope, stimulator) and the experimental techniques used to examine resting potential, action potential and nerve conduction. The student looks at intracellular recording, extracellular recording and how to make recordings from a conscious human. The package is split into three sections: 1. *Simulator and oscilloscope* - the student can vary the controls of a simulated stimulator (frequency of stimulus, delay, output) and oscilloscope (timebase, Y amplifier gain) to find out what each of the controls does; 2. *Recording bioelectric potentials* - the student looks at the ionic mechanisms underlying resting and action potentials in excitable cells, then goes on to look at how to record resting and action potentials in excitable cells using intracellular electrodes and extracellular microelectrodes; 3. *Experiments on a conscious human* - the student looks at the exper-imental set-up used to measure impulses in a conscious human, then goes on to examine: a. How increasing stimulus strength to the nerve affects the amplitude of muscle action potentials and muscle contraction; b. Summation of muscle contraction; c. Nerve conduction velocity. The student also looks at the relationship between initiating muscle contractions voluntarily and initi-ating muscle contractions by artificial stimulation of the nerve.

Medium: CD-ROM
System requirements: Available in Windows and web/intranet versions. The Windows version (compatible with Windows 95/98/NT) is supplied on a CD-ROM installation disk and can be installed to a local hard disk or network drive; requires a PC with minimum 100 MHz Pentium processor, 8 MB RAM and a VGA monitor capable of displaying 16-bit colour at 640 x 480 resolution. The web version is supplied on a CD-ROM installation disk for installation to a web server and runs on PC clients only; requires a 200 MHz Pentium processor with 32 MB RAM and a SVGA monitor capable of displaying 16-bit colour at 800 x 600 resolution; it is compatible with both Netscape Navigator 4.x and Internet Explorer 4 or better and requires Java and JavaScript to be enabled on browsers
Price: £220.00 (excl. VAT at 17.5% for UK and EU orders, and £20.00 handling charge per order)
Source: COACS

Filtration in Bivalve Molluscs

See description of this title under VIDEO.

Language: French
Year of production: Original film made in 1999
Medium: CD-ROM (MPEG4 format)
System requirements: Windows Media 7 (or Windows Player 6.4 for WinNT4 and Win95)
Price: Individual use: €15.00 (Europe), €30.00 (rest of the world); Institutional use: €30.00 (Europe), €45.00 (rest of the world)
Note: The original title of this program is *La Filtration chez les mollusques bivalves*
Source: SFRS

[The] Frog Gastrocnemius Muscle - Sciatic Nerve Preparation (v3.0)

This preparation is a classical physiology model used to introduce undergraduate students in a wide range of scientific disciplines to the underlying principles of nerve conduction and skeletal muscle contraction. Contents: *1. Introduction; 2. Experimental set-up; 3. Recruitment; 4. Summation; 5. Tetanic contraction; 6. Fatigue; 7. Conduction velocity.* The preparation had previously been the subject of a CAL package, which did not have the advantage of multimedia programming techniques. That program based the simulation on the use of electronic recording equipment. It was felt that a representation of the older mechanical equipment would give students a clearer appreciation of the underlying principles, without having to undergo the frustrations associated with setting up such equipment. Consequently, the kymograph has been resurrected as an animation. Animations are used throughout and students are provided with a simulated stimulator and nerve - muscle preparation with which to explore the effects of increasing voltage and frequency. Concepts addressed in this exercise are as follows: the structure and recruitment of motor units (motor neurone + the muscle fibre/s innervated); the generation of tetanic contraction to yield fused smooth responses in skeletal muscles; summation of muscular contractions; nerve and muscle fatigue; the velocity of nerve impulse conduction. The package has been developed at the Welsh School of Pharmacy (UK).

Medium: CD-ROM
System requirements: available in Windows and web/intranet versions. The Windows version (compatible with Windows 95/98/NT) is supplied on a CD-ROM installation disk and can be installed to a local hard disk or network drive; requires a PC with minimum 100 MHz Pentium processor, 8 MB RAM and a VGA monitor capable of displaying 16-bit colour at 640 x 480 resolution. The web version is supplied on a CD-ROM installation disk for installation to a web server and runs on PC clients only; requires a 200 MHz Pentium processor with 32 MB RAM and a SVGA monitor capable of displaying 16-bit colour at 800 x 600 resolution; it is compatible with both Netscape Navigator 4.x and Internet Explorer 4 or better and requires Java and JavaScript to be enabled on browsers
Price: £230.00 (excl. VAT at 17.5% for UK and EU orders, and £20.00 handling charge per order)
Source: COACS

 ## Frog Heart

An interactive, menu-driven program which simulates a number of experiments performed on the *in situ* heart of a pithed frog. High-resolution simulations of the frog heart contractions, derived from real data, are presented on a scrolling display to simulate a chart recorder. The trace may be paused to facilitate measurement of heart rate or to assess changes in the amplitude of atrial or ventricular contraction. Experiments include: the effects of adrenaline, acetylcholine (with physostigmine or atropine), and temperature, together with an investigation of the refractory period and electrical conduction through the heart (Stannius ligatures). Each experiment is prefaced by introductory text and includes an experiment guide and assignments.

Medium: 3.5" disk; CD-ROM
System requirements: Windows only - Win3.1/95/98/NT
Price: £199.00 (departmental multiuser/network licence; includes documentation - program manual and, where appropriate, student's workbook and tutor's notes - and postage)
Source: Sheffield BioScience Programs

 ## Frog Skin

An interactive menu-driven program which simulates experiments performed on the frog skin preparation to teach the principles of ions transport across epithelia. Background information describing the method, apparatus and physiological basis of the experiment is presented as text supported by high-resolution graphics. Then the user can investigate either passive or active transport in the presence or absence of certain drugs and generates data based upon accepted mathematical models. In the passive transport experiment, the user may alter the mucosal and serosal concentrations of sodium and potassium and can take measurements from a simulated voltmeter. In the active transport experiment ion flux may be calculated from measurements taken using either a short circuit current technique or a radioactive tracer one. Results are presented in an attractive display from which measurements may be taken.

Medium: 3.5" disk; CD-ROM
System requirements: MS-DOS
Price: £120.00 (departmental multiuser/network licence; includes documentation - program manual and, where appropriate, student's workbook and tutor's notes - and postage)
Source: Sheffield BioScience Programs

GASP: A Teaching Exercise on Chemical Control of Ventilation

This is a simulated experiment based on a model of the chemical control of the respiratory system (*MacPuf*; Dickinson *et al*). Users are required to make predictions about the effects of each of 11 experiments on 11 parameters before obtaining the actual results. Prediction errors serve as triggers for corrective discussion.

Medium: 3.5" disk
System requirements: MS-DOS
Price: US$375.00; US$450.00 (*GASP* and *CIRCSIM*); US$500.00 (*GASP, CIRCSIM, Cardiovascular Physiology Parts I & II*)
Note: The newest versions of Windows no longer support this DOS product. The authors are in the process of revising some of their programs, as well as developing some new ones. When these are ready, they will be available for free downloading from PERC's website (http://www.physiologyeducation.org)
Source: Rush Medical College

GENESIS (GEneral NEural SImulation System)

GENESIS (short for *GEneral NEural SImulation System*) is a general purpose simulation platform which was developed to support the simulation of neural systems, ranging from complex models of single neurons to simulations of large networks made up of more abstract neuronal components. *GENESIS* has provided the basis for laboratory courses in neural simulation at both California Institute of Technology (Caltech) and the Marine Biological Laboratory in Woods Hole, Massachussetts, USA, as well as many other institutions. Most current *GENESIS* applications involve realistic simulations of biological neural systems, and are the result of an intensive collaboration between multiple centres, including the Theoretical Neurobiology unit at the University of Antwerp (Belgium). Although the software can also model more abstract networks, other simulators are more suitable for back propagation and similar connectionist modeling.

Year of production: 2001 (version 2.2)
Medium: available via FTP from:
ftp://genesis-sim.org/pub/genesis (US site)
ftp://bbf-ftp.uia.ac.be/genesis (European mirror site)
System requirements: *GENESIS* and its graphical front-end *XODUS* are written in C and are known to run under the following UNIX-based systems with the X Window System (X11R5, and X11R6): Intel x86-based Linux systems (Red Hat Linux 5, 6, and 7; Mandrake Linux 7.0; Debian Linux with kernel 2.x, glibc2.1 and egcs-2.91.66); Intel x86-based FreeBSD 4.1; PPC-based Linux systems running LinuxPPC and SUSE 7.0; Sun SPARC-based systems running Solaris 2.6, and 2.7; SGI MIPS-based systems running IRIX 5.x and 6.5.x; IBM SP2 systems running

AIX 4.2 and 4.3. It is likely that *GENESIS* will also work on systems running other revisions of the operating systems listed; however, the developers only have direct experience with the particular systems listed
Price: Freeware
Note: Any enquiries should be addressed by e-mail to: genesis@genesis-sim.org
Source: http://www.genesis-sim.org/GENESIS (US site)
http://bbf-www.uia.ac.be/SOFT/GENESIS_info.shtml (European mirror site)

Graphic Brain - Neurophysiology

This computer animated neuroscience software covers many aspects of neuroscience, including: neural membrane, resting/action potential, neuromuscular junction, synaptic transmission and neurochemistry, plasticity, development, ligand and voltage gated channels, G-protein mediated postsynaptic responses, auditory sensation, visual sensation, mechanical/chemical sensation, reflexes, cerebellum. Each of its topical modules (chapters) is a self-contained teaching unit (playing time 10-15 mins.). *Graphic Brain - Neurophysiology* complements most neuroscience texts and contains about 3 hours of animated instruction. It is particularly useful in teaching/learning about time- and space-varying phenomena, which it illustrates in a dynamic way (ion flow across membranes, axonal conduction, sensory transduction, muscle contraction, second messenger dynamics, neural network operation, etc.). Suitable for medical/graduate neuroscience courses and advanced undergraduate psychobiology courses.

Year of production: 1993
Medium: 3.5" disk
System requirements: MS-DOS, Windows, PowerMac; Local Area Networks (LANs) compatible; 22 MB HDD space
Price: US$100.00 (individual licence); US$350.00 (5-site licence; additional sites are $50.00 each); on-line demo available on website or can be requested on 3.5" disk (enclose full postal address and indicate the format)
Source: Didactic Systems

Hemodynamics Simulator 2002

The *Hemodynamics Simulator* is a computer program that will help you review haemodynamic monitoring, cardiovascular physiology and vasoactive infusions. Follow the 20 self-directed lessons to explore non-invasive versus direct arterial blood pressure measurements, monitor central venous pressures, insert the pulmonary artery catheter and learn to interpret the pressure waveforms in a variety of clinical scenarios. Topics cover: preload, afterload, contractility, LV diastolic compliance, pressure-volume loop, Frank-Starling curve, myocardial ischemia, congestive heart failure, valvular heart disease, hypovolaemic shock, anaphylaxis, pulmonary embolism.

Medium: CD-ROM
System requirements: Windows only, with Internet Explorer 4.01 or later or Netscape 4.x
Price: US$69.00 (single licence), US$399.00 (network licence - up to 10 concurrent users on one network), US$1,199.00 (departmental licence - up to 60 concurrent users)
Source: Anesoft Corporation

Interactive Physiology

This is a series of interactive CD-ROM modules - one CD-ROM per body system - co-developed by Benjamin-Cummings and A.D.A.M. Perfect for lecture or lab, this bundle is filled with detailed graphics, animation, sound, video, and engaging quizzes to bridge the gap between simply memorising a concept and truly understanding it. The Student's Edition contains 7 modules: *Cardiovascular; Muscular; Respiratory; Urinary; Nervous (I & II); Fluids & electrolytes*. The Instructor's Edition contains all these 7 modules, plus two other CD-ROMs: *Anatomy Practice* (allows students to review thousands of pinned structures within hundreds of anatomical images; students can compare up to 4 images simultaneously, including illustrations, radiographs and cadaver photographs) and *Instructor's Guide* (contains everything one needs to integrate the software into the classroom, from suggested course outlines to sample tests). Each interactive CD-ROM contains topics that fit the following criteria: a. The toughest topics in the course - those topics that students find most difficult to master and teachers find difficult to teach; b. Physiological processes that lend themselves well to multimedia - things that move, change over time, or involve correlating multiple and simultaneous events. An on-line version (*IPweb*) is also available.

Medium: CD-ROM; world wide web
System requirements: CD-ROM - Windows (all versions); Macintosh OS 7.0 or later; *IPweb* - Windows 95 or later with 166 MHz processor and 32 MB RAM, Macintosh OS 8.1 or later with 120 MHz PowerPC and 18 MB RAM; Netscape 4.07 or Internet Explorer 4.0 also required
Price: US$33.95 (individual Student's Edition modules), US$149.95 (full Student's Edition series), US$99.95 (individual Instructor's Edition modules), US$495.95 (full Instructor's Edition series); for *IPweb* subscriptions see website
Source: A.D.A.M.; Benjamin Cummings; for *IPweb* see WORLD WIDE WEB

Intestinal Absorption

An interactive computer-simulation of experiments which may be performed on one of the classical *in vitro* techniques used to study intestinal absorption: the isolated, everted intestinal sac of the rat. The program simulates experiments designed to demonstrate the important character-istics of the transport of two important nutrients - hexoses and amino acids - in the small intestine. *Introduction* and *Methods* use a combination of text and high-resolution graphics to explain the everted sac preparation, the process of carrier-mediated transport of these nutrients and the methods used to measure it (using radiolabelled galactose, glycine and methionine and a scintil-lation counting technique). The *Experiments* section allows users to: 1. Measure the transport of these nutrients; 2. Demonstrate the Na^+ dependence of the transport process; 3. Investigate the mutual interaction of the hexose and amino acid transport systems by performing a series of exper-iments (including a kinetic analysis and calculation of apparent K_m and V_{max} for the transport process) to assess whether the interaction is due to competition for energy or competition at the carrier level. The data is based on predictive models of carrier-mediated transport which have been verified by experiment.

Medium: 3.5" disk; CD-ROM
System requirements: Windows only - Win95/98/NT
Price: £199.00 (departmental multiuser/network licence; includes documentation - program manual and, where appropriate, student's workbook and tutor's notes - and postage)
Source: Sheffield BioScience Programs

Intestinal Motility

A highly interactive program to teach the principles of intestinal motility using isolated rat colon. *Introduction* and *Methods* use a combination of text and high resolution colour graphics, as well as an animated section, to describe the nervous control of intestinal longitudinal and circular muscle, the apparatus used to measure longitudinal muscle activity and the propulsion of fluid through the gut. The *Experiments* section allows users to investigate the action of a range of drugs (acetylcholine, carbachol, neostigmine, atropine, adrenaline and a laxative - phenolphthalein) on the preparation. The action of each drug, or drug combination, is demonstrated on basal activity and on the peristaltic reflex response induced by raising the intraluminal pressure and is presented in high resolution graphics on a simulated chart recorder display which shows longitudinal muscle tension and fluid propulsion (measured from a drop counter).

Medium: 3.5" disk; CD-ROM
System requirements: MS-DOS
Price: £120.00 (departmental multiuser/network licence; includes documentation - program manual and, where appropriate, student's workbook and tutor's notes - and postage)
Source: Sheffield BioScience Programs

Intestinal Motility and its Regulation

See description of this title under VIDEO.

Language: French
Year of production: Original film made in 1957
Medium: CD-ROM (MPEG4 format)
System requirements: Windows Media 7 (or Windows Player 6.4 for WinNT4 and Win95)
Price: Individual use: €15.00 (Europe), €30.00 (rest of the world); Institutional use: €30.00 (Europe), €45.00 (rest of the world)
Note: The original title of this program is *La motricité intestinale et sa régulation*
Source: SFRS

When contacting producers and distributors,
please cite *from Guinea Pig to Computer Mouse*

JPCalc / JPCalcW

JPCalc and *JPCalcW*, the full stand-alone Windows version (reprogrammed for Windows by Axon Instruments and incorporated in some of their recent software packages), are interactive graphical research programs designed to: 1. Show graphically how junction potentials arise in a variety of different patch-clamp configurations and other electrophysiological situations; 2. Enable the ready calculation of junction potential corrections, given the solution data; 3. Show clearly how those junction potential corrections need to be applied to the appropriate physiological measurements. In addition to their direct usefulness in research they are also useful for teaching research students about the importance and role of liquid junction potentials in electrophysiological measurements. A listing of supplied ionic mobilities with full ion names for the program *JPCalc/JPCalcW* is also available on-line on the world wide web.

Medium: 3.5" disk; CD-ROM
System requirements: MS-DOS, Windows 95 and later, Macintosh with a fully compatible Windows/DOS emulation package
Price: US$175.00 (*JPCalc/JPCalcW* software package, User's Manual and a laboratory licence for one or more computers). A free demo of *JPCalc* can be downloaded from website
Source: Prof. Peter H. Barry (University of New South Wales, Australia)

Mac Series of Physiological and Medical Simulations

This interactive teaching course for use in physiology and pharmacology is a collaboration between the Centre for Health Informatics and Multiprofessional Education (CHIME), University College London Medical School, UK, and the Health Sciences Centre, McMaster University, Canada. It contains 4 packages that allow students to learn about human circulation, respiration, body fluids and electrolytes, and pharmacokinetics through experiments using computer simulations. The accompanying manuals are available for download in Acrobat PDF format.

- *MacDope Software Package.* MacDope demonstrates how drugs and their metabolites are distributed in the body as a function of time following administration. Students can monitor the levels of a drug in the blood, the amount protein-bound, in the gastro-intestinal tract, distributed outside the plasma, and excreted in the urine. Students can compare levels from a single dose with those obtained with multiple dosing. Patient characteristics may be altered, including size, weight, urinary pH, renal function, and liver function. A number of preset subjects simulating some common clinical prescribing problems are provided, and further subjects can be created by the user. *MacDope* allows up to 4 drugs to be administered simultaneously from a list of over 20 familiar drugs. *MacDope* is not programmed with data such as volume of distribution and half-life of drugs. Instead it generates this information by solving equations which combine the patient's characteristics with descriptions of the drug's features, including what metabolites occur, how they are produced, and their pharmaco-kinetic properties.

- *MacMan Software Package*. MacMan provides a foundation to understanding the behaviour of the cardiovascular system through simulations exploring the mechanisms which regulate blood pressure and cardiac output. The model includes the effects of baroreceptors in the aorta and the carotid sinus, the brainstem vasomotor centre, the autonomic innervation of the heart, cardiac contractility, and smooth muscle tone in arterioles and veins. The MacMan model helps students understand questions such as why jugular venous pressure goes up in cardiogenic shock and down in haemorrhagic shock, and why it is that positive pressure ventilation causes profound circulatory disturbances.

- *MacPee Software Package*. The interaction between the cardiovascular system, the kidneys, and electrolyte balance is so complex that it can be difficult for students to predict the effects of changes in one system on another. *MacPee* will help students to understand renal physiology, the regulation of salt and water balance, and long term effects on blood pressure. It does this by allowing students to perform many experiments (altering dietary sodium, renal perfusion, or levels of hormone excretion) some of which would not be possible on human subjects. They can also monitor the concentrations of a wide range of substances in many body compartments. The complex interactions between renin, vasopressin, and aldosterone can thus be elucidated. *MacPee* also allows medical students to analyse the changes in important clinical conditions (myocardial infarction, nephrotic syndrome, haemorrhage) and to monitor the effects of diuretic drugs or hormones, away from the practical complications of managing sick patients.

- *MacPuf Software Package*. A superficial grasp of respiration is inadequate for anyone who plans to work in acute medicine. Management of shock, heart failure, hypoxia, breathlessness, use of blood gas measurements, and oxygen all require a quantitative familiarity with respiration. The MacPuf model is particularly useful for teaching. It allows students to follow in more detail than with a real patient, for example, the complicated consequences of a failure in the delivery of oxygen. The volumes of different compartments and their gas concentrations, the responsiveness of the respiratory system to different stimuli, and the measures of ventilatory function are all quantified in *MacPuf*, so that students can study when, where, and how changes occur. *MacPuf* provides 120 individual subject factors and physiological variables which can be manipulated and studied. Bag collection and rebreathing experiments can be modelled; and the effects of high altitude, anaemia, pulmonary emboli, and obstructive airways diseases are all easily demonstrated.

Year of production: 1995
Medium: Downloadable from website
System requirements: Any IBM compatible computer
Price: Free of charge subject to the terms and conditions of use, and registration
Note: These programs were developed for use on PCs running DOS and EGA graphics, the original authors no longer work with CHIME and there are currently no plans to create Windows versions of the programs. The programs will work with Windows but there may be problems with the display on newer versions. The material is offered as it is, and no technical support is provided
Source: http://www.chime.ucl.ac.uk/Models (CHIME, UK)

MemCableW / MEMCABLE

MemCable for Windows (*MemCableW*) and its DOS version (*MEMCABLE*) is a teaching programs designed to simulate a microelectrode experiment which illustrated the passive time-dependent properties of a spherical neuron and the cable properties of a nerve and muscle fibre.

Medium: 3.5" disk; CD-ROM
System requirements: MS-DOS, Windows 95 and later, Macintosh with a fully compatible Windows/DOS emulation package
Price: US$395.00 (including Instructor's Manual, Student's Note and departmental site licence) for the first program, and US$200.00 each for either of the other two programs in the *Electrophysiology Software* series (*ArtMemW / ARTMEM, MemPotW / MEMPOT*). A special upgrade price from the MS-DOS to the full Windows version is also available. A free demo of each program can be downloaded from website
Source: Prof. Peter H. Barry (University of New South Wales, Australia)

MemPotW / MEMPOT

MemPot for Windows (*MemPotW*) and its DOS version (*MEMPOT*) have been developed as inter-active teaching programs that simulate the measurement of membrane potentials on excitable cells and have been designed to show students how resting membrane potentials and action potential peaks depend on K^+ and Na^+ concentrations and on their relative permeabilities.

Medium: 3.5" disk; CD-ROM
System requirements: MS-DOS, Windows 95 and later, Macintosh with a fully compatible Windows/DOS emulation package
Price: US$395.00 (including Instructor's Manual, Student's Note and departmental site licence) for the first program, and US$200 each for either of the other two programs in the *Electrophysiology Software* series (*ArtMemW / ARTMEM, MemCableW / MEMCABLE*). A special upgrade price from the MS-DOS to the full Windows version is also available. A free demo of each program can be downloaded from website
Source: Prof. Peter H. Barry (University of New South Wales, Australia)

Muscle Control

This self-supporting multimedia program is a realistic alternative for first year students in the biomedical sciences, which allows them to learn in an interactive and attractive way about the contraction behaviour of skeletal, cardiac and smooth muscle. The use of high-quality video during surgery and experiments, together with a scientific research approach (*Introduction, Material and methods, Results, Discussion*), makes this program a worthwhile replacement for experiments on frogs. Students are guided through every stage of real scientific animal experiments, asked to interpret the data, and draw conclusions. They follow the program individually, but it is possible for 2 students to work together.

Language: Dutch, English; other languages possible
Year of production: 2002
Medium: CD-ROM; world wide web
System requirements: Windows 98/ME/2000/XP, Internet Explorer 5+, QuickTime 4, DirectX (newest version recommended); Pentium II with 450 MHz processor, 64 MB RAM, 8 MB video card, 16-bit sound card, high colour display with 800 x 600 24-bit resolution; 300 MB free on the HDD to copy the program (otherwise the movies won't run smoothly). An HTML 1.1 version is under construction at the time of publication
Price: €50.00
Source: University of Gröningen

 ## Muscle Physiology

An interactive menu-driven program which simulates experiments on the isolated frog sciatic nerve - gastrocnemius muscle preparation to illustrate physiological properties of skeletal muscle. The program covers: removal of the preparation; apparatus and method; a series of experiments, in which high resolution graphic simulations of muscle contractions and compound nerve action potentials (CNAP) from sciatic nerve, derived from real experimental data, are displayed in a form similar to an oscilloscope screen or chart-recorder. Experiments include: stimulus voltage/response relationships, summation, tetanus, length-tension relationship (in sartorius muscle), action of curare (on muscle and CNAP). Each experiment is prefaced by introductory text and experiment guide and includes assignements for students to complete.

Medium: 3.5" disk; CD-ROM
System requirements: Windows only - Win3.1/95/98/NT; Macintosh (with Hypercard)
Price: £199.00 (Windows); £120.00 (Macintosh) (departmental multiuser/network licence; includes documentation - program manual and, where appropriate, student's workbook and tutor's notes - and postage)
Source: Sheffield BioScience Programs

 ## Nerve Physiology

An interactive menu-driven program which simulates a number of experiments performed on isolated frog sciatic nerve to illustrate important properties of mixed nerves. The program covers: removal of the preparation; apparatus and method; a series of experiments, in which high resolution graphic simulations of compound nerve action potentials (CNAP), derived from real experimental data, are displayed on a simulated oscilloscope screen. Experiments include: stimulus voltage/response relationships, investigation of refractory period, measurement of conduction velocity, effects of temperature and action of a local anaesthetic. Each experiment is prefaced by introductory text, has a protocol and associated assignments.

Medium: 3.5" disk; CD-ROM
System requirements: Windows only - Win3.1/95/98/NT; Macintosh (with Hypercard)
Price: £199.00 (Windows); £120.00 (Macintosh) (departmental multiuser/network licence; includes documentation - program manual and, where appropriate, student's workbook and tutor's notes - and postage)
Source: Sheffield BioScience Programs

NEURON

NEURON is a simulation environment for developing and exercising models of neurons and networks of neurons. It is particularly well-suited to problems where cable properties of cells play an important role, possibly including extracellular potential close to the membrane, and where cell membrane properties are complex, involving many ion-specific channels, ion accumulation, and second messengers. It evolved from a long collaboration between Michael Hines at the Department of Computer Science, Yale University School of Medicine, and John W. Moore at the Department of Neurobiology, Duke University Medical Center. Their express goal was to create a tool designed specifically for solving the equations that describe nerve cells. *NEURON* allows users to focus on the important anatomical and biophysical features of the model, without being distracted by computational issues such as compartmental size. It does this in part through the notion of continuous cable 'sections' which are connected together to form any kind of branched architecture and which are endowed with properties that can vary continuously with position along the section. User-defined properties of membrane and cytoplasm are expressed in terms of kinetic schemes and sets of simultaneous equations. Membrane voltage and states are computed efficiently by compiling these model descriptions and using an implicit integration method optimised for branched structures. Variable-order variable-stepsize integration can be chosen to achieve increased accuracy and/or speed. *NEURON* realises a tremendous degree of flexibility by using an object-oriented interpreter to set up the anatomical and biophysical properties of the model, define the appearance of the graphical interface, control simulations, and plot results. Two recent additions to the graphical user interface deserve special mention: the 'CellBuilder' enables users to create new models from scratch and modify existing models without writing any code; and the 'Multiple Run Fitter' greatly facilitates optimisation of models that have high-dimensional parameter spaces.

Medium: Downloadable from: http://www.neuron.yale.edu/neuron/install/install.html
System requirements: Initially developed in the UNIX/Linux environment, NEURON was subsequently ported to Windows (all versions) and Mac OS. It is the only neural simulator that runs on all popular hardware platforms, from sub-US$1,000 microcomputers to supercomputers, bringing the ability to perform research-quality simulations within reach of neuroscientists around the world
Price: Freeware
Source: http://www.neuron.yale.edu (Yale University, USA)
http://neuron.duke.edu (Duke University, USA)

Neurons in Action: Computer Simulations with NeuroLab

Neurons in Action is a unique learning tool, a combination of text and interactive simulations of laboratory experiments called *NeuroLab*. The user carries out interactive simulations of laboratory experiments on digital neurons with the professional research computer simulator called *NEURON*. *NEURON* is a neuronal simulator that calculates currents and voltages throughout nerve cells of all types. It runs on the three major platforms (Unix, Mac, Windows) and is available on the internet sites both at Duke and at Yale Universities (see *NEURON* under SOFTWARE). The foundation of

Neurons in Action is the set of equations developed by Alan Hodgkin and Andrew Huxley (HH) in the 1950s to describe the results of their experiments on the squid's giant axon. These equations remain the reference standard for describing the behaviour of excitable membranes. Their unparalled accuracy allows computer simulations to predict nerve function under the wide variety of circumstances encompassed by these tutorials. Thus the simulations in *Neurons in Action* reproduce the results of real experiments with remarkable fidelity. The tutorials give the student the chance to perform experiments beginning with charging a plain lipid bilayer membrane. By changing the neuron's geometry, channel density, degree of myelination, and ionic environment, the student can experiment with resting and action potentials in an isopotential patch, propagation of action potentials in axons under a variety of conditions, voltage clamping, synaptic potentials, integration of synaptic inputs on dendrites and spike initiation, and action potential invasion of a presynaptic terminal arbour. The ability of *NEURON* to display a movie of the changing voltage patterns at each point in space throughout a nerve cell provides yet another level of ease in comprehension because it is a natural way to envision what is happening. The morphologies of the nerve cells simulated in these experiments range from a patch of membrane at a uniform potential (such as a cell soma), through axons with uniform properties, to axons with morphological discontinuities such as branches and spines. Unless otherwise indicated, the standard (default) HH parameters have been set up throughout. However, the user will be able to make an almost unlimited number of changes in these parameters. The simulated experiments performed will yield results that are similar to those found in experiments on living preparations.

Year of production: 2000
Medium: CD-ROM
System requirements: Windows 95/98/NT, Macintosh OS 7.0 or better with G3 or PowerPC, Netscape browser (Netscape 4 included on CD)
Price: US$31.95 (single user); for site licence please contact the source
Source: Sinauer Associates

 ## NeuroSim - Neural Function Simulator (v3.0)

NeuroSim is a package for use in teaching neurophysiology at the undergraduate and beginning graduate-student level. It also provides useful insights for experienced neurophysiologists. Each of its 5 programs operates independently and simulates a particular aspect of neural function, but with a common style of interface. The screen display is similar to that of an oscilloscope in a genuine experiment. Parameters can be varied to explore the effects of various conditions and can be saved as disk files. Each simulation can be configured for use at different levels, so that students are only exposed to details appropriate to their learning objectives. Tutors can hide specified parameter values from users, so that students can be set the task of discovering them by experiment.

a. *HH* simulates the Hodgkin-Huxley model of a nerve impulse. Two stimulus pulses can be applied in either current clamp or voltage clamp mode, each with square or ramp waveform and user-defined amplitude and timing. A wide range of phenomena can be simulated, including refractory period, threshold accommodation, voltage clamp tail currents, single channel patch clamp conductances and many others. An animated cartoon shows the action of molecular gates in the cell membrane. Various drugs can be applied and the temperature and ionic concentrations can be varied.

b. *NEURON* models voltage-dependent and synaptic conductances. It is for investigating more complex cellular systems than that of the standard HH model, but it provides similar current clamp and voltage clamp experimental facilities. Up to 9 voltage-dependent channel types can be included, each with user-defined maximum conductance and equilibrium potential, and with activation and inactivation kinetics defined using a built-in equation editor. Intracellular calcium concentration fluctuations can be simulated, and any channel can be made calcium dependent. *NEURON* replicates many classical simulations from the literature. In addition to the voltage-dependent channels, up to 5 ligand gated (synaptic) channel types can also be included.

c. *PATCH* simulates the kinetic properties of single ion channels. Three ready-made models are supplied: a simple 2-state (open/shut) channel, a 3-state agonist-activated channel (shut/unbound, shut/bound, open/bound), and a 3-state (shut/open/blocked) channel. The program can also model a channel with up to 5 states with user-defined transition rate constants. The simulation develops open-time and shut-time histograms in combination with animated cartoons showing the molecular states of the channels. Multi-exponential curves can be superimposed on the histograms, with a chi-squared goodness-of-fit measure. Raw data of open and shut times can be exported as ASCII files.

d. *NETWORK* allows the user to construct arbitrary circuits of neurons interconnected by non-spiking or spiking chemical synapses and rectifying or non-rectifying electrical synapses. Many of the membrane properties of each neuron can be set individually, including making it an endogenous burster. Although active membrane events are simplified for speed optimisation, spike characteristics such as threshold accommodation can be included. Experimental current pulses of defined amplitude and timing can be injected into any neuron. Many different types of synapses can be defined. The display shows the membrane potential of up to 5 neurons against time as in a standard oscilloscope recording. Membrane potentials of all neurons can be displayed as an animated bar graph, or the spike activity of all neurons can be displayed as an animated scatter graph against time.

e. *CABLE* simulates passive conduction in a long non-spiking length of axon. It demonstrates how signal attenuation is dependent on the properties of time constant and space constant, and shows how these relate to the fundamental axon characteristics of membrane resistance and capacitance, and axon diameter. Temporal summation can be demonstrated.

Year of production: 1998
Medium: 3.5" disk; CD-ROM
System requirements: Windows (all versions)
Price: US$399.00, £199.00, €399.00; free demo downloadable fromwebsite
Source: Biosoft

 Nodus

Nodus is a user-friendly package designed to simulate the electrical behaviour of neurons and small networks on Macintosh computers. It supports any format using Hodgkin-Huxley type algorithms for user-specified conductances in excitable membrane models. *Nodus* combines a powerful simulator with sophisticated model database management. Models are defined in separate files: conductance definition files, neuron definition files and network definition files. For Simulations two integration methods are available: an accurate Fehlberg method (5th order Runge-Kutta) and a fast forward Euler method, both with variable time steps. The value of any simulation database parameter can be manipulated by the user during simulations. Colour graphic output and/or text output to disk of all membrane potentials, ionic and synaptic conductances and currents, conductance (in)activation factors and time constants, transmitter release, concentrations, injected and voltage clamp currents is supported. Up to 24 variables can be plotted on 4 axes. On-screen measurement of plotted results is possible. Currents (constant, repetitive pulses, ramps, sinus, noise, from text file) can be injected in any compartment of the model. One can voltage clamp two neurons simultaneously, with superposition of traces. Networks are 'hard-wired', with up to 200 neurons and a maximum of 60 synaptic connections with a delay and/or 20 electric connections for each neuron. Neurons can have up to 4,000 compartments. With a maximum of 6 connections per compartment (soma compartment: 24 connections), there is automatic control over connection consistency. Compartments can be split or fused manually or automatically to keep their electrotonic length within user-defined bounds. Conductances can be specified by a standard Hodgkin-Huxley equation, or any type of equation can be used to generate an external conductance parameter file (either activation factor and tau, or alpha and beta). Conductances can be calcium-dependent.

Year of production: 1999 for current version (v3.2)
Medium: Downloadable from: http://www.bbf.uia.ac.be/SOFT/NODUS_load.html
System requirements: Macintosh OS 7-9. Nodus 3.2 is available in three versions. Most users will want to use the PowerMac version *Nodus 3.2P*. The older versions (the Standard version *Nodus 3.2* which runs on any Mac with 68020/30/40 CPU and a FPU and the Quadra version *Nodus 3.2Q* which runs only on Macs with a 68040 CPU) are provided for backward compatibility. An extensive user manual is available
Price: Freeware
Note: The author does not intend to further upgrade or debug this program; but as many users still find it a useful resource, it is still distributed. Please cite "De Schutter E.: Computer software for development and simulation of compartmental models of neurons. Computers in Biology and Medicine 19: 71-81 (1989)" in any publications or work using this free copy of *Nodus*
Source: http://www.bbf.uia.ac.be/SOFT (Prof. Erik De Schutter, Belgium)

PHYPRAK (Computer based PHYsiological PRAKtical Training)

The *PHYPRAK* programs are based on digital video sequences of animal experiments connected with synchronous and synchronised presentation of the related measurement data. Each experiment is subdivided into an introduction with theoretical information about the experiment, a preparation section, the experiment itself, an analysing section of the data and a question section. Additionally there is information about the physiology and anatomy of the subject (text, graphic, animation) and further proceedings in the experiment as well as a demonstration of the dissection (text, video). The programs visualise physiological processes in sometimes tiny objects (frog heart) and allow replays as often as desired. The following experiments can be performed: Straub heart, effect of temperature, Stannius ligatures, ECG, neuronal control of cardiac action and biopotentials in the brain (EEG).

Language: German
Year of production: 1998 (update release in work)
Medium: 3.5" installation disk and CD-ROM (data)
System requirements: Windows only - Win3.x/95/98
Price: On request
Source: Plietz und Steinbis GbR

Physio Sim Lab

This interactive suite consists of 5 electrophysiology practicals. Electrophysiology normally entails the dissection of animals (traditionally frog dissection models) and the investigation of various stimuli on the heart, muscle and nerves. This software prevents any dissection through the use of simulated videoclips and provides an interactive laboratory environment, in which students can observe the effects of various variables upon the virtual preparations, be it frog heart or nerve/muscle. Thus students are able to investigate the same factors that would be present in the traditional practical. The software also alleviates the need for lecturers and lab technicians to prepare practical manuals, as the third aspect of each experiment contains the printable manual and includes worksheets which students can complete and submit as part of their practical reports. In the virtual lab environment, heart rate and strength of contraction are made evident to students by graphical representation (whereby amplitude of the wave form represents strength of contraction and the time scale allows students to calculate heart rate). The software allows the student to: increase/decrease the temperature of the frog heart (*Temperature of Frog Heart*), or increase the calcium of the frog heart (*Calcium on Frog Heart*), and then observe the variations in heart rate and contractile strength; identify the hierarchy of pacemakers existing in the frog heart by ligaturing the primary and then secondary pacemakers, and observing the effectiveness of each successive pacemaker, as well as studying ventricular escape (*Stannius Ligatures on Frog Heart*); stimulate the frog heart at different phases of cardiac contraction and relaxation, via the virtual electrodes, and observe the phenomenon of extrasystole (*Extra-Systole on Frog Heart*); increase/decrease the temperature of the frog nerve-muscle preparation and then observe the variations in contraction, relaxation and latent period and contractile strength (*Temperature on Frog Gastrocnemius Muscle and Sciatic Nerve*).

Year of production: 2001
Medium: CD-ROM
System requirements: Windows only - Win98, Media Player 7 with Codecs; Pentium II processor (300 MHz), 32 MB RAM, 8 MB graphics card
Price: (5 CD-ROM Suite) US$75.00 (student licence); US$500.00 (institution licence - 10 users). Prices excl. postage
Source: Saints Web Design

When contacting producers and distributors,
please cite *from Guinea Pig to Computer Mouse*

PhysioEx 4.0 - Laboratory Simulations in Physiology

This easy-to-use software consists of 10 physiology lab simulations that may be used to supplement or substitute for wet labs. It allows students to repeat labs as often as they like, perform experiments without harming live animals, and conduct experiments that may be difficult to perform in a wet lab environment due to time, cost, or safety concerns. Students also have the flexibility to change the parameters of an experiment and observe how outcomes are affected. Topics covered include: *The cell - transport mechanisms and cell permeability*; *Skeletal muscle physiology*; *Neurophysiology of nerve impulses*; *Endocrine system physiology*; *Cardiovascular dynamics*; *Frog cardiovascular physiology*; *Chemical and physical processes of digestion*; *Respiratory system mechanics*; *Renal physiology*. It is available either as a standalone CD-ROM edition, or as standalone web version package (for the latter see WORLD WIDE WEB).

Medium: CD-ROM; world wide web
System requirements: CD-ROM - Windows 95 or later, Macintosh OS 7.1 or later, with minimum 16 MB RAM; web version - Windows 95 or later with 266 MHz processor, Macintosh OS 8.6 or later with 240 MHz PowerPC, with 64 MB RAM (128 recommended), 800 x 600 screen resolution, millions of colour; Netscape 4.6 or Internet Explorer 5.0 and Flash 6 plug-in also required
Price: US$16.80 (CD-ROM); for on-line version subscriptions see website
Source: Benjamin Cummings

PhysioLogical

This program is an elegant and simple schematic aid to the understanding of respiratory and cardio-vascular physiology, developed solely by Mark Colson.

Medium: Downloadable from: http://home.primus.com.au/colsonline/PhysioLogical.exe
Price: Freeware
Note: 1. The current version 2.11, released 15 January 2002, is about 1.1 MB in size, can be downloaded from the website, and requires no installation, being a fully self-contained EXE file. **2.** This program may be freely distributed
Source: http://home.primus.com.au/colsonline/pl.html (Dr. Mark Colson, Australia)

Rabbit Arterial Blood Pressure – Extrinsic Innervation, Pharmacodynamic Agents

See description of this title under VIDEO

Language: French
Year of production: Original film made in 1974
Medium: CD-ROM (MPEG4 format)
System requirements: Windows Media 7 (or Windows Player 6.4 for WinNT4 and Win95)

Price: Individual use: €15.00 (Europe), €30.00 (rest of the world); Institutional use: €30.00 (Europe), €45.00 (rest of the world)
Note: The original title of this program is *La Pression artérielle du lapin – Innervation extrinsèque, agents pharmacodynamiques*
Source: SFRS

Recording the Electrical and Mechanical Activity of the Frog Heart *In Situ*

See description of this title under VIDEO.

Language: French
Year of production: Original film made in 1969
Medium: CD-ROM (MPEG4 format)
System requirements: Windows Media 7 (or Windows Player 6.4 for WinNT4 and Win95)
Price: Individual use: €15.00 (Europe), €30.00 (rest of the world); Institutional use: €30.00 (Europe), €45.00 (rest of the world)
Note: The original title of this program is *Enregistrement de l'activité électrique et mécanique du coeur de grenouille in situ*
Source: SFRS

Rhbit

This simulated physiology experiment teaches how simple neural networks function, and demonstrates the principles of neuroscience investigation. Using a simulated frog as a model, with 8 interconnected neurons forming its nervous system, the student gathers data from the neurons, and stimulates and lesions them. The relationships between certain neurons and the sense organs and muscles are to be determined in the practical, along with the relationships between the neurons themselves and the excitatory or inhibitory synapses formed.

Medium: Downloadable from: ftp://ftp.ai.mit.edu/pub/ekm/RhBit
System requirements: *Rhbit* is Java-based and will run on a variety of platforms; included is the Java runtime environment for Windows
Price: Freeware
Source: http://www.ai.mit.edu/people/ekm/Rhbit.htm (Massachusetts Institute of Technology, USA)

SimBioSys Physiology Labs v3

This program is built around an interactive on-screen textbook, with animations, quizzes, and illustrations. At its heart is *SimBioSys*, a simulation engine which uses mathematical models of the heart, vessels, lungs, kidney, and their neural control. It reproduces over 1,000 physiological parameters, creating a real-time simulation environment that allows virtual experimentation.

General, respiratory, cardiovascular, and renal physiology are covered in 19 chapters. Throughout the program, 68 guided laboratory exercises allow the user to experiment with a simulated living, breathing patient; thus, blood loss can be modeled, a host of drugs or fluids given, clinical tools (such as a pacemaker or a mechanical ventilator) used, and clinically unavailable parameters such as cardiac contractility, lung inflation, glomerular filtration, controlled and altered. Such interventions help the user understand how the body works, by observing the effects of various changes on different systems. _SimBioSys Physiology Labs Plus_ is designed for the teacher who wants to incorporate simulations into his or her own teaching, and for the physiologist who wants to study responses to interventions in a modeled system. The 'plus' in _Labs Plus_ refers to customisability: it gives teachers the ability to create and modify their own local curriculum, with exercises, and it offers students log-in and on-screen tracking.

Medium: CD-ROM
System requirements: Windows only - Win95/98; Pentium processor, 16 MB RAM (32 MB recommended), minimum 10 MB HDD space
Price: US$99.00 (single user licence for individual version); US$595.00 (single user licence for Plus version); site licence price on request
Source: Critical Concepts

 SimHeart

SimHeart is an interactive computer program focusing on the mechanisms of the cardiac muscle and the effects of cardioactive drugs. All experiments are conducted on the so-called 'Langendorff heart'. The program has 3 sections: _Preparation_ - 3 audiovisual sequences which show the Langendorff preparation using the heart of a rat; _Chemical Lab_ - features the preparation of the experimental solutions from among a range of chemical and pharmacological substances (acetylcholine [ACh], atropine, epinephrine [Adr], phentolamine, propanolol, verapamil, strophanthin); _Practical Course_ - the interactive part of the program, which allows the student to perform numerous experiments in the virtual laboratory, using a Langendorff apparatus, a thermostat, an amplifier, and a perfusor. Ingenious mathematical algorithms freshly compute the behaviour of the specimen according according to the curent parameter settings, while the specimen itself displays realistic behaviour: after program start, an individual and unique profile of properties is calculated for each specimen, thus simulating the biological range of variation of the specimens. The experiments featured are: inotropic and chronotropic Adr effects; functional antagonism between Adr and ACh; atropine as a competitive inhibitor for ACh; alpha- and beta-blockers; calcium-channel blockers (verapamil); cardiac glycosides (G-strophanthin). In addition, _SimHeart_ includes a high-performance analysis module to save, comment and print experimental results. This simulation program is an effective introduction to live laboratory work and an alternative to the classic Langendorff experiments.

Language: German, English
Year of production: 1998
Medium: CD-ROM
System requirements: Windows 3.x or later; Macintosh OS 7 or later; 12 MB RAM; sound card; monitor with at least 256 colours (32k recommended)

Price: US$499.00 / €449.00 (English Version), €699.00 (German version) (both include user's manual); US$1,899.00 / €1,685.00 (complete set of all 5 programs in the *Virtual Physiology Series: SimNerv, SimMuscle, SimVessel, SimHeart, SimPatch* - English version), €2,680.00 (complete *Virtual Physiology Series* - German version); special price for multiple copies and site licence on request. Note that prices for the German version include the German VAT, while those for the English version do not (if no VAT Registration Number is provided, 16% VAT should be added to them). Free demo versions available on CD-ROM
Note: Readers of this book are entitled to a special reduction in price from Thieme; please cite *from Guinea Pig to Computer Mouse* when ordering
Source: Georg Thieme Verlag; Dr. Hans A. Braun (University of Marburg, Germany)

 SimMuscle

SimMuscle is an interactive computer program focusing on the physiology of the striated muscle. It provides a virtual laboratory where the students can perform experiments on the leg muscle of a frog. The program has 3 sections: *Wetlands*, which shows still pictures of six different species of frogs in their natural environment and plays their sounds; *Preparation* - 7 audiovisual sequences demonstrating the dissection process from the decapitation to isolation of gastrocnemius preparation; *Practical Course* - the interactive part of the program, which contains all standard experiments performed by the student in the virtual laboratory, using a length and force transducer, an electric stimulator, and an oscilloscope. Here, intelligent algorithms ensure that the nerve specimen evidences absolutely realistic behaviour; for example, after the program starts, each nerve specimen assumes new, individual, and physiologically-plausible properties, and simulates a realistic range of experimental results. The experiments featured are: single twitch as a function of stimulation intensity; superimposition of double stimuli; tetanic contractions; resting-tension curve; curves of isometric and isotonic maximum values; force-shortening velocity relationship; fatigue. Different muscle preparations with different physiological profiles are available which demonstrate biological variability.

Language: German, English
Year of production: 1998
Medium: CD-ROM
System requirements: Windows 3.x or later; Macintosh OS 7 or later; 12 MB RAM; sound card; monitor with at least 256 colours (32k recommended)
Price: US$499.00 / €449.00 (English Version), €699.00 (German version) (both include user's manual); US$1,899.00 / €1,685.00 (complete set of all 5 programs in the *Virtual Physiology Series: SimNerv, SimMuscle, SimVessel, SimHeart, SimPatch* - English version), €2,680.00 (complete *Virtual Physiology Series* - German version); special price for multiple copies and site licence on request. Note that prices for the German version include the German VAT, while those for the English version do not (if no VAT Registration Number is provided, 16% VAT should be added to them). Free demo versions available on CD-ROM
Note: Readers of this book are entitled to a special reduction in price from Thieme; please cite *from Guinea Pig to Computer Mouse* when ordering
Source: Georg Thieme Verlag; Dr. Hans A. Braun (University of Marburg, Germany)

SimNerv

SimNerv is an interactive computer program simulating the classical frog sciatic nerve experiments, still often required of life science students. It has 3 sections: *Wetlands*, which shows still pictures of six different species of frogs in their natural environment and plays their sounds; *Preparation* - 7 audiovisual sequences demonstrating the preparation of the sciatic nerve, from decapitation to nerve excision; *Practical Course* - the interactive part of the program, which contains all standard experiments performed by the student in the virtual laboratory, featuring an electric stimulator, an oscilloscope, and an experimental chamber. Here, intelligent algorithms ensure that the nerve specimen evidences absolutely realistic behaviour; for example, after program start, each nerve specimen assumes new, individual, and physiologically-plausible properties, and simulates a realistic range of experimental results. The experiments featured are: determination of the relative and absolute refractory period; compound action potential (CAP) amplitudes as a function of stimulation activity or of stimulation duration; monophasic CAP after ligating the nerve; anode opening excitation as a function of the stimulation duration; effects of changed electrode positions; nerve conduction velocity.

Language: German, English
Year of production: 1995
Medium: CD-ROM
System requirements: Windows 3.x or later; Macintosh OS 7 or later; 12 MB RAM; sound card; monitor with at least 256 colours (32k recommended)
Price: US$499.00 / €449.00 (English Version), €699.00 (German version) (both include user's manual); US$1,899.00 / €1,685.00 (complete set of all 5 programs in the *Virtual Physiology Series: SimNerv, SimMuscle, SimVessel, SimHeart, SimPatch* - English version), €2,680.00 (complete *Virtual Physiology Series* - German version); special price for multiple copies and site licence on request. Note that prices for the German version include the German VAT, while those for the English version do not (if no VAT Registration Number is provided, 16% VAT should be added to them). Free demo versions available on CD-ROM
Note: Readers of this book are entitled to a special reduction in price from Thieme; please cite *from Guinea Pig to Computer Mouse* when ordering
Source: Georg Thieme Verlag; Dr. Hans A. Braun (University of Marburg, Germany)

SimPatch

SimPatch is an interactive computer program simulating the electrophysiology of the ion channel and the 'patch-clamp' technique. It provides a complete virtual laboratory environment where the students can investigate voltage dependent ion channels (Na^+, Ca^{++}, K^+, normal and Ca-dependent) in the membrane of the retinal neurons. The program has 3 sections: *Overview* - 7 audiovisual sequences introducing the student to the experiments and equipment; *Presentation* - 8 audiovisual sequences presenting the experiments in detail step by step; *Practical Course* - the interactive part of the program, which allows the student to perform numerous experiments in the virtual laboratory, using a patch-clamp amplifier, a pulse generator and an oscilloscope. Ingenious mathematical algorithms simulate not only the cell responses, but also the passive stimulation artefacts, thus permitting practically any parameter constellation. In addition, *SimPatch* offers several interactive modules, allowing the user to: select the composition of the intra- and extra-cellular solutions from among a range of chemical and pharmacological substances, the experiment temperature, and the Nernst potential (*Solutions* module); select the retina cell type (photoreceptors, horizontal cells, bipolar cells, amacrine cells, ganglion cells) and retinal tissues from various mammals (*Microscope* module); define and save voltage-pulse protocol (*Pulse* module); present and save experimental results (*Analysis* module).

Language: German, English
Year of production: 1998
Medium: CD-ROM
System requirements: Windows 3.x or later; Macintosh OS 7 or later; 12 MB RAM; sound card; monitor with at least 256 colours (32k recommended)
Price: US$499.00 / €449.00 (English Version), €699.00 (German version) (both include user's manual); US$1,899.00 / €1,685.00 (complete set of all 5 programs in the *Virtual Physiology Series: SimNerv, SimMuscle, SimVessel, SimHeart, SimPatch* - English version), €2,680.00 (complete *Virtual Physiology Series* - German version); special price for multiple copies and site licence on request. Note that prices for the German version include the German VAT, while those for the English version do not (if no VAT Registration Number is provided, 16% VAT should be added to them). Free demo versions available on CD-ROM
Note: Readers of this book are entitled to a special reduction in price from Thieme; please cite *from Guinea Pig to Computer Mouse* when ordering
Source: Georg Thieme Verlag; Dr. Horst Schneider (University of Marburg, Germany)

Simulations in Physiology: The Renal System

A set of 6 computer simulations (one tutorial - *Water movement in the kidney* - and 5 laboratory experiments - *Glomerular capillary dynamics, Proximal tubular reabsorption, The distal nephron, The total nephron* and *Acid-base balance*) that provide tutorial and laboratory experiment formats for teaching glomerular filtration, function of proximal and distal tubules, effects of hormones on the kidney, and acid-base control. A laboratory manual provides directions for student 'experiments'.

Year of production: 1994
Medium: 3.5" disk
System requirements: MS-DOS, Macintosh (not OS 9 compatible)
Price: US$300.00 for set of 6 programs (includes permission to make enough copies for students)
Note: The newest versions of Windows no longer support this MS-DOS product. PERC is in the process of revising some of its programs, as well as developing new ones. When these are ready, they will be available for free downloading from PERC's website
Source: PERC

Simulations in Physiology: The Respiratory System

A series of 11 simulated clinical and laboratory situations, each dealing with a limited number of concepts relevant to the physiology of the respiratory system and comparing data from up to 7 'experiments'. Four general areas of study are included, and the simulations in each of them build in complexity. There are 4 mechanics models - *Static relationships* (elastic properties of the lung, chest wall, and total respiratory system), *Dynamic relationships I* (effects of lung compliance and airway resistance on tidal volume development), *Work of breathing* (oxygen cost of elastic, resistive, and total work during inspiration), *Dynamic relationships II* (respiratory dynamics of the total respiratory system); 3 general gas exchange models - *Alveolar gas exchange*, O_2 *and* CO_2 *dissociation curves*, *Exchange from atmosphere to tissues* (influence of alveolar ventilation, cardiac output, and anatomic shunt flow on arterial blood composition and gas exchange at the tissues); 3 VA/Q relationships models - *Gas exchange in a single alveolus* (effects of ventilation-perfusion ratio and inspired gas composition on exchange in a single exchange unit), *The non-uniform lung* (gas exchange from atmosphere to tissues with VA/Q mismatching in the lung), *Overall gas exchange* (gas exchange from atmosphere to tissues with VA/Q mismatching and a true shunt), and one acid-base balance model - *Acid-base balance* (from a base excess viewpoint).

Medium: Downloadable fromwebsite
System requirements: Compatible with Windows or Windows Emulator
Price: Freeware
Source: PERC

Simulator for Neural Networks and Action Potentials (SNNAP)

SNNAP was designed as a tool for the rapid development and simulation of realistic models of single neurons and small neural networks. The electrical properties of individual neurons are described with Hodgkin-Huxley type voltage- and time-dependent ionic currents. The connections among neurons can be made by either electrical or chemical synapses. *SNNAP* also includes mathematical descriptions of intracellular second messengers and ions, thus being able to simulate the modulation, either enhancement or inhibition, of membrane currents and synaptic transmission, as well as the current flow in multicompartment models of neurons (by using the equations describing electrical coupling). Some of the advantages of *SNNAP* include: a graphical user interface; the ability to simulate common experimental manipulations (e.g. injection of external currents into multiple cells, removal of individual conductances to simulate pharmacological agents, modulation of membrane currents via application of modulatory transmitters and voltage-clamping cells); the modular organisation of input files. There are several versions of *SNNAP*. The number of neurons that can be included in a network has been increased from 100 (v7) to 500 (v7a). The number of synaptic connections has been increased to 2,000 chemical synapses, 2,000 electrical synapses, and 2,000 modulatory synapses.

Medium: Downloadable from website
System requirements: Windows 95/98/NT/2000, Macintosh, Linux/UNIX
Price: Freeware
Source: http://snnap.uth.tmc.edu (University of Texas-Houston Medical School, USA)

SimVessel

SimVessel is an interactive computer program demonstrating the physiological behaviour of smooth muscle strips from the antrum gastricum and the aorta of the rat. It includes 3 sections: *Preparation* - 7 audiovisual sequences showing the preparation of the vessels; *Chemical Lab*, featuring the preparation of experimental solutions from among a range of chemical and pharmacological substances (acetylcholine [ACh], atropine, norepinephrine [NE], phentolamine, propanolol, verapamil); *Practical Course* - the interactive part of the program, which allows the student to perform numerous experiments in the virtual laboratory, using a transducer, an amplifier, a chart recorder, and a large storage glass tube. There is a facility to accelerate the experiment by a time factor of 2 or 4. Ingenious mathematical algorithms freshly compute the behaviour of the specimen according according to the current parameter settings, while the specimen itself displays a realistic behaviour: after program start, an individual and unique profile of properties whithin the physiological range is calculated for each specimen. The experiments featured are: myogenic automaticity; tonic and phasic contraction forms; competitive inhibition; functional antagonism of ACh and NE; calcium channel blockers. In addition, *SimVessel* includes a high-performance analysis module to save, comment and print experimental results.

Language: German, English
Year of production: 1998
Medium: CD-ROM
System requirements: Windows 3.x or later; Macintosh OS 7 or later; 12 MB RAM; sound card; monitor with at least 256 colours (32k recommended)
Price: US$499.00 / €449.00 (English Version), €699.00 (German version) (both include user's manual); US$1,899.00 / €1,685.00 (complete set of all 5 programs in the *Virtual Physiology Series: SimNerv, SimMuscle, SimVessel, SimHeart, SimPatch* - English version), €2,680.00 (complete *Virtual Physiology Series* - German version); special price for multiple copies and site licence on request. Note that prices for the German version include the German VAT, while those for the English version do not (if no VAT Registration Number is provided, 16% VAT should be added to them). Free demo versions available on CD-ROM
Note: Readers of this book are entitled to a special reduction in price from Thieme; please cite *from Guinea Pig to Computer Mouse* when ordering
Source: Georg Thieme Verlag; Dr. Hans A. Braun (University of Marburg, Germany)

Sponges – Cellular Motility and Co-ordination

See description of this title under VIDEO.

Language: French
Year of production: Original film made in 1978
Medium: CD-ROM (MPEG4 format)
System requirements: Windows Media 7 (or Windows Player 6.4 for WinNT4 and Win95)
Price: Individual use: €15.00 (Europe), €30.00 (rest of the world); Institutional use: €30.00 (Europe), €45.00 (rest of the world)
Note: The original title of this program is *Motricité cellulaire et coordination chez les éponges*
Source: SFRS

Squid Axon

This interactive program simulates a number of experiments which may be performed on the isolated giant axon of the squid to investigate the biophysical properties of nerve. The *Methods* section uses a combination of text and high-resolution colour graphics to describe the preparation, the apparatus used to record the resting potential of the axon and the techniques of current and voltage clamping. The *Experiments* section is highly interactive and may be used to investigate: the resting potential (where students may vary the concentrations of Na^+, K^+ and Cl^- in the extra-cellular fluid [ECF] and axoplasm, then record changes in the resting membrane potential) and the action potential (where students may design experimental protocols which allow them to perform current clamp and voltage clamp experiments). With current clamp experiments the ECF concentrations of Na^+, K^+ and Cl^- may be varied individually and single or paired stimuli applied; records of voltage or conductance changes are then displayed. With voltage clamp experiments the student may set a membrane holding potential and up to 3 command potentials to voltage clamp the axon and record membrane current or conductance changes. The intracellular fluid [ICF] and ECF concentrations of Na^+, and ICF K^+ may be changed and the action of tetrodotoxin and tetraethy-lammonium investigated. Results are derived from widely accepted algorithms (Goldman-Hodgkin-Katz, Hodgkin & Huxley models) and displayed on a simulated oscilloscope screen from which students are able to take accurate measurements.

Medium: 3.5" disk; CD-ROM
System requirements: MS-DOS
Price: £120.00 (departmental multiuser/network licence; includes documentation - program manual and, where appropriate, student's workbook and tutor's notes - and postage)
Source: Sheffield BioScience Programs

Study of the Voluntary Striated Muscle

See description of this title under VIDEO.

Language: French
Year of production: Original film made in 1959
Medium: CD-ROM (MPEG4 format)
System requirements: Windows Media 7 (or Windows Player 6.4 for WinNT4 and Win95)
Price: Individual use: €15.00 (Europe), €30.00 (rest of the world); Institutional use: €30.00 (Europe), €45.00 (rest of the world)
Note: The original title of this program is *Étude du muscle strié volontaire*
Source: SFRS

Synaptic Transmission in the CNS

This program aims to teach the basic principles of chemical transmission at synapses in the CNS. It is divided into several sections accessed from the main menu: *Introduction*; *Neuronal structure* (structure of the neurone, sites of excitation, neurotransmitter chemicals and their chemical characterisation, basis of resting and action potentials); *Synaptic transmission* (the transmission process, synthesis, storage, release, termination of effects); *Neurotransmitters and postsynaptic receptors* (ligand-gated ion channels and G-protein coupled receptors); *Neurotransmitters and neuronal excitability* (generation and properties of EPSPs and IPSPs and their interaction to determine excitability).

Year of production: Revised 2002
Medium: CD-ROM; world wide web
System requirements: CD-ROM version Windows only; internet version both Windows and Macintosh
Price: £75.00 (UK Higher Education only); £250.00 (others). Prices include full multiuser site licence for unlimited copies, tutor's guide, and telephone support. For internet version price contact the source
Source: British Pharmacological Society

Taxis, Narcosis and Electrical Tetany in Fish

See description of this title under VIDEO.

Language: French, English, Spanish
Year of production: Original film made in 1963
Medium: CD-ROM (MPEG4 format)
System requirements: Windows Media 7 (or Windows Player 6.4 for WinNT4 and Win95)
Price: Individual use: €15.00 (Europe), €30.00 (rest of the world); Institutional use: €30.00 (Europe), €45.00 (rest of the world)
Note: The original title of this program is *Taxies, narcose et tétanies électriques chez les poissons*
Source: SFRS

When contacting producers and distributors,
please cite *from Guinea Pig to Computer Mouse*

Veterinary Physiology

This is the first comprehensive veterinary physiology multimedia CD-ROM. It aims to serve 3 needs. First, it can be used as a teaching material in the lecture theatre by the professor, since the material follows the 'writing with chalk on a blackboard' principle. Second, it can serve the needs of a student who prefers learning independently, since all the sketches can be unfolded step by step throughout the material. Third, it allows self-testing, since it contains an extensive multiple-choice question repertory for each chapter. Based on an experience of more than 6 years in multi-media teaching, the author included approximately 900 pages of textual information, 1,000 figures that can be displayed step by step, 200 animations, 60 short video-clips, 50 summary tables on physiological data, 2,000 multiple-choice questions. Fast and easy navigation and orientation are ensured by a series of tools including the quick-map, the glossary, the list of abbreviations, the navigation buttons, and the help and info sections.

Language: Hungarian, English, German, Spanish
Medium: CD-ROM
System requirements: Windows 3.x/95 (best), Windows 98 (not so good), Windows NT (not recommended); minimum 2 MB HDD space, mins. 16 MB RAM, mins. 8X CD-ROM drive speed recommended
Price: €35.00 (Spanish); US$60.00 (other languages); excl. postage. Special rates available for large orders
Source: Prof. Dr. Péter Rudas (Szent István University, Hungary)

VIDEO

Calcium Waves in Isolated Cardiomyocytes

Demonstration and comparison of intracellular calcium waves with digitised fluorescence microscopic images. It shows how conduction and contraction profiles can be altered by temperature and pharmaceutics.

Language: German, English
Year of production: 1990
Format: VHS PAL, SECAM, NTSC
Running time: 13 mins.
Price: €25.05
Source: IWF Wissen und Medien gGmbH

Capillary Circulation in the Frog Web

The circulation of the frog web is examined under a microscope noting the difference between the arterial and venous flow. Vasoconstriction resulting from the administration of adrenalin is also shown.

Year of production: 1982
Format: VHS PAL
Running time: 15 mins.
Price: £25.00 (different for bulk copies and other standards and formats)
Source: Leeds University Television

 Cardiovascular Physiology

This video shows various experiments on the isolated heart of a rat, and the *in vivo* (dog) model of a number of common heart disorders. High-quality video recordings demonstrate the effect of the presynaptic system, represented by the vagus nerve. The heart fibrilation condition is demonstrated using a dog and the effects of heart massage and electrical defibrillation. All experiments demonstrate both physiological effects and the ECG output of the demonstrated conditions. The film was intentionally produced without background narration, since it was demonstrated that students pay more attention when the explanation is given by the teacher, and not the video, but it does have text labels.

Year of production: 2000
Format: VHS PAL
Price: On request
Source: Dr. Gabriel Shavit (Tel Aviv University, Israel)

 Control of Ventilation: Effects of Chemo and Mechano Receptors

Experiments demonstrate the effects on respiratory control of central and peripheral chemoreceptors, as well as those of intrapulmonary stretch receptors. The effects on ventilation of increased carbon dioxide (hypercapnia), decreased oxygen (hypoxia), and the two stimuli combined are documented in the first half of the video. In the second half, the effects of the intrapulmonary stretch receptors in producing the Hering-Breuer reflex are examined. This reflex is studied in the intact animal and after bilateral vagotomy.

Year of production: 1986
Format: VHS NTSC, PAL
Running time: 40 mins.
Price: US$50.00
Source: University of California (UC Davis)

Electrical Activity of the Isolated Nerve of a Batrachian

After showing the dissection of a frog, and the isolation, removal and placement of its sciatic nerve in a tank, this film presents the experimental device which allows the stimulation of the nerve and the recording of its response. Several experiments are then shown, illustrating the study of biphasic action potentials, excitation threshold, maximal excitation, refractory period, and the effects of various chemical agents on the electrical response amplitude.

Language: French, English
Year of production: 1962
Format: VHS PAL, SECAM, NTSC. Also available on CD-ROM (see under SOFTWARE)
Running time: 18 mins.
Price: Individual use: €15.00 (Europe), €30.00 (rest of the world); Institutional use: €30.00 (Europe), €45.00 (rest of the world); the NTSC format is available at an additional cost of €15.00
Note: The original title of this program is *Activité électrique du nerf isolé de batracien*
Source: SFRS

Electrical Activity of the Myocardium and Transmembrane Ionic Currents

This film presents the experimental recording technique of transmembrane potentials using the 'voltage clamp' and the 'current clamp' methods. Atrial action potential phases are identified by recording the effects of a solution with different ionic concentrations and the effects of various pharmacodynamic agents, and traces recorded on an oscilloscope with memory and explanation of results through animation.

Language: French
Year of production: 1970
Format: VHS PAL, SECAM, NTSC. Also available on CD-ROM (see under SOFTWARE)
Running time: 36 mins.
Price: Individual use: €15.00 (Europe), €30.00 (rest of the world); Institutional use: €30.00 (Europe), €45.00 (rest of the world); the NTSC format is available at an additional cost of €15.00
Note: The original title of this program is *Activité électrique du myocarde et les courants ioniques transmembranaires*
Source: SFRS

Equine Foot Studies

This program uses slow motion video, X-ray images and dissections to show the range of motion of the equine foot and the effect of various biomechanical forces, including hoof testers. A hydraulic press recreates the downward movement of the fetlock during weight bearing and shows expansion and contraction of the heels. Radiopaque dyes and live action X-ray image intensification are used to show how blood circulates within the foot and the venous return mechanism. Computerised subtraction angiography clearly shows the pathways of the circulation during pastern extension, and period of sole pressure. The effect on the circulation of shoeing with a heart-bar shoe and a raised heel is also shown.

Year of production: 1992
Format: VHS PAL
Running time: 23 mins.
Price: £30.00 (excl. VAT and postage)
Source: Royal Veterinary College

Experimental Study of Gastric Complex Motility in Sheep

This program is a descriptive study of the gastric complex in ruminant herbivores. It details the study technique of mechanical and electrical phenomena linked to contraction, the analytical examination of pre-stomachs motor cycle and the nervous and humoral regulation of mechanical phenomena.

Language: French, English, Spanish
Year of production: 1967
Format: VHS PAL, SECAM, NTSC. Also available on CD-ROM (see under SOFTWARE)
Running time: 22 mins.
Price: Individual use: €15.00 (Europe), €30.00 (rest of the world); Institutional use: €30.00 (Europe), €45.00 (rest of the world); the NTSC format is available at an additional cost of €15.00
Note: The original title of this program is *Étude expérimentale de la motricité du complexe gastrique chez le mouton*
Source: SFRS

Experiments on Impulse Generation and Impulse Conduction in the Frog Heart

This film begins with a short introduction to the anatomy of the heart and the physiology of electrical generation and conduction. The first and second Stannius ligatures interrupt the conduction, which leads to the secondary and tertiary pacemaker centres taking over. Electrical stimuli of the ventricle demonstrate that the heart muscle - unlike the skeletal muscle - cannot be tetanised. When the sympathetic and parasympathetic parts of the vagal nerve are electrically stimulated the characteristic changes in impulse generation and impulse conduction of the heart can be observed.

Language: German, English
Year of production: 1992
Format: VHS PAL, SECAM, NTSC
Running time: 14 mins.
Price: €25.05
Source: IWF Wissen und Medien gGmbH

Experiments on Single Ventricular Myocytes

Alterations in the action potentials of isolated myocytes are investigated under different experimental conditions: patch-clamp and voltage-clamp methods, generation of an action potential, effect of cadmium and adrenalin, dependence of action potentials on stimulation frequency, absolute and relative time of refraction.

Language: German, English
Year of production: 1993
Format: VHS PAL, SECAM, NTSC
Running time: 18 mins.
Price: €30.17
Source: IWF Wissen und Medien gGmbH

Experiments on the Isolated Heart of a Rabbit in the Langendorff Apparatus

An isolated, still-beating heart is perfused with solutions of adrenalin, acetylcholine and verapamil. The alterations in contractility and heart rate are shown and discussed. Finally the cooling of the sinus node (primary pacemaker) and its typical reactions are demonstrated.

Language: German, English
Year of production: 1990
Format: VHS PAL, SECAM, NTSC
Running time: 13 mins.
Price: €25.05
Source: IWF Wissen und Medien gGmbH

Experiments on the Physiology of Heart and Circulation of a Rabbit

The experiments on an intact rabbit thorax illustrate control mechanisms of heart and circulation function. ECG, frequency and blood pressure are constantly monitored. The following procedures are performed: clamping of both carotid arteries, electrical stimulation of the vagal nerves, and injection of acetylcholine, adrenalin and verapamil.

Language: German, English
Year of production: 1990
Format: VHS PAL, SECAM, NTSC
Running time: 19 mins.
Price: €30.17
Source: IWF Wissen und Medien gGmbH

Filtration in Bivalve Molluscs

Few films have been made on the biology of bivalve molluscs. This one shows a collection of several Mediterranean species and their behaviour in an aquarium where the conditions are close to those of the natural environment. One sees the molluscs bury themselves and use siphons to breathe and to eat particles in suspension. The film captures for the first time, in several species, the formation of a mucous film moving along the branchiae and serving as a filter. This mucous film is evidenced in many electron scanning microscope photographs, which show significant structural differences between the mucous filters of the 6 species studied.

Language: French
Year of production: 1999
Format: VHS PAL, SECAM, NTSC. Also available on CD-ROM (see under SOFTWARE)
Running time: 16 mins.
Price: Individual use: €15.00 (Europe), €30.00 (rest of the world); Institutional use: €30.00 (Europe), €45.00 (rest of the world); the NTSC format is available at an additional cost of €15.00
Note: The original title of this program is *La Filtration chez les mollusques bivalves*
Source: SFRS

 Fundamentals of Blood Gas Analysis: Collection, Measurement and Interpretation

This video describes how blood gas analysers work, how samples for blood gas analysis should be collected and handled, and presents a series of experiments that affect gas exchanged and interprets the changes in blood gas valves that result from these manipulations.

Year of production: 1987
Format: VHS NTSC, PAL
Running time: 33 mins.
Price: US$50.00
Source: University of California (UC Davis)

 Intestinal Motility and Its Regulation

This program focuses on the various types of intestinal movement. It presents experiments performed on an isolated intestine, as well as on a living animal – the recording of contractions, regulation of motility, action of the sympathetic, parasympathetic and extrinsic systems, and intestinal reflexes.

Language: French
Year of production: 1957
Format: VHS PAL, SECAM, NTSC. Also available on CD-ROM (see under SOFTWARE)

Running time: 23 mins.
Price: Individual use: €15.00 (Europe), €30.00 (rest of the world); Institutional use: €30.00 (Europe), €45.00(rest of the world); the NTSC format is available at an additional cost of €15.00
Note: The original title of this program is *La motricité intestinale et sa régulation*
Source: SFRS

[An] Investigation of Active Transport

A great deal of research is being carried out on the mechanism of the sodium pump, which maintains the differences across cell membranes of a relatively high concentration of K^+ ions and a very low concentration of Na^+ ions inside the cell and the reverse in the fluid bathing the cells. The frog skin is an example of a tissue which has such pumps on only one side of the cells. The experiments in this program demonstrate the uptake of radioactive sodium (^{24}Na) through the skin of a frog's hindlegs, right side out and everted; a counter determines the amount of sodium taken up. The second experiment measures the electrical potential across the skin. The third experiment shows the effect of inhibiting the sodium transport on the transepithelial potential. The drug ouabain - a specific inhibitor of the enzyme Na^+/K^+ ATP-ase (which constitutes the sodium pump) - is added to both the outside and the inside of the skin and readings of the potential are taken. The fourth experiment illustrates the effect of a hormone produced in the frog's pituitary gland.

Format: VHS NTSC
Running time: 15 mins.
Price: US$59.95
Source: Films for the Humanities and Sciences (United States and Canada only)

Locomotion of the Horse

Using slow-motion photography, the flexion and extension patterns of the horse's joints are demonstrated at various phases of locomotion. The standard bred amble, pace and trot, as well as the thoroughbred walk, trot, canter, and gallop are shown from the side and front viewpoints.

Format: VHS NTSC
Running time: 18.30 mins.
Price: US$95.00; other formats available at additional cost
Source: Michigan State University

Motility of the Gastric System of Ruminants

The anatomy and motility of the gastric system of the goat and the sheep, shown radiographically, endoscopically and in animated film.

Language: German, English
Year of production: 1979
Format: VHS PAL, SECAM, NTSC
Running time: 29 mins.
Price: €30.17
Source: IWF Wissen und Medien gGmbH

Muscle Contractility

Compares fast and slow contracting muscles of the cat, using isometric recordings integrated with muscle histochemistry. To illustrate determination of resting length, a length-tension curve is constructed for the medial gastrocnemius muscle, which is then compared in detail to the soleus by means of isometric recordings.

Year of production: 1976
Format: VHS NTSC, PAL
Running time: 19 mins.
Price: US$50.00
Source: University of California (UC Davis)

[The] Nature of the Nerve Impulse

What makes a locust jump when a shadow - for example, of a hand - passes over it? One of the most thoroughly studied of all insect neurones is the descending contralateral movement detector (DCMD) of the locust. The DCMD runs from the 'brain' to the metathoracic ganglion, and responds to movement in the visual field. These experiments use a female locust with legs and wings removed, which is secured by the dorsal surface of the thorax to the shaft of the electrodes by means of beeswax. The locust's field of vision is restricted, visual stimulus provided by passing a circular spot on a strip of white paper in front of the locust's eye, and the locust's response measured. The experiments show the effect of different speeds of movement of a spot across the locust's visual field. The resulting data provides a useful index of the behaviour of locusts as demonstrated in the capacity to respond to different sizes of spots and different speeds.

Format: VHS NTSC
Running time: 15 mins.
Price: US$59.95
Source: Films for the Humanities and Sciences (United States and Canada only)

When contacting producers and distributors,
please cite *from Guinea Pig to Computer Mouse*

Nerve Physiology & Pharmacology

See under 'Pharmacology'.

Normal Swallowing in the Dog

The 3 phases of the swallowing process - oropharyngeal, oesophageal and gastro-oesophageal - are thoroughly explained using illustrations, anatomical prosections and videofluoroscopy. The latter is presented in real time and ultra-slow motion so that all muscular movements may be clearly observed.

Year of production: 1978
Format: VHS NTSC, PAL
Running time: 22 mins.
Price: US$50.00
Source: University of California (UC Davis)

Properties of Isolated Cardiac Muscle

The experiment is performed first on an isolated perfused rabbit heart and then on an isolated atrial strip. In both experiments the apparatus is first described and effects of the alteration of various physical parameters, and of the administration of several drugs, is then demonstrated.

Year of production: 1982
Format: VHS PAL
Running time: 39 mins.
Price: £40.00 (different for bulk copies and other standards and formats)
Note: A short version of this film (12 mins.) is also available for £25.00
Source: Leeds University Television

Rabbit Arterial Blood Pressure - Extrinsic Innervation, Pharmacodynamic Agents

Video detailing the preparation of the experimental material (in particular, the Ludwing manometer); anaesthesia of the rabbit; filling the manometer; dissection: carotid artery and innervation; cannulation and recording (total pressure); stimulation of the vagus nerve; stimulation of the Cyon nerve; stimulation of the sympathetic nerve; adrenaline injections; and acetylcholine injections.

Language: French
Year of production: 1974
Format: VHS PAL, SECAM, NTSC. Also available on CD-ROM (see under SOFTWARE)
Running time: 27 mins.
Price: Individual use: €15.00 (Europe), €30.00 (rest of the world); Institutional use: €30.00 (Europe), €45.00 (rest of the world); the NTSC format is available at an additional cost of €15.00
Note: The original title of this program is *La Pression artérielle du lapin - Innervation extrinsèque, agents pharmacodynamiques*
Source: SFRS

Recording the Electrical and Mechanical Activity of the Frog Heart *In Situ*

Simultaneous recordings of mechanogram and electrocardiogram (ECG), of mechanogram and lesion potentials, and of mechanogram and intracellular electrical activity of a frog heart *in situ* allows the identification of the ECG's main phases.

Language: French
Year of production: 1969
Format: VHS PAL, SECAM, NTSC. Also available on CD-ROM (see under SOFTWARE)
Running time: 11 mins.
Price: Individual use: €15.00 (Europe), €30.00 (rest of the world); Institutional use: €30.00 (Europe), €45.00 (rest of the world); the NTSC format is available at an additional cost of €15.00
Note: The original title of this program is *Enregistrement de l'activité électrique et mécanique du coeur de grenouille in situ*
Source: SFRS

Renal Microcirculation

Demonstration of the renal microcirculation using the model of the hydronephrotic kidney in the small mammal: dissection of the hydronephrotic kidney, visualisation of the blood vessels by passage of dye, alterations of vessel lumen after electrical stimulation and application of angiotensin II, and visualisation of glomerular microcirculation by fluorescence marked erythrocytes and dextran.

Language: German
Year of production: 1996
Format: VHS PAL, SECAM, NTSC
Running time: 12 mins.
Price: €25.05
Source: IWF Wissen und Medien gGmbH

Reptiles and Amphibians

Reptiles and amphibians are important in the evolutionary history of life because they bridged the gap between aquatic and terrestrial ecosystems. This program deals with reptilian physiology and behaviour and with the natural history of amphibians - amazing semi-aquatic creatures that can even withstand total freezing. It also broaches the fascinating yet unresolved question of the extinction of the dinosaurs.

Year of production: 1990
Format: VHS NTSC
Running time: 23 mins.
Price: US$89.95
Source: Films for the Humanities and Sciences (United States and Canada only)

Sponges - Cellular Motility and Co-ordination

General presentation of the structure and physiology of sponges, analysed in relation to the motor behaviour of cells and tissues. Includes movement and differentiation of cells during the morpho-genesis (action of various drugs); water circulation facilitated by choanocytes (flagellate cells); and physiology and structural support of contractile, rhythmic and spontaneous activity. Filmed in accelerated microcinematography.

Language: French
Year of production: 1978
Format: VHS PAL, SECAM, NTSC. Also available on CD-ROM (see under SOFTWARE)
Running time: 24 mins.
Price: Individual use: €15.00 (Europe), €30.00 (rest of the world); Institutional use: €30.00 (Europe), €45.00 (rest of the world); the NTSC format is available at an additional cost of €15.00
Note: The original title of this program is *Motricité cellulaire et coordination chez les éponges*
Source: SFRS

Structure and Function of the Skeletal Muscle

Video includes preparation of a single muscle fibre of the frog semitendinosus muscle, electrical stimulation of the muscle, rising stimulation intensity results in different contraction response (subthreshold, supramaximal and tetanus).

Language: German, English
Year of production: 1977
Format: VHS PAL, SECAM, NTSC

Running time: 18 mins.
Price: €30.17
Source: IWF Wissen und Medien gGmbH

Study of the Voluntary Striated Muscle

The voluntary striated muscle is studied using mechanical phenomena (stimulation study methods, variation of stimulus intensity and frequency, muscle elasticity, fatigue of the isolated muscle) and electrical phenomena (electromyography in the human). Also details neuro-muscular transmission, and shows curarisation of a frog and a rabbit.

Language: French
Year of production: 1959
Format: VHS PAL, SECAM, NTSC. Also available on CD-ROM (see under SOFTWARE)
Running time: 30 mins.
Price: Individual use: €15.00 (Europe), €30.00 (rest of the world); Institutional use: €30.00 (Europe), €45.00 (rest of the world); the NTSC format is available at an additional cost of €15.00
Note: The original title of this program is *Étude du muscle strié volontaire*
Source: SFRS

Taxis, Narcosis and Electrical Tetany in Fish

The reactions of fish placed in an homogenous electrical field depend upon their position in relation to the field polarity, and upon the potentials to which they are subjected. In this video, the main reactions of the trout and eel are identified, with an explanation of the underlying neurophysiological mechanism, and the identification of the nervous or muscular structures involved through transverse sectioning of the central nervous system.

Language: French, English, Spanish
Year of production: 1963
Format: VHS PAL, SECAM, NTSC. Also available on CD-ROM (see under SOFTWARE)
Running time: 19 mins.
Price: Individual use: €15.00 (Europe), €30.00 (rest of the world); Institutional use: €30.00 (Europe), €45.00 (rest of the world); the NTSC format is available at an additional cost of €15.00
Note: The original title of this program is *Taxies, narcose et tétanies électriques chez les poissons*
Source: SFRS

When contacting producers and distributors,
please cite *from Guinea Pig to Computer Mouse*

MODELS, MANNEKINS, SIMULATORS

   ## Biopac Student Lab

More than just a data recorder, the *Biopac Student Lab* is an integrated set of hardware, software, and documentation that guides students through a series of teaching sessions which illustrate fundamental physiological principles. It comes complete with 17 built-in lessons that require no additional programming, each supported by on-line detailed series of instructions that complement the Lab Manual and guide the student through from start to finish and is always on screen. Lessons cover the following topics: electromyography; electroencephalography; electrocardiography and plethysmography; periferic pressure pulse; respiratory physiology; galvanic skin response and the polygraph; electro-oculogram; reaction time; biofeedback - relaxation and arousal; aerobic exercise physiology - cardiovascular and respiratory adjustments; heat exchange. Students attach electrodes and transducers to themselves (or their lab partners) as instructed by the lesson text window, while on-screen measurement tools allow them to analyse data simply by clicking a mouse button. During the lessons the user can stop and measure data to determine wave parameters like: peak to peak, maximum, minimum, slope, standard deviation, frequency, BPM, Delta time, mean, area and integral. In addition to the *Biopac Student Lab* lessons, the system also includes the powerful PRO software, which allows students to create their own experiments. The *Biopac Student Lab* is suitable for human and animal studies, is non-invasive and safe, and is compatible with other programs.

Medium: Apparatus and CD-ROM
System requirements: System configurations: ULTIMATE - can perform all the lessons in the Laboratory Manual; ADVANCED - can perform 14 lessons; BASIC - can only perform a subset of the Laboratory Manual lessons. The lesson descriptions indicate which system is required. An Upgrade Kit is available, to bring the system up to the next configuration. Computer requirements: any PC (USB) running Windows 98/ME/2000/XP; Macs (USB) with OS 8.6 to 9.1
Note: The *Biopac* software is available in English, French, Spanish and Japanese. Italian is under production, and Chinese is also planned
Price: Starts at US$2,995.00
Source: Biopac Systems

   ## Neurosimulator

The *Neurosimulator* system has been designed to realistically simulate the functions and electrical characteristics of neuronal synapses. It comprises up to 4 neuron units (NU), one operating unit (OU) and one signal lead and several connecting cords. The OU comprises the power supply for up to 4 NU, 3 touch simulators with a variable simulating intensity and an optic sensor. The NU simulates a general nerve cell with an apical dendrite and its synaptic contacts, a cell body (soma) and a nerve fibre (axon) with myelin sheaths and a Ranvier's node. The dendrite comprises exciting, inhibiting, presynaptic and Hebb's synapses, marked by colour-coded sockets. Here the axons end in presynaptic buttons, represented together with a part of the (afferent) fibre providing the signal. The connection between the (efferent) axon of a NU which leads away or the stimulus output socket of the OU and a synapse is established by means of a white cable inserted into the desired synapse socket. The height of the intracellular potential is shown by the luminous intensity of the diode at the electrode point, whilst the action (axon) potential can be made audible with the aid of an integrated acoustic monitor. This allows - similar to what is happening in a neuro-physiological laboratory - a direct evaluation of the cell activity. The neuron units can be combined to form a network so that the characteristics of nerve cells are being represented and studied as a group, and the performances of natural neuronal networks are being demonstrated in a very comprehensive way.

Medium: Simulator
Price: €551.00 (NU); €493.00 (OU); €19.60 (signal lead); €2,519.00 (equipment set 4NU + 1OU)
Source: Phywe Systeme

 TeleHeart - an Exosomatic ECG Biotelemetry System

This new system, developed by Koullis Pitsillides Consulting (USA) together with Prof. Michael Axelsson at the University of Gothenburg (Sweden), replaces and improves upon conventional physiology practicals where standard ECG equipment was used to record ECG traces from both humans (students) and frogs. Using telemetry technology and custom-written software, cardiovascular parameters such as resting heart rate, orthostatic reaction - barostatic reflexes, heart rate changes during mental work and exercise, and the diving reflex, can be determined. The *Exosomatic ECG Biotelemetry System* comes in a sturdy case and consists primarily of an ECG/G-force biotelemetry transmitter unit (TX-unit), and a receiver unit (RX-unit) which can be connected to a desktop or laptop computer, or other digital recorder. The TX-unit amplifies the ECG signal from two electrodes placed on the subject. For investigating G (gravitational) forces, a small G-force unit is used. The output from the RX-unit consists of the raw ECG signal, the pulse for each R wave and the X- and Y-axis G-forces. For investigating heart rate, the pulse signal is fed into a computer running the *TeleHeart* software. The beat-to-beat heart rate will be plotted on the screen. To visualise the raw ECG signal or to record G-forces, an analogue-to-digital (A-D) converter is used. As the subject does not need to be physically linked to the recording unit, the system is highly flexible. It has a range of at least 100m in an open environment, and can be used in the field, for face-to-face teaching, and for problem-based and distance learning by students.

Medium: Apparatus and CD-ROM
System requirements: For acquisition, transmission and reception of data - the *Exosomatic ECG Biotelemetry System* (ECG electrodes, TX-unit, G-force unit, RX-unit, connecting cables, 2 antennas); for data processing using the *TeleHeart* software - PC with Pentium processor, monitor with 1024 x 768 resolution, one free serial or parallel port (COM1, COM2, or LPT1), A-D converter (optional, for raw ECG and G-force signals)
Price: On request
Source: Koullis Pitsillides Consulting

WORLD WIDE WEB

Action Potential Laboratory

http://www.neurophys.wisc.edu/~cai/software/hhsimu/hhsimu.html
University of Wisconsin Medical School, USA

BioInteractive

http://www.biointeractive.org
Howard Hughes Medical Institute, USA

Biology Labs On-Line

http://biologylab.awlonline.com
California State University system and Benjamin Cummings, USA

Interactive Physiology (IPweb)

http://www.interactivephysiology.com
A.D.A.M. and Benjamin Cummings, USA (see this title also under SOFTWARE)

PhysioEx 4.0

http://www.physioex.com
Benjamin Cummings, USA (see this title also under SOFTWARE)

10. Miscellaneous

SOFTWARE

Biodisc Cell Biology

Two collections of microscope slide images that provides teachers and students with a tool to use along with, or as replacement for, microscope slides. The *First collection* (available for either Windows or Macintosh) contains 4,748 images covering general botany, general zoology, comparative histology, human pathology, and wood technology, while the *Second collection* (available in hybrid Windows/Macintosh version) contains 684 images and covers Monera, Protista, Fungi, Plants, Zoology, and Histology.

Year of production: 1995
Medium: CD-ROM
System requirements: Windows 95 or later, Macintosh OS 7.5 or later
Price: US$50.00 (*First collection*); US$25.00 (*Second collection*)
Source: Nasco

BioLab: Fly

A perfect introduction to Mendelian genetics, *BioLab: Fly* is a virtual fruit fly genetics lab covering F1, F, and sex-linked crosses. Equipped with *Fly Breeder* that allows students to analyse 26 different characteristics. Also available as part of the *BioLab Virtual Lab Series Package* from Carolina Biological Supply.

Medium: CD-ROM
System requirements: Windows 95, Macintosh OS 7.5, or later
Price: Carolina Biological Supply: US$49.00 (single), US$209.00 (lab pack of 5), US$369.00 (lab pack of 10), US$899.00 (lab pack of 30); Neo/Sci: US$59.95 (single CD-ROM), US$199.95 (lab pack of 5)
Source: Carolina Biological Supply; Neo/Sci

When contacting producers and distributors,
please cite *from Guinea Pig to Computer Mouse*

Biologica - A Survey of Biology

A tremendous resource of photographic images, videoclips, animations, diagrams, and more - all supported by extensive background information. Covers the entire breadth of life science including cells, genetics, evolution, plants, and animals. Videoclips provide detailed information of preparation techniques and procedures for microscopy while animation is used to elaborate on basic biochemical processes. The program also includes an extensive glossary of science terms, electronic notepad, and comprehensive tutorial and assessment systems.

Year of production: 1999
Medium: CD-ROM
System requirements: Windows only (all versions)
Price: US$99.95 (single); US$199.95 (lab pack of 5)
Source: Nasco

Biology Simulations

This disk contains 4 programs designed to allow pupils to plan investigations, to record, display and interpret data, and to experience practical experimental situations which are otherwise too sensitive or time-consuming to be available in schools. 1. *Plant mineral requirements* allows the student to supply plants with various combinations of mineral ions, following which various quantitative comparisons can be made to a control plant. 2. *Metabolism* allows the metabolic rate of four different animals (2 homeotherms and 2 poikilotherms) of chosen mass to be studied over a range of temperatures. It introduces all the experimental details and develops the recording skills associated with respirometry work. 3. *Quadrat sampling in ecology* illustrates how, by varying the size and number of random quadrats, approximations to the density of organisms in the wild may be achieved, and the distribution pattern of those organisms may be deduced. 4. *Population genetics* allows the student to discover the changes in gene frequency in a population when factors such as population size, strength of selection, and/or dominance are varied. All the programs make use of full graphic facilities, and have been compiled and tested by experienced teachers.

Medium: 3.5" disk
System requirements: MS-DOS; Acorn
Price: Single user - £38.50 / ~ US$59.68 (excl. VAT), £45.24 / ~ €77.00 (incl. VAT); network version (MS-DOS version only) - £96.00 / ~ US$148.80 (excl. VAT), £112.80 / ~ €192.00 (incl. VAT); site licence - £115.50 / ~ US$179.03 (excl. VAT), £135.71 / ~ €231.00 (incl. VAT). Prices incl. VAT apply to orders from the EU, prices excl. VAT apply to orders from the rest of the world
Source: AVP

When contacting producers and distributors,
please cite *from Guinea Pig to Computer Mouse*

Biology: The Study of Life

A lively introduction to the fascinating science of biology. Full-colour graphics and special effects are used to illustrate important scientific concepts such as what it means to be alive, how observations can be used in reasoning, the process of developing a hypothesis, and more. A variety of interactive tutorials reinforce concepts such as identifying signs of life and the correct sequence of events when applying scientific methodology. Topics include: *Signs of life; Themes in biology including energy, systems and interactions; Stability; Evolution; Unity within diversity; Inductive and deductive reasoning; Scientific methodology;* and *From hypothesis to theory.*

Medium: CD-ROM
System requirements: Windows (all versions); Macintosh (all versions)
Price: Single user - £55.00 / US$85.25 (excl. VAT), £64.63 / ~ €109.87 (incl. VAT); 10 user network or 5 user multipack - £170.00 / ~ US$263.50 (excl. VAT), £199.75 / ~ €339.58 (incl. VAT); 15 user network or 10 user multipack - £285.00 / ~ US$441.75 (excl. VAT), £334.88 / ~ €569.30 (incl. VAT); 30 user network or 15 user multipack - £400.00 / ~ US$620.00 (excl. VAT), £470.00 / ~ €799.00 (incl. VAT). Prices incl. VAT apply to orders from the EU, prices excl. VAT apply to orders from the rest of the world
Source: AVP

[A] Closer Look at Pondlife

Using close-up photography, this CD-ROM brings students face-to-face with the inner workings of a freshwater pond, the myriad creatures and plants that reside there, and the dynamic interactions that go on beneath the surface. The disk features a library of reference information, images, illustrations, clip art, videoclips and more. *Section 1* provides an overview of ecosystems in general and the pond ecosystem in particular, and introduces the life forms that reside there. *Section 2* delves into microscopic pond life; it covers the different types of cells, eubacteria, cyanobacteria, euglenoids, diatoms, desmids, dinoflagellates, flagellates, amoebas, ciliates, suctorians and green protists. *Section 3* presents pond plants and information about how they grow and reproduce, and what lives on and among them. *Section 4* presents the small invertebrate life that is so plentiful amid the shallow water vegetation and pond sediments; it covers rotifers, gastrotrichs, hydras, flatworms, nematodes, bryozoans, microannelids, cladocerans (water fleas), and microcrustaceans. *Section 5* introduces food chains and trophic levels, photosynthesisers, herbivores, carnivores, omnivores and decomposers. *Section 6* provides field trip and laboratory tips. *Section 7* is a unique curriculum that provides the means to link the vast library of resources to key, curriculum-based science topics.

Medium: CD-ROM
System requirements: Windows, Macintosh
Price: US$99.95 (single user); US$199.95 (lab pack of 5); US$659.95 (lab pack of 20); US$239.95 (network version - single server, one building)
Source: Educational Images

Complete Survey of the Animal Kingdom

This exhaustive, award-winning multimedia review of the great variety of animal life found on Earth provides in one encyclopaedic package a library full of carefully organised information. There are 10 programs on 10 CD-ROMs, containing thousands of images - eye-stopping photographs of live animals augmented by graphics where appropriate. Each program is available individually or as part of a series. Scientific names are provided.

Complete Survey of the Invertebrates

- *Part I: Sponges, Anemones, Corals and Flatworms*. By surveying the protozoa and parazoa and introducing the most primitive metazoans, this program presents the transition from simple unicellular animals, to colonial forms, to complex multicellular creatures. Photographic coverage includes volvox, euglenas, amoebas, ciliates, numerous sponges, *Cnidaria*, nematocysts, anemonies, jellyfish, hydras, man-of-war, corals, flatworms, tapeworms, round worms, rotifers, bryozoans and brachiopods.

- *Part II: Molluscs, Segmented Worms and Minor Phyla*. Presents detailed coverage of such molluscs as chitons, abalones, limpets, cowries, periwinkles, conches, cones, whelks, murexes, nudibranchs, sea hares, land snails, slugs, bivalves, octopuses, nautiluses and squids; segmented worms such as featherduster, myxicola, earthworm and leech; and tardigrades or waterbears.

- *Part III: Insects*. Illustrates the great range and variety of insect adaptations, elaborately details their development and anatomy, and portrays their great diversity. Photographic coverage of live insects is very comprehensive and wide-ranging. Among the many insects and insect stages covered in this program are beetles, silverfish, springtails, caddisflies, dragonflies, mayflies, grasshoppers, cockroaches, mantis, walking stick, termites, lice, true bugs, cicadas, aphids, ladybird, dobsonfly, long-horned pine sawyer beetle, dung beetle, moths, butterflies, mosquitoes, maggots, horsefly eye, fleas, bees, egg, larva, pupa, cocoon and caterpillar. Differences in development and types of metamorphosis provide the basis for insect classification into subclasses. These variations are presented here as well. In addition, the physical and functional differences that occur in social insects like termites, ants and bees resulting in castes, are also detailed.

- *Part IV: Non-insect Arthropods and Echinoderms*. This program surveys the remaining 11 classes of arthropods. There are about 88,000 species of non-insect arthropods. Some are aquatic, some terrestrial, but unlike the insects, none can fly. These include: krill, shrimp, lobster, crayfish, crabs, spiders, scorpions, mites, ticks, millipedes, centipedes and some less well-known groups. The program also examines the phylum *Echinodermata*, which includes: starfish, sea cucumbers, brittlestars, crinoids, sand dollar and sea urchins.

Complete Survey of the Vertebrates

- *Part I: Urochordates and Craniata (Vertebrata) through Fish*. This informative 40-minute multimedia presentation traces the evolutionary transition from urochordates to fish, the first true vertebrates, and provides extensive coverage of the modern bony fish. It introduces the subphylums *Urochordata* and *Cephalochordata* (the tunicates and lancelets which have vertebrate characteristics for only part of their life cycles), then explores the three classes of fish: jawless fish such as the lamprey (this is the class to which the first vertebrates belong); cartilaginous fish, the sharks and rays; and bony fish, the most highly evolved and diverse class of fishes. Individual species examined include tunicate, lamprey, hagfish, sharks, rays, paddlefish, sturgeon, tarpon, moray, gar, bowfin, shad, trout, salmon, pike, pickerel, muskellunge, electric eel, piranha, goldfish, catfish, cod, molly, seahorse, scorpionfish, mullet, bass, dolphinfish, barracuda, remora, puffer, coelacanth, lungfish, and many more. The presentation includes an examination of the rare and unusual coelacanth, a lobe-finned fish thought to share a common ancestry with the first terrestrial vertebrates.

- *Part II: Amphibians and Reptiles.* In-depth coverage is provided of the three amphibian orders (*Gymnophiona* or *Apoda*, caecilians; *Anura*, frogs and toads; *Urodela*, newts and salamanders), and. the four reptile orders (*Rhynchocephalia*, tuataras; *Chelonia*, tortoises and turtles; *Squamata*, snakes; and *Crocodilia*, crocodiles and alligators). Poikilothermic temperature regulation is described in detail, as is the larval stages, respiration, reproduction, significance of amniotic eggs, evolution and adaptation. Animals portrayed include salamanders, newts, frogs, toads, turtles, tortoises, boas, pythons, coral snakes, African mambas, cobras, rattlesnakes, tropical banded sea snakes, geckos, chameleons, iguanas, gila monsters, tuataras, alligators, crocodiles, Komodo dragons, and even the thorny devil or Moloch from Australia.

- *Part III: Birds - Ostrich through Guinea Fowl.* This 35-minute multimedia presentation provides a comprehensive introduction to the class *Aves*, the birds of the world. The living members of this class are generally grouped into 27 orders and 155 families. This program presents the first 13 orders, illustrated by 31 families. (A companion program, *Part IV: Birds - Cranes through Passerines*, presents an additional 12 orders and 59 families, so that together a total of 25 of 27 orders and 90 of 155 families are covered.) Beginning with the large flightless ratites, ostriches, emus, rheas and cassowaries, the program then covers such diverse aquatic birds as penguins, loons, grebes, albatrosses, pelicans, cormorants, darters, frigate birds, egrets, bitterns, storks, ibises, spoonbills, flamingos, ducks, geese, and swans. Birds of prey such as condors, vultures, hawks, eagles and falcons are presented in detail, as are various fowl , including chickens, turkeys and guinea fowl.

- *Part IV: Birds - Cranes through Passerines.* This 40-minute multimedia presentation completes the comprehensive introduction to the class Aves - birds of the world. It picks up where the previous program (*Part III: Birds - Ostrich through Guinea Fowl*) ends, presenting 12 additional orders, illustrated by 59 families. Among the many birds pictured are cranes, coots, sandpipers, puffins, gulls, terns, doves, parrots, roadrunners, owls, whip-poor-wills, swifts, hummingbirds, kingfishers, toucans, woodpeckers, larks, swallows, waxwings, wrens, nuthatches, wood warblers, tanagers, jays, crows, finches, sparrows, blackbirds, orioles, and such thrushes as the robin and mountain bluebird.

- *Part V: Mammals - Echidna through Whales.* This 45-minute multimedia presentation, and its companion program (*Part VI: Mammals - Canids through Sheep*) provide a comprehensive introduction to the world's mammals. Together they detail mammals' relationships to the other classes of vertebrates, explain the different reproductive and developmental process of the three main groups, and describe the behaviours and mechanisms that have enabled mammals to be so successful and widespread. The animals presented include the monotremes (echidna, platypus), marsupials (Tasmanian devils, kangaroos, koalas, opossums), and placentals. Placentals include the *Insectivora* (moles, hedgehogs and shrews), *Chiroptera* (bats - the second largest group of mammals), Primates (lemurs, monkeys, great apes and humans), *Edentata* (sloths, anteaters and armadillos), *Lagomorpha* (rabbits, hares and pikas), Rodents (the largest group of mammals, including prairie dogs, squirrels, beavers, rats, hamsters, porcupines, muskrats, agoutis, etc.), and *Cetacea* (whales, dolphins and porpoises).

- *Part VI: Mammals - Canids through Sheep.* In this 40-minute multimedia presentation, the study of mammals started in its companion program (*Part V: Mammals - Echidna Through Whales*) is completed, beginning with the order *Carnivora* (the meat eaters, such as badgers, bears, foxes, wolves, raccoons, mongooses, lions, tigers, etc.), continuing with the *Tubulidentata* (aardvark), *Pinnipedia* (sea lions, seals and walruses), *Proboscidea* (elephants), *Hyracoidea* (hyraxes), *Sirenia* (manatee), and ending with the *Perissodactyla* (horses, rhinos and tapirs) and the *Artiodactyla* (okapi, camels, hippos, pigs, sheep, etc.), the odd and even-toed hoofed mammals.

Medium: CD-ROM
System requirements: Windows, Macintosh
Price: US$49.95 (individual programs); US$149.95 (lab pack of 5, same title); US$174.95 (*Invertebrates* series, 4 CD-ROMs); US$274.95 (*Vertebrates* series, 6 CD-ROMs)
Source: Educational Images

Explorations in Human Biology

This set of 16 interactive animations enables students to examine issues related to the human side of biology. Contents: *Cystic fibrosis; Active transport; Life span and lifestyle; Muscle contraction; Evolution of the human heart; Smoking and cancer; Diet and weight loss; Nerve conduction; Synaptic transmission; Drug addiction; Hormone action; Immune response; AIDS; Constructing a genetic map; Heredity in families; Pollution of a freshwater lake.*

Medium: CD-ROM
System requirements: Windows (all versions); Macintosh (all versions)
Price: Single user - £36.59 / ~US$56.71 (excl. VAT), £42.99 / ~ €73.00 (incl. VAT). Prices incl. VAT apply to orders from the EU, prices excl. VAT apply to orders from the rest of the world
Source: AVP

When contacting producers and distributors,
please cite *from Guinea Pig to Computer Mouse*

Exploring Animal Life

This multimedia program is both a curriculum-oriented presentation and an instant encyclopaedia, filled with superb photographs, informative text, exciting videoclips, printable diagrams and illustrations, and lab activities - all on one CD-ROM. It provides a fascinating survey of the major divisions of animal life and their characteristics: sponges, molluscs, insects, arthropods, fish, reptiles, birds and mammals. The program gives students instant access to an extensive library of animal illustrations and diagrams to supplement their textbooks. At the end of each section are over 40 printable laboratory activities and tips to help make your labs and field trips more successful.

Medium: CD-ROM
System requirements: Windows, Macintosh
Price: US$99.95 (single user); US$199.95 (lab pack of 5)
Source: Educational Images

Exploring Freshwater Communities

This interactive CD-ROM is a complete resource for studying freshwater biomes. It provides a fascinating survey of the ecology of swamps, bogs, marshes, wetlands, streams, ponds, lakes and the Everglades. It also explores the various organisms commonly found associated with these waters - fish, plankton, protozoa, aquatic insects, amphibians, reptiles, birds and plants, and emphasises their special adaptations, feeding habits and the complex interactions among them. The extensive library of illustrations and diagrams supplements those found in textbooks. The *Protist Culture Database* makes it easy to find over 125 protist genera, and includes morphologic characteristics, culture parameters and media formulations.

Medium: CD-ROM
System requirements: Windows, Macintosh
Price: US$99.95 (single user); US$199.95 (lab pack of 5)
Source: Educational Images

Genetics Simulation

An excellent introduction to the topic of genetics. Execute a series of experiments on this fascinating topic - quickly and easily - in an electronic laboratory. Students will perform a variety of self-monohybrid and dihybrid crosses which, if produced in an actual lab, would take several seasons of growth. Gaining the true advantages of the scientific method, students change their tactics as they progress and repeat the experiments until the desired results are achieved.

Year of production: 1999
Medium: CD-ROM
System requirements: Windows only (all versions)
Price: US$79.95 (single); US$159.95 (lab pack of 5)
Source: Nasco

GET*it Genetics

One of 4 CD-ROMs in this innovative series, GET*it Genetics covers mitosis, meiosis, the monohybrid cross, the dihybrid cross, variations on dominance, genetics of viruses and bacteria, human genetic diseases, DNA replication, the flow of genetic information, regulation of prokaryotic gene expression, regulation of eukaryotic gene expression, RNA processing in eukaryotes, basic gene splicing, cancer, some classic experiments in biology, and a guide to biological terminology. It features more than 750 topics, minicourses that guide students through topic areas, interactive self-quizzing with more than 600 true-false questions, advanced hypertext navigation, extensive index function, hundreds of original illustrations, photos and animations, narration and spoken pronunciations of terms.

Medium: CD-ROM
System requirements: Windows 3.1/95/98/NT, 486 processor (Pentium or better recommended) with 16 MB RAM or better and Super VGA monitor; Macintosh OS 7.0 or later, 68040 or better with 24 MB RAM (32 MB recommended)
Price: US$14.95
Source: Sinauer Associates

Images of Advanced Level Biology

An interactive resource of micrographs, videoclips and animations of topics relating to advanced level biology. Text descriptions and voice-overs make the key teaching points of each image. Includes over 50 sequences of light micrographs sub-divided into broad areas for convenient access. Step, zoom and inspection 'tour' functions are available for specimens. A series of micrographs show changes in the state of specimens over time. Ideal as a whole-class teaching resource and for individual private study.

Medium: CD-ROM
System requirements: Windows only (all versions)
Price: Single user - £51.50 / US$79.83 (excl. VAT), £60.51 / ~ €103.00 (incl. VAT); pack of 3 CD-ROMs - £99.96 / ~ US$154.94 (excl. VAT), £117.45 / ~ €200.00 (incl. VAT); pack of 5 CD-ROMs - £135.27 / ~ US$209.67 (excl. VAT), £158.94 / ~ €270.00 (incl. VAT). Prices incl. VAT apply to orders from the EU, prices excl. VAT apply to orders from the rest of the world
Source: AVP

It's Biology

A series of 4 programs covering:

- *Cell biology and genetics*: cytology, DNA, genetics, mitosis and meiosis, molecules and respiration
- *Nutrition, adaptation and the environment*: diet and digestion, photosynthesis, plant water relations, classification, adaptation, carbon cycle, nitrogen cycle, succession, ecosystem structure and population dynamics, deforestation, desertification, the greenhouse effect, ozone depletion, biological control and conservation
- *Biological systems and processes*: gas exchange and excretion, transport systems, nervous co-ordination, chemical co-ordination, movement and support, reproduction
- *Microbiology and biotechnology*: micro-organisms structure, function and diversity, microbiological techniques, genetic engineering, industrial and agricultural applications, food and drink production, micro-organisms and disease

Medium: CD-ROM
System requirements: Windows only (all versions)
Price: Individual programs: single user - £19.99 / US$30.98 (excl. VAT), £23.49 / ~ €40.00 (incl. VAT); network version - £49.99 / US$77.48 (excl. VAT), £58.74 / ~ €100.00 (incl. VAT); pack of 4 CD-ROMs single user - £70.00 / ~ US$108.50 (excl. VAT), £82.25 / ~ €140.00 (incl. VAT); pack of 4 CD-ROMs network version - £150.00 / ~ US$232.50 (excl. VAT), £176.25 / ~ €300.00 (incl. VAT); multipack of all 4 programs: single user - £70.00 / ~ US$108.50 (excl. VAT), £82.25 / ~ €140.00 (incl. VAT); network version - £150.00 / US$232.50 (excl. VAT), £176.25 / ~ €300.00 (incl. VAT). Prices incl. VAT apply to orders from the EU, prices excl. VAT apply to orders from the rest of the world
Source: AVP

Key to Insects

This multimedia CD-ROM contains a comprehensive collection of vivid photographs, exquisite drawings and rare video footage - all supported with extensive background information. Students will be challenged to develop their taxonomic knowledge as they classify insects to the order level. The unique program allows them to use any characteristic to identify and organism at any level. A perfect means for students to explore taxonomy quickly and easily - without prior knowledge of the five kingdoms.

Year of production: 1999
Medium: CD-ROM
System requirements: Windows only (all versions)
Price: US$79.95 (single); US$159.95 (lab pack of 5)
Source: Nasco

Sniffy, the Virtual Rat

This is a fun, interactive software program that simulates a wide range of learning phenomena, typically discussed in courses on the Psychology of Learning. It outputs the response measures employed by research psychologists. Sniffy, a realistic digital rat in an operant chamber (Skinner Box), gives students hands-on experience setting up and conducting experiments that demonstrate most of the major phenomena of operant and classical conditioning. Users begin by training Sniffy to press a bar to obtain food and progress to studies of complex learning phenomena. There are two versions of *Sniffy, the Virtual Rat: Sniffy Lite* demonstrates the most basic phenomena of operant and classical conditioning, but does not have the complexity and flexibility for advanced learning topics; *Sniffy Pro* is a comprehensive simulation of advanced learning phenomena, as described in detail on the website. The classical conditioning phenomena simulated by *Sniffy Lite* are: acquisition, extinction and spontaneous recovery. *Sniffy Pro* also includes: pre-exposure and effects of manipulating the intensity of the CS and US, compound conditioning, blocking, overshadowing, over-expectation effect, inhibitory conditioning, sensory preconditioning, higher-order/background conditioning, nature of the classical conditioning association (S-S or S-R). The operant conditioning phenomena that *Sniffy Lite* simulates include: magazine training, shaping, extinction, spontaneous recovery, primary and secondary reinforcement, and the effects of variable-interval, variable-ratio, fixed-interval, and fixed-ratio schedules. *Sniffy Pro* also simulates: the partial reinforcement effect; simple and complex stimulus discrimination learning; and stimulus generalisation.

Year of production: 2000
Medium: CD-ROM
System requirements: Windows 95/98/NT; Macintosh OS 7 or above; 16 MB RAM (32 MB highly recommended)
Price: US$21.95 / £14.99 (excl. VAT) (*Lite Version*); US$25.95 / £19.99 (excl. VAT) (*Pro Version*). Both versions include a Lab Manual
Source: Thomson Learning

Videodiscovery Digital Library (VDL)

The *Videodiscovery Digital Library (VDL)* is an on-line collection of 30,000 images and movies with associated descriptive text, lessons and retrieval software. It represents the culmination of over 200 person/years of research and development resulting in a comprehensive treatment of biology, genetics, anatomy and physiology, chemistry, physics, geology, atmospheric science, oceanography and astronomy. The biology, oceanography and anatomy and physiology collections contain hundreds of progressive animal dissections, human cadaver dissections as well as virtual and actual physiology experiments. This unique resource offers teachers and students a comprehensive, high quality, highly organised science media collection that can improve science learning at all levels. It allows students and teachers to prepare custom presentations ('mediashows') using built-in authoring tools. Teachers precisely control access to the *VDL*, adjusting for grade level, subject focus and appropriateness. *VDL* is a living collection – it is continually growing and being revised to keep up-to-date. It is delivered on a dedicated server located at each site and is available to qualified institutions as a yearly subscription.

Medium: Dedicated server appliance and in some cases also CD-ROM

System requirements: The *VDL* is a rich media collection delivered across an institution's high speed local area network using an innovative and cost effective system. There should be one server appliance per school subnet or when suitable bandwidth is available one or more machines can be housed in a central district network facility. Each server appliance comes completely loaded with the *VDL* images, videos, interface and text databases. Updates and administration can be performed remotely. *VDL* is accessed through a minimum Internet Explorer 5 or Netscape Navigator 4 web browser. The computer can be a Macintosh or PC with a sound card and a 200+ MHz processor, and should have a Windows Media Player 7 plug-in

Price: The *VDL* licence is US$2.00 per student per year based on the Full Time Equivalent (FTE) count of students in the institution. The licence fee pays for student and teacher access, and for routine service upgrades, up-to-date revisions or additions to the collection and supporting resources. Videodiscovery sells the server appliance, fully loaded with the *VDL* content and software for US$2,000 per machine, which will be owned by the institution and should be dedicated to the *VDL*

Note: Although the *VDL* is easy to learn and use, Videodiscovery offers a variety of staff training services including phone teleconference, training-the-trainers workshops in Seattle (USA), and on-site training by Videodiscovery staff

Source: Videodiscovery

VIDEO

 [The] Dogwhelk: A Study in Adaptation

We might expect shores that are exposed to considerable wave action to harbour marine life of a type different from that of a more sheltered shore. Using *Nucella lapillus*, a species of dogwhelk, these experiments compare substantial samples of dogwhelks taken from both locations. The two groups are compared for shell height and shape, body form, wet tissue weight, shell volume, and the amount of force required to remove it when attached. The dogwhelks are eaten by various predators, and a further experiment is carried out with the most important of these, certain littoral crabs. These crabs are present in far greater quantity at the sheltered than at the wave-swept site; the severity of the wave action and the lack of suitable refuge sites are probably responsible. In the experiment, the crabs are offered a choice of dogwhelks in different size ranges and with thin or thick shell lips. Some are eaten and others rejected. From what they have observed and data given in the guide, students will be able to make deductions about the relationships between location and shell shape and size.

Format: VHS NTSC
Running time: 15 mins.
Price: US$59.95
Source: Films for the Humanities and Sciences (United States and Canada only)

Equine Euthanasia

The humane euthanasia of an animal is one of the most important tasks a veterinarian can perform. The last few moments of an animal's life should be as peaceful and pleasant as possible. Planning and preparation will help to minimise stress on the animal and the people involved. The horse is a special case with regard to euthanasia. The large size of a horse and a tendency to remain standing until losing consciousness are complicating factors. The goal of the video is to teach students, veterinary hospital personnel, and clients that the euthanasia of a large standing animal, the horse, can be quiet and peaceful. The accompanying booklet provides information for veterinarians and their employees. In the step by step procedures of scheduled euthanasia and recommendations for emergency situations, the objective is to provide the information needed to ensure a humane death for the horse, safety for all personnel involved, and emotional support for the client and the veterinary hospital team.

Format: VHS NTSC
Price: US$75.00 (incl. workbook); other formats available at additional cost
Source: Michigan State University

Science Bank: Biology

An invaluable resource bank of practical demonstrations that teachers often find difficult to carry out, with graphical explanations and real-life applications. Contains three 15-minute programs: 1. *Biological reactions*: photosynthesis, respiration and enzymes; 2. *Cells and tissues*: animal cells, plant cells and cell division; 3. *Energy and cycles in nature*: energy transfer in nature, carbon cycle and nitrogen cycle.

Format: VHS PAL
Running time: 45 mins.
Price: £17.90 / ~ US$27.74 (excl. VAT), £21.03 / ~ €36.00 (incl. VAT). Prices incl. VAT apply to orders from the EU, prices excl. VAT apply to orders from the rest of the world
Source: AVP

When contacting producers and distributors,
please cite *from Guinea Pig to Computer Mouse*

Stimulus Response

This video program looks at behaviour in farm animals. Pigs show how they perceive stimuli in the first moments of life. Hens run obstacle courses and show that they have the mental co-ordination to learn from videos. Calves make us aware of their internal as well as external effectors, and we see the ways in which these animals are able to respond to the stimuli in their environment. All these steps are made memorable by familiar animals revealed as they have never been seen before.

Language: English, German; other language versions are also being developed
Year of production: second edition 2000
Format: VHS PAL, NTSC
Running time: 26 mins.
Price: £5.00 (ASAB members); £10.00 (non-ASAB members), incl. postage and a 12-page booklet with notes and exercises
Source: ASAB

part d **further resources**

1. Web resources

1.1 Databases

1.1.1 Alternatives in education

Databases that provide detailed information on individual alternatives for life science education. See also 'Websites'.

AVAR (Association of Veterinarians for Animal Rights) - Alternatives in Education Database
http://www.avar.org

EURCA (European Resource Centre for Alternatives in Higher Education) - Database and Product Reviews
http://www.eurca.org

InterNICHE (International Network for Humane Education) - from Guinea Pig to Computer Mouse
http://www.interniche.org

NORINA Database on Alternatives
http://oslovet.veths.no/NORINA

1.1.2 Other databases, networks and information points

Databases and similar resources that provide detailed information on alternatives in general, on other issues relating to life science research, testing and education, and on animal protection organisations worldwide. See also 'Websites' and 'Organisations'.

1.1.2.1 Research, testing & education

Akademie für Tierschutz - Databank for Alternative Methods
http://www.tierschutzbund.de

ALIS (Animals in Labs Information Service)
http://www.alisdatabase.org

Altweb (Alternatives to Animal Testing website)
http://altweb.jhsph.edu

Biome - Gateway to Internet Resources in the Health and Life Sciences
http://biome.ac.uk/biome.html

Biosis
http://www.biosis.org/index.htm

BUBL Information Service
http://bubl.ac.uk

BUFVC (British Universities Film & Video Council) - HERMES Database of Audio-Visual Materials
http://www.bufvc.ac.uk/databases

CONVINCE Database
http://www.convince.org

DIMDI (German Institute for Medical Documentation and Information)
http://www.dimdi.de

Dr. Felix's Free MEDLINE Page
http://www.beaker.iupui.edu/drfelix

ECVAM (European Centre for the Validation of Alternative Methods) - Scientific Information Service
http://ecvam-sis.jrc.it

Electric Editors
http://www.electriceditors.net

ERIC - Education Information
http://askeric.org/Eric

FRAME (Fund for the Replacement of Animals in Medical Experiments)
http://www.frame.org.uk

MERLOT - Multimedia Educational Resource for Learning and Online Teaching
http://www.merlot.org

National Agricultural Library - Agricola
http://www.nal.usda.gov/ag98

NCA (Netherlands Centre Alternatives to Animal Use)
http://www.nca-nl.org

PREX - Biomedical and Veterinary Databases
http://www.prex.org

TextBase
http://oslovet.veths.no/TextBase

UCCAA - University of California Center for Animal Alternatives
http://www.vetmed.ucdavis.edu/Animal_Alternatives/main.htm

US National Library of Medicine
http://www.ncbi.nlm.nih.gov/PubMed

www Virtual Library - NetVet Veterinary Resources and the Electronic Zoo
http://netvet.wustl.edu

ZEBET (Centre for Documentation and Evaluation of Alternatives to Animal Experiments)
http://www.bfr.bund.de

1.1.2.2   Animal protection

Animal Concerns
http://www.animalconcerns.org

Animal Contacts Directory
http://www.veggies.org.uk/acd.htm

Animal World Directory
http://www.animalworlddirectory.com

World Animal Net Directory
http://worldanimalnet.org

1.2   Websites

1.2.1   Priority sites on alternatives in education

Major websites that address replacement alternatives in life science education. See also 'Databases' and 'Organisations'.

Animalearn
http://www.animalearn.org
http://www.humanestudent.org

AVAR (Association of Veterinarians for Animal Rights)
http://www.avar.org

Educational Memorials (Body Donation Programs)
http://www.educationalmemorial.org

ESEC (Ethical Science and Education Coalition)
http://www.neavs.org/esec

EURCA (European Resource Centre for Alternatives in Higher Education)
http://www.eurca.org

HSUS (Humane Society of the United States)
http://www.hsus.org

HSUS / Jonathan Balcombe - The Use of Animals in Higher Education: Problems, Alternatives, and Recommendations
http://www.hsus.org/ace/13059

InterNICHE (International Network for Humane Education)
http://www.interniche.org

InterNICHE Brazil - Information Network for Humane Education
http://www.internichebrasil.org

NAVS (National Anti-Vivisection Society) (US)
http://www.navs.org

Novivisezione (Novivisection)
http://www.novivisezione.org

PCRM (Physicians Committee for Responsible Medicine)
http://www.pcrm.org

SATIS (Student Workgroup Against Animal Misuse in Education)
http://www.tierrechte.de/satis

1.2.2   On-line educational resources

A non-exhaustive list of websites with exemplary and otherwise useful on-line resources, including course material for students and teachers, and general life science information. See also 'Databases'. For on-line alternatives, see 'Part C - Alternatives File'.

1.2.2.1   Anatomy

Anatomically Correct: The On-line Cat Dissection - Think Quest
http://library.thinkquest.org/15401

Animal Dissection Page
http://www.d91.k12.id.us/www/skyline/teachers/robertsd/dissect.htm

Articulation Page - Portland State University
http://www-adm.pdx.edu/user/bio/articula/home.html

CALnet Programmes for Veterinary Science Students - University of Bristol Comparative Morphology Centre / University College Dublin Department of Veterinary Anatomy
http://137.222.110.150/calnet/Introvet/Introvet.htm

Comparative Mammalian Brain Collections
http://brainmuseum.org

Dog Abdomen Series - School of Veterinary Studies, Murdoch University
http://numbat.murdoch.edu.au/dog_abdomen_series/index_high.html

Earthworm, Perch, Crayfish and Frog Dissection
http://www.flushing.k12.mi.us/srhigh/tippettl/biology/lum/index.html

Gross Anatomy - University of Pennsylvania School of Veterinary Medicine
http://caltest.nbc.upenn.edu/grossanat

Horse Head Series - School of Veterinary Studies, Murdoch University
http://numbat.murdoch.edu.au/horse_head_series/horse_head_series.html

Interactive Atlas of Zebrafish Vascular Anatomy - Weinstein Lab, National Institute of Child Health and Human Development **(NICHD)**
http://mgchd1.nichd.nih.gov:8000/zfatlas/Intro%20Page/intro1.html

Interactive Fly - Society for Developmental Biology
http://sdb.bio.purdue.edu/fly/aimain/1aahome.htm

Interactive Frog Dissection (Net Frog): An On-line Tutorial - The Curry School of Education, University of Virginia
http://curry.edschool.virginia.edu/go/frog

Nemestrina Monkey Brain Atlas - UCLA Laboratory of Neural Imaging
http://www.loni.ucla.edu/Research_Loni/atlases/nemestrina.html

Neuroscience - University of Pennsylvania School of Veterinary Medicine
http://cal.vet.upenn.edu/neuro/N_Index.html

Photographic Dissection of the Ox and Sheep - Ohio State University College of Veterinary Medicine
http://www.vet.ohio-state.edu/docs/ATCenter/VM522/toc.html

QTVR (Quick Time Virtual Reality) Anatomical Resource
http://www.anatomy.wright.edu/QTVR/links.html

Radiographic Images of the Dog - Texas A&M University College of Veterinary Medicine
http://classes.cvm.tamu.edu/vaph910/radiogra.htm

Rat Anatomy - University of Tennessee at Martin
http://www.utm.edu/~rirwin/RatAnat.htm

The Dog in Cross-Section - Purdue University School of Veterinary Medicine
http://www.vet.purdue.edu/bms/mri_cd/index.htm

Veterinary Anatomy and Radiology - University of Georgia College of Veterinary Medicine
http://www.vet.uga.edu/var/index.htm

Veterinary Anatomy at the University of Minnesota
http://vanat.cvm.umn.edu/WebSites.html

Veterinary Dissection Images - Department of Veterinary Anatomy, University College Dublin
http://hermes.ucd.ie/~vetanat/images/image.html

Virtual Creatures - Stanford University
http://k-2.stanford.edu/

Virtual Pig Dissection - Fort Kent Community High School
http://mail.fkchs.sad27.k12.me.us/fkchs/vpig

Visible Animal Viewer
http://www.anat.vetmed.uni-muenchen.de/VisibleAnimal/VisibleAnimalViewer.html

Visible Human Project - (US) National Library of Medicine
http://www.nlm.nih.gov/research/visible/visible_human.html

WebAnatomy - General College, University of Minnesota
http://www.gen.umn.edu/faculty_staff/jensen/1135/webanatomy

Whole Brain Atlas
http://www.med.harvard.edu/AANLIB/home.html

Whole Frog Project: Interactive Frog Dissection Kit and Virtual Frog Builder Game -
Lawrence Berkeley National Laboratory, California
http://www-itg.lbl.gov/vfrog

1.2.2.2   Biology

About.com - Biology
http://biology.about.com

Animal Diversity Web - University of Michigan Museum of Zoology
http://animaldiversity.ummz.umich.edu/

Biodidac: Digital Resource Bank for Teaching Biology
http://biodidac.bio.uottawa.ca

Biology Labs On-Line - California State University / Addison Wesley Longman
http://biologylab.awlonline.com

Biology Online - Information in the Biological Sciences
http://www.biology-online.org

Biology Website References for Students and Teachers
http://www.hoflink.com/~house

Field-Based Animal Research Approach for Teaching Learning & Motivation - Center for the Advancement of Science Education / Department of Psychology, Northeastern University
http://www.casdn.neu.edu/~nucase/library/cohenandblock.html

Kimball's Biology Pages: Online Biology Textbook
http://www.ultranet.com/~jkimball/BiologyPages

MIT Biology Hypertextbook
http://esg-www.mit.edu:8001/esgbio/7001main.html

On-line Biology Book - Estrella Mountain Community College
http://gened.emc.maricopa.edu/bio/bio181/BIOBK/BioBookTOC.html

Online Material for Biology and Mathematics - Eduvinet / Kreisgymnasium Bad Krozingen
http://www.eduvinet.de/mallig/defaultb.htm#rep

The Biology Place - Peregrine Publishers
http://www.biology.com

The Biology Project - University of Arizona
http://www.biology.arizona.edu

The Laboratory Rat: A Natural History - Manuel Berdoy, University of Oxford
http://www.ratlife.org/

Tree of Life Web Project: Collaborative Internet Project on Phylogeny and Biodiversity
http://tolweb.org/tree/phylogeny.html

Virtual Creatures - Stanford University
http://k-2.stanford.edu/

Centre for Educational Resources on the Internet
http://biologie.zum.de

Zoo Lab: a Website for Animal Biology - University of Wisconsin, La Crosse
http://bioweb.uwlax.edu/zoolab

1.2.2.3   Embryology & Developmental Biology

Developmental Biology On-line - University of Guelph
http://www.uoguelph.ca/zoology/devobio/dbindex.htm

Dynamics of Development Tutorial
http://worms.zoology.wisc.edu/embryology_main.html

Embryo Images: Normal and Abnormal Mammalian Development - University of North Carolina
http://www.med.unc.edu/embryo_images

Frog Developmental Biology - University of Texas at Austin
http://www.utexas.edu/courses/zoo321/movies321.html

Interactive Fly - Society for Developmental Biology
http://sdb.bio.purdue.edu/fly/aimain/1aahome.htm

Neural Crest - Caroline Moran, University of Manchester
http://www.teaching-biomed.man.ac.uk/moran

Virtual Embryology - Kyoto University
http://www.kuhp.kyoto-u.ac.jp/multimed/VE/VE.html

1.2.2.4 Histology

Atlas of Microscopic Anatomy - Virtual Hospital, University of Iowa College of Medicine
http://www.vh.org/Providers/Textbooks/MicroscopicAnatomy/MicroscopicAnatomy.html

Histology - Department of Anatomy and Human Biology, University of Western Australia
http://131.229.114.77/Histology

Histology - University of Georgia College of Veterinary Medicine
http://www.vet.uga.edu/var/histo00/index.htm

Histology Imagebase - School of Veterinary Studies, Murdoch University
http://numbat.murdoch.edu.au/histology/index_low.html

Histology: Reproductive Systems - Oklahoma State University College of Veterinary Medicine
http://handlin.cvm.okstate.edu/histology/index.htm

Histology Self-Teaching Program - Hannover School of Veterinary Medicine
http://www.tiho-hannover.de/einricht/anat/lit/mwenth/histo_e.htm

Histology Tutorial - University of Florida College of Medicine
http://www.medinfo.ufl.edu/year1/histo

Histology Website - University of Prince Edward Island, Faculty of Veterinary Medicine
http://www.upei.ca/~morph/webct/home2.html

Histology Websites - University of Iowa College of Medicine
http://www.medicine.uiowa.edu/pathed/virtual_laboratory/Histology_Website_Page/histology_websites.html

HistoWeb - University of Kansas Medical Center
http://www.kumc.edu/instruction/medicine/anatomy/histoweb

Internet Atlas of Histology - University of Illinois College of Medicine at Urbana-Champaign
http://www.med.uiuc.edu/histo/medium/atlas/index.htm

Mammalian Histology - University of Delaware
http://www.udel.edu/Biology/Wags/histopage/histopage.htm

1.2.2.5 Human Medicine

Computer Assisted Teaching System (CATS) - University of Vermont College of Medicine
http://cats.med.uvm.edu

Eye Simulation Application
http://axis.cbcu.cam.ac.uk/mirrors/eyesim/eyesim.htm

Howard Hughes Medical Institute Holiday Lectures on Science
http://www.hhmi.org/lectures/index.htm

Integrated Medical Curriculum - Gold Standard Multimedia network
http://www.imc.gsm.com

LectureLinks - Johns Hopkins School of Medicine Office of Academic Computing
http://oac.med.jhmi.edu/LectureLinks

Medicalstudent.com: Digital Library of Medical Information - Michael P. D'Alessandro
http://medicalstudent.com

MedWeb - Emory University
http://www.medweb.emory.edu/MedWeb

Trauma.org - Trauma Moulage
http://www.trauma.org/resus/moulage/moulage.html

TraumaTraining.org
http://www.traumatraining.org

Supercourse: Epidemiology, the Internet and Public Health
http://www.liv.ac.uk/PublicHealth/super1

1.2.2.6   Pathology

Bristol Biomedical Image Archive: Medical, Dental and Veterinary Images for Teaching
http://www.brisbio.ac.uk

Internet Pathology Laboratory for Medical Education - Florida State University College of Medicine
http://www-medlib.med.utah.edu/WebPath/webpath.html

IPLAB.net - Interactive Pathology Laboratory
http://iplab.net

Museum of Human Disease - University of New South Wales, Sydney
http://129.94.18.13/pathmus

Pathology Tutorial - Johns Hopkins School of Medicine Office of Medical Informatics Education
http://omie.med.jhmi.edu/pathconcepts

PathWeb: the Virtual Pathology Museum - University of Connecticut Health Center
http://pathweb.uchc.edu

peir.net: Pathology Education Instructional Resource - University of Alabama at Birmingham
http://www.peir.net

PERLjam Online - Pathology, Histology and Laboratory Medicine - Indiana University
http://erl.pathology.iupui.edu

Renal Pathology - University of Florida College of Veterinary Medicine
http://www.vetmed.ufl.edu/path/teach/vem5162/urinary/urinary.htm

The Lightning Hypertext of Disease - Pathology Informatics
http://www.pathinfo.com

Urbana Atlas of Pathology - University of Illinois College of Medicine at Urbana-Champaign
http://www.med.uiuc.edu/PathAtlasf/titlepage.html

Veterinary General Pathology - University of Florida College of Veterinary Medicine
http://www.vetmed.ufl.edu/path/pbteach/wlc/vem5161/vem5161.htm

Veterinary Pathology Tutorials - University of Bristol
http://www.bris.ac.uk/Depts/PathAndMicro/CPL/tut.html

Veterinary Systemic Pathology - University of Florida College of Veterinary Medicine
http://www.vetmed.ufl.edu/path/teach/vem5162/vem5162.htm

1.2.2.7 Pharmacology

First Course in Pharmacokinetics and Biopharmaceutics - David Bourne
http://www.boomer.org/c/p1

ISAP - Internet Self-Assessment in Pharmacology
http://www.horsetooth.com/ISAP/welcome.html

Principles of Pharmacology - Purdue University School of Veterinary Medicine
http://www.vet.purdue.edu/bms/courses/bms513/index.htm

Veterinary Clinical Pharmacology - Virginia-Maryland Regional College of Veterinary Medicine
http://cpharm.vetmed.vt.edu

1.2.2.8 Physiology

Acid-Base Balance Tutorial - Tulane University School of Medicine, Department of Anesthesiology
http://www.tmc.tulane.edu/anes/acid

Animations for Learning Reproductive Biology in Farm Animals - Oklahoma State University Department of Animal Science
http://www.ansi.okstate.edu/resource-room/reprod/all/animations/index.htm

Cardiovascular Physiology Web Resource - Ohio University College of Osteopathic Medicine
http://www.oucom.ohiou.edu/CVPhysiology

Human Physiology Lecture Notes - Eastern Kentucky University
http://www.biology.eku.edu/RITCHISO/301syl.htm

Interactive Respiratory Physiology - Johns Hopkins School of Medicine Office of Medical Informatics Education
http://omie.med.jhmi.edu/res_phys/index.HTML

McGill Virtual Physiology Lab - McGill University
http://www.medicine.mcgill.ca/physio/vlabonline/virtual_lab.htm

Online Teaching Resources - GKT School of Biomedical Sciences, Kings College London
http://www.umds.ac.uk/physiology/teach.htm

Open Course Harvey Project - Physiology on the Web
http://www.harveyproject.org

Physiology Files and Software Archive - Physiology Online
http://www.physoc.org/Software

1.2.2.9   Veterinary Medicine

AltVetMed - **Complementary and Alternative Veterinary Medicine**
http://www.altvetmed.com

American Holistic Veterinary Medical Association - University of Florida Student Chapter
http://neuro.vetmed.ufl.edu/alt_med/ahvma.html

Canine Cardiology - University of Saskatchewan, Western College of Veterinary Medicine
http://www.usask.ca/wcvm/canine

Cardiology Service - Texas A&M University College of Veterinary Medicine
http://www.cvm.tamu.edu/cardiology/default.html

Case Studies in Clinical Pharmacology - University of Pennsylvania School of Veterinary Medicine
http://cal.vet.upenn.edu/pharm/index.html

Case Studies in Small Animal Cardiovascular Medicine - UC-DAVIS Veterinary Medical Teaching Hospital
http://www.vmth.ucdavis.edu/cardio/cases

Clinical Cases - University of Minnesota College of Veterinary Medicine
http://www.cvm.umn.edu/academics/course_web/current/ClinSkill_3

Clinical Pathology Modules - Cornell University College of Veterinary Medicine
http://web.vet.cornell.edu/public/popmed/clinpath/CPmodules

Clinical Problem Solving in Internal Medicine - Ohio State University College of Veterinary Medicine
http://www.vet.ohio-state.edu/docs/lapdog/index.html

Computer-Aided Learning Pilot Project - University of Pennsylvania School of Veterinary Medicine
http://cal.vet.upenn.edu/cal

Cyberpet Veterinary Hospital Waiting Room - The Ohio State University College of Veterinary Medicine
http://www.vet.ohio-state.edu/case/testpg.html

Dermatology Case Review - Oklahoma State University College of Veterinary Medicine
http://www.cvm.okstate.edu/instruction/mm_curr/dermatology/dermatology.htm

Human-Animal Bond and Pet Therapy Web Links - University of Guelph Library
http://www.lib.uoguelph.ca/pathfinders/habond/web_links.htm

IVIS: International Veterinary Information Service
http://www.ivis.org

Large Animal Courses - University of Georgia College of Veterinary Medicine
http://lam.vet.uga.edu/LAM/LM000003.HTML

Merck Veterinary Manual
http://www.MerckVetManual.com

On-line Quizzes - School of Veterinary Medicine Tuskegee University
http://192.203.127.60/frontend/syllab.html

Radiology Teaching - Ohio State University College of Veterinary Medicine
http://www.vet.ohio-state.edu/docs/ClinSci/radiology/Teaching.htm

Small Animal Cardiology: Interactive Tutorial - University of Pennsylvania
http://caltest.nbc.upenn.edu/smcardiac

Small Animal Nephrology and Urology - University of Wisconsin College of Veterinary Medicine
http://www.vetsites.vin.com/Kidney/VMIIN.HTML

Veterinary Clinical Cardiology - Ontario Veterinary College
http://www.vetgo.com

Veterinary Instructional Materials On-line - University of Florida College of Veterinary Medicine
http://www.vetmed.ufl.edu/teaching.htm

Veterinary Musculoskeletal System: Case-based Problem Solving - Virginia-Maryland Regional College of Veterinary Medicine
http://www.bsi.vt.edu/vetmed/vm8284/cases/index.html

Veterinary Parasitology Images - Oklahoma State University
http://www.cvm.okstate.edu/~users/jcfox/htdocs/clinpara/clinpara.htm

VetScape: Veterinary Internet Resource Network
http://www.vetscape.net

Virtual Veterinary Center - Martindale's Health Science Guide 2003
http://www-sci.lib.uci.edu/HSG/Vet.html

www Virtual Library - Veterinary Medicine
http://netvet.wustl.edu/vetmed.htm

1.2.2.10 Miscellaneous

Access Excellence - National Health Museum
http://www.accessexcellence.org

Basic Immunology Overview - V.V. Klimov, Siberian State Medical University / Tomsk State University
http://www.immunology.klimov.tom.ru/index.html

Center for Problem-Based Learning - Illinois Mathematics and Science Academy
http://www.imsa.edu/team/cpbl/cpbl.html

College and University Instructional Technology Support Centers
http://it.csumb.edu/atms/centers

Critical Thinking Consortium
http://www.criticalthinking.org

CSU Bioweb: Biological Sciences Webserver - California State University
http://arnica.csustan.edu

E-Biosci: European Platform for Information in the Life Sciences
http://www.e-biosci.org

Electron Micrographs of Animal Viruses - Queen's University of Belfast
http://www.qub.ac.uk/afs/vs/vsd6.html

Hypertexts for Biomedical Sciences - Colorado State University
http://arbl.cvmbs.colostate.edu/hbooks/index.html

Instructional Multimedia - University of Alberta, Biological Sciences
http://www.biology.ualberta.ca/facilities/multimedia/

International Network on Feminist Approaches to Bioethics
http://www.georgetown.edu/research/kie

Medical Biochemistry Page - Michael W. King / Indiana State University School of Medicine
http://www.dentistry.leeds.ac.uk/biochem/thcme/home.html

NetBioChem: Biochemistry tutorial - Allegheny University of the Health Sciences / University of Utah
http://www.auhs.edu/netbiochem/NetWelco.htm

NOAH: New York Online Access to Health
http://www.noah-health.org

The Technology Source - Michigan Virtual University
http://ts.mivu.org

World Lecture Hall
http://www.utexas.edu/world/lecture

1.3   Listserves

1.3.1   Priority listserves

Listserves that focus on alternatives in life science education and on conscientious objection.

Animals and Alternatives in Education (Japan)
c/o Makiko Nakano
http://www.egroups.co.jp/group/alt-edu-animal

AVARStudents
c/o AVAR (Association of Veterinarians for Animal Rights)
http://www.avar.org

HumEdANZ (Humane Education - Australia and New Zealand)
c/o Animals Australia
http://www.animalsaustralia.org

interniche-l
c/o InterNICHE (International Network for Humane Education)
http://www.interniche.org

animalista
c/o InterNICHE Brazil - Information Network for Humane Education
http://www.internichebrasil.org

1.3.2   Other listserves

There are a small number of other listserves that address humane education amongst other animal issues, including **I-CAAN (Inter-Campus Animal Advocacy Network)**, run by the HSUS (Humane Society of the United States). Various professional, 3R's and animal rights listserves sometimes carry mailings on alternatives in education too.

2. Printed and video resources

2.1   Priority resources

Printed and video resources that address replacement alternatives in life science education, and conscientious objection.

2.1.1   Books

Animals in Education: The Facts, Issues and Implications - Lisa Ann Hepner (Richmond Publishers, 1994)

from Guinea Pig to Computer Mouse: Alternative Methods for a Progressive, Humane Education (2ⁿᵈ ed) - Nick Jukes, Mihnea Chiuia (InterNICHE, 2003)

Hidden Values: Ethics and the Use of Animals in Education - Thales Tréz (MA thesis, Leuven University, 2001)

Humane Education - Animals and Alternatives in Laboratory Classes: Aspects, Attitudes and Implications - Helena Pedersen (Stiftelsen Forskning utan Djursförsök, 2002)

The Use of Animals in Higher Education: Problems, Alternatives and Recommendations - Jonathan Balcombe (Humane Society Press, 2000)

Vivisection and Dissection in the Classroom: A Guide to Conscientious Objection - Gary L. Francione & Anna E. Charlton (AAVS, 1992)

2.1.2   Academic papers, reports and proceedings

For published academic papers addressing alternatives, please see the references and notes following the chapters in this book and in the other priority publications mentioned above. Proceedings from meetings such as the biennial **InterNICHE conference** and the triennial **World Congress on Alternatives** report on some of the latest developments in the field. Journals such as *ATLA* (Alternatives to Laboratory Animals), *ALTEX* (Alternativen zu Tierexperimenten), *Animal Welfare*, *JAAWS* (Journal of Applied Animal Welfare Science) and other scientific publications sometimes carry papers on alternatives in education. There is also a wide range of other journals addressing related issues - for example, *Anthrozoös* and *Society and Animals* on human-animal interaction.

2.1.3   Booklets, pamphlets, leaflets and magazines

A variety of useful documents and campaigning packs are available from all the organisations which have a major focus on alternatives in education. For example:

The **'Viewpoints 2000 Series'** (NEAVS, 2000) and **Veterinary Education Packet** are available in hard copy from ESEC (Ethical Science and Education Coalition), and the majority also on-line at http://www.neavs.org/esec.

The 'Ethics in Medical Education' series of leaflets is available from PCRM (Physicians Committee for Responsible Medicine) and is on-line at http://www.pcrm.org.

'Comparative Studies of Dissection and Other Animal Uses' (HSUS, 1999) is produced by the HSUS (Humane Society of the United States), and is also on-line at http://www.hsus.org and the InterNICHE website http://www.interniche.org.

'Ethically-Sourced Cadaver Surgery - A Submission to Murdoch University's Division of Veterinary & Biomedical Sciences' (Knight, 2000) is available in hard copy from InterNICHE and in part at http://www.interniche.org.

'Learning without Killing: A Guide to Conscientious Objection' (Knight, 2002) is available in hard copy from InterNICHE, and can be downloaded from http://www.interniche.org and from the AVAR (Association of Veterinarians for Animal Rights) website http://www.avar.org.

A booklet of testimonies written by student conscientious objectors is available from InterNICHE, and is also on-line at http://www.interniche.org.

There are also numerous printed animal protection magazines available from different organisations. Some are also on-line, such as the Animals Agenda at http://www.animalsagenda.org and Animal People at http://www.animalpeoplenews.org.

2.1.4   Video and CD-ROM

HSUS (Humane Society of the United States):

'Animal Dissection - A Student's Choice' (1996)
Video available in VHS NTSC format only. Running time: 6 mins.

InterNICHE (International Network for Humane Education):

'Alternatives in Education: New Approaches for a New Millennium' (1999-2003)
Video available in VHS PAL and VHS NTSC formats. Running time: 33 mins.

Subtitled or dubbed translations available in Croatian, Czech, Estonian, French, German, Georgian, Hungarian, Polish, Portuguese (Brazilian), Romanian, Russian, Serbian, Slovenian, Spanish, and Ukrainian. Mandarin Chinese, Arabic, Turkish, Hebrew and others under production. Text transcription available in Japanese. Web and CD-ROM versions under production.

PCRM (Physicians Committee for Responsible Medicine):

'Advances in Medical Education, with Henry Heimlich, MD' (1997)
Video available in VHS PAL and VHS NTSC formats. Running time: 19 mins.

'Innovations in Trauma Training, with Henry Heimlich, MD' (1997)
Video available in VHS NTSC format only. CD-ROM version available. Running time: 9 mins.

PETA (People for the Ethical Treatment of Animals):

'Classroom Cut-Ups: A Look at Dissection' (1990)
Video available in VHS PAL, VHS NTSC and at the website http://www.petatv.com/viv.html. Running time: 15 mins.

2.2   Other recommended reading

Other publications that address a range of issues relevant to students, teachers, campaigners and others. Issues include alternatives, curricular design, ethics, the human-animal bond, and empowerment. See also 'Priority Resources'.

2.2.1   Humane education, conscientious objection and alternatives

Animal Use in Education: Proceedings of the 2nd International Conference 1989 - B.S. Close, F. Dolins and G. Mason (eds) (EuroNICHE / Humane Education Centre, 1989)

Animals in Education: The Use of Animals in High School Biology Classes and Science Fairs - Heather McGiffin & Nancy Brownley (Institute for the Study of Animal Problems, 1980)

Beyond Dissection: Innovative Teaching Tools for Biology Education (3rd ed) - Larson, S. (ed.) (NEAVS, 1998)

New Teaching Approaches in the Life Sciences - Proceedings from the 1st InterNICHE Conference 2001 - Nick Jukes & Bruno Lecomte (eds) (InterNICHE, 2003)

SATIS-Studie '95 - C. Gericke, B. Völlm, T. Rieg, M. Keller (SATIS, 1995)

Über Leichen Zum Examen (2nd ed) - Timo Rieg, Birgit Völlm, Anya Feddersen, Corina Gericke (Timona Verlag, 1996)

2.2.2   General animal use and alternatives

Animal Experimentation: A Harvest of Shame - Moneim Fadali (Hidden Springs Press, 1997)

Animal Research: For and Against - Lesley Grayson (The British Library, 2000)

Animal Research Takes Lives - Bette Overell (NZAVS, 1993)

Biology, Ethics and Animals - Rosemary Rodd (Oxford University Press, 1994)

Brute Science: Dilemmas of Animal Experimentation - Hugh Lafollette & Niall Shanks (Routledge, 1996)

Cruel Deception: The Use of Animals in Medical Research - Robert Sharpe (Thorsons, 1990)

Experimentação Animal: A Sua Saúde em Perigo - Sergio Greif & Thales Tréz (Sociedade Educacional 'Fala Bicho', 2000)

In the Name of Science: Issues in Responsible Animal Experimentation - F. Barbara Orlans (Oxford University Press, 1993)

Lethal Laws: Animal Testing, Human Health, and Environmental Policy - Alex Fano (St. Martin's Press, 1977)

Lives in the Balance: The Ethics of Using Unimals in Biomedical Research - Jane A. Smith and Kenneth M. Boyd (Eds) (Oxford University Press, 1991)

Net Vet: Mosby's Veterinary Guide to the Internet - Ken Boschert (Mosby, 1998)

Sacred Cows and Golden Geese: The Human Cost of Experiments on Animals - C. Ray Greek & J. Greek (Continuum, 2000)

Searching for Information on Non-Animal Replacement Alternatives - Bottrill, K. (FRAME, 1999)

The Principles of Humane Experimental Technique - W.M.S. Russell & R.L. Burch (UFAW, 1992)

The Unheeded Cry: Animal Consciousness, Animal Pain, and Science (Expanded ed) - Bernard E. Rollin (Iowa State University Press, 1998)

Vivisection or Science? (2nd ed) - Pietro Croce (St. Martin's Press, 1999)

2.2.3   Pedagogics and the curriculum

Animal Care from Protozoa to Small Mammals - F. Barbara Orlans (Addison-Wesley Longman, 1977)

Democracy and Education: An Introduction to the Philosophy of Education - John Dewey (The Free Press, 1916)

Deschooling Society - Ivan Illich (Marion Boyars, 1996)

Dissection and Vivisection in the European Renaissance - Roger K. French (Ashgate Publishing Company, 1999)

Ecology Projects: Ideas and Projects for the Journal of Biological Education - D. Harding (Institute of Biology, 1992)

Empowering Education: Critical Teaching for Social Change - Ira Shor (University of Chicago Press, 1992)

Feeling Power: Emotions and Education - Megan Boler (Routledge, 1999)

Ideology and Curriculum - Michael W. Apple (2nd ed) (Routledge, 1990)

Laboratory Investigations in Human Physiology - George K. Russell (Macmillan, 1978)

Paulo Freire on Higher Education: A Dialogue at the National University of Mexico - Michael Escobar, Miguel Escobar, with Alfredo L. Fernandex (State University of New York Press, 1994)

Pedagogy of Freedom: Ethics, Democracy, and Civic Courage - Paulo Freire (Rowman & Littlefield, 1998)

Problem Based Service Learning: A Fieldguide for Making a Difference in Higher Education - Rick Gordon, Peter Temple, Amy McGlashan (Antioch New England Graduate School, 2000)

Teaching to Transgress: Education as the Practice of Freedom - bell hooks (Routledge, 1994)

The Courage to Teach: Exploring the Inner Landscape of a Teacher's Life - P J Palmer (Jossey-Bass, 1997)

The Hidden Curriculum in Higher Education - Eric Margolis (Routledge, 2001)

The Power of Problem-Based Learning: A Practical "how to" for Teaching Undergraduate Courses in Any Discipline - Barbara J. Duch, Deborah E. Allen, Susan E. Groh (eds) (Stylus Publishing, 2001)

Understanding by Design - Grant Wiggins & Jay McTighe (Association for Supervision & Curriculum Development, 1998)

Values across the Curriculum - Peter Tomlinson & Margaret Quinton (eds) (Taylor & Francis, 1986)

When Students Have Power: Negotiating Authority in a Critical Pedagogy - Ira Shor (University of Chicago Press, 1996)

2.2.4   Animal rights, ethics and critical thinking

A Practical Companion to Ethics - Anthony Weston (Oxford University Press, 1996)

Animal Liberation - Peter Singer (Pimlico 2nd ed, 1995)

Animal Revolution (Updated ed) - Richard Ryder (Berg Publishers, 2000)

Animal Rights and Human Morality (Revised ed) - Bernard Rollin (Prometheus, 1992)

Animal Rights and Human Obligations - Tom Regan & Peter Singer (eds) (2nd ed, Prentice Hall, 1989)

Animals and Why They Matter - Mary Midgley (University of Georgia Press, 1998)

Beyond Prejudice: The Moral Significance of Human and Nonhuman Animals - Evelyn B. Pulhar (Duke University Press, 1995)

Rain Without Thunder: The Ideology of the Animal Rights Movement - Gary L. Francione (Temple University Press, 1996)

Rattling the Cage: Toward Legal Rights for Animals - Steven M. Wise (Perseus, 2001)

Taking Animals Seriously - David DeGrazia (Cambridge University Press, 1996)

The Animal World of Albert Schweitzer - Albert Schweitzer, Charles R. Joy (ed) (HarperCollins, 1996)

The Case for Animal Rights - Tom Regan (University of California Press, 1985)

The Extended Circle - Jon Wynne-Tyson (ed) (Cardinal, 1990)

The Human Use of Animals: Case Studies in Ethical Choice - F. Barbara Orlans, Rebecca Dresser, John P. Gluck (eds) (Oxford University Press, 1998)

The Lives of Animals - J. M. Coetzee (Princeton University Press, 2001)

The Universal Declaration of Animal Rights: Comments and Intentions - Georges Chapouthier & Jean-Claude Nouet (eds) (Ligue Française des Droits de l'Animal, 1998)

The Words of Albert Schweitzer - Norman Cousins (Newmarket Press, 1996)

Tools of Critical Thinking: Metathoughts for Psychology - David A. Levy (Allyn & Bacon, 1996)

2.2.5   Animal lives and the human-animal bond

Animal Equality: Language and Liberation - Joan Dunayer (Ryce Publishing, 2001)

Animal Grace: Entering a Spiritual Relationship with Our Fellow Creatures - Mary Lou Randour & Susan Chernak McElroy (New World Library, 2000)

Biological Exuberance: Animal Homosexuality and Natural Diversity - Bruce Bagemihl (Profile, 1999)

Dogs That Know When Their Owners Are Coming Home - Rupert Sheldrake (Three Rivers Press, 2000)

Dolphin Dreamtime - Jim Nollman (Anthony Blond, 1985)

In the Company of Animals: A Study of Human-Animal Relationships - James Serpell (Cambridge University Press, 1996)

The Ape and the Sushi Master: Cultural Reflections of a Primatologist - Frans De Waal (Basic Books, 2001)

The Man Who Listens to Horses - Monty Roberts (Arrow, 1997)

The Parrot's Lament: And Other True Tales of Animal Intrigue, Intelligence, and Ingenuity - Eugene Linden (Dutton / Plume, 2000)

The Parrot Who Owns Me: The Story of a Relationship - Joanna Burger (Random House, 2001)

The Sacred Depths of Nature - Ursula Goodenough (Oxford University Press, 1998)

The Voice of the Infinite in the Small: Revisioning the Insect-Human Connection - Joanne E. Lauck (Granite, 1999)

When Elephants Weep - Jeffrey Masson & Susan McCarthy (Vintage, 1996)

2.2.6   Power, patriarchy, and links between oppressions

An Unnatural Order - Jim Mason (Continuum, 1997)

Animal Geographies: Place, Politics, and Identity in the Nature-Culture Borderlands - Jennifer Wolch & Jody Emel (eds) (Verso, 1998)

Animals and Women - Carole Adams (Duke University Press, 1995)

Beyond Animal Rights - Carole Adams (Continuum, 2000)

Child Abuse, Domestic Violence and Animal Abuse - Frank Ascione and Phil Arkow (Purdue, 1998)

Earth Ethics: Environmental Ethics, Animal Rights and Practical Applications - James P. Sterba (ed) (2nd ed, Prentice Hall, 1994)

Ecofeminism: Women, Animals and Nature - Greta Gaard (ed) (Temple University Press, 1993)

Feminism and Ecological Communities: An Ethic of Flourishing - Chris J. Cuomo (Routledge, 1998)

'Feminism and Ecology' in Society and Nature Journal (Vol 1, No 2) (Institute of Social Ecology / Society and Nature Press, 1993)

Feminism, Animals and Science: The Naming of the Shrew - Lynda Birke (Taylor & Francis, 1994)

More than the Parts: Biology and Politics - Lynda Birke & Jonathan Silvertown (eds) (Pluto Press, 1984)

Natural Relations: Ecology, Animal Rights and Social Justice - Ted Benton (Verso, 1993)

Neither Man nor Beast - Carole Adams (Continuum, 1994)

On Killing: The Psychological Cost of Learning to Kill in War and Society - Dave Grossman (Little, Brown & Co, 1996)

Rape of the Wild - Andrée Collard (Women's Press, 1988)

Science as Salvation: A Modern Myth and Its Meaning - Mary Midgley (Routledge, 1994)

The Animal Rights/Environmental Ethics Debate: The Environmental Perspective - Eugene C. Hargrove (ed) (State University of New York Press, 1992)

The Dreaded Comparison: Human and Animal Slavery - Marjorie Spiegel (Mirror, 1997)

The New Conscientious Objection: From Sacred to Secular Resistance - Charles C. Moskos & John Whiteclay Chambers (eds) (Oxford University Press, 1994)

The Old Brown Dog: Women, Workers, and Vivisection in Edwardian England - Carol Lansbury (University of Wisconsin Press, 1985)

The Rebirth of Nature - Rupert Sheldrake (Bantam, 1992)

The Rights of Nature: A History of Environmental Ethics - Roderick Frazier Nash (University of Wisconsin Press, 1989)

The Sexual Politics of Meat (10th Anniversary ed) - Carole Adams (Continuum, 1999)

The Turning Point - Fritjof Capra (Harper Collins, 1982)

Truth or Dare - Starhawk (Harper & Row, 1990)

Wisdom of the Elders: Honoring Sacred Native Visions of Nature - David T. Suzuki & Peter Knudtson (Bantam Books, 1993)

2.2.7   Personal empowerment

Coming Back to Life - Joanna R. Macy and Molly Young Brown (New Society, 1998)

Ethics into Action: Henry Spira and the Animal Rights Movement - Peter Singer (Rowman & Littlefield Publishers, 2000)

Growing Whole: Self-Realization on an Endangered Planet - Molly Young Brown (Hazleden, 1993)

In Our Nature: Stories of Wildness - Donna Seaman (ed) (Dorling Kindersley, 2001)

Pure Lust - Mary Daly (Women's Press, 2001)

Speaking Out for Animals: True Stories about Real People Who Rescue Animals - Kim W. Stallwood (ed) (Lantern Books, 2001)

Spiritual Intelligence - Danah Zohar and Ian Marshall (Bloomsbury, 2001)

The Path of Least Resistance - Robert Fritz (Fawcett Columbine, 1989)

The Primal Wound: A Transpersonal View of Trauma, Addiction, and Growth - John Firman and Ann Gila (State University of New York Press, 1997)

What We May Be: Techniques for Psychological and Spiritual Growth through Psychosynthesis - Piero Ferrucci (Thorsons, 1995)

3. Alternatives loan systems

3.1   Loan systems worldwide

Libraries of alternatives that can be borrowed by teachers, students and others. Small-scale 'micro-Loan Systems' are also being set up in Brazil, Russia, India and Japan - please contact InterNICHE for more details.

Each telephone code is written with a '+' to represent the international dialling code required from a specific country, followed by the country code. For calls made within the same country, the '+' and country code should not be dialled, and '0' added before the area code.

Animalearn
The Science Bank
801 Old York Road # 204
Jenkintown, PA 19046
USA
tel: +1 215 887 0816
fax: +1 215 887 2088
e-mail: info@animalearn.org
http://www.animalearn.org
http://www.humanestudent.org

ESEC (Ethical Science and Education Coalition)
Alternative Resource Center
333 Washington Street, Suite 850
Boston, MA 02108
USA
tel: +1 617 367 9143
fax: +1 617 523 7925
e-mail: esec@ma.neavs.com
http://www.neavs.org/esec

HSI (Humane Society International) (Australia)
Humane Education Loan Program - HELP
P.O. Box 439
Avalon NSW 2107
Australia
tel: +61 2 9973 1728
fax: +61 2 9973 1729
e-mail: alternatives@hsi.org.au
http://www.hsi.org.au

HSUS (Humane Society of the United States)
Humane Education Loan Program - HELP
Animal Research Issues
2100 L Street, NW
Washington, D.C. 20037
USA
tel: +1 301 258 3042
fax: +1 301 258 7760
e-mail: ari@hsus.org
http://www.hsus.org/ace/11378

InterNICHE (International Network for Humane Education)
Alternatives Loan System
Jurčičeva 18
9240 Ljutomer
Slovenia
tel: +386 2 583 1311
fax: +386 2 584 1407
e-mail: loansystem@interniche.org
http://www.interniche.org

NAVS (National Anti-Vivisection Society) (US)
Dissection Alternative Loan Program
53 W. Jackson Blvd., Suite 1552
Chicago, IL 60604
USA
tel: +1 312 427 6065
fax: +1 312 427 6524
e-mail: navs@navs.org
http://www.navs.org

RSPCA / InterNICHE
Ukraine Alternatives Library
c/o International Society for the Protection of Animals 'SOS'
Volodymyrska Str. 29
Kyiv 253003
Ukraine
tel/fax: +380 44 229 4295
e-mail: tamara@i-c.com.ua

3.2   InterNICHE Alternatives Loan System

A full list of products held in the InterNICHE Alternatives Loan System, according to discipline and medium. Further details of most products can be found in 'Part C - Alternatives File'. Products can be borrowed by teachers, students and others. As this is an evolving resource, please contact InterNICHE for the latest content.

Anaesthesia & Critical Care

 SOFTWARE

'Anaesthesia of Rats' (BSL)

'Innovations in Trauma Training' (PCRM)

'Virtual Ventilator' (Dr. R. D. Keegan, Washington State University)

 VIDEO

'Innovations in Trauma Training' (PCRM)

Anatomy

 SOFTWARE

'Anatomy Revealed' (Medical College of Ohio)

'Canine Osteology: An Interactive Atlas and Quiz' (UC Davis School of Veterinary Medicine)

'Cat Dissection Laboratory' (Neotek)

'Catworks' (Science Works)

'Comparative Anatomy: Mammals, Birds and Fish' (UC Davis School of Veterinary Medicine)

'DigiDiss' (DigiDiss Education AB)

'DissectionWorks Deluxe' (Science Works)

'Equine Osteology: An Interactive Atlas and Quiz' (UC Davis School of Veterinary Medicine)

'Frog Dissection Laboratory' (Neotek)

'MediClip Veterinary Anatomy' (Lippincott Williams & Wilkins)

'ProDissector: Frog' (Schneider & Morse Group)

'The Digital Frog 2' (Digital Frog International)

'The Dogfish' (University of Portsmouth)

'The Frog' (University of Portsmouth)

'The Heart in Depth' (Neotek)

'The Pigeon' (University of Portsmouth)

'The Rat - a Functional Anatomy' (University of Portsmouth)

'The Virtual Heart' (UC Davis School of Veterinary Medicine)

 VIDEO

'Dissection Techniques - Introduction and Muscles' (UC Davis School of Veterinary Medicine)

'Innervation of Superficial Structures of the Head' (UC Davis School of Veterinary Medicine)

'The Anatomy of the Freshwater Mussel' (Carolina Biological Supply)

'The Dissection of the Crab' (University of Liverpool)

'The Dogfish' (Media Development Centre)

'The Frog' (Media Development Centre)

'The Pigeon' (Media Development Centre)

'The Rat' (Media Development Centre)

 MODELS, MANNEKINS, SIMULATORS

'Plastinated Frog' (InterNICHE)

'Plastinated Rat' (InterNICHE)

Biochemistry & Cell Biology

 SOFTWARE

'Biochemical Simulations: Computer Simulation of Laboratory Exercises' (Dr. D. A. Bender)

'Investigation of Gluconeogenesis' (CLIVE)

'The Cell Is A City' (Neotek)

Clinical Skills & Surgery

 SOFTWARE

'P.O.P. Trainer' demo CD-ROM (OPTIMIST)

 VIDEO

'Catheterisation Techniques - Venous and Arterial' (UC Davis School of Veterinary Medicine)

'Early-age Neutering: A Practical Guide for Veterinarians' (AVAR, UC Davis School of Veterinary Medicine)

'Ovariohysterectomy in the Dog' (UC Davis School of Veterinary Medicine)

'P.O.P. Trainer' demo video (OPTIMIST)

'Surgical Anatomy of Superficial Vessels and Endotracheal Intubation' (UC Davis School of Veterinary Medicine)

'Suture and Suturing' (UC Davis School of Veterinary Medicine)

 MODELS, MANNEKINS, SIMULATORS

'Canine Foreleg Vascular Access Model' (UC Davis School of Veterinary Medicine)

'Canine Head Vascular Access Model' (UC Davis School of Veterinary Medicine)

'Critical Care 'Fluffy' CPR Mannekin' (Rescue Critters)

'Female K-9 Urinary Catheter Training Mannekin' (Rescue Critters)

'Hollow Organ Surgical Simulator' (Dr. D. D. Smeak)

''Jerry' K-9 CPR mannekin' (Rescue Critters)

'K-9 Intubation Trainer' (Rescue Critters)

'Koken Rat' (B&K Universal)

'P.O.P. Trainer' (OPTIMIST)

'Skin / Suture Pattern Simulator' (Dr. D. D. Smeak)

'Suture Trainer Arm' (Rescue Critters)

'Suture Trainer Skin Pad' (Soft Options)

'Intestine Anastomosis Model' (Alternavitae, Sawbones)

Pathology

 SOFTWARE

'Veterinary Neuropathology Modules' (UC Davis School of Veterinary Medicine)
'Veterinary Systemic Pathology' (UC Davis School of Veterinary Medicine)

Pharmacology

 SOFTWARE

'Basic Psychopharmacology' (COACS)
'Cat Nictitating Membrane' (Sheffield BioScience Programs)
'Langendorff Heart' (Sheffield BioScience Programs)
'Microlabs for Pharmacologists' (Dr. H. van Wilgenburg, University of Amsterdam)
'Mouse Watch' (British Pharmacological Society)
'Neuromuscular Pharmacology' (Sheffield BioScience Programs)
'Pictures Instead of Animals' (University of Newcastle upon Tyne)
'Respiratory Pharmacology' (Sheffield BioScience Programs)
'Simulations of Pharmacological Experiments on the Guinea Pig Ileum' (COACS)
'Simulations of Pharmacological Experiments on the Rabbit Jejunum' (COACS)
'The Pharmacology of Inflammation' (Sheffield BioScience Programs)

 VIDEO

'Control of Ventilation: Effects of Chemo and Mechano Receptors' (UC Davis School of Veterinary Medicine)
'Neuromuscular Blocking Agents' (UC Davis School of Veterinary Medicine)

Physiology

 SOFTWARE

'BioPac Student Lab' demo CD-ROMs (BioPac Systems)

'Cardiovascular System / Autonomic Nervous System Tutor' v3.0 (University of Aston, PCCAL)

'cLabs Neuron' (Dr. H. A. Braun, University of Marburg)

'Essentials of Human Physiology' (Gold Standard Multimedia)

'Experiments in Human Neuro-Muscular Physiology' (COACS)

'Frog Gastrocnemius Muscle - Sciatic Nerve Preparation' (COACS)

'Frog Heart' (Sheffield BioScience Programs)

'Hemodynamics Simulator 2001' (Anesoft)

'Intestinal Absorption' (Sheffield BioScience Programs)

'Muscle Control' (University of Gröningen)

'Muscle Physiology' (Sheffield BioScience Programs)

'Nerve Physiology' (Sheffield BioScience Programs)

'PhysioEx 3.0 - Laboratory Simulations in Physiology' (Benjamin Cummings)

'SimBioSys Physiology Labs' (Critical Concepts)

'SimHeart' (Georg Thieme Verlag)

'SimMuscle' (Georg Thieme Verlag)

'SimNerv' (Georg Thieme Verlag)

'SimPatch' (Georg Thieme Verlag)

'SimVessel' (Georg Thieme Verlag)

'Veterinary Physiology' (Prof. P. Rudas, Szent István University)

 VIDEO

'Advances in Medical Education' (PCRM)

'Fundamentals of Blood Gas Analysis: Collection, Measurement and Interpretation' (UC Davis School of Veterinary Medicine)

'Muscle Contractility' (UC Davis School of Veterinary Medicine)

Various Russian-language physiology videos

Miscellaneous

 Sᴏꜰᴛᴡᴀʀᴇ

'BioLab: Fly' (Carolina Biological Supply)
'Essentials of Immunology' (Gold Standard Multimedia)
'HyperCELL 1998' (Garland Publishing)
'Invertebrates Zoology: Multimedia Lab Assistant' (Tangent Scientific)
'Sniffy the Virtual Rat' (Thomson Learning)

 Vɪᴅᴇᴏ

'Alternatives in Education' (InterNICHE)
'Stimulus Response' (Association for the Study of Animal Behaviour)

4. Organisations

4.1   International

Organisations with an international remit that address alternatives in education, alternatives in general, humane education, and animal protection. Organisations may vary in their emphasis on replacement alternatives.

Each telephone code is written with a '+' to represent the international dialling code required from a specific country, followed by the country code. For calls made within the same country, the '+' and country code should not be dialled, and '0' added before the area code.

DLRM (Doctors & Lawyers for Responsible Medicine)
P.O. Box 302
London N8 9HD
UK
tel/fax: +44 208 340 9813
e-mail: dlrm@gn.apc.org
http://www.dlrm.org

ECOPA (European Consensus - Platform for Alternatives)
c/o Prof. Vera Rogiers
Vrije Universiteit Brussel
Faculteit Geneeskunde en Farmacie
Dienst Farmacognosie, Fytochemie en Toxicologie
Laarbeeklaan 103
B-1090 Brussel
Belgium
fax: +32 2 477 4582
e-mail: vera@fafy.vub.ac.be
http://ecopa.vub.ac.be

ECVAM (European Centre for the Validation of Alternative Methods)
European Commission
Joint Research Centre
Institute for Health and Consumer Protection
ECVAM Unit
21020 Ispra (VA)
Italy
tel: +39 0332 786256
fax: +39 0332 785 336
http://ecvam.jrc.it

EURCA (European Resource Centre for Alternatives in Higher Education)
http://www.eurca.org

c/o Jan van der Valk
NCA (Netherlands Centre Alternatives to Animal Use)
Faculty of Veterinary Sciences

Utrecht University
Yalelaan 17
NL-3584 CL Utrecht
The Netherlands
tel: +31 30 253 2163 / 2186
fax: +31 30 253 9227
e-mail: valk@las.vet.uu.nl

c/o David Dewhurst
Learning Technology Section
Faculty Group of Medicine & Veterinary Medicine
The University of Edinburgh
Hugh Robson Link Building
15 George Square
Edinburgh EH8 9XD
UK
tel/fax: +44 131 651 1564
e-mail: d.dewhurst@ed.ac.uk

Eurogroup for Animal Welfare
6 rue des Patriotes
1000 Brussels
Belgium
tel: +32 2 740 08 20
fax: +32 2 740 08 29
e-mail: info@eurogroupanimalwelfare.org
http://www.eurogroupanimalwelfare.org

European Coalition to End Animal Experiments
16a Crane Grove
London N7 8LB
UK
tel: +44 171 700 4888
fax: +44 171 700 0252
e-mail: eceae@buav.org
http://www.tierrechte.de/european-coalition

IAAPEA (International Association Against Painful Experiments on Animals)
P.O. Box 14
Hayling Island
Hampshire PO11 9BF
UK
tel/fax: +44 2392 463 738
e-mail: iaapea@hotmail.com
http://www.iaapea.com

InterNICHE (International Network for Humane Education)
19 Brookhouse Avenue
Leicester LE2 0JE
UK
tel/fax: +44 116 210 9652
e-mail: coordinator@interniche.org
http://www.interniche.org

PETA (People for the Ethical Treatment of Animals)
501 Front St.
Norfolk, VA 23510
USA
tel: +1 757 622 7382
fax: +1 757 622 0457
e-mail: info@peta-online.org
http://www.peta.org

RSPCA (Royal Society for the Prevention of Cruelty to Animals)
International Department
Wilberforce Way
Southwater
Horsham
West Sussex RH13 7WN
UK
tel: +44 870 754 0373
fax: +44 870 753 0373
e-mail: international@rspca.org.uk
http://www.rspca.org.uk

UFAW (Universities Federation for Animal Welfare)
The Old School
Brewhouse Hill
Wheathampstead
Hertfordshire AL4 8AN
tel: +44 1582 831 818
fax: +44 1582 831 414
e-mail: ufaw@ufaw.org.uk
http://www.ufaw.org.uk

WSPA (World Society for the Protection of Animals)
89 Albert Embankment
14th Floor
London SE1 7TP
UK
tel: +44 207 587 5000
fax: +44 207 793 0208
e-mail: wspa@wspa.org.uk
http://www.wspa.org.uk

4.2 By Country

Organisations that address alternatives in education, alternatives in general, humane education, and animal protection. Some countries also have local groups focusing on these issues, for example at individual universities. Organisations may vary in their emphasis on replacement alternatives.

Each telephone code is written with a '+' to represent the international dialling code required from a specific country, followed by the country code. For calls made within the same country, the '+' and country code should not be dialled, and '0' added before the area code.

Argentina

ADDA Argentina (Association for the Defence of Animal Rights)
P.O. Box 99 - Suc. 5 B
Buenos Aires
tel: +54 11 4856 7028
fax: +54 11 4857 1644
e-mail: adda@infovia.com.ar
http://usuarios.advance.com.ar/adda

Ánima
C.C. No. 3098 - Correo Central
C1000WBE
Buenos Aires
tel/fax: +54 11 4392 1478
http://www.anima.org.ar

Australia

AAHR (Australian Association for Humane Research)
P.O. Box 779
Darlinghurst NSW 1300
tel: +61 2 9360 1144
fax: +61 2 9361 6448
e-mail: humane@aahr.asn.au
http://www.aahr.asn.au

Animal Liberation Qld
P.O. Box 463
Annerley 4103
Brisbane
Queensland
tel: +61 7 3255 9572
fax: +61 7 3392 6102
e-mail: alibqld@powerup.com.au
http://www.powerup.com.au/~alibqld

ANZCAART (Australian and New Zealand Council for the Care of Animals in Research and Teaching)
Room 128, Darling Building
Department of Environmental Biology
Adelaide University
South Australia 5005
tel: +61 8 8303 7586
fax: +61 8 8303 7587
e-mail: anzccart@adelaide.edu.au
http://www.adelaide.edu.au/ANZCCART

ANZFAS (Australian and New Zealand Federation of Animal Societies)
Animals Australia - Humane Education Division
P.O. Box 1023
Collingwood
Victoria 3066
tel: +61 3 9329 6333
fax: +61 3 9329 6441
e-mail: enquiries@animalsaustralia.org
http://www.animalsaustralia.org

HSI (Humane Society International) (Australia)
P.O. Box 439
Avalon NSW 2107
Australia
tel: +61 2 9973 1728
fax: +61 2 9973 1729
e-mail: enquiry@hsi.org.au
http://www.hsi.org.au

InterNICHE Contact
Cynthia Burnett
c/o ANZFAS
Animals Australia - Humane Education Division
tel: +61 7 3379 2461
fax: +61 7 3716 0050
e-mail: cynthia@powerup.com.au

MAWA Trust (Medical Advances Without Animals)
P.O. Box 779
Darlinghurst NSW 1300
tel: +61 2 9360 1144
e-mail: info@mawa.asn.au
http://www.mawa.asn.au/

Austria

MEGAT (Middle European Society for Alternative Methods to Animal Testing)
P.O. Box 210
A-4021 Linz
tel: +43 1 815 1023
fax: +43 1 817 9404
e-mail: info@zet.or.at
http://www.zet.or.at/MEGAT

Belarus

Vitebsk Charitable Society 'Animal Friends'
Pravdy str. 8, Flat 19
Vitebsk   210015
tel: +375 0 212 23 66 56
e-mail: animalfriendsorg@rambler.ru
http://animals-friend.iatp.by

Belgium

APMA (Action Against Laboratory Animal Abuse)
De Burletlaan 4
B-2650 Edegem
tel: +32 3 449 4908
fax: +32 3 448 2663
e-mail: apma@pandora.be
http://www.apma.be

GAIA (Global Action in the Interest of Animals)
Paleizenstraat 90
1030 Brussels
tel: +32 2 245-29-50
fax: +32 2 215-09-43
e-mail: info@gaia.be
http://www.gaia.be

InterNICHE contact (Flemish-speaking)
René Votion
c/o APMA
tel: +32 3 449 4908
fax: +32 3 448 2663
e-mail: apma@pandora.be

InterNICHE contact (French-speaking)
Bruno Lecomte
c/o S.E.A.-S.E.D.
Koninksemstraat 156
3700 Tongeren
tel/fax: +32 12 672 551
e-mail: lbruno@wanadoo.be

S.E.A.-S.E.D. (Stop Experiments on Living Animals)
Rue Saint-Nicolas 84
5000 Namur
tel/fax: +32 81 26 26 90
e-mail: lbruno@wanadoo.be
http://sea-sed.org

UBAEAV (Belgian Union for the Abolition of Experimentation on Living Animals)
Rue Henri Van Zuylen 21
1180 Brussels
tel: +32 2 376 82 23

Brazil

ARCA Brasil (Brazil Ark Humane Society)
Rua Pascoal Vita, 336
São Paulo - SP - CEP 05445-000
tel: +55 11 3031 6991
e-mail: arcabrasil@arcabrasil.org.br
http://www.arcabrasil.org.br

FBAV (Brazilian Front for the Abolition of Vivisection)
Caixa Postal 8169
CEP 21032-970 Rio de Janeiro, RJ
tel: +55 (21) 9962 1526
fax: +55 (21) 260 9103
e-mail: bastompa@antares.com.br
http://www.geocities.com/Petsburgh/8205

InterNICHE Brazil - Information Network for Humane Education
Caixa Postal 758
CEP 88010-970
Florianópolis/SC
tel: +55 48 233 2410
e-mail: info@internichebrasil.org
http://www.internichebrasil.org

InterNICHE contact
Thales Tréz
c/o InterNICHE Brazil
tel: +55 48 233 2410
e-mail: thalestrez@yahoo.com

'Fala Bicho' Educational Society
Caixa Postal 31047
CEP: 20732-970, Rio de Janeiro - RJ
tel: +55 21 568 1708
e-mail: falabicho@infolink.com.br
http://www.falabicho.org.br

Canada

ADLC (Animal Defence League of Canada)
P.O. Box 3880, Stn. C
Ottawa, ON
K1Y 4M5
tel/fax: +1 613 233 6117
http://www.ncf.ca/animal-defence

Alberta SPCA (Society for the Prevention of Cruelty to Animals)
10806 124 St.
Edmonton AB
T5M 0H3
tel: +1 780 447 3600
fax: +1 780 447 4748
e-mail: info@albertaspca.org
http://www.albertaspca.org

Animal Alliance of Canada
221 Broadview Avenue, Suite 101
Toronto, ON
M4M 2G3
tel: +1 416 462 9541
fax: +1 416 462 9647
e-mail: info@animalalliance.ca
http://www.AnimalAlliance.ca

Canadian Council on Animal Care
315-350 Albert Street
Ottawa, ON
K1R 1B1
tel: +1 613 238 4031, ext. 29
fax: +1 613 238 2837
e-mail: mbedard@ccac.ca
http://www.ccac.ca

Canadian Federation of Humane Societies
102-30 Concourse Gate
Nepean, ON
K2E 7V7
tel: +1 613 224 8072
fax: +1 613 723 0252
e-mail: info@cfhs.ca
http://www.cfhs.ca

Centre for Compassionate Living
Waterloo Public Interest Research Group
University of Waterloo
Student Life Centre, Room 2139
200 University Avenue West
Waterloo, ON
N2L 3G1
tel: +1 519 888 4882
fax: +1 519 725 3093
e-mail: info@wpirg.org
http://wpirg.org

Croatia

InterNICHE contact
Sonja Desnica
Maretićeva 4
10000 Zagreb
tel: +385 1 667 3260
e-mail: ratfroglive@yahoo.com

Cuba

InterNICHE contact
Ulpiano Pérez Marqués
c/o TOXIMED
tel: +53 226 643838
fax: +53 226 687188
e-mail: uperez@toxi.scu.sld.cu

TOXIMED (Centre for Toxicology and Biomedicine)
Autopista Nacional Km 1.5
Apartado 4033, C.P. 90400
Santiago de Cuba
tel: +53 226 643838
fax: +53 226 687188
e-mail: uperez@toxi.scu.sld.cu

Czech Republic

InterNICHE contact
Markéta Pecková
c/o Spolecnost pro zvířata
tel/fax: +420 2 74 78 24 97
e-mail: s.pro.zvirata@ecn.cz

Nadace na ochranu zvířat (Animal Protection Trust)
Olbrachtova 3
140 00 Prague 4
tel: +420 241 440012
fax: +420 241 441005
e-mail: nadace@core.cz
http://www.ochranazvirat.cz

Společnost pro zvířata (Society for Animals)
P.O. Box 121
140 21 Prague 4
tel: +420 603 851 334
e-mail: s.pro.zvirata@ecn.cz
http://www.spolecnostprozvirata.cz

Svoboda zvířat (Animal Freedom)
Koterovska 84
326 00 Plzeň
tel/fax: +420 377 444 084
e-mail: svoboda.zvirat@email.cz
http://www.svobodazvirat.cz

Denmark

Alternativfondet (Alternatives Fund)
c/o Forsøgsdyrenes Værn
http://www.forsoegsdyrenes-vaern.dk

Dyrenes Beskyttelse (Animal Protection Society)
Alhambravej 15
1826 Frederiksberg C
tel: +45 3 322 3222
e-mail: db@dyrenes-beskyttelse.dk
http://www.dyrenes-beskyttelse.dk

Dyrenes Venner (Animal Friends)
Nordre Strandvej 194 N
3140 Ålsgårde

tel: +45 7027 3717
e-mail: dv@dyrenes-venner.dk
http://www.dyrenes-venner.dk

Forsøgsdyrenes Værn (Society for the Protection of Laboratory Animals)
Øster Søgade 32
DK-1357 Copenhagen K
tel: +45 33 32 00 16
fax: +45 33 32 81 12
http://www.forsoegsdyrenes-vaern.dk

InterNICHE contact
Mrs Bente Lakjer
c/o Forsøgsdyrenes Værn
tel: +45 33 32 00 16
fax: +45 33 32 81 12
e-mail: education@rats.dk

Estonia

Estonian Academic Society for Animal Welfare
Kreutzwaldi 62
51014 Tartu
tel: +37 27 313206
fax: +37 27 422582
e-mail: aland@eau.ee
http://www.eau.ee/~ereintam/easaw.htm

InterNICHE contact
Evald Reintam
Kreutzwaldi 62
51014 Tartu
tel: +37 27 313206
fax: +37 27 422582
e-mail: ereintam@eau.ee

Finland

Animalia - Federation for the Protection of Animals
Porvoonkatu 53
00520 Helsinki
tel: +358 9 146 4866
fax: +358 9 148 4622
e-mail: asiakaspalvelu@animalia.fi
http://www.animalia.fi

InterNICHE contact
Hanna Kurppa
Viljelijantie 4-6 B 43
00410 Helsinki
tel: +358 50 369 6902
e-mail: hkurppa@uiah.fi

Juliana von Wendt's Fund
Porvoonkatu 53
00520 Helsinki
tel: +358 9 146 4865
fax: +358 9 148 4622
e-mail: jvws@jvws.fi
http://www.animalia.fi/jvw-saatio.htm

France

InterNICHE contact
Anne Leenknegt
1 Rue Maurice Ravel
59166 Bousbeque
tel/fax: +33 3 20 23 60 21
e-mail: anne-leenknegt@wanadoo.fr

LFCV (French League Against Vivisection)
84, rue Blanche
75009 Paris
e-mail: lfcv@club-internet.fr
http://perso.club-internet.fr/lfcv

Pro Anima
16, rue Vézelay
75008 Paris
tel: +33 1 45 63 10 89
fax: +33 1 45 63 47 94
e-mail: pro.anima@wanadoo.fr
http://perso.wanadoo.fr/proanima

Georgia

Animal Rights Committee
c/o Manana Gabashvili
9 Barnov Street, Apt. 6
Tbilisi, 380008

tel: +995 (8) 77 469 197
fax: +995 32 251501
e-mail: arc@animalrights.ge
http://www.animalrights.ge

InterNICHE contact
Irina Tsirkvadze
c/o Manana Gabashvili
9 Barnov Street, Apt. 6
Tbilisi 380008
tel: +995 77 469197
fax: +995 32 251501
e-mail: irina_tsirkvadze@hotmail.com

Germany

Akademie für Tierschutz (Academy for Animal Protection)
Spechtstr. 1
D-85579 Neubiberg
tel: +49 89 60 02910
fax: +49 89 6 00 291 15
e-mail: akademie@tierschutzbund.de
http://www.tierschutzbund.de

Ärzte gegen Tierversuche (Doctors Against Animal Experiments)
Nußzeil 50
D-60433 Frankfurt/Main
tel: +49 69 51 94 11
fax: +49 69 51 95 07
e-mail: info@aerzte-gegen-tierversuche.de
http://aerzte-gegen-tierversuche.tierrechte.de

BVTVG (Federal Association Against Vivisection - People for Animal Rights Germany)
Roermonder Straße 4a
D-52072 Aachen
tel: +49 2 41 15 72 14
fax: +49 2 41 15 56 42
e-mail: info@tierrechte.de
http://www.tierrechte.de

InterNICHE contact
Astrid Schneider
e-mail: batty89@yahoo.de

SATIS (Student Workgroup Against Animal Misuse in Education)
Roermonder Straße 4a
52072 Aachen
tel: +49 241 157 214
fax: +49 241 155 642
e-mail: satis@tierrechte.de
http://www.tierrechte.de/satis

SET (Foundation for the Promotion of Research on Replacement and Complementary Methods to Reduce Animal Testing)
Kaiserstraße 60
55116 Mainz
tel: +49 6131 23 77 89
fax: + 49 6131 23 56 98
e-mail: info@tierversuche-ersatz.de
http://www.tierversuche-ersatz.de

ZEBET (Centre for Documentation and Evaluation of Alternatives to Animal Experiments)
Federal Institute for Risk Assessment (BfR)
Diedersdorfer weg 1
D-12277 Berlin
tel: +49 1 888 412 2270
fax: +49 1 888 412 2958
e-mail: zebet@bfr.bund.de
http://www.bfr.bund.de

Greece

Doctors in Greece for Responsible Medicine
P.O. Box 77022
Pales Falirs 17501
Athens
tel: +30 1 983 3101

Hungary

InterNICHE contact
Dávid Karátson
Öv u. 114 / 6
1141 Budapest
tel: +36 1 252 2441
fax: +36 1 209 0555
e-mail: dkarat@ludens.elte.hu

Fauna Egyesűlet (Fauna Society)
Vadász u. 29
H-1054 Budapest
tel/fax: +36 1 302 1686
e-mail: fauna@zpok.hu
http://www.fauna.enviroweb.org

India

Blue Cross of India
1 Eldams Road
Chennai - 600 018
tel: +91 44 2434 1778
fax: +91 44 2234 9801
e-mail: bluecross@aspick.com
http://www.bluecross.org.in

CPCSEA (Committee for the Purpose of Control and Supervision of Experiments on Animals)
AWBI Complex
3rd Seaward Road
Valmiki Nagar
Thiruvanmiyur
Chennai 600 041
tel: +91 44 2441 6914
fax: +91 44 2440 3531
e-mail: cpcsea@eth.net
http://www.cpcsea.org

InterNICHE contact
Shiranee Pereira
c/o CPCSEA
tel: +91 44 2441 6914
fax: +91 44 2440 3531
e-mail: shiraneep@hotmail.com

People for Animals
14, Ahoka Road
New Delhi 110 001
tel: +91 11 2335 5883
fax: +91 11 2335 4321
e-mail: gandhim@alpha.nic.in

Israel

HaKol Chai (All Life)
P.O. Box 51858
Tel Aviv
tel: +972 3 624 3242
fax: +972 3 561 7937
e-mail: shiraskolnik@hotmail.com
http://www.chai.org.il

InterNICHE contact
Tamir Lousky
8th Keren Ha Yessod St.
Apartment #16
Bat-Yam 59624
tel: +972 3 553 6397
fax: +972 3 552 5013
e-mail: ns_tamirl@bezeqint.net

ISAV (Israeli Society for the Abolition of Vivisection)
P.O. Box 519
Givatayim 53104
tel: +972 3 635 9014
e-mail: isav@isav.org.il
http://www.isav.org.il

Italy

CSA (Scientific Committee Against Vivisection)
Via P. A. Micheli 62
00197 Rome
tel: +39 6 322 0720
fax: +39 6 322 5370
e-mail: csafin@iol.it
http://www.antivivisezione.it

InterNICHE contact
Marina Berati
Via Pragelato 9
10139 Torino
e-mail: interniche_italia@yahoo.co.uk

LAV (Anti-Vivisection League)
Via Sommacampagna 29
00185 Roma
tel: +39 6 446 1325
fax: +39 6 446 1326

e-mail: lav@infolav.org
http://www.infolav.org

LEAL (Anti-Vivisectionist League)
Via Settala 2
20124 Milano
tel: +39 2 2940 1323
e-mail: parliamone@leal.it
http://www.leal.it

MOUSE (University Movement of Objectors to Animal Experiments)
Via Chini 17
38100 Trento
tel: +39 0461 922040
fax: +39 0461 398765
e-mail: mouse@unimondo.org

Novivisezione (Novivisection)
tel: +39 0335 671 6494
e-mail: info@novivisezione.org
http://www.novivisezione.org

Japan

ALIVE (All Life in a Viable Environment)
1-17-16 Honkomagome
Bunkyo-ku
Tokyo 113-0021
tel: + 81 3 5978 6272
fax: + 81 3 5978 6273
e-mail: alive@jca.apc.org
http://www.alive-net.net

AVA-net (Anti-Vivisection Action)
c/o ALIVE
tel: +81 3 5978 6272
fax: +81 3 5978 6273
e-mail: office@ava-net.net
http://www.alive-net.net

InterNICHE contact
Makiko Nakano
2-34-11 Shichirigahama-higashi
Kamakura City
Kanagawa-Ken 248
tel/fax +81 467 31 7202
e-mail: me437799@members.interq.or.jp

JAVA (Japan Anti-Vivisection Association)
4-9-18-411 Shibaura
Minami-ku
Tokyo 108-0023
tel: +81 3 5419 8106
fax: +81 3 5419 8107
e-mail: java@blue.ocn.ne.jp
http://java.enviroweb.org

JSAAE - Japanese Society for Alternatives to Animal Experiments
http://jsaae.jp

[The] Netherlands

InterNICHE contact
Heleen van Kernebeek
Boschplein 9
9671 GB Winschoten
tel: +31 59 742 2198
e-mail: H.R.J.van.Kernebeek@student.rug.nl

NCA (Netherlands Centre Alternatives to Animal Use)
Department for Animals and Society
Faculty of Veterinary Medicine
Utrecht University
Yalelaan 17
NL-3584 CL Utrecht
tel: +31 30 253 2186
fax: +31 30 253 9227
e-mail: valk@las.vet.uu.nl
http://www.nca-nl.org

NVBD (Dutch Society for the Protection of Animals)
Floris Grijpstraat 2
Postbus 85980
NL - 2508 CR Den Haag
tel: +31 70 314 2700
fax: +31 70 314 2777
e-mail: info@dierenbescherming.nl
http://www.dierenbescherming.nl

Proefdiervrij
Groot Hertoginnelaan 201
2517 ES Den Haag
tel: +31 70 306 24 68
fax: +31 70 306 24 64
e-mail: info@proefdiervrij.nl
http://www.proefdiervrij.nl

New Zealand (Aotearoa)

ANZCAART (Australian and New Zealand Council for the Care of Animals in Research and Teaching)
The Executive Officer
C/- The Royal Society of New Zealand
P.O. Box 598
Wellington
tel: +64 4 472 7421
fax: +64 4 473 1841
e-mail: anzccart@rsnz.govt.nz
http://anzccart.rsnz.govt.nz

ARLAN (Animal Rights Legal Advocacy Network)
Birkenhead
P.O. Box 6065
Wellesley St.
Auckland
e-mail: contact@arlan.org.nz
http://www.arlan.org.nz

AVA (Anti-Vivisection Association)
P.O. Box 7213
Wellesley St
Auckland
e-mail: avanz@paradise.net.nz

InterNICHE contact
Deidre Bourke
26 Lloyd Ave.
Mt. Albert
Auckland
tel: +64 9 846 8933
e-mail: dbourke@paradise.net.nz

NZAVS (New Zealand Anti-Vivisection Society)
P.O. Box 9387
Christchurch
e-mail: phil@kiwimail.net.nz
http://www.nzavs.org.nz

SAFE (Save Animals From Exploitation)
P.O. Box 13366
Armagh
Christchurch
tel/fax: +64 3 379 9711
e-mail: safe@chch.planet.co.nz
http://www.safe.org.nz

Norway

Dyrebeskyttelsens Fond for Alternativ Forskning (Fund for Alternatives)
c/o Dyrebeskyttelsen Norge
tel: +47 23 13 92 50
fax: +47 23 13 92 51
e-mail: post@dyrebeskyttelsen.no
http://www.dyrebeskyttelsen.no

InterNICHE contact
Siri Martinsen
c/o NOAH
tel/fax: +46 570 40135
e-mail: siri@noahonline.org

NOAH - for Animal Rights
Osterhausgt. 12
0183 Oslo
Norway
tel/fax: +47 22 114163
e-mail: noah@noahonline.org
http://www.noahonline.org

Dyrebeskyttelsen Norge (Norwegian Federation for Animal Protection)
Karl Johans gate 6
0154 Oslo
tel: +47 23 13 92 50
fax: +47 23 13 92 51
e-mail: post@dyrebeskyttelsen.no
http://www.dyrebeskyttelsen.no

Poland

InterNICHE contact
Liza Kodym-Flanagan
05-090 Raszyn
P.O. Box (SKR.) 40
tel: +48 504 570 947
e-mail: lizakodym.interniche@poczta.fm

Portugal

InterNICHE contact
Maria Eugénia Webb
New University of Lisbon
Faculty of Science and Technology
2829-516 Portugal
tel: +351 21 412 04 26
fax: +351 21 294 85 54
e-mail: MariaEWebb@netscape.net

Romania

InterNICHE contact
Alina Bodnariu
Str. Vistiernic Stavrinos, Nr. 15
Bl. 55, Ap. 44, Sector 6
Bucharest 77629
tel: +40 21 769 9642
e-mail: alinare@email.ro

Russia

CETA - Centre for the Ethical Treatment of Animals
39-3-23 Volzsky Bulvar
Moscow 109462
tel: +7095 172 8633
fax: +7095 170 7029
e-mail: ceta_russia@mail.ru
http://greenlife.narod.ru

InterNICHE contact
Elena Maroueva
Mutnaye 62-93

Moscow 115191
tel/fax: +7095 95 49279
e-mail: Elena-Maroueva@yandex.ru

Slovakia

InterNICHE contact
Jana Bohdanová
Havličkova 39
04 001 Košice
tel: +421 55 63 37852
e-mail: bohdaj@kiwwi.sk

Sloboda Zvierat (Animal Freedom)
Sološnická 10
841 04 Bratislava 4
tel/fax: +421 2 6542 1961
e-mail: info@sloboda.sk
http://www.slobodazvierat.sk

Slovenia

InterNICHE contact
Monika Perčić
Jurčičeva 18
9240 Ljutomer
tel: +386 2 583 1311
fax: +386 2 584 1407
e-mail: lolioli@hotmail.com

South Africa

Humane Education Trust
Suite 191 Postnet
Private Bag X29
Somerset West 7129
tel: +27 21 852 8160
fax: +27 21 852 4402
e-mail: avoice@yebo.co.za
http://www.animal-voice.org

InterNICHE contact
Gina Walsh
P.O. Box 84
Florida, Johannesburg 1710
tel: +27 11 672 7404
fax: +27 11 674 3278
e-mail: alfwalsh@iafrica.com

SAAV (South Africans for the Abolition of Vivisection)
P.O. Box 3018
Honeydew, Johannesburg 2040
tel/fax: +27 11 472 2380
e-mail: saav@sn.apc.org
http://www.saav.org.za

Spain

ADDA (Association for the Defence of Animal Rights)
c/ Bailén 164
local 2 interior
08037 Barcelona
tel: +34 93 459 1601
e-mail: adda@addaong.org
http://www.addaong.org

ALA (Alternatives for Animal Liberation)
c/ Montera 34 6o 1
28013 Madrid
tel/fax: +34 91 532 84 95
e-mail: liberacion@gmx.net
http://www.liberacionanimal.org

Fundación Altarriba (Altarriba Foundation)
Rambla de Catalunya 14
08007 Barcelona
tel: +34 93 412 00 73
fax: +34 93 412 15 54
e-mail: altarriba@altarriba.org
http://www.altarriba.org

GTEMA (Spanish Group on Alternative Methods)
Instituto Nacional de Toxicología
Apdo Postal 863
41080 - Sevilla
tel: +34 9 5 437 1233
fax: +34 9 5 437 0262
e-mail: repetto@cica.es
http://tox.umh.es/aet/gtema

InterNICHE contact
Nuria Querol i Viñas
Baixada de l'Alba 16 2o 1a
08190 St. Cugat del Vallès
Barcelona
tel: +34 93 674 6883
e-mail: gevha@AnimalProtector.com

Sweden

Djurens Rätt (Animal Rights Sweden)
Box 2005
SE-125 02 Älvsjö
tel: +46 8 555 914 00
fax: +46 8 555 914 50
e-mail: info@djurensratt.org
http://www.djurensratt.org

FSMD (Researchers and Students Against Speciesism)
c/o Mikael Mildén
Dept. of Botany, Stockholm University
SE-10691 Stockholm
e-mail: c_sahlgren@hotmail.com
http://welcome.to/fsmd

InterNICHE contact
Ursula Zinko
Istidsgatan 53
SE-906 55 Umea
tel: +46 90 197740
e-mail: tussen@kommunicera.umea.se

NICA (Nordic Information Centre for Alternative Methods)
Vintervägen 17
SE-182 74 Stocksund
tel: +46 8 622 55 65
fax: +46 8 753 49 51
e-mail: c.clemedson@cctoxconsulting.a.se
http://www.cctoxconsulting.a.se/nica.htm

Swedish Fund for Research Without Animal Experiments
Gamla Huddingevägen 437
SE-125 42 Älvsjö
tel: +46 8 749 03 40
fax: +46 8 749 13 40
e-mail: info@stifud.a.se
http://www.algonet.se/~stifud

Switzerland

FFVFF (Fund for Animal-Free Research)
Hegarstrasse 9
Postfach 1766
CH-8032 Zürich
tel: +41 1 422 7070
fax: +41 1 422 8010
e-mail: ffvff@bluewin.ch
http://www.ffvff.ch

InterNICHE contact
Vanna Maria Tatti
18 Rue Albert Gos
1206 Geneva
tel: +41 22 347 5196
e-mail: vanna@infomaniak.ch

LSCV (Swiss League Against Vivisection)
3 chemin des Arcs-en-Ciel
1226 Thônex GE
tel: +41 22 349 73 37
fax: +41 22 349 19 54
e-mail: lscv@bluewin.ch
http://www.lscv.ch

3R Research Foundation
Postfach 1372
CH-3110 Münsingen
tel: +41 31 722 08 30
fax: +41 31 721 70 80
e-mail: Secretary.3r@bluewin.ch
http://www.forschung3r.ch

Ukraine

Centre for the Ethical Treatment of Animals (CETA) - 'LIFE'
Stepnaya Str. 23
Malaya Danilovka
Dergachevsky raion
Kharkovskaya oblast 62341
tel/fax: +380 576 331 825
e-mail: cry@3s.kharkov.ua

International Society for the Protection of Animals 'SOS'
Volodymyrska Str. 29
Kyiv 253003
tel/fax: +380 44 229 4295
e-mail: tamara@i-c.com.ua

InterNICHE contact
Anya Yushchenko
ul. Sumskaya, 74, kv.7
Kharkov 310078
tel: +380 572 438133
e-mail: agyu@3s.kharkov.ua

UK

Advocates for Animals
10 Queensferry Street
Edinburgh EH2 4PG
tel: +44 131 225 6039
fax: +44 131 220 6377
e-mail: mail@advocatesforanimals.com
http://www.advocatesforanimals.org.uk

Animal Aid
The Old Chapel, Bradford Street
Tonbridge
Kent TN9 1AW
tel: +44 (0)1732 364546
fax: +44 (0)1732 366533
e-mail: info@animalaid.org.uk
http://www.animalaid.org.uk

BUAV (British Union for the Abolition of Vivisection)
16a Crane Grove
London N7 8NN
tel: +44 207 700 4888
fax: +44 207 700 0252
e-mail: info@buav.org
http://www.buav.org

Dr. Hadwen Trust
84A Tilehouse Street
Hitchin
Hertfordshire SG5 2DY
tel: +44 1462 436819
fax: +44 1462 436844
e-mail: info@drhadwentrust.org.uk
http://www.drhadwentrust.org.uk

FRAME (Fund for the Replacement of Animals in Medical Experiments)
Russell & Burch House
96-98 North Sherwood Street
Nottingham NG1 4EE
tel: +44 115 958 4740
fax: +44 115 950 3570
e-mail: frame@frame.org.uk
http://www.frame.org.uk

InterNICHE (International Network for Humane Education)
19 Brookhouse Avenue
Leicester LE2 0JE
tel/fax: +44 116 210 9652
e-mail: coordinator@interniche.org
http://www.interniche.org

Lord Dowding Fund for Humane Research
c/o NAVS
tel: 020 8846 9777
fax: 020 8846 9712
e-mail: info@ldf.org.uk
http://www.ldf.org.uk

NAVS (National Anti-Vivisection Society)
261 Goldhawk Road
London W12 9PE
tel: 020 8563 0250
fax: 020 8563 8146
e-mail: info@navs.org.uk
http://www.navs.org.uk

RSPCA (Royal Society for the Prevention of Cruelty to Animals)
Wilberforce Way
Southwater
Horsham
West Sussex RH13 7WN
tel: +44 870 010 1181
fax: + 44 870 753 0048
http://www.rspca.org.uk

St. Andrew Animal Fund
c/o Advocates for Animals
tel: +44 131 225 2116
fax: +44 131 220 6377
e-mail: mail@advocatesforanimals.com
http://www.advocatesforanimals.org.uk

Students for Ethical Science (The Open University)
c/o 6 Monks Park
Ridgegrove Hill
Launceston
Cornwall PL15 9QW
tel: +44 1566 776327
e-mail: vivien.karuna@tinyonline.co.uk

Uncaged Campaigns
2nd Floor
St. Matthews House
45 Carver Street
Sheffield S1 4FT
tel: +44 114 272 2220
fax: +44 114 272 2225
e-mail: info@uncaged.co.uk
http://www.uncaged.co.uk

USA

AAVS (American Anti-Vivisection Society)
801 Old York Road # 204
Jenkintown, PA 19046
tel: +1 215 887 0816
fax: +1 215 887 2088
e-mail: aavs@aavs.org
http://www.aavs.org

AFAAR (American Fund for Alternatives to Animal Research)
175 West 12th St.
New York, NY 10011
tel: +1 212 989 8073

ALDF (Animal Legal Defense Fund)
127 Fourth Street
Petaluma, CA 94952
tel: +1 707 769 7771
fax: +1 707 769 0785
e-mail: info@aldf.org
http://www.aldf.org

Animal Emancipation
5632 Van Nuys Boulevard, Suite 50
Van Nuys, CA 91401
tel: +1 805 655 5735
e-mail: aeinc@mainnet.com
http://www.aeinc-online.org

Animal Rights Legal Foundation, Inc.
108 N. Columbus Street
Alexandria, VA 22314
tel: +1 866 206 9066 x9259
e-mail: info@animalrightslaw.org
http://www.animalrightslaw.org

Animal Rights Online
e-mail: EnglandGal@aol.com
http://www.geocities.com/RainForest/1395

Animalearn
801 Old York Road # 204
Jenkintown, PA 19046
tel: +1 215 887 0816
fax: +1 215 887 2088
e-mail: info@animalearn.org
http://www.animalearn.org
http://www.humanestudent.org

Animals Voice
1354 East Avenue #252
Chico, CA 95926
fax: +1 530 343 2498
e-mail: info@animalsvoice.com
http://www.Animalsvoice.com

ARDF (Alternatives Research and Development Foundation)
15050 Cedar Ave. S. / PMB 343
Apple Valley, MN 55124
fax: +1 952 949 2619
e-mail: ardfjmc@aol.com
http://www.aavs.org

ASPCA (American Society for the Prevention of Cruelty to Animals)
424 E. 92nd St
New York, NY 10128
tel: +1 212 876 7700
fax: +1 212 860 3435
e-mail: education@aspca.org
http://www.aspca.org

AVAR (Association of Veterinarians for Animal Rights)
P.O. Box 208
Davis, CA 95617
tel: +1 530 759 8106
fax: +1 530 759 8116
e-mail: info@avar.org
http://www.avar.org

AWI (Animal Welfare Institute)
P.O. Box 3650
Washington, DC 20007
tel: +1 202 337 2332
fax: +1 202 338 9478
http://www.awionline.org

AWIC (Animal Welfare Information Center)
U.S. Department of Agriculture
Agricultural Research Service
National Agricultural Library
10301 Baltimore Avenue, 5th Floor
Beltsville, MD 20705
tel: +1 301 504 6212
fax: +1 301 504 7125
e-mail: awic@nal.usda.gov
http://www.nal.usda.gov/awic

CAAT (Johns Hopkins Center for Alternatives to Animal Testing)
Johns Hopkins University Bloomberg School of Public Health
111 Market Place / Suite 840
Baltimore, MD 21202
tel: +1 410 223 1693
fax: +1 410 223 1603
e-mail: caat@jhsph.edu
http://caat.jhsph.edu

CHAI (Concern for Helping Animals in Israel)
P.O. Box 3341
Alexandria, VA 22302
tel: +1 703 658 9650
fax: +1 703 941 6132
e-mail: chai_us@compuserve.com
http://www.chai-online.org

Doctors Against Dog Labs
e-mail: nlharrison@cox.net
http://www.doctorsagainstdoglabs.com

Doris Day Animal League
227 Massachusetts Ave.
NE Suite 100
Washington, DC 20002
tel: +1 202 546 1761
fax: +1 202 546 2193
e-mail: info@ddal.org
http://www.ddal.org

EETA/CRABS (Ethologists for the Ethical Treatment of Animals / Citizens for Responsible Animal Behavior Studies)
e-mail: bekoffm@spot.colorado.edu
http://www.ethologicalethics.org

ESAR (Engineers and Scientists for Animal Rights)
173 Hawthorne Way
San Jose, CA 95110
tel/fax: +1 408 971 6657
e-mail: ESAR01@aol.com

ESEC (Ethical Science and Education Coalition
333 Washington St., Suite 850
Boston, MA 02108
tel: +1 617 367 9143
fax: +1 617 523 7925
e-mail: esec@ma.neavs.com
http://www.neavs.org/esec

Feminists for Animal Rights
P.O. Box 41355
Tucson AZ 85717
tel: +1 520 825 6852
e-mail: far@farinc.org
http://www.farinc.org

HSUS (Humane Society of the United States)
2100 L Street, NW
Washington, DC 20037
tel: +1 301 258 3042
fax: +1 301 258 7760
e-mail: ari@hsus.org
http://www.hsus.org/ace/14028

Humane Education Network
P.O. Box 7434
Menlo Park, CA 94026
tel: +1 650 854 8921
e-mail: hennet2@aol.com
http://www.hennet.org

IFER (International Foundation for Ethical Research)
53 West Jackson Boulevard
Suite 1552
Chicago, IL 60604
tel: +1 312 427 6025
e-mail: ifer@navs.org
http://www.ifer.org

In Defense of Animals
131 Camino Alto
Suite E
Mill Valley, CA 94941
tel: +1 415 388 9641
fax: +1 415 388 0388
e-mail: ida@idausa.org
http://www.idausa.org

International Institute of Humane Education - Center for Compassionate Living
P.O. Box 260
Surry, ME 04684
tel/fax: +1 207 667 1025
e-mail: ccl@acadia.net
http://www.compassionateliving.org

InterNICHE contact
Katherine Lewis
8120 Eastern Avenue
Wyndmoor, PA 19038
tel: +1 215 233 1162
fax: +1 215 233 5445
e-mail: katherinealewis@hotmail.com

Jane Goodall Institute
P.O. Box 14890
Silver Spring, MD 20911
tel: +1 301 565 0086
fax: +1 301 565 3188
http://www.janegoodall.org

Latham Foundation
Latham Plaza Bld.
1826 Clement Avenue
Alameda, CA 95401
tel: +1 510 521 0920
fax: +1 510 521 9861
e-mail: Info@Latham.org
http://www.latham.org

MRMC (Medical Research Modernization Committee)
3200 Morley Rd
Shaker Heights, OH 44122
tel/fax: +1 216 283 6702
e-mail: stkaufman@pol.net
http://www.mrmcmed.org

NAHEE (National Association for Humane and Environmental Education)
P.O. Box 362
East Haddam, CT 06423
tel: +1 860 434 8666
e-mail: nahee@nahee.org
http://www.nahee.org

NAVS (National Anti-Vivisection Society)
53 W. Jackson Blvd., Suite 1552
Chicago, IL 60604
tel: +1 312 427 6065
fax: +1 312 427 6524
e-mail: navs@navs.org
http://www.navs.org

NEAVS (New England Anti-Vivisection Society)
333 Washington Street
Suite 850
Boston, MA 02108
tel: +1 617 523 6020
fax: +1 617 523 7925
e-mail: info@ma.neavs.com
http://www.neavs.org

New World Vision
1327 Elsinore Ave.
McLean, VA 22102
tel: +1 703 848 3822
e-mail: info@newworldvision.org
http://www.newworldvision.org

PCRM (Physicians Committee for Responsible Medicine)
5100 Washington Avenue, Suite 400
Washington, DC 20016
tel: +1 202 686 2210
fax: +1 202 686 2216
e-mail: pcrm@pcrm.org
http://www.pcrm.org

PETA (People for the Ethical Treatment of Animals)
501 Front St.
Norfolk, VA 23510
tel: +1 757 622 7382
fax: +1 757 622 0457
e-mail: peta@peta.org
http://www.peta.org

PsyETA (Psychologists for the Ethical Treatment of Animals)
P.O. Box 1297
Washington Grove, MD 20880
tel/fax: +1 301 963 4751
e-mail: fran@psyeta.org
http://www.psyeta.org

Rutgers University School of Law - Animal Rights Law Project
Rutgers Law School
123 Washington Street
Newark, NJ 07102
tel: +1 973 353 5989
fax: +1 973 353 1445
e-mail: director@animal-law.org
http://www.animal-law.org

SCAW (Scientists Center for Animal Welfare)
7833 Walker Drive, Suite 410
Greenbelt, MD 20770
tel: +1 301 345 3500
fax: +1 301 345 3503
e-mail: info@scaw.com
http://www.scaw.com

Seeds of Change Humane Education
P.O. Box 13343
La Jolla, CA 92039
tel: +1 858 824 1975
fax: +1 858 457 8683
e-mail: dani@seedsofchangeonline.org
http://www.seedsofchangeonline.org

UC Center for Animal Alternatives
School of Veterinary Medicine
University of California, Davis
One Shields Avenue
Davis, CA 95616
tel: +1 530 757 8448
e-mail: animalalternatives@ucdavis.edu
http://www.vetmed.ucdavis.edu/Animal_Alternatives/main.htm

Vertebrate View
e-mail: mail@vview.org
http://vview.org

Yugoslavia

InterNICHE contact
Dražen Vicić
Stevana Filipovića 29
11000 Belgrade
tel: +381 11 653 628
e-mail: vicicdra@softhome.net

ORCA - The Animal Welfare Organisation of the Faculty of Veterinary Medicine
Bulevar JNA 18
11000 Belgrade
Yugoslavia
tel: +381 11 361 5436 (loc.343)
fax: +381 11 685 936
e-mail: orca_vet@yahoo.com
http://www.orca.org.yu

5. Producers

Contact details of producers or main distributors of alternatives detailed in 'Part C - Alternatives File'.

Each telephone code is written with a '+' to represent the international dialling code required from a specifi country, followed by the country code. For calls made within the same country, the '+' and country cod should not be dialled, and '0' added before the area code.

A.D.A.M., Inc.
1600 RiverEdge Parkway
Suite 800
Atlanta, GA 30328
USA
tel: +1 770 980 0888
fax: +1 770 955 3088
e-mail: edsales@adamcorp.com
http://education.adam.com

Anesoft Corporation
18606 NW Cervinia Court
Issaquah, WA 98027
USA
tel: +1 425 643 9388
          877 287 0188 (toll-free North America only)
fax: +1 425 643 0092
e-mail: info@anesoft.com
http://www.anesoft.com

ASAB (Association for the Study of Animal Behaviour)
ASAB Membership Secretary
82A High Street
Sawston
Cambridge CB2 4HJ
UK
tel: +44 1223 830 665
fax: +44 1223 839 804
e-mail: asab@grantais.demon.co.uk
http://www.societies.ncl.ac.uk/asab

AVAR (Association of Veterinarians for Animal Rights)
P.O. Box 208
Davis, CA 95617
USA
tel: +1 530 759 8106
fax: +1 530 759 8116
e-mail: info@avar.org
http://www.avar.org

AVP
School Hill Centre
Chepstow
Monmouthshire NP16 5PH
UK
tel: +44 1291 625 439
fax: +44 1291 629 671
e-mail: info@avp.co.uk
http://www.avp.co.uk

B&K Universal, Ltd.
Grimston, Hull
East Yorkshire HU11 4QE
UK
tel: +44 1964 527 555
fax: +44 1964 527 006
e-mail: info@bku.com
http://www.bku.com

Barry, Prof. Peter H.
Department of Physiology & Pharmacology
School of Medical Sciences
University of New South Wales
Sydney NSW 2052
Australia
tel: +61 2 9385 1101
fax: +61 2 9385 1099 / 1059
e-mail: p.barry@unsw.edu.au
http://www.med.unsw.edu.au/PHBSoft

Bender, Dr. David A.
49 Draycott Avenue
Kenton
Middlesex HA3 0BL
UK
tel: +44 20 8933 7970
    +44 20 7679 2196 (weekdays)
fax: +44 20 8907 9933
e-mail: dab@biochem.ucl.ac.uk
http://www.dabender.freeserve.co.uk/dabcomp.html

Benjamin Cummings
1301 Sansome Street
San Francisco, CA 94111
USA
tel: +1 415 402 2500
fax: +1 415 402 2590
e-mail: bcfeedback@aw.com
http://www.aw.com/bc

Biopac Systems, Inc.
42 Aero Camino
Santa Barbara, CA 93117
USA
tel: +1 805 685 0066
fax: +1 805 685 0067
e-mail: info@biopac.com
http://www.biopac.com

Biosoft
2D Dolphin Way
Stapleford
Cambridge CB2 5DW
UK
tel: +44 1223 841 700
fax: +44 1223 841 802
e-mail: info@biosoft.com
http://www.biosoft.com
(orders from Euro zone and elsewhere, except North America)

Biosoft
P.O. Box 10938
Ferguson, MO 63135
USA
tel: +1 314 524 8029
fax: +1 314 524 8129
e-mail: info@biosoft.com
http://www.biosoft.com
(orders from North America only)

Blackwell Science Ltd.
Osney Mead
Oxford OX2 0EL
UK
tel: +44 1865 206 206
fax: +44 1865 721 205
e-mail: edward.crutchley@blacksci.co.uk
http://www.vetsite.net

Blue Cross of India
1 Eldams Road
Chennai - 600 018
India
tel: +91 44 2434 1778
fax: +91 44 2234 9801
e-mail: bluecross@aspick.com
http://www.bluecross.org.in

Branch, Dr. Charles E.
Department of Anatomy, Physiology and Pharmacology
Greene Hall 208
College of Veterinary Medicine
Auburn University, AL 36849
USA
tel: +1 334 844 5414 / 334 444 8148
fax: +1 334 844 5388
e-mail: branch@mail.auburn.edu
http://www.vetmed.auburn.edu/~branch/cvl

Braun, Dr. Hans A.
Laboratory of Neurodynamics
Institute of Physiology
University of Marburg
Deutschhausstr. 2
D-35037 Marburg
Germany
tel: +49 6421 286 2305
fax: +49 6421 286 6967
e-mail: braun@mailer.uni-marburg.de
http://www.cLabs.de

British Pharmacological Society
pharma-CAL-ogy
16 Angel Gate, City Road
London EC1V 2SG
UK
tel: +44 207 417 0382
fax: +44 207 417 0114
e-mail: cal@bps.ac.uk
http://www.bps.ac.uk

BSL (Bohn Stafleu Van Loghum)
Customer Service
P.O. Box 246
3990 GA Houten
The Netherlands
tel: +31 30 638 3736
fax: +31 30 638 3999
e-mail: klantenservice@bsl.nl
http://www.bsl.nl

BVA (British Veterinary Association) Postal Bookshop
6 Bourne Enterprise Centre
Wrotham Road
Borough Green
Kent TN15 8DG
UK
tel: +44 1732 886 422
fax: +44 1732 886 686
e-mail: cairns@mcmslondon.co.uk

Carolina Biological Supply Company
International Sales Department
P.O. Box 6010
Burlington, NC 27216
USA
tel: +1 336 584 0381
        800 334 5551 (US customers)
        800 387 2474 (Canadian customers)
fax: +1 336 584 7686
        800 222 7112 (US customers)
        800 374 6714 (Canadian customers)
e-mail: internationalsales@carolina.com
http://www.carolina.com

CHIME (Centre for Health Informatics and Multiprofessional Education)
Royal Free & University College Medical School
University College London
Holborn Union Building
The Archway Campus
Highgate Hill
London N19 3UA
UK
tel: +44 20 7288 3366
fax: +44 20 7288 3322
e-mail: chime@ucl.ac.uk
http://www.chime.ucl.ac.uk/Models

CLEARVUE / eav
6465 North Avondale Avenue
Chicago, IL 60631
USA
tel: +1 773 775 9433
        800 253 2788 (toll-free North America only)
fax: +1 773 775 9855
        800 444 9855 (toll-free North America only)
e-mail: custserv@clearvue.com
http://www.clearvue.com

CLIVE (Computer-aided Learning In Veterinary Education)
Royal (Dick) School of Veterinary Studies
The University of Edinburgh
Summerhall
Edinburgh EH9 1QH
UK
tel: +44 131 650 6113
fax: +44 131 650 6576
e-mail: clive@ed.ac.uk
http://www.clive.ed.ac.uk

COACS (Commercial and Academic Services), Ltd.
Kimbolton House
Mount Beacon
Lansdown
Bath BA1 5QP
UK
tel: +44 1225 312 992
fax: +44 1225 315 339
e-mail: coacs@coacs.com
http://www.coacs.com/PCCAL

Colson, Dr. Mark
P.O. Box 3008
Geelong
Victoria 3220
Australia
tel: +61 3 5221 3732
mobile: +61 419 557 481
e-mail: colsonline@primus.com.au
http://home.primus.com.au/colsonline/pl.html

Critical Concepts, Inc.
2845 Haven Lane
Lindenhurst, IL 60046
USA
tel: +1 847 265 4826
fax: +1 928 396 7548
e-mail: info@critcon.com
http://www.critcon.com

CyberEd, Inc.
P.O. Box 3480
Chico, CA 95927
USA
tel: +1 530 899 1212
        888 318 0700 (toll-free North America only)
fax: +1 530 899 1211
e-mail: info@cyber-ed.com
http://www.cybered.net

Cytographics Pty., Ltd.
47 St. Leonards Road
Ascot Vale
Victoria 3032
Australia
tel: +613 8344 4519
fax: +613 9349 3268
e-mail: info@cytographics.com
http://www.cytographics.com

DASIE International
c/o Dr. David L. Holmberg
89 Callander Drive
Guelph, ON N1E 4H9
Canada
e-mail: dasieinternational@hotmail.com
        holmberg@uoguelph.ca
http://www.dasie.com

Davies, Alexander S.
Associate Professor in Veterinary Anatomy
Institute of Veterinary, Animal and Biomedical Sciences 412
Massey University
Private Bag 11 222
Palmerston North
New Zealand
tel: +64 6 356 9099 ext. 7508
fax: +64 6 350 2263
e-mail: a.s.davies@massey.ac.nz

De Schutter, Prof. Erik
Born-Bunge Foundation
University of Antwerp (UIA)
Universiteitsplein 1
B-2610 Antwerpen
Belgium
fax: +32 3 820 2669
e-mail: erik@bbf.uia.ac.be
http://www.bbf.uia.ac.be/SOFT

Denoyer Geppert International
5225 Ravenswood Avenue
Chicago, IL 60640
USA
tel: +1 847 965 9600
        800 621 1014 (toll-free North America only)
fax: +1 866 531 1221 (toll-free North America only)
e-mail: customerservice@denoyer.com
http://www.denoyer.com

Didactic Systems
Prof. Tim Teyler
2756 Hartwood Circle
Stow, OH 44224
USA
tel: +1 330 673 4066 / 325 6640
fax: +1 330 325 5916
e-mail: tjt@neoucom.edu
http://web.neoucom.edu/~tjt/headerc.html

DigiDiss Education AB
Karl Gustavsgatan 12B
SE-41125 Gothenburg
Sweden
tel: +46 31 773 1000
e-mail: info@digidiss.com
http://www.digidiss.com

Digital Frog International, Inc.
Trillium Place
RR #2, 7377 Calfass Road
Puslinch, ON N0B 2J0
Canada
tel: +1 519 766 1097
fax: +1 519 767 9994
e-mail: info@digitalfrog.com
http://www.digitalfrog.com

eBioMEDIA
BioMEDIA Associates
P.O. Box 1234
Beaufort, SC 29901
USA
tel: +1 843 470 0236
     877 661 5355 (toll-free North America only)
fax: +1 843 470 0237
e-mail: ggerber@ebiomedia.com (Gwen Gerber)
http://www.ebiomedia.com

Educational Images, Ltd.
P.O. Box 3456
West Side Station
Elmira, NY 14905
USA
tel: +1 607 732 1090
     800 527 4264 (toll-free North America only)
fax: +1 607 732 1183
e-mail: edimages@edimages.com
http://www.educationalimages.com

FFVFF (Fund for Animal-Free Research)
Hegarstrasse 9
P.O. Box 1766
CH-8032 Zürich
Switzerland
tel: +41 1 422 7070
fax: +41 1 422 8010
e-mail: ffvff@bluewin.ch
http://www.ffvff.ch

Films for the Humanities and Sciences
P.O. Box 2053
Princeton, NJ 08543
USA
tel: +1 609 419 8000
         800 257 5126 (toll-free North America only)
fax: +1 609 275 3767
e-mail: custserv@films.com
http://www.films.com

Gabrielsson, Johan
AstraZeneca
e-mail: johan.gabrielsson@astrazeneca.com

Georg Thieme Verlag
International Sales & Marketing
P.O. Box 30 11 20
D-70451 Stuttgart
Germany
tel: +49 711 89310
fax: +49 711 8931 410
e-mail: custserv@thieme.de
http://www.thieme.de
(all orders except from the Americas; see 'Thieme New York' for orders from the Americas)

Gold Standard Multimedia
320 West Kennedy Blvd., Suite 400
Tampa, FL 33606
USA
tel: +1 813 258 4747
         800 375 0943 (toll-free North America only)
fax: +1 813 259 1585
e-mail: sales@gsm.com
http://www.gsm.com

Hubbard Scientific / Scott Resources / National Teaching Aids
401 W. Hickory Street
P.O. Box 2121
Fort Collins, CO 80522
USA

tel: +1 970 484 7445
  800 446 8767 (toll-free North America only)
fax: +1 970 484 1198
e-mail: bevans@amep.com
http://www.shnta.com

Institute of Pharmaceutical Sciences ETH
Prof. Dr. Heidi Wunderli-Allenspach
Biopharmacy, Department of Applied BioSciences
Winterthurerstrasse 190
CH-8057 Zürich
Switzerland
tel: +41 1 635 6040
fax: +41 1 635 6882
e-mail: wunderli-allenspach@pharma.anbi.ethz.ch
http://www.pharma.ethz.ch/biopharmacy

IWF Wissen und Medien gGmbH
P.O.Box 2351
D-37013 Göttingen
Germany
tel: +49 551 50240
fax: +49 551 5024 400
e-mail: iwf-goe@iwf.de
http://www.iwf.de

Keegan, Dr. R.D.
Department of Veterinary Clinical Sciences
College of Veterinary Medicine
Washington State University
Pullman, WA 99164
USA
tel: +1 509 335 0770
fax: +1 509 335 0880
e-mail: rdk@vetmed.wsu.edu
http://www.vetmed.wsu.edu/academic/vent.html

Kisállatklinika Ltd.
Fűtőház Street 1
H-8000 Székesfehérvár
Hungary
tel: +36 22 338 238
fax: +36 22 506 177
e-mail: info@mail.dokisoft.com
http://www.dokisoft.com

Kofránek, Dr. Jiří
Institute of Pathological Physiology
1st Faculty of Medicine, Charles University
U Nemocnice 5
128 53 Prague 2
Czech Republic
tel: +420 2 249 65912
        777 686 868
fax: +420 2 2491 2834
        777 407 890
e-mail: kofranek@cesnet.cz
http://www.physiome.cz

Koullis Pitsillides Consulting
3461 Rancho Rio Way
Sacramento, CA 95834
USA
tel: +1 916 359 2562
e-mail: koullis@winfirst.com

Kronen Osteo
21416 Chase Street #1
Canoga Park, CA 91304
USA
tel: +1 818 709 7991
fax: +1 818 709 7993
e-mail: kronen@boneclones.com
http://www.boneclones.com

Künzel, Prof. Wolfgang
Institute of Anatomy
University of Veterinary Medicine Vienna
Veterinärplatz 1
A-1210 Vienna
Austria
tel: +43 1 25077 / 2502
fax: +43 1 25077 / 2590
e-mail: wolfgang.kuenzel@vu-wien.ac.at
http://www.vu-wien.ac.at/i101

Leeds University Television
University of Leeds
Leeds LS2 9JT
UK
tel: +44 113 233 2660
fax: +44 113 233 2655
e-mail: television@leeds.ac.uk
http://mediant.leeds.ac.uk/vtcatalogue

Limbs & Things, Ltd.
Sussex Street
St Philips
Bristol BS2 0RA
UK
tel: +44 117 311 0500
fax:+44 117 311 0501
e-mail: sales@limbsandthings.com
http://www.limbsandthings.com

Lippincott Williams & Wilkins
P.O. Box 1600
Hagerstown, MD 21741
USA
tel: +1 301 223 2300
    800 638 3030 (toll-free North America only)
fax: +1 301 223 2365
http://www.wwilkins.com

Marcus Sommer Somso Modelle
Friedrich-Rückert-Strasse 54
Postfach 2942
96418 Coburg
Germany
tel: +49 9561 85740
fax: +49 9561 857411
e-mail: somso@somso.de
http://www.somso.de

Massachusetts Institute of Technology
Department of Brain and Cognitive Sciences
77 Massachusetts Avenue, E25-406
Cambridge, MA 02139
USA
tel: +1 617 253 5748
http://www.ai.mit.edu/people/ekm/Rhbit.htm

METI (Medical Education Technologies, Inc.)
6000 Fruitville Road
Sarasota, FL 34232
USA
tel: +1 941 377 5562
fax: +1 941 377 5590
e-mail: gcarlson@meti.com (Grace Carlson)
http://www.meti.com

Michigan State University
Instructional Media Center
Marketing Division
P.O. Box 710
East Lansing, MI 48826
USA
tel: +1 517 353 9229
fax: +1 517 432 2650
e-mail: omalleyb@pilot.msu.edu
http://msuvmall.msu.edu/imc

Microsurgical Developments
P.O. Box 2045
6201 CC Maastricht
The Netherlands
tel: +31 43 388 1595
fax: +31 36 546 9781
e-mail: info@microdev.nl
http://www.microdev.nl

Nasco, Inc.
901 Janesville Avenue
P.O.Box 901
Fort Atkinson, WI 53538
USA
tel: +1 920 563 2446
       800 558 9595 (toll-free North America only)
fax: +1 920 563 8296
e-mail: info@enasco.com
http://www.enasco.com

Neo/Sci, Inc.
P.O. Box 22729
Rochester, NY 14692
USA
tel: +1 800 526 6689 (toll-free North America only)
fax: +1 800 657 7523 (toll-free North America only)
e-mail: customerservice@neosci.com
http://www.neosci.com

NEOTEK
6540 Northumberland Street
Pittsburgh, PA 15217
USA
tel: +1 412 521 1111
fax: +1 412 521 0313
e-mail: support@neotek.com
http://www.neotek.com

OPTIMIST Handelsges.m.b.H.
Ölrainstrasse 24
A-6900 Bregenz
Austria
tel: +43 5574 53653
mobile: +43 664 104 8050
fax: +43 5574 54651
e-mail: pop@optimist.at
http://www.optimist.at

Pacific Research Laboratories
10221 SW 188th Street
P.O. Box 409
Vashon, WA 98070
USA
tel: +1 206 463 5551
fax: +1 206 463 2526
e-mail: info@sawbones.com
http://www.sawbones.com

PERC (Physiology Educational Research Consortium)
Dr. Harold Modell, Director
P.O. Box 51187
Seattle, WA 98115
USA
tel: +1 206 522 6045
e-mail: modell@physiologyeducation.org
http://www.physiologyeducation.org

Phywe Systeme GmbH
Robert-Bosch-Breite 10
D-37079 Göttingen
Germany
tel: +49 551 604 0
fax: +49 551 604 107 / 115
e-mail: info@phywe.de
http://www.phywe.de
http://www.phywe.com

PIDATA
Prof. Ian E. Hughes
The Old Vicarage
Church Lane
Horsforth, Leeds
West Yorkshire LS18 5LA
UK
tel/fax: +44 113 258 4576
e-mail: i.e.hughes@leeds.ac.uk

Pioneer Electronics (USA), Inc.
Business Solutions Division
Industrial Video Group
2265 East 220ᵗʰ Street
Long Beach, CA 90810
USA
tel: +1 310 952 2000
fax: +1 310 952 2990
e-mail: tchristall@pnmt.com
http://www.tools4teachers.com

PLATO Learning (UK), Ltd.
10 Lancaster Court
Coronation Road
Cressex Business Park
High Wycombe
Buckinghamshire HP12 3TD
UK
tel: +44 1494 686 910
fax: +44 1494 686 931
e-mail: ukinfo@plato.com
http://www.platolearning.co.uk

Plietz und Steinbis GbR
Lutherstrasse 66
07743 Jena
Germany
tel: +49 3641 421904
fax: +49 36692 20138
e-mail: phyprak@gmx.de
http://people.freenet.de/phyprak

Purves, Dr. Robert D.
Pharmacology Department
Otago School of Medical Sciences
University of Otago
P.O. Box 913, Dunedin
New Zealand
tel: +64 3 479 7266
fax: +64 3 479 9140
e-mail: robert.purves@stonebow.otago.ac.nz

Quentin-Baxter, Dr. Megan
Faculty of Medicine Computing Centre
University of Newcastle
Newcastle upon Tyne NE2 4HH
UK
tel: +44 191 222 5888
e-mail: megan.quentin-baxter@ncl.ac.uk
http://www.staff.ncl.ac.uk/megan.quentin-baxter
http://www.ltsn-01.ac.uk/resources/features/rats

Queue, Inc.
1450 Barnum Avenue
Suite 207
Bridgeport, CT 06610
USA
tel: +1 203 335 0908
        800 232 2224 (toll-free North America only)
fax: +1 203 336 2481
e-mail: sales@queueinc.com
http://www.queueinc.com

Rescue Critters, LLC
P.O. Box 261972
Encino, CA 91426
USA
tel: +1 818 780 7860
fax: +1 818 780 1078
e-mail: emsca@aol.com
http://www.rescuecritters.com

Royal Veterinary College
Continuing Professional Development Unit
Hawkshead Lane
North Mymms, Hatfield
Hertfordshire AL9 7TA
UK
tel: +44 1707 666 333
fax: +44 1707 646 540
e-mail: jmills@rvc.ac.uk (John Mills)
http://www.rvc.ac.uk/Courses/Continuing_Education/Videos/Index.cfm

Rudas, Prof. Dr. Péter
Department of Physiology and Biochemistry
Faculty of Veterinary Science
Szent István University
István Street 2
1078 Budapest
Hungary
tel: +36 1 478 4163
fax: +36 1 478 4165   ·
e-mail: prudas@univet.hu
http://www.physiol.univet.hu

Rush Medical College
Laboratory of Drs. Joel Michael and Allen Rovick
Department of Molecular Biophysics & Physiology
Presbyterian - St. Luke's Medical Center
Chicago, IL 60612
USA

tel: +1 312 942 6454
fax: +1 312 942 8711
e-mail: jmichael@rush.edu
        arovick@rush.edu
http://www.physiologyeducation.org

Saints Web Design
677 Main Road
Northdene
Durban 4093 KZN
South Africa
tel: +27 31 708 1425
mobile: +27 83 777 4946
fax: +27 31 708 1391
e-mail: admin@saintsweb.co.za
http://www.saintsweb.co.za

Schneider & Morse Group
7901 Hedingham Road
Sylvania, OH 43560
USA
tel: +1 419 885 2803
e-mail: artimiss55@aol.com
http://www.prodissector.com

Schneider, Dr. Horst
Laboratory of Neurodynamics
Institute of Physiology
University of Marburg
Deutschhausstr. 2
D-35037 Marburg
Germany
tel: +49 6421 286 2305
fax: +49 6421 286 6967
e-mail: hschneid@mailer.uni-marburg.de

Scholastic, Inc.
2931 East McCarty Street
Jefferson City, MO 65101
USA
tel: +1 573 636 5271
        800 724 6527 (toll-free North America only)
fax: +1 573 635 7630
e-mail: custserv@scholastic.com
http://www.scholastic.com

Science Works, Inc.
808 Retford Circle
Winston-Salem, NC 27104
USA

tel: +1 336 712 0353
      800 478 8476 (toll-free North America only)
fax: +1 336 712 0004
e-mail: info@scienceclass.com
http://www.scienceclass.com
http://www.k12sciencestore.com

Scottish Knowledge plc
1ˢᵗ Floor
6-8 Wemyss Place
Edinburgh EH3 6DH
Scotland, UK
tel: +44 131 625 2600
fax: +44 131 625 2609
e-mail: info@scottishknowledge.com
http://www.scottishknowledge.co.uk

SFRS (Service du Film de Recherche Scientifique)
CERIMES (Multimedia Resources and Information Centre for Higher Education)
6 Avenue Pasteur
92170 Vanves (Hauts de Seine)
France
tel: +33 1 4123 0880
fax: +33 1 4529 1099
e-mail: info@sfrs.fr
http://www.cerimes.education.fr

Shavit, Dr. Gabriel
Department of Physiology and Pharmacology
Sackler School of Medicine
Tel Aviv University
Ramat Aviv
Tel Aviv 69978
Israel
tel: +972 3 640 8735
fax: +972 3 640 9113
e-mail: pharm6@post.tau.ac.il

Sheffield BioScience Programs
Dr. David Dewhurst
Flat 1, Salisbury Heights
31 Salisbury Road
Edinburgh EH16 5AA
UK
tel: +44 131 662 8225
mobile: +44 7985 179 130
e-mail: d.dewhurst@ed.ac.uk
http://www.sheffbp.co.uk

Simulab Corporation
1440 NW 53rd Street
Seattle, WA 98107
USA
tel: +1 206 297 1260
fax: +1 253 681 7667
e-mail: info@simulab.com
http://www.simulab.com

Sinauer Associates, Inc.
23 Plumtree Road
P.O. Box 407
Sunderland, MA 01375
USA
tel: +1 413 549 4300
fax: +1 413 549 1118
e-mail: orders@sinauer.com
http://www.sinauer.com

Smeak, Dr. Daniel D.
Head, Small Animal Surgery
The Ohio State University
College of Veterinary Medicine
601 Vernon L. Tharp Street
Columbus, OH 43210
USA
tel: +1 614 292 3551
fax: +1 614 292 0895
e-mail: surgicalsimulators@yahoo.com

Soft Options, Ltd.
326 Kensal Road
London W10 5BZ
UK
tel: +44 208 964 3355
fax: +44 208 964 3357
e-mail: anyone@softoptions-sfp.com
http://www.softoptions-sfp.com

Sophus Medical A/S
Esplanaden 18
DK-1263 Copenhagen K
Denmark
tel: +45 3337 7900
fax: +45 3337 7901
e-mail: mail@sophusmedical.dk
http://www.resussim.com

Surgical Specialties Corporation
100 Dennis Drive
Reading, PA 19606
USA
tel: +1 610 404 1000
        800 523 3332 (toll-free North America only)
fax: +1 610 404 4010
e-mail: info@surgicalspecialties.com
http://www.surgicalspecialties.com
http://www.surgspec.com
http://www.sharpoint.com

Tangent Scientific Supply, Inc.
P.O. Box 705
Lewiston, NY 14092
USA
tel: +1 905 704 1500
        800 363 2908 (toll-free North America only)
fax: +1 905 704 1555
        877 704 1555 (toll-free North America only)
e-mail: sales@tangentscientific.com
http://www.tangentscientific.com

Texas A&M University
College of Veterinary Medicine
Media Resources, MS4461
College Station, TX 77843
USA
tel: +1 979 845 1780
fax: +1 979 845 6737
e-mail: rcrow@cvm.tamu.edu (Ralph M. Crow)
http://www.cvm.tamu.edu

Thieme New York
333 Seventh Avenue
New York, NY 10001
USA
tel: +1 212 760 0888
        800 782 3488 (toll-free North America only)
fax: +1 212 947 1112
e-mail: customerservice@thieme.com
http://www.thieme.com
(*orders from the Americas only; see 'Georg Thieme Verlag' for orders from the rest of the world*)

Thomson Learning
Thomson Distribution Center
Customer Service
10650 Toebben Drive
Independence, KY 41051
USA
tel: +1 859 525 6620
        800 354 9706 (USA toll-free)
fax: +1 859 647 5023
        800 487 8488 (USA toll-free)
e-mail: esales@thomsonlearning.com
http://www.wadsworth.com/psychology_d/special_features/sniffy.html

University of Arkansas for Medical Sciences
Biomedical Biotechnology Center
Charles Cook, Contracts & Licensing Associate
4301 West Markham Street
Slot 718
Little Rock, AR 72205
USA
tel: +1 501 686 5431
fax: +1 501 686 8501
e-mail: cookcharlesa@uams.edu
http://www.uamsbiotech.com

University of California (UC Davis)
School of Veterinary Medicine
Dean's Office - Academic Programs
One Shields Avenue
Davis, CA 95616
USA
tel: +1 530 752 1324
fax: +1 530 752 2801
e-mail: svmacadprog@ucdavis.edu
http://www.calf.vetmed.ucdavis.edu

University of Georgia
College of Veterinary Medicine
Department of Pathology
Athens, GA 30602
USA
tel: +1 706 542 5837
fax: +1 706 542 5828
e-mail: noah@vet.uga.edu
http://www.vet.uga.edu/vpp/noah

University of Gröningen
Department of Animal Physiology
Dr. Anne J. H. de Ruiter
P.O. Box 14
9750 AA Haren
The Netherlands
tel: +31 50 363 2346 / 2340
fax: +31-50 363 5205 / 2331
e-mail: a.j.h.de.ruiter@biol.rug.nl
http://www.biol.rug.nl/neuro

University of Miami School of Medicine
Center for Research in Medical Education
Prof. Michael S. Gordon, Director
P.O. Box 016960 (D-41)
Miami, FL 33101
USA
tel: +1 305 243 6491
fax: +1 305 243 6136
e-mail: mgordon@miami.edu
http://crme.med.miami.edu

University of Minnesota
College of Veterinary Medicine
Department of Veterinary PathoBiology
Prof. Thomas F. Fletcher
1988 Fitch Avenue
St. Paul, MN 55109
USA
tel: +1 612 624 9765
fax: +1 612 625 0204
e-mail: fletc003@tc.umn.edu
http://vanat.cvm.umn.edu/vanatCrsware/Crsware.html

University of Newcastle upon Tyne
Prof. Paul Flecknell
Comparative Biology Centre
Medical School
Framlington Place
Newcastle upon Tyne NE2 4HH
UK
tel: +44 191 222 6715
fax: +44 191 222 8688
e-mail: p.a.flecknell@ncl.ac.uk
http://www.lal.org.uk/digital.htm

University of Portsmouth
Learning Development Centre
Buckingham Building
Lion Terrace
Portsmouth PO1 3HE
UK
tel: +44 23 9284 6510
fax: +44 23 9284 6511
e-mail: ldc@port.ac.uk
http://www.port.ac.uk/departments/ldc

University of Strathclyde
Dr. John Dempster
Department of Physiology and Pharmacology
Institute for Biomedical Sciences
27 Taylor Street
Glasgow G4 ONR
UK
tel: +44 141 548 2320
fax: +44 141 552 2562
e-mail: j.dempster@strath.ac.uk
http://innovol.sibs.strath.ac.uk/physpharm/sims.shtml

University of Texas-Houston Medical School
Dr. Douglas A. Baxter
Associate Professor of Research
Department of Neurobiology and Anatomy
Room MSB 7.171
Houston, TX 77225
USA
tel: +1 713 500 5565
fax: +1 713 500 0621
e-mail: douglas.baxter@uth.tmc.edu
http://snnap.uth.tmc.edu

University of Washington
Health Sciences Center for Educational Resources
Box 357161
Seattle, WA 98195
USA
tel: +1 206 685 1186
fax: +1 206 543 8051
e-mail: center@u.washington.edu
http://www.hscer.washington.edu/hscer

Ventura Educational Systems
P.O. Box 425
Grover Beach, CA 93483
USA
tel: +1 805 473 7387
     800 336 1022 (toll-free North America only)
fax: +1 805 473 7382
     800 493 7380 (toll-free North America only)
e-mail: sales@venturaes.com
http://www.venturaes.com

Videodiscovery
1700 Westlake Avenue North
Suite 600
Seattle, WA 98109
USA
tel: +1 206 285 5400
     800 548 3472 (toll-free North America only)
fax: +1 206 285 9245
e-mail: sales@videodiscovery.com
http://www.videodiscovery.com

Ward's Natural Science
5100 West Henrietta Road
P.O. Box 92912
Rochester, NY 14692
USA
tel: +1 585 359 2502
     800 962 2660 (toll-free North America only)
fax: +1 585 334 6174
e-mail: customer_service@wardsci.com
http://www.wardsci.com

Wilgenburg, Dr. Henk van
University of Amsterdam
Academic Medical Centre
Department of Pharmacology
Meibergdreef 15
1105 AZ Amsterdam
The Netherlands
tel: +31 20 566 4669
fax: +31 20 691 9149
e-mail: h.vanwilgenburg@amc.uva.nl

Yale University Press
Order Department
P.O. Box 209040
New Haven, CT 06520
USA
tel: +1 203 432 0940 / 60
    800 987 7323 (toll-free North America only)
fax: +1 203 432 0948
    800 777 9253 (toll-free North America only)
e-mail: custservice.press@yale.edu
http://www.yale.edu/yup
(*orders from North and South America, Australia, Japan, South Korea and Taiwan*)

Yale University Press
23 Pond Street
London NW3 2PN
UK
tel: +44 20 7431 4422
fax: +44 20 7431 3755
e-mail: sales@yaleup.co.uk
http://www.yale.edu/yup
(*orders from Europe, Africa and Asia*)

appendix

InterNICHE Policy on the Use of Animals and Alternatives in Education

This Policy addresses the use of animals and alternatives in education. It presents specific policies addressing dissection, the sourcing of animal cadavers and tissue, and the use of live animals in the clinic and the field, from the perspective of designing and carrying out practical courses. It also presents a specific policy on the use of animals for making alternatives. To facilitate replacement of harmful animal use in non-ideal circumstances, specific policies relating to the non-ideal sourcing of animals, and the non-ideal use of animals for making alternatives, are included.

Contents

1. Position statement

2. Definition of alternatives in education

3. Definition of harm

4. Policy on animal dissection

5. Policy on ethical sourcing of animal cadavers and tissue

6. Policy on non-ideal sourcing of animal cadavers and tissue

7. Policy on live animal use for clinical skills and surgery training

8. Policy on live animal field studies

9. Policy on the ethical use of live animals, animal cadavers and tissue for making alternatives

10. Policy on the non-ideal use of live animals, animal cadavers and tissue for making alternatives

1.   Position statement

InterNICHE supports a high quality humane education within the life sciences, and the use of alternatives to meet teaching objectives. InterNICHE is against all harmful use of animals in education, including the harming and killing of animals for their cadavers and tissue, for live experimentation and skills training, for ethology and field studies, and for making alternatives.

2.   Definition of alternatives in education

Alternatives are humane educational aids and teaching approaches that can replace harmful animal use or complement existing humane education. Alternatives may be non-animal alternatives, or approaches that involve neutral or beneficial work with animals. They comprise:

- Film and video
- Models, mannekins and simulators
- Multimedia computer simulation
- Ethically-sourced animal cadavers and tissue
- Clinical work with animal patients and volunteers
- Student self-experimentation
- *In vitro* labs
- Field studies

3.   Definition of harm

Harm comprises any action, deliberate or otherwise, that impinges on an animal's current and future well-being by denying or limiting any of the following freedoms:

- Freedom to live
- Freedom to express full natural behaviour
- Freedom to be part of a social structure and ecosystem
- Freedom from hunger and thirst
- Freedom from discomfort
- Freedom from pain, injury and disease
- Freedom from fear and distress

Harm caused to an animal within education is only acceptable when it is the unavoidable consequence of action taken to benefit the individual animal, and in certain circumstances when the action is taken to benefit the species or to produce an alternative, given the harm inflicted is only brief and minor (see 7, 8, 9, 10). In these cases, cost-benefit analyses concerning harm and potential benefit to the individual animal, the species, and to other animals, should be conducted.

4. Policy on animal dissection

InterNICHE accepts that animal dissection can be a useful tool for knowledge and skills acquisition, and may encourage an appreciation of life, when all of the following conditions are met:

4.1 The animal cadaver is ethically-sourced (see 5)

4.2 The dissection is performed at the university level, and no lower

4.3 The dissection is relevant for the student's career

4.4 The student's ethical position concerning dissection is respected

4.5 The dissection is performed within the context of respect for life and respect for the cadaver

4.6 The dissection is complemented by observation of free-living animals of the same species, wherever possible

4.7 Instructors are ethically aware and responsible, and have appropriate training and competence for all activity and procedures that involve animals

4.8 Ethics, including animal rights and welfare, animal use, alternatives, and the human-animal bond, are explored openly and fully

5. Policy on ethical sourcing of animal cadavers and tissue

InterNICHE is against all harmful use of animals in education, including the harming and killing of animals for sourcing cadavers and tissue. Such material may provide a useful resource for knowledge and skills acquisition, however, and InterNICHE accepts its use when it has been ethically sourced. InterNICHE recognises an animal cadaver or tissue as ethically-sourced when all of the following conditions are met:

5.1 The animal was wild, stray, or a companion animal before death

5.2 The animal was not captured, bought, bred, kept, harmed or killed to provide the cadaver or tissue

5.3 The animal died from natural causes or an accident, or was humanely euthanised secondary to natural terminal disease or serious non-recoverable injury (see 5.4)

5.4 The decision to euthanise the animal was made by a qualified veterinarian with consent of the animal's guardian (if any), based on the interests of the animal and not motivated by practical or financial interests

5.5 Consent for the animal cadaver or tissue to be used in education has been given by the animal's guardian (if any)

5.6 Ethically-sourced tissue from living animals comprises only left-over tissue deriving from beneficial surgery or clinical procedures, and scheduled for disposal; or tissue deriving from natural activity such as giving birth, and abandoned by the animal

5.7 Neither the cadaver nor the tissue is needed for the clinical benefit of another animal, or for the benefit of the species

5.8   Those involved in the process of sourcing are ethically aware and responsible, and have appropriate training and competence for all activity and procedures that involve animals

5.9   All stages of the process of sourcing are carried out within the context of respect for life and respect for the cadaver or tissue; and to the highest ethical, welfare, health and safety standards

6.   Policy on non-ideal sourcing of animal cadavers and tissue

Animal cadavers and tissue are usually obtained from sources where animals suffer harm or are killed, such as animal breeders, research facilities, some animal shelters, farms, slaughterhouses and sporting events. InterNICHE does not consider material from these sources, including so-called 'waste' or 'surplus' material, to be ethically-sourced: its ethical nature has been compromised or negated by the harming, killing and/or marketing of the animal at some stage of his/her life.

However, cadavers and tissue from species of animal that are less common as wild, stray, or companion animals, may be hard to source ethically. In these cases, non-ideal sources of material, such as the above, may in certain circumstances provide an appropriate solution to the ethical challenge.

Deriving animal cadavers and tissue from non-ideal sources is an acceptable compromise, when all of the following conditions are met:

6.1   Animal cadavers or tissue are genuinely required for practical work or for making an alternative, and no ethically-sourced and appropriate material is available

6.2   The animal was not captured, bought, bred, kept, harmed or killed to provide the cadaver or tissue

6.3   The animal has died from natural causes or an accident, or was humanely euthanised secondary to natural terminal disease or serious non-recoverable injury; or the cadaver or tissue is destined for disposal, or has been abandoned by the animal (see 6.4)

6.4   The decision to euthanise the animal was made by a qualified veterinarian with consent of the animal's guardian (if any), based on the interests of the animal and not motivated by practical or financial interests

6.5   Neither the cadaver nor the tissue is needed for the clinical benefit of another animal or for the benefit of the species

6.6   The process of sourcing provides zero support and validation for activity involving animal harm or killing, and no market for the material is created or supported

6.7   Those involved in the process of sourcing are ethically aware and responsible, and have appropriate training and competence for all activity and procedures that involve animals

6.8   All stages of the process of sourcing are carried out within the context of respect for life and respect for the cadaver or tissue; and to the highest ethical, welfare, health and safety standards

7.   Policy on live animal use for clinical skills and surgery training

InterNICHE considers the use of live animals in the clinical setting to be an integral part of knowledge and skills acquisition for veterinary students, acceptable when all of the following conditions are met:

7.1   Opportunities for clinical skills and surgery training are built around the needs and well-being of individual wild, stray and companion animal patients, and healthy companion animal volunteers

7.2   The animal is not captured, bought, bred, kept, harmed or killed for the purpose of training, except for harm and/or euthanasia in certain circumstances with animal patients (see 7.5, 7.6, 7.7, 7.8)

7.3   Clinical skills training with a companion animal volunteer is beneficial or neutral in its effect on the individual animal, with rewards not punishment given as encouragement; and the training stopped whenever fear or discomfort is evidenced

7.4   The clinical procedure and/or treatment chosen for an animal patient is the most appropriate and best possible for the well-being of the individual animal, and is aimed at healing, unless the animal requires euthanasia

7.5   Harm caused to an animal patient during a clinical procedure and/or treatment is acceptable when it is the minimum harm necessary for successful work aimed at healing the animal; and in certain circumstances during procedures involving an animal that is suffering from natural terminal disease or serious non-recoverable injury; or when it comprises the act of humane euthanasia (see 7.6, 7.7, 7.8)

7.6   Clinical skills and surgery training that involves a terminal procedure is acceptable only when an animal is suffering from natural terminal disease or serious non-recoverable injury; and for whom a decision to euthanise has been made by a qualified veterinarian with the consent of the animal's guardian (if any), based on the interests of the animal and not motivated by practical or financial interests (see 7.7, 7.8)

7.7   Harm caused during an invasive and/or terminal procedure on an animal that is suffering from natural terminal disease or serious non-recoverable injury is acceptable only when the harm is not subjectively experienced by the animal (e.g. under general anaesthesia); when the harm is minimised; and/or when it comprises the act of humane euthanasia (see 7.8)

7.8   Euthanasia is acceptable when an animal is suffering from natural terminal disease or serious non-recoverable injury; and for whom the decision to euthanise has been made by a qualified veterinarian with the consent of the animal's guardian (if any), based on the interests of the animal and not motivated by practical or financial interests

7.9   The student's ethical position concerning the use of live animals in the clinical setting is respected

7.10   Instructors are ethically aware and responsible, and have appropriate training and competence for all activity and procedures that involve animals

7.11   Clinical skills and surgery training with an animal patient or companion animal volunteer should be supervised by a qualified instructor at all times

7.12 The student should have the appropriate level of skills mastery, accomplished using non-animal alternatives, prior to participation in clinical skills and surgery training with an animal patient or companion animal volunteer

7.13 All elements of clinical skills and surgery training are carried out within the context of respect for life and respect for the animal; and to the highest ethical, welfare, health and safety standards

7.14 Ethics, including animal rights and welfare, animal use, alternatives, and the human-animal bond, are explored openly and fully

8. Policy on live animal field studies

InterNICHE considers the educational study of free-living wild or stray animals to be a valuable experience, acceptable when all of the following conditions are met:

8.1 Opportunities for field studies are built around the needs and well-being of individual wild and stray animals, animal species, and the ecosystem

8.2 The animal is not captured, bought, bred, kept, harmed or killed for the purpose of the study, except for capture and/or harm in certain circumstances that are beneficial to the individual animal, species or ecosystem (see 8.4, 8.5)

8.3 Field studies should cause zero or minimal disturbance to an animal, his/her social structure and the ecosystem; or have a beneficial impact on an animal, species or ecosystem

8.4 Capture and/or harm caused to an animal is acceptable only when the animal is a patient, or will benefit from a clinical procedure

8.5 Capture and/or harm caused to an animal for the benefit of the species or ecosystem is acceptable only when it comprises minor, temporary harm and/or capture of very short duration, with no physical pain; and should not jeopardise the animal's future well-being

8.6 Field studies should avoid threatened or endangered species and ecosystems, unless considerable benefit for an individual animal, species or ecosystem is expected to be derived

8.7 The student's ethical position concerning the study of wild and stray animals is respected

8.8 The use of cadavers and tissue from wild and stray animals accords with the 'Policy on ethical sourcing of animal cadavers and tissue' or 'Policy on non-ideal sourcing of animal cadavers and tissue' (see 5, 6)

8.9 Clinical work with wild or stray animals accords with the 'Policy on live animal use for clinical skills and surgery training' (see 7)

8.10 The use of wild or stray animals for making alternatives accords with the 'Policy on the ethical use of live animals, animal cadavers and tissue for making alternatives' or 'Policy on the non-ideal use of live animals, animal cadavers and tissue for making alternatives' (see 9, 10)

8.11 Instructors are ethically and environmentally aware and responsible, and have appropriate training and competence for all activity that involves animals and that impacts on ecosystems

8.12 Field studies should be supervised by a qualified instructor at all times

8.13 All elements of field studies are carried out within the context of respect for life, respect for the animal, species and ecosystem; and to the highest ethical, welfare, health and safety standards

8.14 Ethics, including environmental ethics, animal rights and welfare, animal use, alternatives, and the human-animal bond, are explored openly and fully

9. Policy on the ethical use of live animals, animal cadavers and tissue for making alternatives

InterNICHE is against all harmful use of animals in education, including that for the creation of alternatives. If a live animal or animal cadaver or tissue is required for making an alternative, InterNICHE accepts this use when all of the following conditions are met:

9.1 An alternative for the practical does not already exist or is not practicably available

9.2 The animal is not captured, bought, bred, kept, harmed or killed for the purpose of making the alternative, except for harm and/or euthanasia in certain circumstances during procedures involving invasive and/or terminal live animal use (see 9.4, 9.5)

9.3 The animal cadaver or tissue is ethically-sourced (see 5)

9.4 Invasive and/or terminal live animal use is acceptable only when an animal is suffering from natural terminal disease or serious non-recoverable injury; and for whom a decision to euthanise has already been made by a qualified veterinarian with the consent of the animal's guardian (if any), based on the interests of the animal and not motivated by practical or financial interests (see 9.5)

9.5 Harm caused during an invasive and/or terminal procedure on an animal is acceptable only when the harm is not subjectively experienced by the animal (e.g. under general anaesthesia); when the harm is minimised; and/or when it comprises the act of humane euthanasia

9.6 All persons involved in making alternatives are ethically aware and responsible, and have appropriate training and competence for all activity and procedures that involve animals

9.7 All stages of the process of making the alternative are carried out within the context of respect for life, respect for the live animal, animal cadaver or tissue; and to the highest ethical, welfare, health and safety standards

10. Policy on the non-ideal use of live animals, animal cadavers and tissue for making alternatives

Live animals and animal cadavers and tissue used in the process of making alternatives are usually obtained from sources where animals suffer harm or are killed, such as animal breeders, research facilities and farms. InterNICHE does not support using these sources for live animals, animal cadavers and tissue, as their ethical nature has been compromised or negated by the harming, killing and/or marketing of the animal at some stage of his/her life.

When a wild, stray or companion animal suffering from terminal disease or serious non-recoverable injury is not available for invasive and/or terminal live use for making an alternative, then deriving so-called 'waste' or 'surplus' live animals from non-ideal sources, such as the above, may in certain circumstances provide an appropriate solution to the ethical challenge. Similarly, when an ethically-sourced animal cadaver or tissue is not available, then non-ideal sources may provide a solution.

Deriving a live animal for use in invasive and/or terminal procedures, or an animal cadaver or tissue, from non-ideal sources, is an acceptable compromise for the purpose of making an alternative when all of the following conditions are met:

10.1   An alternative for the practical does not already exist or is not practicably available

10.2   The animal is genuinely required for making the alternative, and no ethical source of a live animal or animal cadaver or tissue is available

10.3   The alternative to be made will replace harmful animal use in education, and will be available for other students to use

10.4   The live animal was destined for killing or slaughter before being sourced, and was not captured, bought, bred, harmed or killed for use in making the alternative, except for harm and/or euthanasia in certain circumstances during procedures involving invasive and/or terminal live animal use (see 10.5, 10.6, 10.8, 10.9)

10.5   If live animal use is required, priority is given to the sourcing and use of an animal when he/she is suffering from natural terminal disease or serious non-recoverable injury; and for whom a decision to euthanise has already been made by a qualified veterinarian with consent of the animal's guardian (if any), based on the interests of the animal and not motivated by practical or financial interests (see 10.8, 10.9)

10.6   If an animal could be recovered and rehomed, then he/she should be recovered and rehomed, and not used for a terminal procedure or one that will necessitate euthanasia

10.7   All non-ideal sourcing of a live animal and invasive non-terminal live animal use should result in some direct or indirect benefit for the animal, such as being saved from euthanasia, being neutered during a procedure, and being recovered and rehomed

10.8   All invasive live animal use should cause zero additional harm to the animal, and should not jeopardise the animal's future well-being, except in certain circumstances during procedures involving an animal that is suffering from natural terminal disease or serious non-recoverable injury (see 10.9)

10.9   Harm caused during an invasive and/or terminal procedure on an animal is acceptable only when the harm is not subjectively experienced by the animal (e.g. under general anaesthesia); when the harm is minimised; and/or when it comprises the act of humane euthanasia

10.10 The sourcing of animal cadavers and tissue accords with the 'Policy on ethical sourcing of animal cadavers and tissue' or 'Policy on non-ideal sourcing of animal cadavers and tissue' (see 5, 6)

10.11 The process of sourcing provides zero support and validation for activity involving animal harm or killing, and no market for the animals is created or supported

10.12 All persons involved in making alternatives are ethically aware and responsible, and have appropriate training and competence for all activity and procedures that involve animals

10.13 All stages of the process of sourcing are carried out within the context of respect for life and respect for the animal; and to the highest ethical, welfare, health and safety standards

index

Product index

D

G

H

HorseTrek, *see* CALVE, *160*
Howling Monkey Skulls, *see* Skulls of Anthropoids
Models Series, *226*
HPS (Human Patient Simulator), *153*
Humane K-9 & Cat Trainer, *272*
Hydra
- Model, *219*
- Set Model, *220*

I

Ileum - Isolated Guinea Pig Ileum Simulator, *320*
Images of Advanced Level Biology, *396*
In Vitro Development of a Viviparous
Toothcarp, *294, 300*
Individual MI-OWN Frog Models, *220*
Inflammation Pharmacology, *321*
Inguinal Canal of the Horse, *see* CALVE, *160*
Initial Evaluation and Management of the Ill Neonatal
Foal, *259*
Injection and Dissection of the
- Chick, *174, 199*
- Frog, *175, 199*
Innervation of Superficial Structures of the Head, *200*
Insect Metamorphosis, *300*
Insects, *see* Complete Survey of the Animal
Kingdom, *392*
Inside the Cell, *240*
Interactive
- Frog Dissection Kit, *see* Whole Frog Project, *234*
- Physiology (Anatomy Practice, Cardiovascular
System, Fluids & Electrolytes, Muscular System,
Nervous System Part I & II, Respiratory System,
Urinary System), *353, 388*
Internet Guide to Veterinary Microscopic Anatomy, *311*
Intestinal
- Absorption, *353*
- Motility, *354*
- Motility and Its Regulation, *354, 379*
Introduction to
- Cell Biology, *241*
- Cells, *247*
- the Living Cell, *248*
Intubation Model, *153*
Invertebrate Anatomy Set, *see* Animal
Anatomy Set, *191*
Invertebrates Zoology: Multimedia Lab Assistant, *175*
Investigation of
- Active Transport, *380*
- Gluconeogenesis, *241*
IPWeb, *see* Interactive Physiology, *388*
Isolated Vas Deferens Preparation, *321*
Isolation and Metabolism of Mitochondria, *248*
It's Biology, *397*

J

'Jerry Jr.' First Aid Trainer, *153*
'Jerry' K-9 CPR Mannekin, *154*
Joint Structure, *see* CALVE, *160*
Journey through
- a Sheep Using X-ray Tomography, *175*
- the Cell, *248*
JPCalc / JPCalcW, *355*

K

K-9
- Breath Sounds Simulator, *273*
- Intubation Trainer, *154*
- IV Trainer, *273*
- Ophthalmology Training Mannekins, *273*
- Thoracentesis Mannekin, *273*
K-9 & Cat
- Arrhythmia Simulator, *274*
- Heartbeat Simulator, *274*
- Nursing Mannekins, *274*
- Urinary Catheter Training Mannekins, *274*
Key to Insects, *397*
KinetiClass 5.0, *338*
Kingdom *Protista*, *200*
Klikakat, *see* CALVE, *160*
Koken
- Rabbit, *275*
- Rat, *275*

L

Laboratory
- Animals Anaesthesia, *142*
- Anaesthesia of the Cat and Dog, *see* Laboratory
Animals Anaesthesia, *142*
- Small Mammals Part 2, *see* Laboratory Animals
Anaesthesia, *142*
- Dissection Video Series, *200*
- Preparations 1, 2, *322, 336*
- Surgery and Perioperative Care, *143*
Lancelet, *304*
Langendorff Heart, *322*
Languedoc Scorpion (*Buthus occitanus*), *176, 201*
Laparoscopic
- Cholecystectomy Model, *276*
- Nissen Fundoplication Model, *276*
Large Surgical Dissection Pad, *see* M.A.T. Trainer, *278*

P

Paramecium
- Model, *221*
- Morphology and Biology, *180, 201*
PathWeb - The Virtual Pathology Museum, *316*
PediaSim, *154*
Pelviscopic Operations Model, *280*
Perch
- Dissection, *see* Dissections CD-ROMs *and* DissectionWorks, *166; see* Biological Dissection Series (Part 2), *192; see* Dissection Video Series *and* Dissection Videos, *197*
- Model, *222; see* Zoology Models, *231*
Percutaneous Renal Biopsy: The Ishizaki Technique, *260*
Pet First Aid Trainer Kit for Kids, *155*
PharmaCalc, *325*
Pharmacodynamics Simulator, *325*
Pharmacokinetics Simulations, *326*
PharmaSim, *326*
PharmaTutor, *327*
Photosynthesis and Cellular Respiration, *see* Visualizing Cell Processes, *244, 249*
PHYPRAK, *362*
Physio Sim Lab, *363*
PhysioEx, *364, 388*
PhysioLogical, *364*
Pictures Instead of Animals, *327*
Pig Head Tomography, *see* CALVE, *160*
Pig's
- Hoof with Foot Disease Model, *see* SOMSO Pathological Models, *315*
- Snout with Mouth Disease Model, *see* SOMSO Pathological Models, *315*
Pigeon: A Dissection Guide, *see* Vertebrates Dissection Guides Series, *183, 204*
Planarian
- Model, *222*
- Set Model, *223*
Plant & Animal Mitosis & Meiosis, *243*
P.O.P. Trainer, *280*
Practical Animal Handling - 1. Small Mammals, *253, 261*
PracticeRat, *281*
Pregnant
- Cat Model, *223*
- Shark Model, *223*
Preparation of the Labyrinth of the Small-Spotted Dogfish, *201*
Primates Skulls, *see* Bone Clones Skulls, *207*
Principles of Surgery, *290*
ProDissector, *180*
Properties of Isolated Cardiac Muscle, *382*
Protozoa, *180*
PVC-Rat, *281*

R

Rabbit Arterial Blood Pressure - Extrinsic Innervation, Pharmacodynamic Agents, *364, 382*
Ramifications, *see* CALVE, *160*
Rat
- A Dissection Guide, *see* Vertebrate Dissection Guides Series, *204*
- A Functional Anatomy, *181*
- A Practical Dissection Guide, *202*
- Blood Pressure, *327*
- Brain Model, *224*
- Dissection, *see* Dissection Videos, *197*
- Dissection/Anatomy Resource Digital Video, *181*
- Model, *224*
- Phrenic Nerve (*In Vitro*), *328*
- Stack, *182*
Recording the Electrical and Mechanical Activity of the Frog Heart *In Situ*, *365, 383*
Renal Microcirculation, *383*
Reptiles and Amphibians, *384*
Respiratory Pharmacology, *329*
ResusSim
- Inhospital, *143*
- Prehospital, *144*
Rhbit, *365*
Rhesus Primate Mannekin, *282*
Rhesus-Ape Skulls, *see* Skulls of Anthropoids Models Series, *226*
RHYTHM 2000, *156*
Right on the Head, *see* CALVE, *160*
Ring Block Injection Set, *see* Skin Simulator Kit - Skin Pads and Lesions, *285*
Ruminant Stomach of the Cow Model, *224*

S

Sanitary CPR Dog, *155*
Sawbones Models, *282*
Science Bank: Biology, *400*
Scrotocat, *see* CALVE, *160*
Sea Anemone Model, *225*
Sedation Simulator 2002, *145*
Selected Animal Tests in Pharmacology and Toxicology, *329*
Shark
- Dissection & Anatomy, *202*
- Head Model, *225*
- Lab, *225*
- Model, *225*
Shave Pad, *see* Skin Simulator Kit - Skin Pads and Lesions, *285*

General index

H

I

J

K

L

M